MATH

McGraw Hill Education

connectED.mcgraw-hill.com

STEM McGraw-Hill is committed to providing instructional materials in Science, Technology, Engineering, and Mathematics (STEM) that give all students a solid foundation, one that prepares them for college and careers in the 21st century.

Send all inquiries to:
McGraw-Hill Education
STEM Learning Solutions Center
8787 Orion Place
Columbus, OH 43240

ISBN: 978-0-07-665708-7
MHID: 0-07-665708-6

Printed in the United States of America.

6 7 8 9 10 11 QVS 19 18 17 16 15

CONTENTS IN BRIEF

Organized by Focal Areas

TEKS Focal Area **Mathematical Processes**

8.1 Mathematical Process Handbook

TEKS Focal Area **Number and Operations**

8.2 **1** Real Numbers

TEKS Focal Area **Proportionality**

8.3, 8.8, 8.10 **2** Similarity and Dilations

8.4, 8.5 **3** Proportional Relationships and Slope

8.5 **4** Functions

TEKS Focal Area **Expressions, Equations, and Relationships**

8.6, 8.7, 8.8 **5** Triangles and the Pythagorean Theorem

8.8, 8.9 **6** Equations and Inequalities

8.6, 8.7 **7** Connect Algebra to Geometry

TEKS Focal Area **Two-Dimensional Shapes**

8.10 **8** Transformations and Congruence

TEKS Focal Area **Measurement and Data**

8.5, 8.11 **9** Scatterplots and Data Analysis

TEKS Focal Area **Personal Financial Literacy**

8.12 **10** Financial Literacy

Problem-Solving Projects

Your assignment's due tomorrow...

but your book is in your locker!

James Woodson/Digital Vision/Getty Images

NOW WHAT?

Even in crunch time, with ConnectED, we've got you covered!

With ConnectED, you have instant access to all of your study materials—anytime, anywhere. From homework materials to study guides—it's all in one place and just a click away. ConnectED even allows you to collaborate with your classmates and use mobile apps to make studying easy.

Resources built for you—available 24/7:

- Your eBook available wherever you are
- Personal Tutors and Self-Check Quizzes whenever you need them
- An Online Calendar with all of your due dates
- eFlashcard App to make studying easy
- A message center to stay in touch

Reimagine Learning

Go Online!

connectED.mcgraw-hill.com

Vocab

Learn about new vocabulary words.

Watch

Watch animations and videos.

Tutor

See and hear a teacher explain how to solve problems.

Tools

Explore concepts with virtual manipulatives.

Check

Check your progress.

eHelp

Get targeted homework help.

Worksheets

Access practice worksheets.

Chapter 1
Real Numbers

What Tools Do You Need? 20
When Will You Use This? 21
Are You Ready? 22
Foldable 23

TEKS

25 **Lesson 1** Rational Numbers 8.2(C)

33 **Lesson 2** Powers and Exponents 8.2(C)

41 **Lesson 3** Negative Exponents 8.2(C)

49 **Lesson 4** Scientific Notation 8.2(C)
57 **Graphing Technology Lab 4-b:** Scientific Notation Using Technology 8.2(C)

61 **Focus on Mathematical Processes:** The Four-Step Plan 8.1(B), 8.2

Mid-Chapter Check 64

65 **Lesson 5** Roots 8.2(B)

73 **Hands-On Lab 6-a:** Roots of Non-Perfect Squares 8.2(B)
75 **Lesson 6** Estimate Roots 8.2(B)

83 **Lesson 7** The Real Number System 8.2(A)

91 **Lesson 8** Compare and Order Real Numbers 8.2(D), 8.2(B)

99 **21st Century Career** Robotics Engineer 8.1(A), 8.2(C)

Chapter Review 101
Chapter Reflect 104

Go to page 99 to learn about a 21st Century Career in
Robotics Engineering!

Chapter 2 Similarity and Dilations

What Tools Do You Need? 106
When Will You Use This? 107
Are You Ready? 108
Foldable 109

Page	Lesson	TEKS
111	**Hands-On Lab 1-a:** Similar Triangles	8.3(A)
113	**Lesson 1** Properties of Similar Polygons	8.3(A)
121	**Lesson 2** Angle-Angle Similarity of Triangles	8.8(D)
129	Focus on Mathematical Processes: Draw a Diagram	8.1(B), 8.7
132	**Mid-Chapter Check**	
133	**Hands-On Lab 3-a:** Model Dilations	8.3(A)
137	**Lesson 3** Dilations	8.3(B), 8.3(C)
145	**Hands-On Lab 4-a:** Changes in Dimensions	8.3(A), 8.10(D)
149	**Lesson 4** Area and Perimeter of Similar Figures	8.3(A), 8.10(D)
157	**21st Century Career** Car Designer	8.1(A), 8.3(A)

Chapter Review 159
Chapter Reflect 162

Go to page 157 to learn about a 21st Century Career in **Car Design!**

Chapter 3 Proportional Relationships and Slope

What Tools Do You Need? 164
When Will You Use This? 165
Are You Ready? 165
Foldable 167

TEKS

169 **Lesson 1** Constant Rate of Change 8.4(B), 8.5(F)
177 **Graphing Technology Lab 1-b:** Rate of Change 8.4(B), 8.4(C)

179 **Lesson 2** Slope 8.4(A), 8.4(C)

187 **Lesson 3** Slope and Similar Triangles 8.4(A), 8.4(C)

195 **Lesson 4** Equations in $y = mx$ Form 8.5(A), 8.4(B)

203 **Lesson 5** Direct Variation 8.5(E), 8.5(A)

211 **Focus on Mathematical Processes:** Guess, Check, and Revise 8.1(B), 8.8

Mid-Chapter Check 214

215 **Hands-On Lab 6-a:** Proportional and Non-Proportional Relationships 8.5(F)
219 **Lesson 6** Equations in $y = mx + b$ Form 8.5(I), 8.4(C)

227 **Lesson 7** Graph a Line Using Intercepts 8.4(C), 8.5(B)

235 **Lesson 8** Write Linear Equations 8.5(B), 8.5(I)
243 **Graphing Technology Lab 8-b:** Proportional and Non-Proportional Relationships 8.4(C), 8.5(C)

245 **21st Century Career** Mastering Engineer 8.1(A), 8.4(C)

Chapter Review 247
Chapter Reflect 250

Go to page 245 to learn about a 21st Century Career in **Music!**

Chapter 4
Functions

What Tools Do You Need? 252
When Will You Use This? 253
Are You Ready? 254
Foldable 255

TEKS

257 **Lesson 1** Represent Relationships — 8.4(B), 8.5(A)

267 **Lesson 2** Relations — 8.5(G)

275 **Hands-On Lab 3-a:** Relations and Functions — 8.5(G)
277 **Lesson 3** Functions — 8.5(G)

285 **Focus on Mathematical Processes:** Make a Table — 8.1(B), 8.5(A), 8.5(B)

Mid-Chapter Check 288

289 **Lesson 4** Linear Functions — 8.5(G), 8.5(A)

299 **Lesson 5** Proportional and Non-Proportional Functions — 8.5(H)

309 **Lesson 6** Write Equations of Functions — 8.4(C), 8.5(I)
317 **Graphing Technology Lab 6-b:** Family of Linear Functions — 8.5(F), 8.5(A)

321 **21st Century Career** Physical Therapist — 8.1(A), 8.5(A)

Chapter Review 323
Chapter Reflect 326

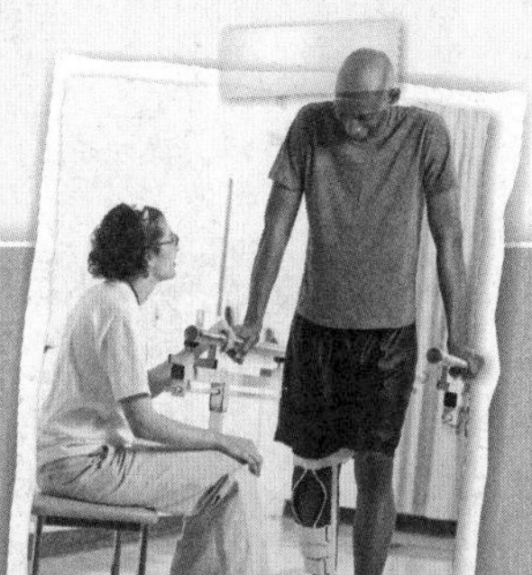

Go to page 321 to learn about a 21st Century Career in
Physical Therapy!

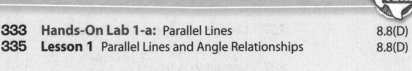

Chapter 5 Triangles and the Pythagorean Theorem

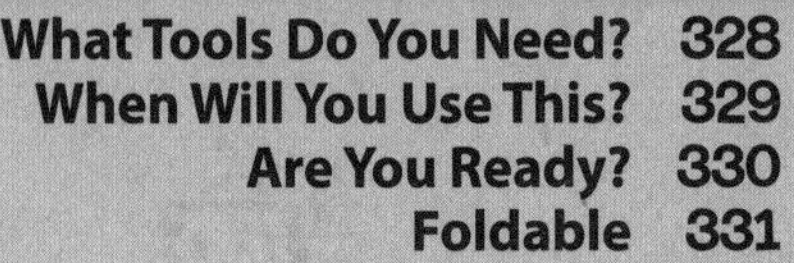

What Tools Do You Need? 328
When Will You Use This? 329
Are You Ready? 330
Foldable 331

		TEKS
333	**Hands-On Lab 1-a:** Parallel Lines	8.8(D)
335	**Lesson 1** Parallel Lines and Angle Relationships	8.8(D)
343	**Hands-On Lab 2-a:** Angles of Triangles	8.8(D)
347	**Lesson 2** Angle Sum and Exterior Angles of Triangles	8.8(D)
355	**Focus on Mathematical Processes:** Look for a Pattern	8.1(B), 8.7
358	**Mid-Chapter Check**	
359	**Hands-On Lab 3-a:** Model Right Triangle Relationships	8.6(C)
361	**Lesson 3** The Pythagorean Theorem	8.7(C)
369	**Hands-On Lab 3-b:** Verify the Pythagorean Theorem	8.6(C)
373	**Lesson 4** Use the Pythagorean Theorem	8.7(C)
381	**Lesson 5** Distance on the Coordinate Plane	8.7(D)
389	**21st Century Career** Travel Agent	8.1(A), 8.7(C), 8.7(D)

Chapter Review 391
Chapter Reflect 394

Go to page 389 to learn about a 21st Century Career in
Travel and Tourism!

Chapter 6 Equations and Inequalities

What Tools Do You Need? 396
When Will You Use This? 397
Are You Ready? 398
Foldable 399

Page	Lesson	TEKS
401	**Lesson 1** Solve Two-Step Equations	8.8(C)
409	**Lesson 2** Write Two-Step Equations	8.8(A)
417	**Virtual Manipulative Lab 3-a:** Model Equations with Variables on Each Side	8.8(A),8.8(C)
421	**Lesson 3** Solve Equations with Variables on Each Side	8.8(A),8.8(C)
429	**Focus on Mathematical Processes:** Work Backward	8.1(B), 8.8(A)
Mid-Chapter Check 432		
433	**Lesson 4** Solve Multi-Step Equations	8.8(A),8.8(C)
441	**Lesson 5** Inequalities with Variables on Each Side	8.8(A),8.8(B)
449	**Graphing Technology Lab 6-a:** Sets of Linear Equations	8.9
451	**Lesson 6** Solve Simultaneous Linear Equations	8.9
461	**Hands-On Lab 6-b:** Analyze Simultaneous Linear Equations	8.9
463	**21st Century Career** Skateboard Designer	8.1(A), 8.8(C)

Chapter Review 465
Chapter Reflect 468

Go to page 463 to learn about a 21st Century Career in **Skateboard Design!**

Chapter 7 Connect Algebra to Geometry

What Tools Do You Need? 470
When Will You Use This? 471
Are You Ready? 472
Foldable 473

Page	Title	TEKS
475	**Lesson 1** Volume of Cylinders	8.6(A), 8.7(A)
483	**Hands-On Lab 2-a:** Model Volume of Cones	8.6(B)
487	**Lesson 2** Volume of Cones	8.7(A), 8.6(A)
495	**Lesson 3** Volume of Spheres	8.7(A)
503	**Focus on Mathematical Processes:** Solve a Simpler Problem	8.1(B), 8.7(A)

Mid-Chapter Check 506

Page	Title	TEKS
507	**Hands-On Lab 4-a:** Nets of Prisms	8.7(B)
511	**Lesson 4** Surface Area of Prisms	8.7(B)
519	**Hands-On Lab 5-a:** Nets of Cylinders	8.7(B)
521	**Lesson 5** Surface Area of Cylinders	8.7(B)
529	**Hands-On Lab 6-a:** Changes in Scale	8.7(A)
531	**Lesson 6** Changes in Dimensions	8.7(A)
539	**21st Century Career** Space Architect	8.1(A), 8.7(A)

Chapter Review 541
Chapter Reflect 544

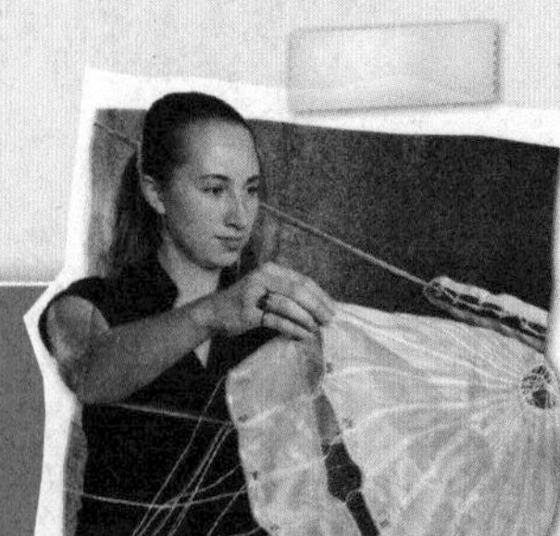

Go to page 539 to learn about a 21st Century Career in Architecture!

Chapter 8 Transformations and Congruence

What Tools Do You Need? 546
When Will You Use This? 547
Are You Ready? 548
Foldable 549

Page		TEKS
551	**Hands-On Lab 1-a:** Transformations	8.10(A)
555	**Lesson 1** Translations	8.10(A), 8.10(B)
563	**Lesson 2** Reflections	8.10(A), 8.10(B)
571	**Focus on Mathematical Processes:** Act It Out	8.1(B), 8.10(C)
574	Mid-Chapter Check	
575	**Hands-On Lab 3-a:** Rotational Symmetry	8.10(A)
577	**Lesson 3** Rotations	8.10(A), 8.10(B)
585	**Hands-On Lab 4-a:** Composition of Transformations	8.10(A), 8.10(B)
589	**Lesson 4** Congruence and Transformations	8.10(A), 8.10(B)
597	**Hands-On Lab 5-a:** Investigate Congruent Triangles	8.10(A), 8.10(B)
601	**Lesson 5** Congruence	8.10(A), 8.10(B)
609	**Geometry Software Lab 5-b:** Transformations and Congruence	8.10(A)
611	**21st Century Career** Computer Animator	8.1(A), 8.10(A)

Chapter Review 613
Chapter Reflect 616

Go to page 611 to learn about a 21st Century Career in
Computer Animation!

Chapter 9
Scatterplots and Data Analysis

What Tools Do You Need? 618
When Will You Use This? 619
Are You Ready? 620
Foldable 621

TEKS

623 **Hands-On Lab 1-a:** Construct Scatterplots 8.5(C), 8.11(A)
625 **Lesson 1** Scatterplots and Association 8.5(C), 8.11(A)

635 **Hands-On Lab 2-a:** Model Trend Lines 8.5(D), 8.11(A)
637 **Lesson 2** Use Trend Lines to Make Predictions 8.5(D), 8.11(A)
645 **Graphing Technology Lab 2-b:** Linear and Non-Linear Association 8.5(C), 8.11(A)

649 **Focus on Mathematical Processes:** Use a Scatterplot 8.1(B), 8.11(A)

Mid-Chapter Check 652

653 **Lesson 3** Descriptive Statistics 8.11(B)

661 **Lesson 4** Mean Absolute Deviation 8.11(B)

669 **Lesson 5** Analyze Data Distributions 8.11(B)

677 **Lesson 6** Random Samples 8.11(C)
685 **Virtual Manipulative Lab 6-b:** Simulate Random Samples 8.11(C)

687 **21st Century Career** Sports Marketer 8.1(A), 8.5(D)

Chapter Review 689
Chapter Reflect 692

Go to page 687 to learn about a 21st Century Career in **Sports Marketing!**

Chapter 10
Personal Financial Literacy

What Tools Do You Need? 694
When Will You Use This? 695
Are You Ready? 696

TEKS

697	**Lesson 1**	Loans and Interest Rates	8.12(A), 8.12(B)
701	**Lesson 2**	Savings and Investments	8.12(C), 8.12(D)
705	**Lesson 3**	Shopping: Payment Methods	8.12(E)
709	**Lesson 4**	Financial Responsibility	8.12(F)
713	**Lesson 5**	Saving for College	8.12(G)

Chapter Review 717
Chapter Reflect 720

Texas Essential Knowledge and Skills, Grade 8

Track Your TEKS Progress

The knowledge and skills that you will learn this year are listed on these pages. Throughout the year, your teacher will ask you to rate how confident you feel about your knowledge of each one. Don't worry if you have no clue **before** you learn about them. You will rate your knowledge before and after you learn them. Your teacher will provide you with more instructions. Watch how your knowledge and skills grow as the year progresses!

☹ I have no clue. 😐 I've heard of it. ☺ I know it!

8.1 Mathematical Process Standards		Before ☹	Before 😐	Before ☺	After ☹	After 😐	After ☺
The student uses mathematical processes to acquire and demonstrate mathematical understanding. The student is expected to:							
8.1(A)	Apply mathematics to problems arising in everyday life, society, and the workplace;						
8.1(B)	Use a problem-solving model that incorporates analyzing given information, formulating a plan or strategy, determining a solution, justifying the solution, and evaluating the problem-solving process and the reasonableness of the solution;						
8.1(C)	Select tools, including real objects, manipulatives, paper and pencil, and technology as appropriate, and techniques, including mental math, estimation, and number sense as appropriate, to solve problems;						
8.1(D)	Communicate mathematical ideas, reasoning, and their implications using multiple representations, including symbols, diagrams, graphs, and language as appropriate;						
8.1(E)	Create and use representations to organize, record, and communicate mathematical ideas;						
8.1(F)	Analyze mathematical relationships to connect and communicate mathematical ideas; and						
8.1(G)	Display, explain, and justify mathematical ideas and arguments using precise mathematical language in written or oral communication.						

8.2 Number and Operations	Before: ☹	Before: 😐	Before: ☺	After: ☹	After: 😐	After: ☺
The student applies mathematical process standards to represent and use real numbers in a variety of forms. The student is expected to:						
8.2(A) Extend previous knowledge of sets and subsets using a visual representation to describe relationships between sets of real numbers;						
8.2(B) Approximate the value of an irrational number, including π and square roots of numbers less than 225, and locate that rational number approximation on a number line;						
8.2(C) Convert between standard decimal notation and scientific notation; and						
8.2(D) Order a set of real numbers arising from mathematical and real-world contexts.						

8.3 Proportionality	Before: ☹	Before: 😐	Before: ☺	After: ☹	After: 😐	After: ☺
The student applies mathematical process standards to use proportional relationships to describe dilations. The student is expected to:						
8.3(A) Generalize that the ratio of corresponding sides of similar shapes are proportional, including a shape and its dilation;						
8.3(B) Compare and contrast the attributes of a shape and its dilation(s) on a coordinate plane; and						
8.3(C) Use an algebraic representation to explain the effect of a given positive rational scale factor applied to two-dimensional figures on a coordinate plane with the origin as the center of dilation.						

8.4 Proportionality	Before: ☹	Before: 😐	Before: ☺	After: ☹	After: 😐	After: ☺
The student applies mathematical process standards to explain proportional and non-proportional relationships involving slope. The student is expected to:						
8.4(A) Use similar right triangles to develop an understanding that slope, *m*, given as the rate comparing the change in *y*-values to the change in *x*-values, $\frac{(y_2-y_1)}{(x_2-x_1)}$, is the same for any two points (x_1, y_1) and (x_2, y_2) on the same line;						
8.4(B) Graph proportional relationships, interpreting the unit rate as the slope of the line that models the relationship; and						
8.4(C) Use data from a table or graph to determine the rate of change or slope and *y*-intercept in mathematical and real-world problems.						

8.5 Proportionality		Before ☹	Before 😐	Before ☺	After ☹	After 😐	After ☺
The student applies mathematical process standards to use proportional and non-proportional relationships to develop foundational concepts of functions. The student is expected to:							
8.5(A)	Represent linear proportional situations with tables, graphs, and equations in the form of $y = kx$;						
8.5(B)	Represent linear non-proportional situations with tables, graphs, and equations in the form of $y = mx + b$, where $b \neq 0$;						
8.5(C)	Contrast bivariate sets of data that suggest a linear relationship with bivariate sets of data that do not suggest a linear relationship from a graphical representation;						
8.5(D)	Use a trend line that approximates the linear relationship between bivariate sets of data to make predictions;						
8.5(E)	Solve problems involving direct variation;						
8.5(F)	Distinguish between proportional and non-proportional situations using tables, graphs, and equations in the form $y = kx$ or $y = mx + b$, where $b \neq 0$;						
8.5(G)	Identify functions using sets of ordered pairs, tables, mappings, and graphs;						
8.5(H)	Identify examples of proportional and non-proportional functions that arise from mathematical and real-world problems; and						
8.5(I)	Write an equation in the form $y = mx + b$ to model a linear relationship between two quantities using verbal, numerical, tabular, and graphical representations.						

8.6 Expressions, Equations, and Relationships	Before: ☹	Before: 😐	Before: ☺	After: ☹	After: 😐	After: ☺
The student applies mathematical process standards to develop mathematical relationships and make connections to geometric formulas. The student is expected to:						
8.6(A) Describe the volume formula $V = Bh$ of a cylinder in terms of its base area and its height;						
8.6(B) Model the relationship between the volume of a cylinder and a cone having both congruent bases and heights and connect that relationship to the formulas; and						
8.6(C) Use models and diagrams to explain the Pythagorean theorem.						

8.7 Expressions, Equations, and Relationships	Before: ☹	Before: 😐	Before: ☺	After: ☹	After: 😐	After: ☺
The student applies mathematical process standards to use geometry to solve problems. The student is expected to:						
8.7(A) Solve problems involving the volume of cylinders, cones, and spheres;						
8.7(B) Use previous knowledge of surface area to make connections to the formulas for lateral and total surface area and determine solutions for problems involving rectangular prisms, triangular prisms, and cylinders;						
8.7(C) Use the Pythagorean Theorem and its converse to solve problems; and						
8.7(D) Determine the distance between two points on a coordinate plane using the Pythagorean Theorem.						

8.8 Expressions, Equations, and Relationships	Before			After		
The student applies mathematical process standards to use one-variable equations or inequalities in problem situations. The student is expected to:						
8.8(A) Write one-variable equations or inequalities with variables on both sides that represent problems using rational number coefficients and constants;						
8.8(B) Write a corresponding real-world problem when given a one-variable equation or inequality with variables on both sides of the equal sign using rational number coefficients and constants;						
8.8(C) Model and solve one-variable equations with variables on both sides of the equal sign that represent mathematical and real-world problems using rational number coefficients and constants; and						
8.8(D) Use informal arguments to establish facts about the angle sum and exterior angle of triangles, the angles created when parallel lines are cut by a transversal, and the angle-angle criterion for similarity of triangles.						

8.9 Expressions, Equations, and Relationships	Before			After		
The student applies mathematical process standards to use multiple representations to develop foundational concepts of simultaneous linear equations. The student is expected to:						
Identify and verify the values of x and y that simultaneously satisfy two linear equations in the form $y = mx + b$ from the intersections of the graphed equations.						

8.10 Two-Dimensional Shapes		Before ☹	Before 😐	Before ☺	After ☹	After 😐	After ☺
The student applies mathematical process standards to develop transformational geometry concepts. The student is expected to:							
8.10(A)	Generalize the properties of orientation and congruence of rotations, reflections, translations, and dilations of two-dimensional shapes on a coordinate plane;						
8.10(B)	Differentiate between transformations that preserve congruence and those that do not;						
8.10(C)	Explain the effect of translations, reflections over the *x*- or *y*-axis, and rotations limited to 90°, 180°, 270°, and 360° as applied to two-dimensional shapes on a coordinate plane using an algebraic representation; and						
8.10(D)	Model the effect on linear and area measurements of dilated two-dimensional shapes.						

8.11 Measurement and Data		Before ☹	Before 😐	Before ☺	After ☹	After 😐	After ☺
The student applies mathematical process standards to use statistical procedures to describe data. The student is expected to:							
8.11(A)	Construct a scatterplot and describe the observed data to address questions of association such as linear, non-linear, and no association between bivariate data;						
8.11(B)	Determine the mean absolute deviation and use this quantity as a measure of the average distance data are from the mean using a data set of no more than 10 data points; and						
8.11(C)	Simulate generating random samples of the same size from a population with known characteristics to develop the notion of a random sample being representative of the population from which it was selected.						

8.12 Personal Financial Literacy	Before ☹	Before 😐	Before ☺	After ☹	After 😐	After ☺
The student applies mathematical process standards to develop an economic way of thinking and problem solving useful in one's life as a knowledgeable consumer and investor. The student is expected to:						
8.12(A) Solve real-world problems comparing how interest rate and loan length affect the cost of credit;						
8.12(B) Calculate the total cost of repaying a loan, including credit cards and easy access loans, under various rates of interest and over different periods using an online calculator;						
8.12(C) Explain how small amounts of money invested regularly, including money saved for college and retirement, grow over time;						
8.12(D) Calculate and compare simple interest and compound interest earnings;						
8.12(E) Identify and explain the advantages and disadvantages of different payment methods;						
8.12(F) Analyze situations to determine if they represent financially responsible decisions and identify the benefits of financial responsibility and the costs of financial irresponsibility; and						
8.12(G) Estimate the cost of a two-year and four-year college education, including family contribution, and devise a periodic savings plan for accumulating the money needed to contribute to the total cost of attendance for at least the first year of college.						

Mathematical Processes Handbook

Texas Essential Knowledge and Skills

Targeted TEKS

8.1 The student uses mathematical processes to acquire and demonstrate mathematical understanding.

Mathematical Processes

8.1, 8.1(A), 8.1(B), 8.1(C), 8.1(D), 8.1(E), 8.1(F), 8.1(G)

Essential Question

WHAT processes help me develop and demonstrate mathematical understanding?

What You'll Learn

MP The mathematical process standards listed below will help you to become a successful problem solver and to use math effectively in your daily life. Throughout this handbook, you will learn about each of these mathematical processes and how they are integrated in the chapters and lessons of this book.

Focus on Mathematical Process A. 3

MP **Apply Math to the Real World** Apply mathematics to problems arising in everyday life, society, and the workplace.

Focus on Mathematical Process B. 5

MP **Use a Problem-Solving Model** Use a problem-solving model that incorporates analyzing given information, formulating a plan or strategy, determining a solution, justifying the solution, and evaluating the problem-solving process and the reasonableness of the solution.

Focus on Mathematical Process C. 7

MP **Select Tools and Techniques** Select tools, including real objects, manipulatives, paper and pencil, and technology as appropriate, and techniques, including mental math, estimation, and number sense as appropriate, to solve problems.

Focus on Mathematical Process D. 9

MP **Use Multiple Representations** Communicate mathematical ideas, reasoning, and their implications using multiple representations, including symbols, diagrams, graphs, and language as appropriate.

Focus on Mathematical Process E. 11

MP **Organize Ideas** Create and use representations to organize, record, and communicate mathematical ideas.

Focus on Mathematical Process F. 13

MP **Analyze Relationships** Analyze mathematical relationships to connect and communicate mathematical ideas.

Focus on Mathematical Process G. 15

MP **Justify Arguments** Display, explain, and justify mathematical ideas and arguments using precise mathematical language in written or oral communication.

Apply the Mathematical Processes to Every Lesson

Use the chart at the beginning of each lesson throughout this text to select which processes you used to solve a particular problem.

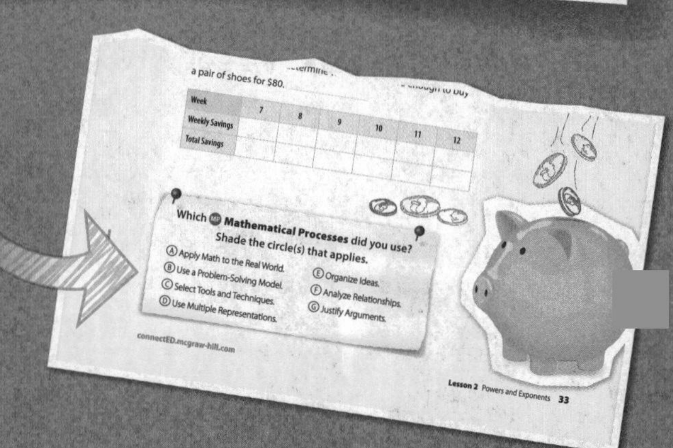

Apply Math to the Real World

How does math fit into your future?

No matter what career path you choose, you are sure to use math in your job or career. Suppose you are a doctor or a nurse. A prescription directs a patient to take 2.5 cc (cubic centimeters) of a medicine per 50 pounds of body weight.

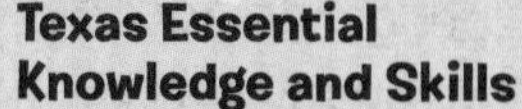

Texas Essential Knowledge and Skills

Targeted TEKS
8.1(A) Apply mathematics to problems arising in everyday life, society, and the workplace.

1. What skill(s) would you use to see how much medicine you should give to a 125 pound person?

   Rasio

2. How much medicine would the 125 pound patient need?

3. What career path interests you? Research that career and complete the graphic organizer below.

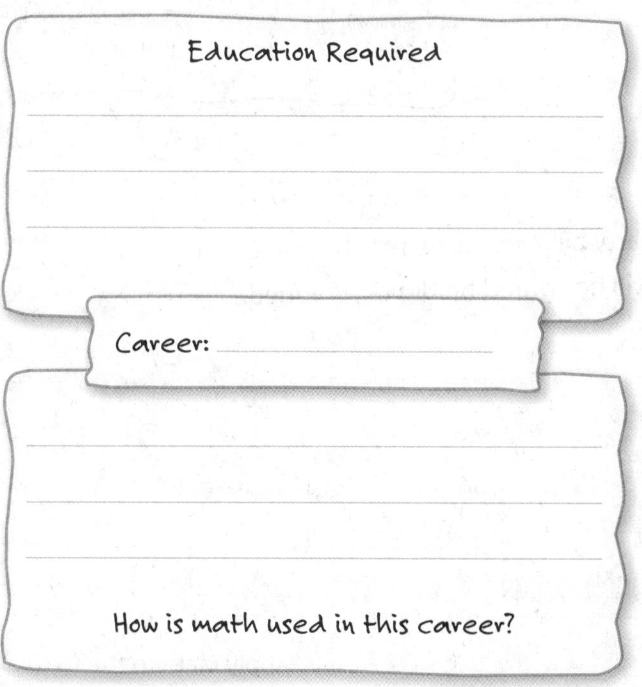

Education Required
Career:
How is math used in this career?

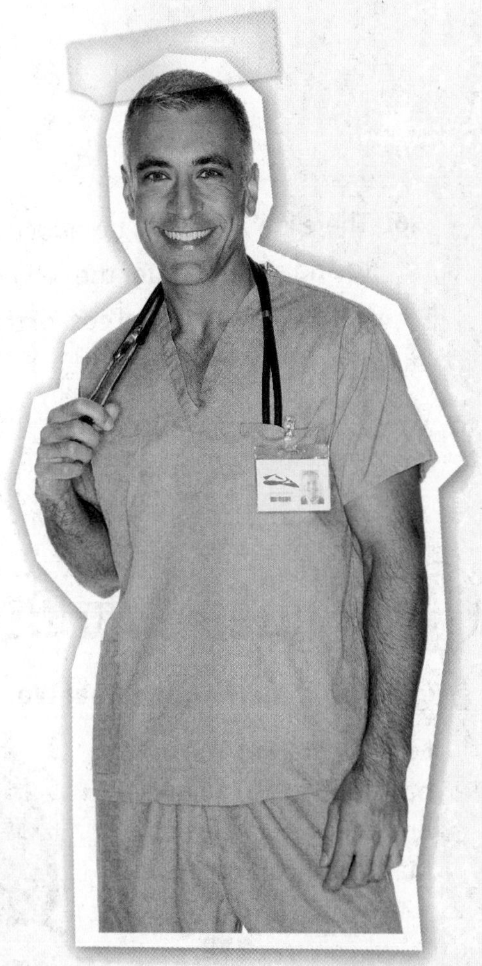

It's Your Turn!

List the skills needed to solve each exercise. Then solve.

4. You are in the pit crew for a driver at a Nascar race. The gas weighs 5.92 pounds per gallon. Your driver uses 0.25 gallon per lap. With 42 laps to go, you put 60 pounds of fuel in the tank of the car. Will your driver finish the race at the same rate without more gas? Explain.

Use the table for Exercises 5 and 6.

5. Mrs. Gutierrez hired a party planner to plan Carina's quinceañera. There will be 125 guests and she wants to offer appetizers and a buffet dinner. What is the cost, before tax, for the party?

Polly's Perfect Parties			
Cost of Food (per person)		Cost of Extras	
Appetizers	\$9.20	Hall	\$250
Buffet	\$18.30	Linens	\$15 per table
Sit-down Dinner	\$25.75	Table and Chair Rental (seats 8)	\$60 per table

6. There is a $7\frac{1}{2}$% sales tax added to the party bill. Mrs. Gutierrez also wants to add an 18% tip for the servers. This will be figured before tax is added. What will be the total cost of the party?

Find it in Your Book!

MP Apply Math to the Real World

Look at Chapter 1. Write the page number(s) where you find these examples of Mathematical Process A.

_______ Apply Math to the Real World exercises

_______ Graphic Novels

_______ 21st Century Career

Use a Problem-Solving Model

Why do I need a problem-solving model?

Texas Essential Knowledge and Skills

Targeted TEKS

8.1(B) Use a problem-solving model that incorporates analyzing given information, formulating a plan or strategy, determining a solution, justifying the solution, and evaluating the problem-solving process and the reasonableness of the solution.

Using a problem-solving model to solve a problem is like using directions to build a piece of furniture. If you follow the directions correctly, there is a good chance you will end up with a solid piece of furniture. If you don't follow the steps in order, who knows what you will have!

You have already used the four-step problem-solving plan in previous courses. Complete the graphic organizer that shows the four steps to solve the given problem.

Of the 480 students at Lincoln Middle School, one third have traveled overseas. Of these, 15% have been to Australia. How many students have not been to Australia?

Step 1. Analyze

What do you need to determine?

Step 2. Plan

What strategy will you use to solve the problem above?

Step 3. Solve

Solve the problem. Show your steps below.

Step 4. Justify and Evaluate

How do you know your answer is reasonable?

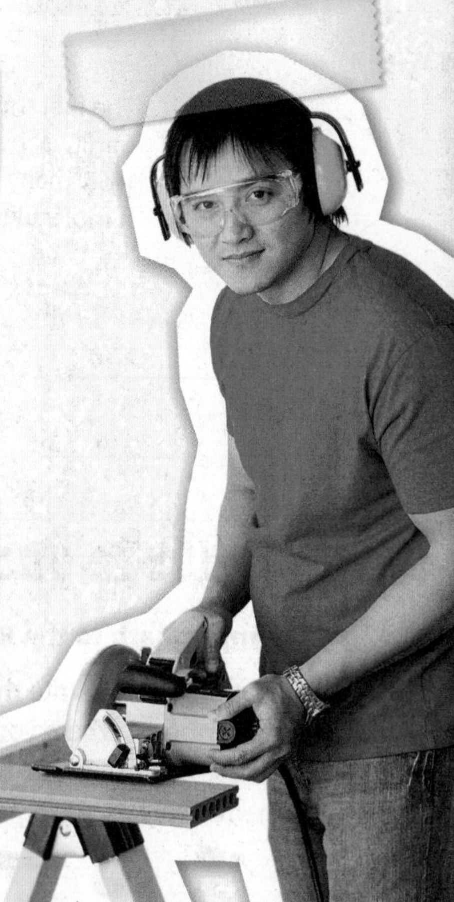

It's Your Turn!

Solve each problem by using the four-step problem-solving model.

1. Seventy percent of the population of Texas lives within a 200-mile radius of Austin. If the total area of Texas is 267,339 square miles, about what percent of the total land area is within 200 miles of Austin?

   Analyze Circle the information you know and underline what you are trying to find. Is there any information you will not use?

   Plan How will you solve this problem?

   Solve Solve the problem. Show your steps below. What is the solution?

   Justify and Evaluate Does your answer make sense? Can you solve the problem another way to check your work?

2. The first three molecules for a certain family of hydrocarbons are shown. How many hydrogen atoms (H) are in a molecule containing 6 carbon atoms (C)?

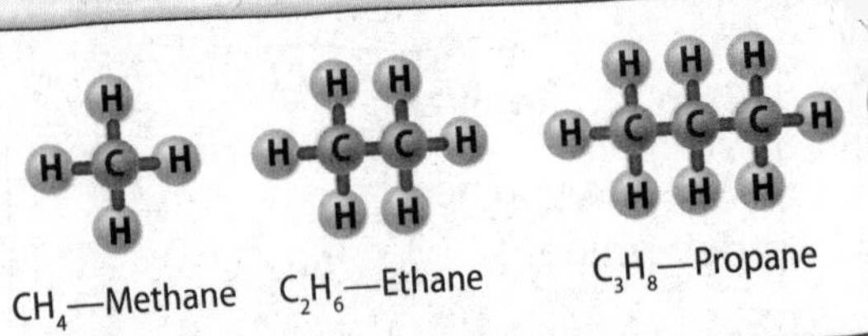

Find it in Your Book!

MP Apply Math to the Real World

Look at Chapter 1. Write the page number(s) where you find these examples of Mathematical Process B.

_____ Use a Problem-Solving Model exercises

_____ Multi-Step Problem-Solving exercises

_____ Focus on Mathematical Processes lesson

Select Tools and Techniques

How do I use tools and techniques in math class?

Texas Essential Knowledge and Skills

Targeted TEKS

8.1(C) Select tools, including real objects, manipulatives, paper and pencil, and technology as appropriate, and techniques, including mental math, estimation, and number sense as appropriate, to solve problems.

Sometimes using math tools and techniques helps make solving problems easier. Math tools are physical objects you use when solving problems. Math tools can be paper and pencil, technology, or calculators.

1. List three other tools you can use to solve math problems.

Math techniques are more like skills or the ability to apply your math knowledge. Some math techniques are mental math, number sense, estimation, drawing a diagram, solving a simpler problem, etc.

2. List three other techniques you can use to solve math problems.

3. Complete the graphic organizer.

Problem	Tool	Technique
You want to leave a 20% tip for your server.		
You want to determine how long it will take to drive from Austin to Dallas.		
You are stuck while in the middle of solving an equation.		

It's Your Turn!

List the tools or techniques you would use to solve each problem. Then solve the problem.

4. A pre-election survey was taken in Ms. Bowen's homeroom. The results for class president are shown in the table.

Class President	
Elan	10
Karam	8
Magdalena	20
Sara	12

   a. Based on the survey, if there are 850 students in the 8th grade, how many votes will Magdalena get?

   ____

   b. A candidate needs to receive at least 51% of the votes to win the election. If every student votes, how many more votes would Magdalena need to win?

   ____

5. A walking path around a lake is in the shape of a pentagon like the one shown. If Natalie wants to walk $4\frac{1}{2}$ miles, how many times does she need to walk around the lake?

____

____

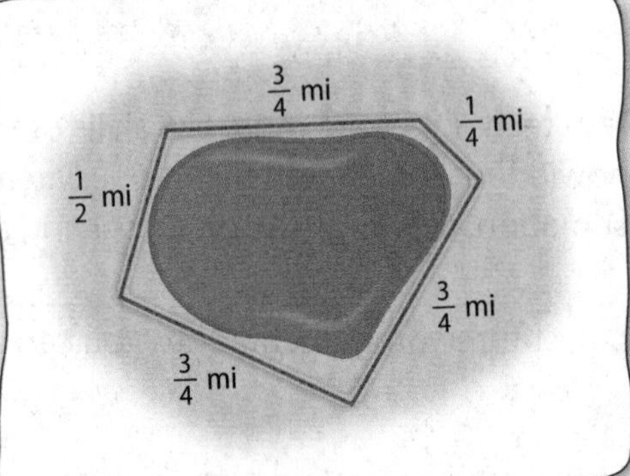

6. The infield for the Texas Longhorns baseball team is a square 90 feet on each side. If a player can run the bases at an average speed of about 8 meters per second, about how long will it take the player to run the bases? Round to the nearest tenth.

____

Find it in Your Book!

MP Select Tools and Techniques

Look at Chapter 1. Write the page number(s) where you find these examples of Mathematical Process C.

__________ Select Tools and Techniques exercises

__________ Hands-On Labs

__________ Graphing Technology Labs

Use Multiple Representations

What does it mean to use multiple representations?

Texas Essential Knowledge and Skills

Targeted TEKS

8.1(D) Communicate mathematical ideas, reasoning, and their implications using multiple representations, including symbols, diagrams, graphs, and language as appropriate.

In math, we use multiple representations to model relationships and to solve problems. Some of the different representations we use are tables, graphs, symbols, diagrams, and words.

Suppose you are training for a marathon. A marathon is 26.2 miles long. You can run 3 miles in 16 minutes. In how many different ways can you represent this relationship?

1. At this rate, how many miles can you run in one hour?

____

2. Assume your rate remains constant. Complete the graphic organizer to show the different representations of the relationship between distance and time.

Words

_______ miles per hour

Numbers

Time (h)	Distance (mi)
1	
2	
3	

Symbols

Let d = distance run and t = time in hours.

d = _______ t

Graph

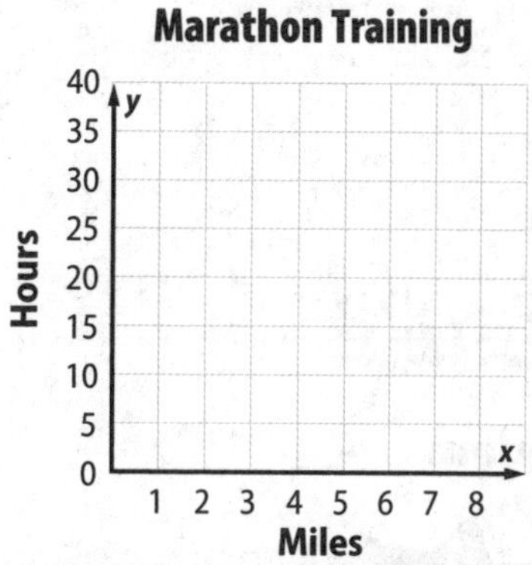

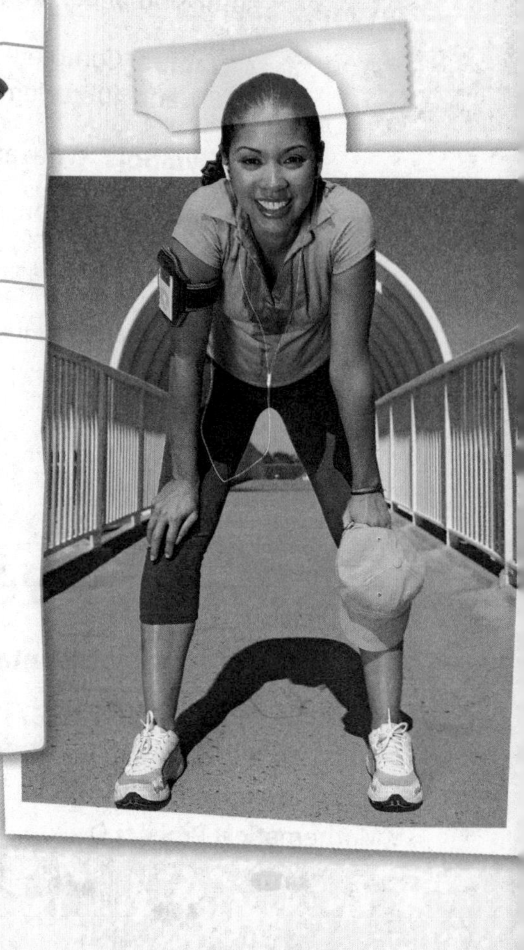

3. About how long will it take to complete the marathon?

____

It's Your Turn!

Use the multiple representations shown to solve each problem.

4. You are saving money to buy a new game system. You received $50 as a birthday gift from your grandparents. You want to save $25 a week from mowing lawns.

    a. **Tables** Complete the table to show the total amount saved after 1, 2, 3, 4, and 5 weeks.

Week, w	Total Saved, s ($)

    b. **Symbols** Write an equation to show the total amount saved s after w weeks. ______

    c. **Algebra** Use the equation to determine the total amount saved after 17 weeks. ______

5. A class trip is scheduled for Six Flags Over Texas. Group admission prices are $31 per student. Parking is $18 per bus.

    a. **Tables** Complete the table to show the total cost for 10, 20, 30, and 40 students.

Number of Students, s	Total Cost, c ($)

    b. **Symbols** Write an equation to show the total cost c if two buses transport s students to the park. ______

    c. **Algebra** There are a total of 78 students attending on two buses. What is the total cost? ______

Find it in Your Book!

MP Use Multiple Representations

Look at Chapter 4. Write the page number(s) where you find these examples of Mathematical Process D.

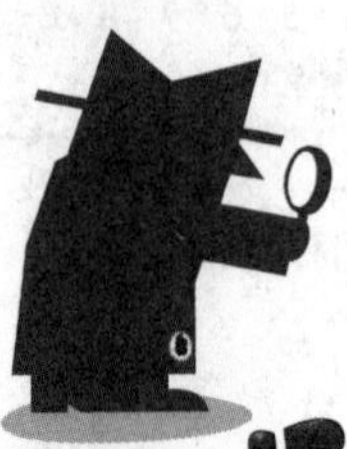

______ Use Multiple Representations exercises

Organize Ideas

What does it mean to organize ideas in math?

Texas Essential Knowledge and Skills

Targeted TEKS

8.1(E) Create and use representations to organize, record, and communicate mathematical ideas.

Suppose you want to suggest a Texas location for the eighth-grade class trip. How can you organize and record the pros and cons about a particular place?

Just like you can record information about a class trip, you can create ways to organize, record, and then communicate mathematical ideas.

1. Complete the graphic organizer to communicate all of the pros and cons of the place you have chosen. You can add more bubbles if needed.

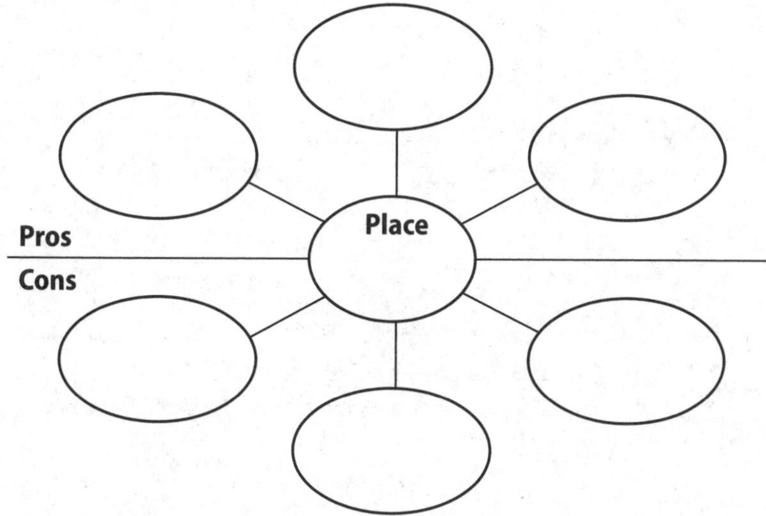

Throughout this text, you will complete graphic organizers and tables to help record and connect mathematical ideas. You can also take notes in the margins of your text and/or on a separate piece of paper.

2. On a separate piece of paper, create a notes page that you can use to organize the information in Chapter 1. You may want to include a column for vocabulary, a column for Key Concepts, and a column for questions you may have.

It's Your Turn!

3. Another kind of graphic organizer is a Foldable. Foldables are three-dimensional graphic organizers that help you create study guides. Look through Chapter 1 in your text. Describe the Foldable you will create for this chapter. How do you think it will help you organize the information you will learn in Chapter 1?

____

____

____

4. Turn to page 25 in your text. Find the vocabulary term *rational number* and complete the graphic organizer for that term.

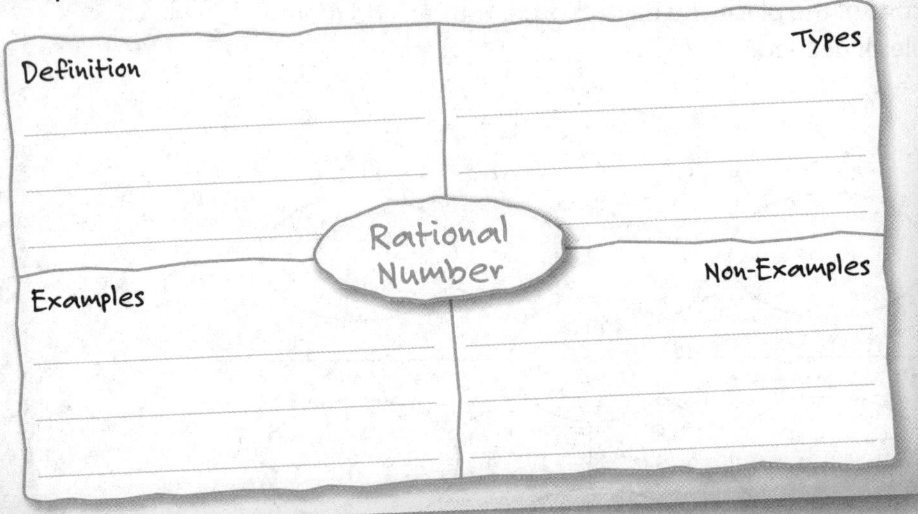

Find it in Your Book!

MP Organize Ideas

Look at Chapter 1. Write the page number(s) where you find these examples of Mathematical Process E.

__________ Organize Ideas exercises

__________ Foldables

__________ Graphic organizers

Analyze Relationships

What does it mean to analyze relationships in math?

Texas Essential Knowledge and Skills

Targeted TEKS

8.1(F) Analyze mathematical relationships to connect and communicate mathematical ideas.

When you analyze relationships in math, you make connections between what you have already seen, what you know, and new situations that use a similar kind of thinking. Making these connections can help you learn and understand related concepts better.

1. The table shows the diameters of several flying discs. Use the relationship between the radius and diameter of a circle to complete the table. Round to the nearest tenth.

Diameter (cm)	Radius (cm)	Circumference (cm)	Area (cm^2)
20			
22			
25			

2. Describe the relationship between the diameter and radius of a circle. ______

3. Describe the relationship between the circumference and diameter of a circle. ______

______

4. Complete the graphic organizer by writing a formula in each box that shows the relationship between each term.

Diameter and Radius

Radius and Circumference

Diameter and Area

It's Your Turn!

The scores for the winning and losing teams in the Cotton Bowl are shown in the double bar graph. Use this information to complete Exercises 5–7.

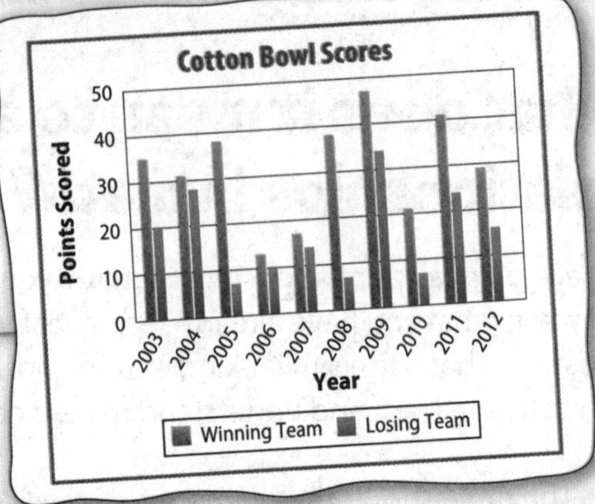

5. In what years was the winning score more than twice the losing score?

6. Using the information given, can you make a prediction about the scores for the 2013 Cotton Bowl? Explain your reasoning.

7. Using the information in the graph, write a question and answer about the relationships shown. Then exchange with a classmate and compare your work.

8. Model trains come in different scales. The ratio for an HO scale train is 1:87, while the ratio for a Z scale train is 1:220. Suppose a Z scale model of a steam engine is 62 millimeters long. What is the length of the HO scale model of the same engine? Round to the nearest millimeter.

Find it in Your Book!

MP Analyze Relationships

Look at Chapter 1. Write the page number(s) where you find these examples of Mathematical Process F.

_______ Analyze Relationships exercises

_______ Analyze exercises in H.O.T. problems

_______ Analyze and Reflect exercises in Hands-On Labs

Justify Arguments

How do I justify an argument in math class?

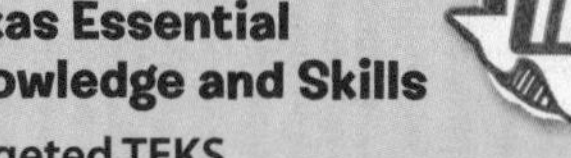

Texas Essential Knowledge and Skills

Targeted TEKS

8.1(G) Display, explain, and justify mathematical ideas and arguments using precise mathematical language in written or oral communication.

Suppose your friend told you that his rectangular flatscreen T.V. has congruent diagonals, simply because it was rectangular. How could you ask your friend to justify his argument? You could use inductive reasoning or deductive reasoning. *Inductive reasoning* uses examples to draw conclusions, while *deductive reasoning* uses definitions, rules, or facts.

1. How could you use *inductive reasoning* to justify why the following statement is true?
   All rectangles have diagonals that are congruent.

2. How could you use *deductive reasoning* to justify why the following statement is false?
   Each angle of an equilateral triangle measures 90°.

3. Complete the graphic organizer to show that the statement below is *sometimes* true.

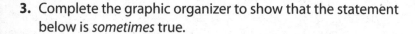

The product of two integers is positive.

Example when it is true:	Example when it is false:

It's Your Turn!

For each of the following statements, determine if the statement is *always*, *sometimes*, or *never* true. Justify your response.

4. The sum of two rational numbers is a rational number.

5. The sum of two odd numbers is an odd number.

6. The volume of a pyramid is less than the volume of a prism with the same size base.

7. The state flag of Texas is in the shape of a rectangle with a width to length ratio of two to three. The shorter side of the blue stripe is one-third of the entire length of the flag. Suppose a flag is 45 inches wide. Kiely thinks the shorter side of the blue stripe should be 15 inches wide. Is she correct? Justify your response.

Find it in Your Book!

MP Justify Arguments

Look at Chapter 1. Write the page number(s) where you find these examples of Mathematical Process G.

______ Justify Arguments exercises

______ Evaluate exercises in H.O.T. problems

Review

Use the Mathematical Processes

Solve.

You are boxing and wrapping gifts for a club fundraiser. The charge to wrap a gift in the shape of a rectangular prism is shown in the table.

Total Surface Area	Cost
up to 35 in^2	$5
36–54 in^2	$8
over 55 in^2	$12

a. Marina wrapped three different boxes with measurements shown in the table. Complete the table with the cost per box and the cost per square inch. Which box has the least cost per square inch? ______

Box	height in.	width in.	length in.	Cost to Wrap	Cost per Square Inch
A	2	4	3		
B	2	5	6		
C	2	3	2		

b. Which of those boxes has the least cost per cubic inch? Explain.

Look Ahead

Determine which mathematical processes you used to determine the solution. Shade the circles that apply.

Which MP Mathematical Processes did you use?
Shade the circle(s) that applies.

Ⓐ Apply Math to the Real World.
Ⓑ Use a Problem-Solving Model.
Ⓒ Select Tools and Techniques.
Ⓓ Use Multiple Representations.
Ⓔ Organize Ideas.
Ⓕ Analyze Relationships.
Ⓖ Justify Arguments.

Reflect

Answering the Essential Question

Use what you learned about the mathematical processes to complete the graphic organizer. List three processes that help you best demonstrate mathematical understand. Then give an example for each process.

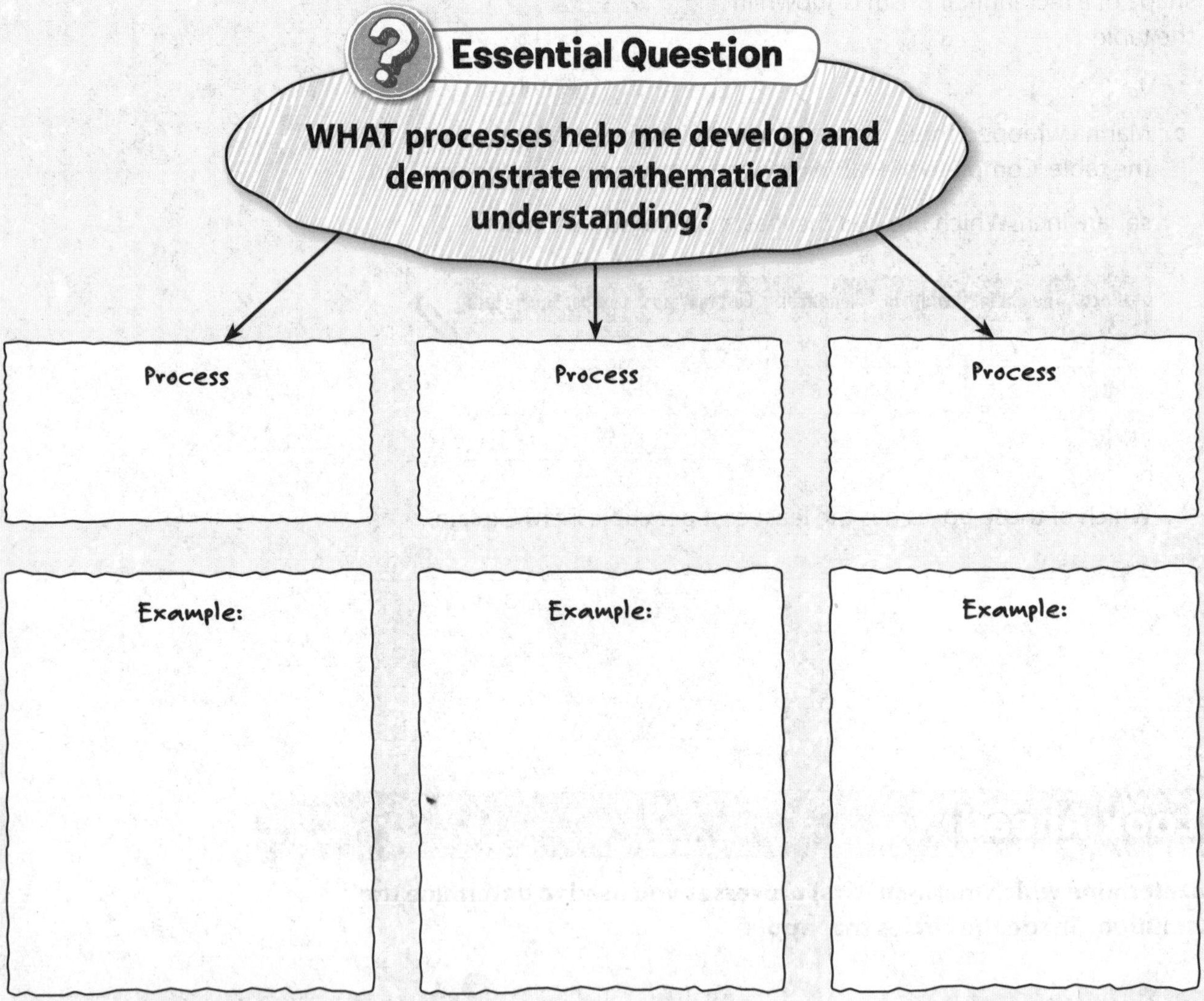

Essential Question

WHAT processes help me develop and demonstrate mathematical understanding?

Process	Process	Process

Example:	Example:	Example:

Answer the Essential Question. WHAT processes help me develop and demonstrate mathematical understanding?

Chapter 1
Real Numbers

Texas Essential Knowledge and Skills

Targeted TEKS

8.2 The student applies mathematical process standards to represent and use real numbers in a variety of forms.

Mathematical Processes

8.1, 8.1(A), 8.1(B), 8.1(C), 8.1(D), 8.1(E), 8.1(F), 8.1(G)

Essential Question

WHY is it helpful to write numbers in different ways?

Math in the Real World

Space The Lyndon B. Johnson Space Center, in Houston, Texas, trains astronauts to prepare them for the extreme speeds they will endure while traveling in space. The International Space Station travels about 17,500 miles per hour while orbiting Earth in about 1.5 hours. Find the distance in miles that the space station would travel in this time.

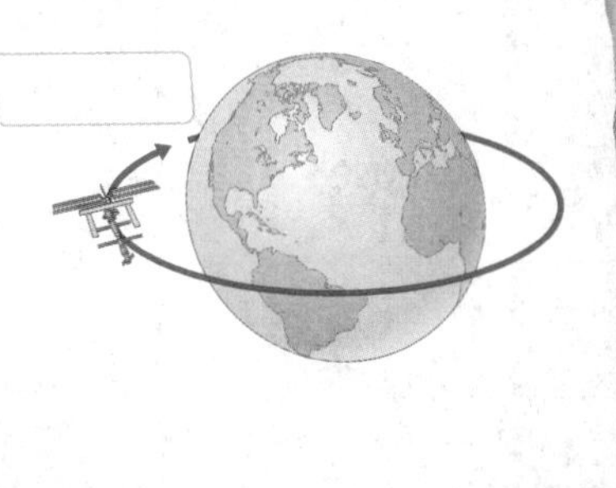

Go Online! www.connectED.mcgraw-hill.com

Watch 
Worksheets 
Vocab 
Tutor 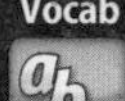
Tools 
Check 

What Tools Do You Need?

Vocabulary

base
cube root
exponent
irrational number
perfect cube
perfect square
power
radical sign
rational number
real number
repeating decimal
scientific notation
square root
terminating decimal

Use a Mnemonic Device

When a mathematical expression has a combination of operations, the order of operations tells you which operation to perform first. How can you remember the orders easily? A mnemonic device is a verse or phrase to help you remember something.

In this case, it is *P*lease *E*xcuse *M*y *D*ear *A*unt *S*ally. Work with a partner to fill in each rung of the ladder with the operation that the mnemonic device represents. Then evaluate the numerical expression step-by-step. Ask your partner for help, if needed.

$3(5 - 15)^2 - 7 \cdot 3 + 24 \div 6$

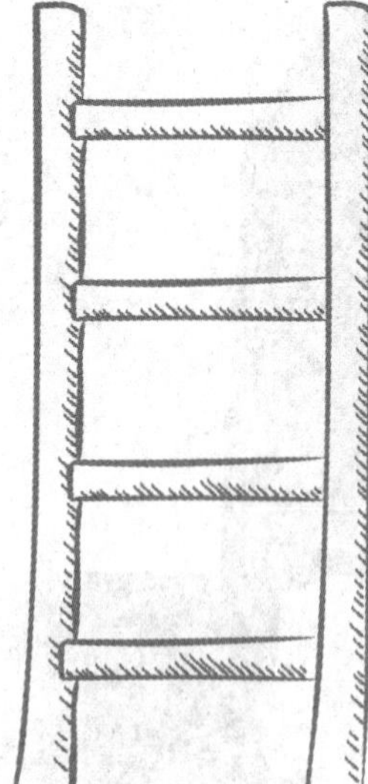

Please Parenthases

Excuse Exponents

My Dear Multiplication Division

Aunt Sally Addition Subtraction

When Will You Use This?

Jacob and Sarah in

Measuring Up

1km=1,
1cm=0.01m
1mm=0.001m
1 nm

The nanometer is a unit for measuring things that are quite small...

... and equals only 1 billionth of a meter.

3.75 m

3.75 m = 3,750,000,000 nm

Hmm, if we can measure a tree that way...

I'm sure we could measure ourselves in nanometers, too.

Looks like you're 1.52 meters tall.

...and I'm 1.7 meters.

So to count nanometers...

I'm going to need a LOT more fingers.

Your Turn! **You will solve this problem in the chapter.**

Are You Ready?

Quick Review

Example 1

Determine 5 • 4 • 5 • 4 • 5.

$$5 \cdot 4 \cdot 5 \cdot 4 \cdot 5 = 4 \cdot 4 \cdot 5 \cdot 5 \cdot 5$$
$$= (4 \cdot 4) \cdot (5 \cdot 5 \cdot 5)$$
$$= 16 \cdot 125$$
$$= 2{,}000$$

Example 2

Determine the prime factorization of 60.

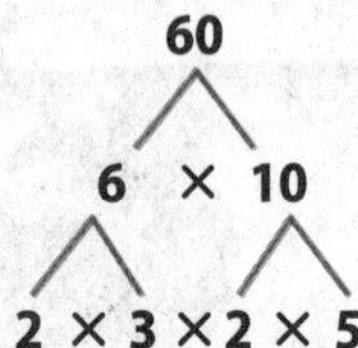

The prime factorization of 60 is $2 \times 2 \times 3 \times 5$.

Quick Check

Simplify Expressions **Determine each product.**

1. $2 \cdot 2 \cdot 4 \cdot 4 \cdot 4 =$ ________

2. $(-8)(-8)(5)(5)(-8) =$ ________

3. The students at Hampton Middle School raised $8 \cdot 8 \cdot 2 \cdot 8 \cdot 2$ dollars to help build a new community center. How much money did they raise? ________

Prime Factorization **Determine the prime factorization of each number.**

4. 36 ________
5. 24 ________
6. 18 ________
7. 100 ________
8. 121 ________
9. −42 ________

How Did You Do?

Which problems did you answer correctly in the Quick Check? Shade those exercise numbers below.

① ② ③ ④ ⑤ ⑥ ⑦ ⑧ ⑨

Lesson 1

Rational Numbers

Launch the Lesson: Vocabulary

Numbers that can be written as a comparison of two integers, expressed as a fraction, are called **rational numbers**.

Complete the graphic organizer.

Examples

Percent

Decimal

Rational Number

Define in your own words

Examples

Fraction

Mixed Numbers

The root of the word *rational* is *ratio*. Describe the relationship between rational numbers and ratios.

Texas Essential Knowledge and Skills

Targeted TEKS

Preparation for 8.2(C) Convert between standard decimal notation and scientific notation.

Mathematical Processes

8.1(A), 8.1(B), 8.1(F)

Vocab

Vocabulary

rational number

repeating decimal

terminating decimal

Essential Question

WHY is it helpful to write numbers in different ways?

Real-World Link

During a recent regular season, a Texas Ranger baseball player had 126 hits and was at bat 399 times. Write a fraction in simplest form to represent the ratio of the number of hits to the number of at bats.

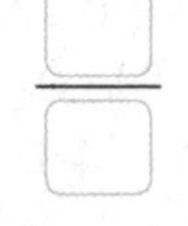

Which MP Mathematical Processes did you use? Shade the circle(s) that applies.

Ⓐ Apply Math to the Real World.

Ⓑ Use a Problem-Solving Model.

Ⓒ Select Tools and Techniques.

Ⓓ Use Multiple Representations.

Ⓔ Organize Ideas.

Ⓕ Analyze Relationships.

Ⓖ Justify Arguments.

Key Concept — Rational Numbers

Words A rational number is a number that can be written as the ratio of two integers in which the denominator is not zero.

Symbols $\frac{a}{b}$, where a and b are integers and $b \neq 0$

Model

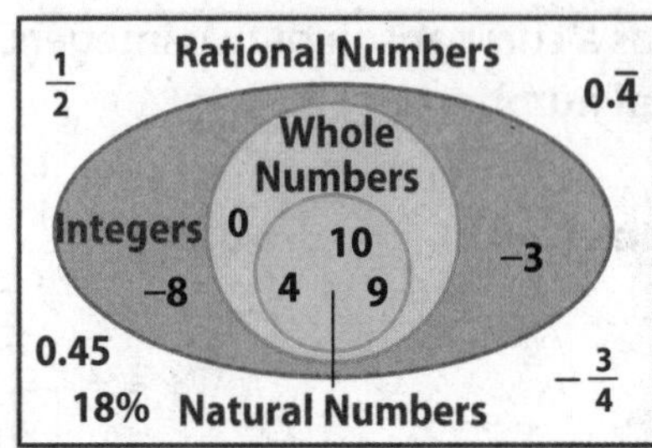

Work Zone

Bar Notation

Bar notation is often used to indicate that a digit or group of digits repeats. The bar is placed above the repeating part. To write 8.636363... in bar notation, write $8.\overline{63}$, not $8.\overline{6}$ or $8.\overline{636}$. To write 0.3444... in bar notation, write $0.3\overline{4}$, not $0.\overline{34}$.

Every rational number can be expressed as a decimal by dividing the numerator by the denominator. The decimal form of a rational number is called a **repeating decimal**. If the repeating digit is zero, then the decimal is a **terminating decimal**.

Rational Number	Repeating Decimal	Terminating Decimal
$\frac{1}{2}$	0.5000...	0.5
$\frac{2}{5}$	0.400...	0.4
$\frac{5}{6}$	0.833...	does not terminate

Examples

Tutor

Express each fraction or mixed number as a decimal.

1. $\frac{5}{8}$

$\frac{5}{8}$ means $5 \div 8$.

$$\begin{array}{r} 0.625 \\ 8\overline{)5.000} \\ -48 \\ \hline 20 \\ -16 \\ \hline 40 \\ -40 \\ \hline 0 \end{array}$$

Divide 5 by 8.

2. $-1\frac{2}{3}$

$-1\frac{2}{3}$ can be rewritten as $\frac{-5}{3}$.

$$\begin{array}{r} 1.6\ldots \\ 3\overline{)5.0} \\ -3 \\ \hline 20 \\ -18 \\ \hline 2 \end{array}$$

Divide 5 by 3 and add a negative sign.

The mixed number $-1\frac{2}{3}$ can be written as $-1.\overline{6}$.

Show your work.

Got It? Do these problems to find out.

a. $\frac{3}{4}$

b. $-\frac{2}{9}$

c. $4\frac{13}{25}$

d. $3\frac{1}{11}$

a. ________

b. ________

c. ________

d. ________

Multi-Step Example

Tutor

3. In a recent season, Albert Pujols had 175 hits in 530 at bats. At this pace, how many hits would Albert Pujols have in 590 at bats?

Step 1 Determine the batting average.

To determine his batting average, divide the number of hits, 175, by the number of at bats, 530.

175 [÷] 530 [ENTER] 0.3301886792

Albert Pujols's batting average was about 0.330.

Step 2 To determine the number of hits, multiply 590 and 0.330.

590 × 0.330 [ENTER] 194.7

At this pace, Albert Pujols would have about 195 hits in 590 at bats.

Got It? **Do these problems to find out.**

e. In a recent season, NASCAR driver Jimmie Johnson won 6 of the 36 total races held. To the nearest thousandth, determine the part of races he won.

e. ______________

Examples

Tutor

4. Express 0.45 as a fraction.

$0.45 = \frac{45}{100}$ — 0.45 is 45 hundredths.

$= \frac{9}{20}$ — Simplify.

5. Express $0.\overline{5}$ as a fraction in simplest form.

Assign a variable to the value $0.\overline{5}$. Let $N = 0.555...$. Then perform operations on N to determine its fractional value.

$N = 0.555...$

$10(N) = 10(0.555...)$ — Multiply each side by 10 because 1 digit repeats.

$10N = 5.555...$ — Multiplying by 10 moves the decimal point 1 place to the right.

$-N = 0.555...$ — Subtract $N = 0.555...$ to eliminate the repeating part.

$9N = 5$ — Simplify.

$N = \frac{5}{9}$ — Divide each side by 9.

The decimal $0.\overline{5}$ can be written as $\frac{5}{9}$.

6. Express $2.\overline{18}$ as a mixed number in simplest form.

Assign a variable to the value $2.\overline{18}$. Let $N = 2.181818....$
Then perform operations on N to determine its fractional value.

$N = 2.181818...$	
$100(N) = 100(2.181818...)$	Multiply each side by 100 because 2 digits repeat.
$100N = 218.181818$	Multiplying by 100 moves the decimal point 2 places to the right.
$-N = 2.181818...$	Subtract $N = 2.181818...$ to eliminate the repeating part.
$99N = 216$	Simplify.
$N = \frac{216}{99}$ or $2\frac{2}{11}$	Divide each side by 99. Simplify.

The decimal $2.\overline{18}$ can be written as $2\frac{2}{11}$.

f. ______________

g. ______________

Got It? Do these problems to find out.

Express each decimal as a fraction or mixed number in simplest form.

f. -0.14

g. $0.\overline{27}$

Guided Practice

Express each fraction or mixed number as a decimal. (Examples 1 and 2)

1. $\frac{9}{16} =$ ______

2. $-1\frac{29}{40} =$ ______

3. $4\frac{5}{6} =$ ______

4. Monica won 7 of the 16 science competitions she entered. To the nearest thousandth, determine her winning average. (Example 3) ______________

Express each decimal as a fraction or mixed number in simplest form. (Examples 4–6)

5. $0.32 =$ ______

6. $-0.\overline{7} =$ ______

7. **Building on the Essential Question** How can you determine if a number is a rational number?

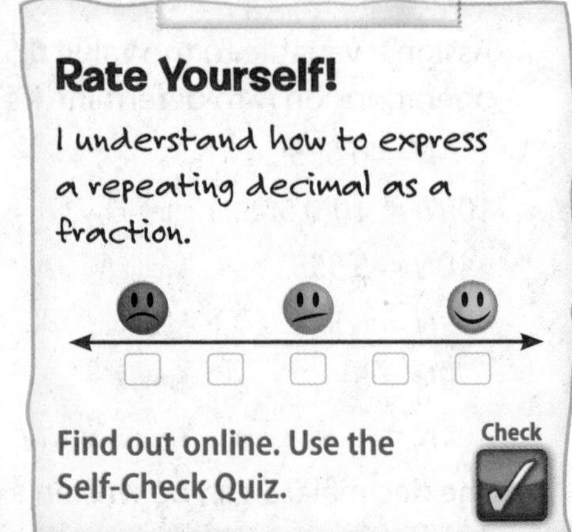

Rate Yourself!
I understand how to express a repeating decimal as a fraction.
Find out online. Use the Self-Check Quiz.
Check

Independent Practice

8.2(C), 8.1(F) TEKS

Express each fraction or mixed number as a decimal. (Examples 1 and 2)

1. $\frac{2}{5}$ = ________

2. $2\frac{1}{8}$ = ________

3. $\frac{33}{40}$ = ________

4. $\frac{4}{33}$ = ________

5. $-\frac{6}{11}$ = ________

6. $-7\frac{8}{45}$ = ________

7. **MP Analyze Relationships** The table shows statistics about the students at Carter Junior High. (Example 3)

Number of Siblings	Fraction of Students
None	$\frac{1}{15}$
One	$\frac{1}{3}$
Two	$\frac{5}{12}$
Three	$\frac{1}{6}$
Four or more	$\frac{1}{60}$

a. Express the fraction of students with no siblings as a decimal.

0.067

b. Express the fraction of students with three siblings as a decimal.

c. Write the fraction of students with one sibling as a decimal.

Round to the nearest thousandth. 0.333

d. Write the fraction of students with two siblings as a decimal.

Round to the nearest thousandth. 0.417

Express each decimal as a fraction or mixed number in simplest form. (Examples 4–6)

8. -0.4 = $-\frac{2}{5}$

9. -7.32 = $-7\frac{8}{25}$

$7\frac{32}{100} = 7\frac{8}{25}$

10. $0.\overline{2}$ = $2/9$

11. 5.65 = $5\frac{13}{20}$

$5\frac{65}{100} = 5\frac{13}{20}$

12. $4.\overline{16}$ = ________

13. 10.312 = $10\frac{39}{125}$

$\frac{312}{1000} = \frac{78}{250} = \frac{39}{125}$

Copy and Solve **Express each decimal as a fraction or mixed number in simplest form. Show your work on a separate piece of paper.** (Examples 4–6)

14. $-0.\overline{45}$ $-\frac{5}{11}$

15. $2.\overline{7}$ $2\frac{7}{9}$

16. 5.55 $5\frac{11}{20}$

$5\frac{55}{100} = \frac{11}{20}$

MP **Analyze Relationships** Write the length of each insect as a fraction or mixed number and as a decimal.

17.

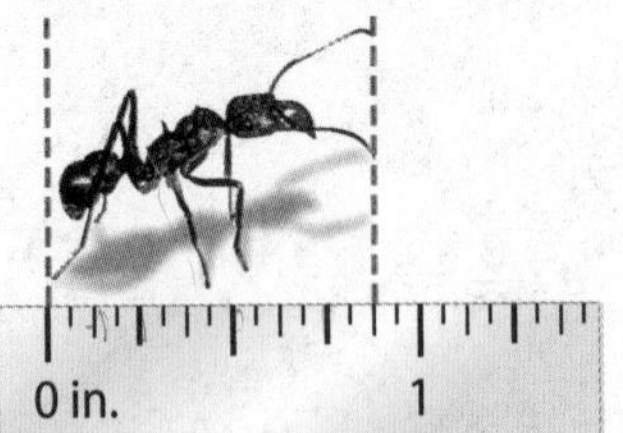

0.8 $\frac{4}{5}$

18.

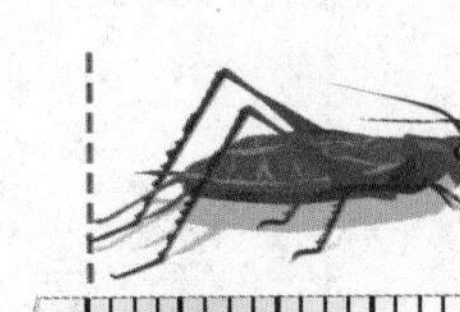

1.0625 $1\frac{1}{16}$

H.O.T. Problems Higher-Order Thinking

19. Analyze Write an example of a repeating decimal where two digits repeat. Explain why your number is a rational number.

20. Evaluate Justify that any rational number is either a terminating or repeating decimal.

21. Analyze Compare 0.1 and $0.\overline{1}$, 0.13 and $0.\overline{13}$, and 0.157 and $0.\overline{157}$ when written as fractions. Make a conjecture about expressing repeating decimals like these as fractions.

22. Create Write two decimals, one repeating and one terminating, with values between 0 and 1. Then write an inequality that shows the relationship between your two decimals.

Name ______________________________

Multi-Step Problem Solving

23. Two teams that have the best win to loss ratio play each other in a one-game playoff. The table shows four teams competing for the playoff spots. Based on the table, which two teams are in the lead to go to the playoffs? N MP

Team	Win	Loss
Blue Sox	97	64
Hawks	96	66
Bombers	95	60
Bears	94	61

Ⓐ Blue Sox and Hawks

Ⓑ Bombers and Bears

Ⓒ Blue Sox and Bombers

Ⓓ Hawks and Bears

Use a problem-solving model to solve this problem.

1 Analyze

Read the problem. Circle the information you know.
Underline what the problem is asking you to find.

2 Plan

What will you need to do to solve the problem? Write your plan in steps.

Step 1 Write the information for each team as a win to loss ratio.

Step 2 Express each ratio as a __________ and compare __________.

3 Solve

Use your plan to solve the problem. Show your steps.

Blue Sox: $\frac{97}{64} \approx$ Hawks: $\frac{96}{66} \approx$

Bombers: $\frac{95}{60} \approx$ Bears: $\frac{94}{61} \approx$

The two greatest values are __________ and __________.

So, the __________ and __________ are in the lead to go to the play-offs. The correct answer is _____. Fill in that answer choice.

When comparing decimals, be sure to round each decimal to the same decimal place.

4 Justify and Evaluate

How do you know your solution is accurate?

____

____

____

N = Number and Operations MP = Mathematical Processes

More Multi-Step Problem Solving

Use a problem-solving model to solve each problem.

24. The table below shows the free throws made (FTM) and the free throws attempted (FTA) for three players on the high school basketball team. As a decimal rounded to the nearest thousandth, what is the combined free-throw percentage of all three players?

Free Throws		
Player	**FTM**	**FTA**
Jones	38	42
Mason	9	10
Rice	9	10

Ⓐ 0.900
Ⓑ 0.903
Ⓒ 0.904
Ⓓ 0.905

25. Express $0.\overline{461538}$ as a fraction in simplest form. Show your steps below. N MP

26. A survey was conducted to determine the favorite sport for members of the eighth grade class. The results are shown in the table. How many students selected either football or baseball? Express your answer as a decimal.

Sport	Part of Class
Football	$\frac{7}{20}$
Baseball	$\frac{1}{5}$
Basketball	$\frac{3}{10}$
Soccer	$\frac{3}{20}$

27. What is the difference of the areas, expressed as a decimal, of the shaded rectangle and the unshaded rectangle? Explain how you determined your answer. N EE MP

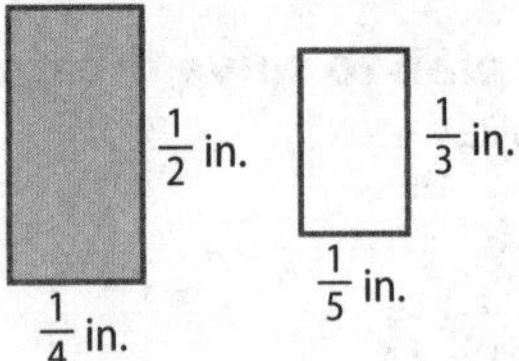

N = Number and Operations EE = Expressions, Equations, and Relationships MD = Measurement and Data MP = Mathematical Processes

Lesson 2

Powers and Exponents

Launch the Lesson: Real World

Texas Essential Knowledge and Skills

Targeted TEKS
Preparation for 8.2(C) Convert between standard decimal notation and scientific notation.

Mathematical Processes
8.1(A), 8.1(B), 8.1(D) 8.1(F)

Vocab

Vocabulary
power
base
exponent

Essential Question
WHY is it helpful to write numbers in different ways?

Yogi decided to start saving money by putting a penny in his piggy bank, then doubling the amount he saves each week. How much money will Yogi save in 8 weeks?

1. Complete the table below to determine the amount Yogi saved each week and the total amount in his piggy bank.

Week	0	1	2	3	4	5	6
Weekly Savings	1¢	2¢					
Total Savings	1¢	3¢					

2. How many 2s are multiplied to determine his savings in Week 4? ☐ Week 5? ☐

3. How much money will Yogi save in Week 8? ________

4. Continue the table to determine when he will have enough to buy a pair of shoes for $80. ________

Week	7	8	9	10	11	12
Weekly Savings						
Total Savings						

Which MP Mathematical Processes did you use? Shade the circle(s) that applies.

Ⓐ Apply Math to the Real World.
Ⓑ Use a Problem-Solving Model.
Ⓒ Select Tools and Techniques.
Ⓓ Use Multiple Representations.
Ⓔ Organize Ideas.
Ⓕ Analyze Relationships.
Ⓖ Justify Arguments.

Work Zone

Express and Evaluate Powers

A product of repeated factors can be expressed as a **power**, that is, using an exponent and a base.

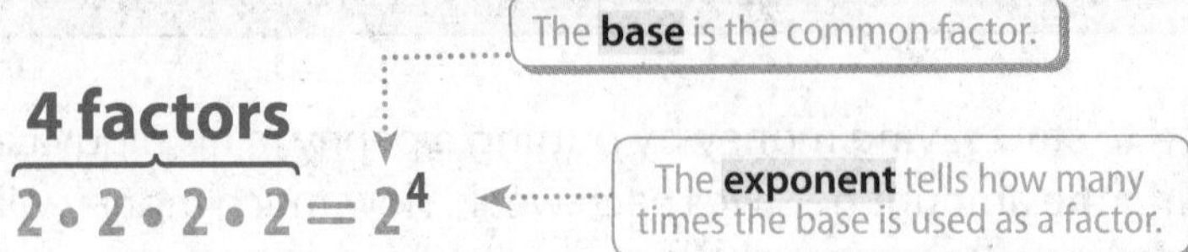

The **base** is the common factor.
4 factors
$2 \cdot 2 \cdot 2 \cdot 2 = 2^4$
The **exponent** tells how many times the base is used as a factor.

Powers are read in a certain way.

Read and Write Powers

Power	Words	Factors
3^1	3 to the first power	3
3^2	3 to the second power or 3 squared	$3 \cdot 3$
3^3	3 to the third power or 3 cubed	$3 \cdot 3 \cdot 3$
3^4	3 to the fourth power or 3 to the fourth	$3 \cdot 3 \cdot 3 \cdot 3$
⋮	⋮	⋮
3^n	3 to the *n*th power or 3 to the *n*th	$\underbrace{3 \cdot 3 \cdot 3 \cdot \ldots \cdot 3}_{n \text{ factors}}$

Examples

Tutor

Express each expression using exponents.

1. $(-2) \cdot (-2) \cdot (-2) \cdot 3 \cdot 3 \cdot 3 \cdot 3$

The base −2 is a factor 3 times, and the base 3 is a factor 4 times.

$(-2) \cdot (-2) \cdot (-2) \cdot 3 \cdot 3 \cdot 3 \cdot 3 = (-2)^3 \cdot 3^4$

2. $a \cdot b \cdot b \cdot a \cdot b$

Use the properties of operations to rewrite and group like bases together. The base *a* is a factor 2 times, and the base *b* is a factor 3 times.

$a \cdot b \cdot b \cdot a \cdot b = a \cdot a \cdot b \cdot b \cdot b$

$= a^2 \cdot b^3$

Got It? Do these problems to find out.

Show your work.

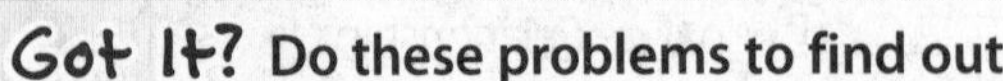

a. $\frac{1}{2} \cdot \frac{1}{2} \cdot \frac{1}{2} \cdot \frac{1}{2}$ **b.** $4 \cdot 4 \cdot 4 \cdot 5 \cdot 5$ **c.** $m \cdot m \cdot n \cdot n \cdot m$

a. $\left(\frac{1}{2}\right)^4$

b. $4^3 \cdot 5^2$

c. $m^3 \cdot n^2$

Example

Tutor

3. **Evaluate $\left(-\frac{2}{3}\right)^4$.**

$\left(-\frac{2}{3}\right)^4 = \left(-\frac{2}{3}\right) \cdot \left(-\frac{2}{3}\right) \cdot \left(-\frac{2}{3}\right) \cdot \left(-\frac{2}{3}\right)$ Write the power as a product.

$= \frac{16}{81}$ Multiply.

Evaluate

Remember that to evaluate an expression means to find its value.

Got It? **Do these problems to find out.**

d. 4^4

e. $(-2)^6$

f. $\left(\frac{1}{5}\right)^3$

d. 256

e. 64

f. 1/125

$\frac{1}{5} \cdot \frac{1}{5} \cdot \frac{1}{5} = \frac{1}{125}$

Example

Tutor

4. **The deck of a skateboard has an area of about $2^5 \cdot 7$ square inches. What is the area of the skateboard deck?**

$2^5 \cdot 7 = 2 \cdot 2 \cdot 2 \cdot 2 \cdot 2 \cdot 7$ Write the power as a product.

$= (2 \cdot 2 \cdot 2 \cdot 2 \cdot 2) \cdot 7$ Associative Property

$= 32 \cdot 7$ or 224 Multiply.

The area of the skateboard deck is about 224 square inches.

Got It? **Do this problem to find out.**

g. A school basketball court has an area of $2^3 \cdot 3 \cdot 5^2 \cdot 7$ square feet. What is the area of a school basketball court?

g. 4200

Examples

Tutor

Evaluate each expression if $a = 3$ and $b = 5$.

5. $a^2 + b^4$

$a^2 + b^4 = 3^2 + 5^4$ Replace a with 3 and b with 5.

$= (3 \cdot 3) + (5 \cdot 5 \cdot 5 \cdot 5)$ Write the powers as products.

$= 9 + 625$ or 634 Add.

6. $(a - b)^2$

$(a - b)^2 = (3 - 5)^2$ Replace a with 3 and b with 5.

$= (-2)^2$ Perform operations in the parentheses first.

$= (-2) \cdot (-2)$ or 4 Write the powers as products. Then simplify.

h. 17

i. 125

j. 747

Show your work.

Got It? Do these problems to find out.

Evaluate each expression if $c = -4$ and $d = 9$.

h. $c^3 + d^2$

$-4^3 + 9^2$
$-64 + 81$

i. $(c + d)^3$

$(-4 + 9)^3$

j. $d^3 - (c^2 - 2)$

$9^3 - (4^2 - 2)$
$729 - (-18)$

$-16 - 2 = -18$

Guided Practice

Express each expression using exponents. (Examples 1 and 2)

1. $(-11)(-11)(-11) =$ -11^3

2. $2 \cdot 2 \cdot 2 \cdot 3 \cdot 3 \cdot 3 =$ $2^3 \cdot 3^3$

3. $r \cdot s \cdot r \cdot r \cdot s \cdot s \cdot r \cdot r =$ $r^5 \cdot s^3$

Evaluate each expression. (Examples 3)

4. $2^6 =$ 64

5. $(-4)^4 =$ 256

6. $\left(\frac{1}{7}\right)^3 =$ $1/343$

$\frac{1}{7} \cdot \frac{1}{7} \cdot \frac{1}{7} =$

7. The table shows the average weights of some endangered mammals. What is the weight of each animal? (Example 4)

Animal	Weight (lb)
Black bear	$2 \cdot 5^2 \cdot 7$
Key deer	$3 \cdot 5^2$
Panther	$2^3 \cdot 3 \cdot 5$

350 ← Black bear
75 ← Key deer
120 ← Panther

Evaluate each expression if $x = 2$ and $y = 10$. (Examples 5 and 6)

8. $x^2 + y^4 =$ 40,000

$2^2 + 10^4 =$

9. $(x^2 + y)^3 =$ 2744

$(2^2 + 10)^3$

10. **Building on the Essential Question** How can I express repeated multiplication using powers?

Rate Yourself!

Are you ready to move on? Shade the section that applies.

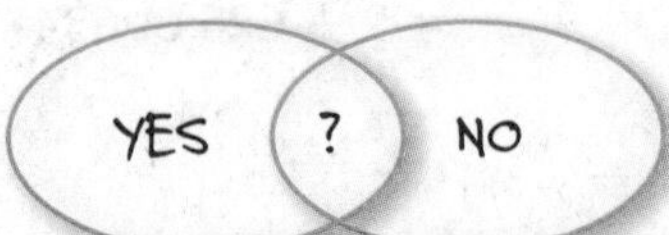

Find out online. Use the Self-Check Quiz.

FOLDABLES Time to update your Foldable!

Name ____________ My Homework ____________

Independent Practice

Preparation for 8.2(C), 8.1(F) TEKS

Express each expression using exponents. (Examples 1 and 2)

1. $(-5)(-5)(-5)(-5) =$

2. $3 \cdot 3 \cdot 5 \cdot q \cdot q \cdot q =$

3. $m \cdot m \cdot m \cdot m \cdot m =$

Evaluate each expression. (Example 3)

4. $(-9)^4 =$

5. $\left(\frac{1}{3}\right)^4 =$

6. $\left(\frac{5}{7}\right)^3 =$

7. **Select Tools and Techniques** In the United States, nearly $8 \cdot 10^9$ text messages are sent every month. About how many text messages is this? Use mental math.

(Example 4) 

8. Interstate 70 stretches almost $2^3 \cdot 5^2 \cdot 11$ miles across the United States. About how many miles long is Interstate 70?

(Example 4) 

Evaluate each expression. (Examples 5 and 6)

9. $g^5 - h^3$ if $g = 2$ and $h = 7$

10. $c^2 + d^3$, if $c = 8$ and $d = -3$

11. $a^2 \cdot b^6$ if $a = \frac{1}{2}$ and $b = 2$

12. $(r - s)^3 + r^2$ if $r = -3$ and $s = -4$

13. **MP Apply Math to the Real World** Refer to the graphic novel frame below for Exercises a–d.

The metric system is based on powers of 10. For example, one kilometer is equal to 1,000 meters or 10^3 meters. Express each measurement in meters as a power of 10.

a. hectometer (100 meters) 10^2

b. megameter (1,000,000 meters) 10^6

c. gigameter (1,000,000,000 meters) 10^9

d. petameter (1,000,000,000,000,000 meters) 10^{15}

H.O.T. Problems Higher-Order Thinking

14. **Create** Write an expression with an exponent that has a value between 0 and 1. ________

15. **Analyze** Describe the following pattern: $3^4 = 81, 3^3 = 27, 3^2 = 9, 3^1 = 3$.

Then use a similar pattern to predict the value of 2^{-1}. ________

16. **Create** Simplify the expressions below to develop a rule for multiplying powers with the same base.

$2^2 \cdot 2^3 = 2^{\square}$ or 32 $\qquad 3 \cdot 3^2 = 3^{\square}$ or 27

$4^3 \cdot 4 = 4^{\square}$ or 256 $\qquad x^2 \cdot x^3 = x^{\square}$

Name ______________________________

Multi-Step Problem Solving

17. The table shows the approximate number of Earth hours there are in one day for two planets. Which of the following is the longest amount of time? N EE MP

Planet	Length of Day (Earth Hours)
Venus	3^5
Neptune	2^4

Ⓐ 8 Venus days

Ⓑ 20 Neptune days

Ⓒ 5 Venus days and 12 Neptune days

Ⓓ 4 Venus days and 15 Neptune days

Use a problem-solving model to solve this problem.

1 Analyze

Read the problem. Circle the information you know.
Underline what the problem is asking you to find.

2 Plan

What will you need to do to solve the problem? Write your plan in steps.

Step 1 Write an expression with exponents for each of the three times.

Step 2 __________ each expression and __________ the values.

3 Solve

Use your plan to solve the problem. Show your steps.

8 Venus days = __________ Earth days

20 Neptune days = __________ Earth days

5 Venus days and 12 Neptune days = __________ Earth days

4 Venus days and 15 Neptune days = __________ Earth days

The greatest value is __________ Earth days. So, the longest amount of time is __________. The answer is ____. Fill in that answer choice.

Read to Succeed!
When evaluating an expression such as $8 \cdot 3^5$, remember to follow the order of operations. Evaluate 3^5 before multiplying by 8.

4 Justify and Evaluate

How do you know your solution is accurate?

____

____

____

N = Number and Operations EE = Expressions, Equations, and Relationships MP = Mathematical Processes

More Multi-Step Problem Solving

Use a problem-solving model to solve each problem.

18. The table shows the approximate number of Earth hours there are in one day for two planets. Which of the following is the same amount of time as 4 Venus days and 6 Neptune days? N EE MP

Planet	Length of Day (Earth Hours)
Venus	3^5
Neptune	2^4

Ⓐ 1,036 Earth hours

Ⓑ 1,068 Earth hours

Ⓒ 1,522 Earth hours

Ⓓ 1,554 Earth hours

19. What is the volume of the cube, in cubic units, if $x = 3$? N EE MP

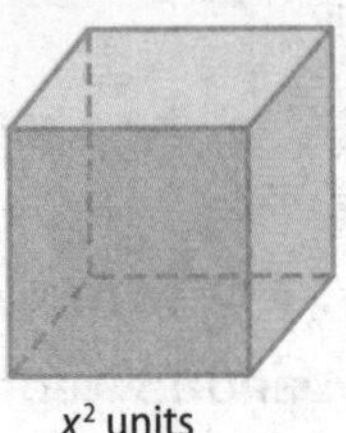

x^2 units

20. If $4^2 \cdot 4^x = 8 \cdot 512$, what is the value of x? Show how you solved the problem. N MP

21. Consider the following equations.

$$1 = 1 = 1^3$$
$$3 + 5 = 8 = 2^3$$
$$7 + 9 + 11 = 27 = 3^3$$
$$13 + 15 + 17 + 19 = 64 = 4^3$$
$$21 + 23 + 25 + 27 + 29 = 125 = 5^3$$

If the pattern continues, what will be the 10th equation? Explain. N EE MP

N = Number and Operations EE = Expressions, Equations, and Relationships MP = Mathematical Processes

Lesson 3

Negative Exponents

Launch the Lesson: Real World

The table shows the approximate wing beats per minute for certain insects.

Insect	Wing Beats per Minute
house fly	10,000
small butterfly	100

1. The ratio in simplest form that compares the number of wing beats for a butterfly to a housefly is $\frac{1}{100}$ or $\frac{1}{10^2}$. What is the relationship between exponential form and standard decimal notation?

2. Complete the 1st 4 rows of the table showing the exponential and standard decimal notation forms of powers of 10.

3. What operation is performed when you move down the table?

____

4. What happens to the exponent?

____

5. Extend the table to include the next three entries.

6. **Analyze** Use the relationship shown in the table to predict the standard decimal notation for 10^{-7}.

____

Exponential Form	Standard Decimal Notation
10^3	
$10^{\square}$	100
10^1	
10^0	

Texas Essential Knowledge and Skills

Targeted TEKS
Preparation for 8.2(C) Convert between standard decimal notation and scientific notation.

Mathematical Processes
8.1(A), 8.1(B), 8.1(F), 8.1(G)

Essential Question

WHY is it helpful to write numbers in different ways?

Which MP Mathematical Processes did you use? Shade the circle(s) that applies.

Ⓐ Apply Math to the Real World.
Ⓑ Use a Problem-Solving Model.
Ⓒ Select Tools and Techniques.
Ⓓ Use Multiple Representations.
Ⓔ Organize Ideas.
Ⓕ Analyze Relationships.
Ⓖ Justify Arguments.

Key Concept

Zero and Negative Exponents

Words Any nonzero number to the zero power is 1. Any nonzero number to the negative n power is the multiplicative inverse of its nth power.

Examples

Numbers	Algebra
$5^0 = 1$	$x^0 = 1, x \neq 0$
$7^{-3} = \frac{1}{7} \cdot \frac{1}{7} \cdot \frac{1}{7}$ or $\frac{1}{7^3}$	$x^{-n} = \frac{1}{x^n}, x \neq 0$

Work Zone

Negative Exponents

Remember that 6^{-3} is equal to $\frac{1}{6^3}$, not -216 or -18.

You can use exponents to represent very small numbers. Negative powers are the result of repeated division.

Tutor

Examples

Express each expression using a positive exponent.

1. 6^{-3}

$6^{-3} = \frac{1}{6^3}$ Definition of negative exponent

2. a^{-5}

$a^{-5} = \frac{1}{a^5}$ Definition of negative exponent

Got It? Do these problems to find out.

a. 7^{-2}

b. b^{-4}

c. 5^0

d. m^{-3}

a. 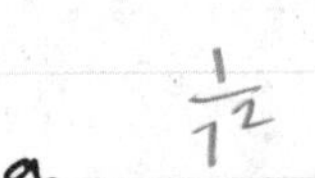 $\frac{1}{7^2}$

b. 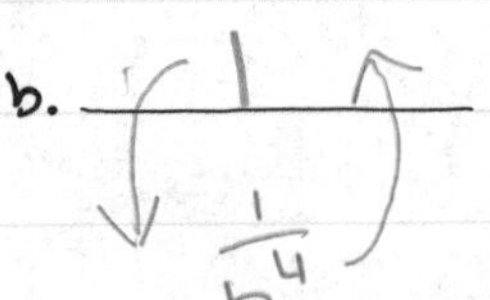 1

c. $\frac{1}{b^4}$

d. 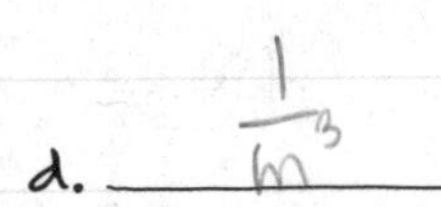 $\frac{1}{m^3}$

Tutor

Examples

Express each fraction as an expression using a negative exponent other than −1.

3. $\frac{1}{5^2}$

$\frac{1}{5^2} = 5^{-2}$ Definition of negative exponent

4. $\frac{1}{36}$

$\frac{1}{36} = \frac{1}{6^2}$ Definition of exponent

$= 6^{-2}$ Definition of negative exponent

Got It? Do these problems to find out.

e. $\frac{1}{8^3}$

f. $\frac{1}{4}$

g. $\frac{1}{c^5}$

h. $\frac{1}{27}$

e. 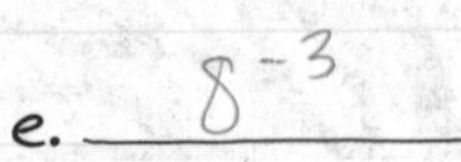 8^{-3}

f. 2^{-2}

g. c^{-5}

h. 3^{-3}

Example

5. **STEM** **One human hair is about 0.001 inch in diameter. Express the decimal as a power of 10.**

$0.001 = \frac{1}{1{,}000}$ Write the decimal as a fraction.

$= \frac{1}{10^3}$ $1{,}000 = 10^3$

$= 10^{-3}$ Definition of negative exponent

A human hair is 10^{-3} inch thick.

STOP and Reflect

Explain below the difference between the expressions $(-4)^2$ and 4^{-2}.

Got It? **Do these problems to find out.**

i. **STEM** A water molecule is about 0.0000000001 meter long. Express the decimal as a power of 10.

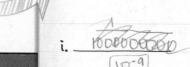

i. 

Variables with Negative Exponents

Expressions with variables can have negative exponents.

Examples

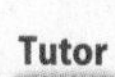

Express each expression without using a negative exponent.

6. x^{-5}

$\frac{1}{x^5}$ Definition of negative exponent

7. $3r^{-10} = 3(r^{-10})$ Think: $3r^{-10}$ is a product of 3 and r^{-10}.

$= \frac{3}{r^{10}}$ Definition of negative exponent

8. $2t^0$

$2t^0 = 2 \cdot 1$ Definition of exponent of zero

$= 2$ Simplify.

Got It? **Do these problems to find out.**

j. x^{-4}

k. y^{-3}

l. $2t^{-7}$

m. $9v^0$

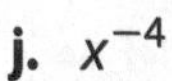

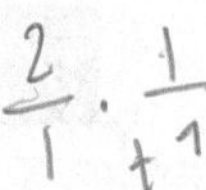

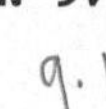

j. 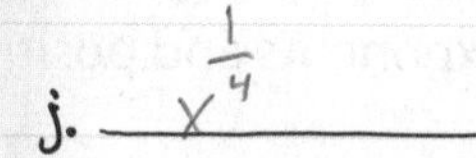

k. 

l. 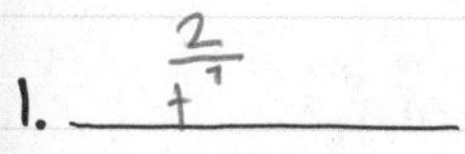

m. 9

Guided Practice

Express each expression using a positive exponent. (Examples 1 and 2)

1. $2^{-4} =$ $\frac{1}{2^4}$

2. $4^{-3} =$ $\frac{1}{4^3}$

3. $a^{-4} =$ $\frac{1}{a^4}$

4. $g^{-7} =$ $\frac{1}{g^7}$

Express each fraction as an expression using a negative exponent other than −1. (Examples 3 and 4)

5. $\frac{1}{3^4} =$ 3^{-4}

6. $\frac{1}{m^5} =$ m^{-5}

7. $\frac{1}{16} =$ 4^{-2}

8. $\frac{1}{49} =$ 7^{-2}

9. An American green tree frog tadpole is about 0.00001 kilometer in length when it hatches. Express this decimal as a power of 10.

(Example 5) $\frac{1}{10000} = 10^{-4}$

Express each expression without using a negative exponent. (Examples 6–8)

10. $k^{-4} =$ $\frac{1}{k^4}$

11. $5m^{-2} =$ $\frac{5}{m^2}$

12. $4b^0 =$ 4

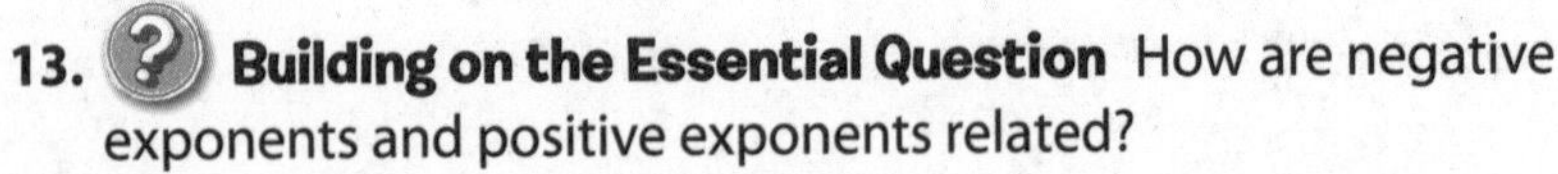

13. **Building on the Essential Question** How are negative exponents and positive exponents related?

Rate Yourself!

How well do you understand negative exponents? Circle the image that applies.

Clear

Somewhat Clear

Not So Clear

Find out online. Use the Self-Check Quiz.

FOLDABLES Time to update your Foldable!

Name ______________________ My Homework ______________________

Independent Practice

Preparation for 8.2(C), 7.1(A) TEKS

Express each expression using a positive exponent. (Examples 1 and 2)

1. 7^{-10} = ________

2. $(-5)^{-4}$ = ________

3. g^{-7} = ________

4. w^{-13} = ________

Express each fraction as an expression using a negative exponent other than −1. (Examples 3 and 4)

5. $\frac{1}{12^4}$ = ________

6. $\frac{1}{(-5)^7}$ = ________

7. $\frac{1}{125}$ = ________

8. $\frac{1}{1{,}024}$ = ________

9. The table shows different metric measurements. Express each decimal as a power of 10. (Example 5) ________

Measurement	Value
Decimeter	0.1
Centimeter	0.01
Millimeter	0.001
Micrometer	0.000001

10. STEM An atom is a small unit of matter. A small atom measures about 0.0000000001 meter. Express the decimal as a power of 10.

(Example 5) ________

Express each expression without using a negative exponent. (Examples 6–8)

11. w^{-3} = ________

12. s^{-7} = ________

13. $4y^{-9}$ = ________

14. $3a^{-2}$ = ________

15. n^0 = ________

16. $6b^0$ = ________

17. $(3r)^0$ = ________

18. c^2d^{-6} = ________

19. **STEM** The mass of a molecule of penicillin is 10^{-18} kilogram and the mass of a molecule of insulin is 10^{-23} kilogram. How many times greater is the mass of a molecule of penicillin than the mass of a molecule of insulin?

20. **MP Justify Arguments** A common flea that is 2^{-4} inch long can jump about 2^3 inches high. About how many times its body size can a flea jump? Explain your reasoning.

H.O.T. Problems Higher-Order Thinking

21. **Analyze** Without evaluating, order 11^{-3}, 11^2, and 11^0 from least to greatest. Explain your reasoning.

22. **Create** Write an expression with a negative exponent that has a value between 0 and $\frac{1}{2}$.

23. **Analyze** Select several fractions between 0 and 1. Determine the value of each fraction after it is raised to the -1 power. Explain the relationship between the -1 power and the original fraction.

24. **Create** For each power, write an equivalent multiplication expression with two factors. The first factor should have a positive exponent and the second factor should have a negative exponent.

a. $10^4 =$ ________

b. $8^2 =$ ________

c. $x^7 =$ ________

Name ____________

Multi-Step Problem Solving

25. The table shows the hair lengths of five samples taken for a laboratory study. Which of the following shows the order of these hair lengths from least to greatest? 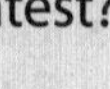

Ⓐ $2^2, 2^{-2}, 2^0, 2^{-1}, 2^{-3}$

Ⓑ $2^0, 2^{-3}, 2^{-2}, 2^{-1}, 2^2$

Ⓒ $2^2, 2^0, 2^{-1}, 2^{-2}, 2^{-3}$

Ⓓ $2^{-3}, 2^{-2}, 2^{-1}, 2^0, 2^2$

Sample	Hair Length (in.)
1	2^2
2	2^{-2}
3	2^0
4	2^{-1}
5	2^{-3}

Use a problem-solving model to solve this problem.

1 Analyze

Read the problem. Circle the information you know.
Underline what the problem is asking you to find.

2 Plan

What will you need to do to solve the problem? Write your plan in steps.

Step 1 Evaluate ____________.

Step 2 ________ and ________ the values.

3 Solve

Use your plan to solve the problem. Show your steps.

$2^2 =$ ________ $2^{-2} =$ ________ $2^0 =$ ________

$2^{-1} =$ ________ $2^{-3} =$ ________

Since ______ < ______ < ______ < ______ < ______, choice ______ is the answer. Fill in that answer choice.

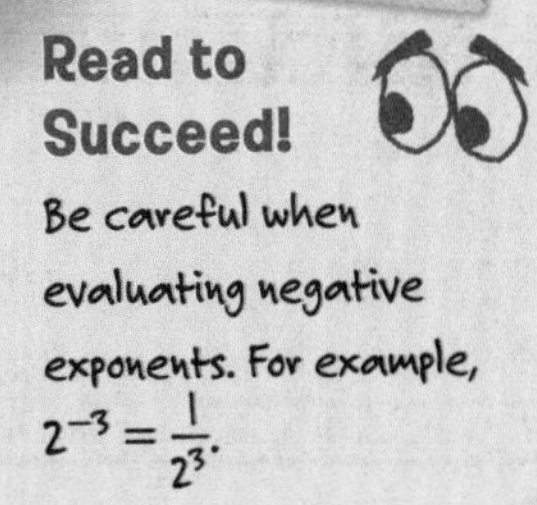

Read to Succeed!
Be careful when evaluating negative exponents. For example, $2^{-3} = \frac{1}{2^3}$.

4 Justify and Evaluate

How do you know your solution is accurate?

____

____

____

____

N = Number and Operations MP = Mathematical Processes

More Multi-Step Problem Solving

Use a problem-solving model to solve each problem.

26. On the number line shown below, the coordinate of point X is 3^{-3} and the coordinate of point Y is 3^{-2}. Which of the following is the coordinate of a point between X and Y? N P MP

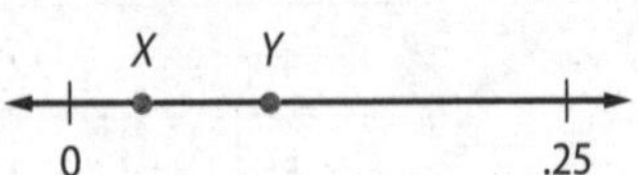

Ⓐ 2^{-5}

Ⓑ 4^{-1}

Ⓒ 5^{-2}

Ⓓ 6^{-1}

27. The table shows the dimensions in feet of four rectangles. What is the difference in area of the rectangle with the greatest area and the rectangle with the least area? N EE MP

Rectangle	Width (ft)	Length (ft)
A	2^{-1}	2^{7}
B	2^{6}	2^{-3}
C	2^{-2}	2^{6}
D	2^{5}	2^{-5}

28. What is the total surface area of the rectangular prism shown below? N EE MP

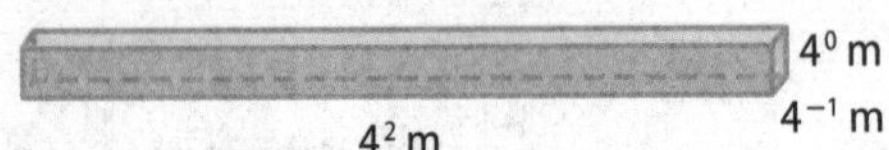

29. If a, b, and c are different negative integers less than -1 and $2^a \cdot 2^b \cdot 2^c = \frac{1}{512}$, what is the absolute value of abc? Explain your answer. N EE MP

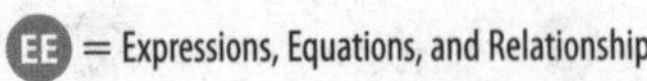
N = Number and Operations P = Proportionality EE = Expressions, Equations, and Relationships MP = Mathematical Processes

Lesson 4

Scientific Notation

Launch the Lesson: Real World

A single sided, single layer DVD has a storage capacity of 4.7 gigabytes. One gigabyte is equal to 10^9 bytes. Write a multiplication expression that represents how many bytes can be stored on the DVD.

1. Complete the table below to discover what happens when a decimal is multiplied by a power of 10.

Expression	Product	Expression	Product
$4.7 \times 10^1 = 4.7 \times 10$	47	$4.7 \times 10^{-1} = 4.7 \times \frac{1}{10}$	0.47
$4.7 \times 10^2 = 4.7 \times 100$		$4.7 \times 10^{-2} = 4.7 \times \frac{1}{100}$	
$4.7 \times 10^3 = 4.7 \times 1{,}000$		$4.7 \times 10^{-3} = 4.7 \times \frac{1}{1000}$	
$4.7 \times 10^4 = 4.7 \times$		$4.7 \times 10^{-4} = 4.7 \times$	

2. If 4.7 is multiplied by a positive power of 10, what relationship exists between the decimal point's new position and the exponent?

3. When 4.7 is multiplied by a negative power of 10, how does the new position of the decimal point relate to the negative exponent?

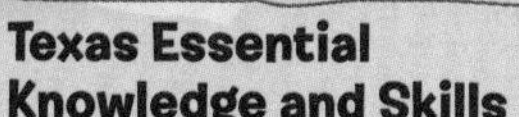

Texas Essential Knowledge and Skills

Targeted TEKS

8.2(C) Convert between standard decimal notation and scientific notation.

Mathematical Processes

8.1(A), 8.1(B), 8.1(D), 8.1(E), 8.1(G)

Vocab

Vocabulary

scientific notation

Essential Question

WHY is it helpful to write numbers in different ways?

Which MP Mathematical Processes did you use?
Shade the circle(s) that applies.

Ⓐ Apply Math to the Real World.
Ⓑ Use a Problem-Solving Model.
Ⓒ Select Tools and Techniques.
Ⓓ Use Multiple Representations.
Ⓔ Organize Ideas.
Ⓕ Analyze Relationships.
Ⓖ Justify Arguments.

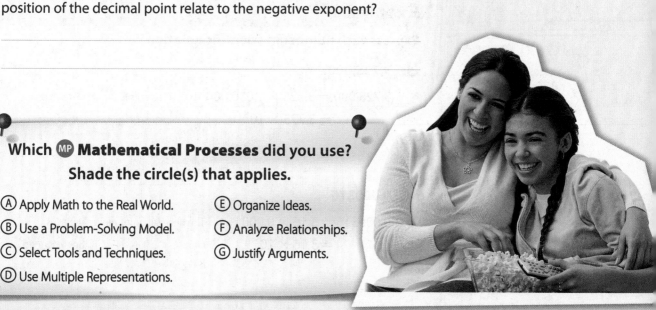

Key Concept Scientific Notation

Words	**Scientific notation** is when a number is written as the product of a factor and an integer power of 10. The factor must be greater than or equal to 1 and less than 10.
Symbols	$a \times 10^n$, where $1 \leq a < 10$ and n is an integer
Example	$425{,}000{,}000 = 4.25 \times 10^8$

Work Zone

Use these rules to express a number in scientific notation.

- If the number is greater than or equal to 1, the power of ten is positive.
- If the number is between 0 and 1, the power of ten is negative.

Powers of Ten

Multiplying a factor by a positive power of 10 moves the decimal point right. Multiplying a factor by a negative power of 10 moves the decimal point left.

Tutor 

Examples

Express each number in standard decimal notation.

1. 5.34×10^4

$5.34 \times 10^4 = 53{,}400.$

2. 3.27×10^{-3}

$3.27 \times 10^{-3} = 0.00327$

Got It? Do these problems to find out.

Show your work.

a. 7.42×10^5 **b.** 6.1×10^{-2} **c.** 3.714×10^2

a. 742000

b. .061

c. 371.4

Tutor 

Examples

Express each number in scientific notation.

3. 3,725,000

$3{,}725{,}000 = 3.725 \times 1{,}000{,}000$

$= 3.725 \times 10^6$

The decimal point moves 6 places. Since $3{,}725{,}000 > 1$, the exponent is positive.

4. 0.000316

$0.000316 = 3.16 \times 0.0001$

$= 3.16 \times 10^{-4}$

The decimal point moves 4 places. Since $0 < 0.000316 < 1$, the exponent is negative.

Got It? Do these problems to find out.

d. 14,140,000 **e.** 0.00876 **f.** 0.114

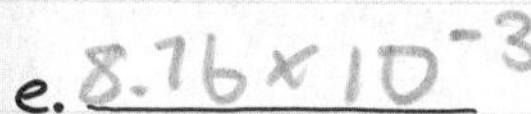

d. 14.14×10^{6}

e. 8.76×10^{-3}

f. 1.14×10^{-1}

Example

Watch Tutor

5. Refer to the table at the right. Order the countries according to the amount of money visitors spent in the United States from greatest to least.

Dollars Spent by International Visitors in the U.S	
Country	**Dollars Spent**
Canada	1.03×10^7
India	1.83×10^6
Mexico	7.15×10^6
United Kingdom	1.06×10^7

Canada and United Kingdom ↓ Mexico and India ↓

Step 1 $\left\{\begin{matrix} 1.06 \times 10^7 \\ 1.03 \times 10^7 \end{matrix}\right\} > \left\{\begin{matrix} 7.15 \times 10^6 \\ 1.83 \times 10^6 \end{matrix}\right\}$ ← Group the numbers by their power of 10.

Step 2 $1.06 > 1.03$ $7.15 > 1.83$ ← Order the decimals.

United Kingdom Canada Mexico India

Got It? Do this problem to find out.

g. Some of the top U.S. cities visited by overseas travelers are shown in the table. Order the cities according to the number of visitors from least to greatest.

U.S. City	Number of Visitors
Boston	7.21×10^5
Las Vegas	1.3×10^6
Los Angeles	2.2×10^6
Metro D.C. area	9.01×10^5

g. L.A., L.V., MetroDC, Boston

Example

Tutor

6. STEM If you could walk at a rate of 2 meters per second, it would take you 1.92×10^8 seconds to walk to the moon. Is it more appropriate to report this time as 1.92×10^8 seconds or 6.09 years? Explain your reasoning.

The measure 6.09 years is more appropriate. The number 1.92×10^8 seconds is very large so choosing a larger unit of measure is more meaningful.

h. ____________

Got It? Do this problem to find out.

h. **STEM** In an ocean, the sea floor moved 475 kilometers over 65 million years. Is it more appropriate to report this rate as 7.31×10^{-5} kilometer per year or 7.31 centimeters per year? Explain your reasoning.

Guided Practice

Express each number in standard decimal notation form. (Examples 1 and 2)

1. $9.931 \times 10^5 =$ 993100

2. $6.02 \times 10^{-4} =$ 0.000602

Express each number in scientific notation. (Examples 3 and 4)

3. 8,785,000,000 = 87.85×10^8

4. 0.524 = 5.24×10^-1

5. The table lists the total value of music shipments for four years. List the years from least to greatest dollar amount. (Example 5)

Year	Music Shipments($)
1	1.22×10^{10}
2	1.12×10^{10}
3	7.15×10^{6}
4	1.06×10^{7}

6. **STEM** A plant cell has a diameter of 1.3×10^{-8} kilometer. Is it more appropriate to report the diameter of a plant cell as 1.3×10^{-8} kilometer or 1.3×10^{-2} millimeter? Explain your reasoning. (Example 6)

7. **Building on the Essential Question** How is scientific notation useful in the real world?

Rate Yourself!

☐ I understand scientific notation.

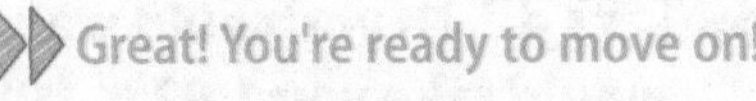

☐ I still have some questions about scientific notation.

FOLDABLES Time to update your Foldable!

Name ______________________ My Homework ______________________

Independent Practice

8.2(C), 8.1(F) TEKS

Express each number in standard decimal notation form. (Examples 1 and 2)

1. $3.16 \times 10^3 =$ 3160

2. $1.1 \times 10^{-4} =$ .00011

3. $2.52 \times 10^{-5} =$ .0000252

Express each number in scientific notation. (Examples 3 and 4)

4. 43,000 = 4.3×10^5

5. 0.0072 = 7.2×10^{-3}

6. 0.0000901 = 9.01×10^{-5}

7. The areas of the world's oceans are listed in the table. Order the oceans according to their area from least to greatest. (Example 5)

____

____

World's Oceans	
Ocean	**Area (mi²)**
Atlantic	2.96×10^7
Arctic	5.43×10^6
Indian	2.65×10^7
Pacific	6×10^7
Southern	7.85×10^6

8. The space shuttle traveled about 8×10^5 centimeters per second. Is it more appropriate to report this rate as 8×10^5 centimeters per second or 8 kilometers per second? Explain. (Examples 6)

____

____

____

____

9. The inside diameter of a certain size of ring is 1.732×10^{-2} meter. Is it more appropriate to report the ring diameter as 1.732×10^{-2} meter or 17.32 millimeters? Explain. (Examples 6)

____

____

____

Fill in each ◯ with <, >, or = to make a true statement.

10. 678,000 (<) 6.78×10^6

6,780,000

11. 6.25×10^3 (<) 6.3×10^3

12. **Apply Math to the Real World** Refer to the graphic novel frame below for Exercises a–c.

a. Find Jacob's and Sarah's heights in nanometers.

b. Write each height using scientific notation.

c. Give an example of something that would be appropriately measured by nanometers.

H.O.T. Problems Higher Order Thinking

13. **Analyze** Determine whether 1.2×10^5 or 1.2×10^6 is closer to one million. Explain.

14. **Analyze** Compute and express each value in scientific notation.

a. $\frac{(130{,}000)(0.0057)}{0.0004} =$

b. $\frac{(90{,}000)(0.0016)}{(200{,}000)(30{,}000)(0.00012)} =$

15. **Create** Write two numbers in scientific notation with values between 100 and 1,000. Then write an inequality that shows the relationship between your two numbers.

Name ______________________________

Multi-Step Problem Solving

16. The attendance records at games for four professional football teams for a recent year are shown in the table. Which of the following lists the teams from greatest attendance to least attendance? N MP

Team	Attendance
W	5.58×10^4
X	5.49×10^5
Y	5.51×10^4
Z	5.53×10^5

Ⓐ W, Z, Y, X

Ⓑ Y, W, X, Z

Ⓒ Z, X, W, Y

Ⓓ X, Y, Z, W

Use a problem-solving model to solve this problem.

1 Analyze

Read the problem. Circle the information you know.
Underline what the problem is asking you to find.

2 Plan

What will you need to do to solve the problem? Write your plan in steps.

Step 1 Express each value in standard decimal notation.

Step 2 Order the numbers from ______________.

3 Solve

Use your plan to solve the problem. Show your steps.

W: $5.58 \times 10^4 =$ ________ **X:** $5.49 \times 10^5 =$ ________

Y: $5.51 \times 10^4 =$ ________ **Z:** $5.53 \times 10^5 =$ ________

Since ________ > ________ > ________ > ________, the teams, in order of greatest to least attendance, are ____, ____, ____, and ____.

So, the correct answer is C. Fill in that answer choice.

Read to Succeed!
When comparing numbers with the same number of decimal places, start at the right and compare digits until you come to the digits that are different.

4 Justify and Evaluate

How do you know your solution is accurate?

____

____

____

N = Number and Operations MP = Mathematical Processes

More Multi-Step Problem Solving

Use a problem-solving model to solve each problem.

17. The table shows the mass of one atom of each of several elements. Which element has the greatest mass per atom? N MP

Element	Mass per Atom
argon	6.64×10^{-23} g
helium	6.65×10^{-24} g
iodine	2.11×10^{-22} g
mercury	3.33×10^{-22} g

Ⓐ argon

Ⓑ helium

Ⓒ iodine

Ⓓ mercury

18. The volume the rectangular prism shown below is 4.8×10^9 cubic meters. What is the height h of the prism expressed in standard decimal notation? N EE MP

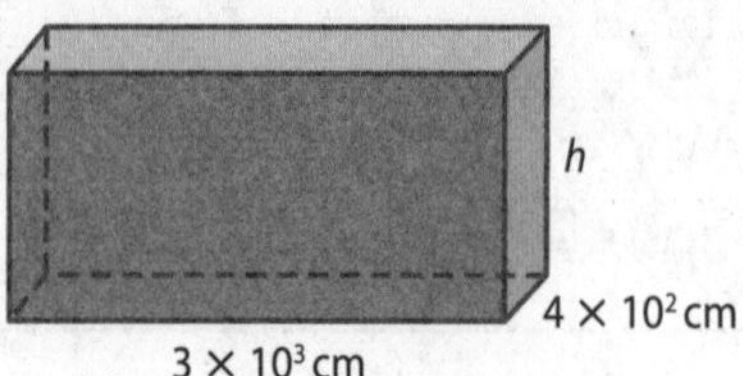

19. The table shows three numerical expressions. Suppose each expression is evaluated and the result is written in scientific notation. What will be the power of 10 of the expression with the greatest value? N EE MP

Calculation Number	Expression
1	$\frac{(28{,}000)(6{,}000)}{400}$
2	$\frac{(7{,}000)(600{,}000)}{3{,}000}$
3	$\frac{(350{,}000)(900{,}000)}{14{,}000}$

20. Light travels at approximately 186,000 miles per second. A light year is the distance that light can travel in one year. How many miles is a light year? Express your answer in scientific notation and explain your work. N P MP

N = Number and Operations 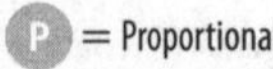 = Proportionality EE = Expressions, Equations, and Relationships MP = Mathematical Processes

Graphing Technology Lab 4-b

Scientific Notation Using Technology

INQUIRY How can I select tools and techniques to express real numbers in scientific notation?

The table shows the mass of some planets in our solar system. What is the mass of Earth written in scientific notation?

Planet	Mass (kg)
Earth	5,973,700,000,000,000,000,000,000
Mars	641,850,000,000,000,000,000,000
Saturn	568,510,000,000,000,000,000,000,000

Texas Essential Knowledge and Skills TEKS

Targeted TEKS
8.2(C) Convert between standard decimal notation and scientific notation.

Mathematical Processes
8.1(C), 8.1(F)

Hands-On Activity 1

You will use a graphing calculator to explore how scientific notation is displayed using technology.

Step 1 Press CLEAR to clear the home screen.

Step 2 Enter the value in standard decimal notation for Earth's mass. Press ENTER.

Copy your calculator screen on the blank screen shown.

Step 3 Express the value for Earth's mass using scientific notation.

____

Investigate

Select Tools and Techniques Work with a partner. Repeat Steps 1 and 2 of the activity on the previous page for each of the following.

1. mass of Mars

2. mass of Saturn

3. What does the E symbol represent on the calculator screen? ______

What does the value after the E symbol represent? ______

4. Based on your answers for Exercise 1 and 2, what are the masses of Mars and Saturn in scientific notation?

Mars: ______ Saturn: ______

Analyze and Reflect

Work with a partner to complete the table.

	Calculator Notation	Scientific Notation	Standard Decimal Notation
5.	3.1E7		
6.		6.39×10^{10}	
7.			0.02357
8.	1.7E-11		

9. **Analyze Relationships** The Moon has a mass of about 73,600,000,000,000,000,000,000 kilograms. Without entering the value in your calculator, predict how the mass of the Moon will be displayed on the calculator screen. ______

Hands-On Activity 2

A human blood cell is about 1×10^{-6} meter in diameter. The Moon is about 3.476×10^{6} meters in diameter. How many times greater is the diameter of the Moon that the diameter of a blood cell?

Step 1 Press CLEAR to clear the home screen.

Step 2 Perform the following keystrokes:

3.476 2nd [EE] 6 ÷ 1 2nd [EE] –6 ENTER

Copy your calculator screen on the blank screen shown.

Step 3 Express the value in standard decimal notation.

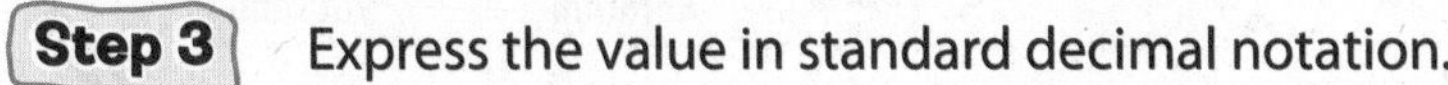

So, the diameter of the Moon is ________________ times greater than the diameter of a human blood cell.

Hands-On Activity 3

When in "Normal" mode, a calculator will show answers in scientific notation only if they are very large numbers or very small numbers. You can set your calculator to show scientific notation for all numbers by using the "Sci" mode.

Step 1 Press CLEAR to clear the home screen. Put your calculator in scientific mode by pressing MODE ▶ ENTER. Then press CLEAR to return to the home screen.

Step 2 Complete the table by entering the numbers in the first column into your calculator.

Enter	Calculator Notation	Standard Decimal Notation
14 ÷ 100		
60 − 950		
360 • 15		
1 + 1		

Investigate

10. **MP Select Tools and Techniques** Work with a partner. Write down the keystrokes and fill in the calculator screen to write $(6.2 \times 10^5)(2.3 \times 10^7)$ using a calculator in "Sci" mode. Express your final answer in standard decimal notation.

Keystrokes: ______________________________

____

Answer in standard decimal notation: ______________

Analyze and Reflect

11. **MP Select Tools and Techniques** A *micrometer* is 0.000001 meter. Use your calculator to determine how many micrometers are in each of the following. Express your answer in both calculator and scientific notation.

	Calculator Notation	Scientific Notation
5,000 meters		
4.08E14 meters		
2.9E–10 meter		

Create

On Your Own

12. **MP Select Tools and Techniques** Write a subtraction expression involving two numbers written in scientific notation. Then write the keystrokes and fill in the calculator screen to write your expression using a calculator in "Sci" mode. Express your final answer in standard decimal notation.

Expression: ______________________________

Keystrokes: ______________________________

____

Answer in standard decimal notation: ______________

13. **INQUIRY** How can I select tools and techniques to express real numbers in scientific notation?

____

____

____

The Four-Step Plan

E-vite

Lilian received an e-vite to a concert. She forwarded the invite to two of her friends. They each forwarded it to two more friends, and so on. At the end of the 8th stage, $\frac{2}{3}$ of the people invited, other than Lilian, accepted the invitation.

How many invites were accepted altogether at the 8th stage?

Mathematical Process
8.1(B) Use a problem-solving model that incorporates analyzing given information, formulating a plan or strategy, determining a solution, justifying the solution, and evaluating the problem-solving process and the reasonableness of the solution.

Targeted TEKS 8.2

Analyze *Read the problem. Circle the information you know.*

Underline what the problem is asking you to find.

2 Plan *What is your strategy to solve this problem?*

I will ____________________

____

3 Solve *How can you apply the strategy?*

Draw a diagram to show the number of invites sent for the first four stages.

1st stage	2
2nd stage	4
3rd stage	8
4th stage	16

The pattern is multiply by 2. So, ☐, ☐, ☐, and ☐ invites were sent during the 5th, 6th, 7th and 8th stages, respectively. At the end of the 8th stage, a total of ☐ invites had been sent. Determine $\frac{2}{3}$ of ☐, which is ☐.

So, ☐ invites were accepted at the end of the 8th stage.

Justify and Evaluate *How do you know your solution is accurate?*

____

____

Green Mileage

In a gas mileage test, a hybrid car was driven 4,840 miles using 88 gallons of gas. The car company wants to improve the gas mileage so that the car can travel this distance using 72 gallons of gas.

How many fewer gallons of gas will the improved hybrid car need than the original tested hybrid to travel a distance of 1,155 miles?

Analyze

Read the problem. Circle the information you know. Underline what the problem is asking you to find.

Plan

What is your strategy to solve this problem?

I will ______________________________

Solve

How can you apply the strategy?

Justify and Evaluate

How do you know your solution is accurate?

____

____

____

____

Multi-Step Problem Solving

Work with a small group to solve the following cases.
Show your work on a separate piece of paper.

1. Class Trip

All of Mr. Bassett's science classes are going to the Natural History Museum. A tour guide is needed for each group of eight students. His classes have 28 students, 35 students, 22 students, 33 students, and 22 students.

How many tour guides are needed?

2. Gardening

Mrs. Lopez is designing her garden in the shape of a rectangle. The area of her garden is 2 times greater than the area of the rectangle shown.

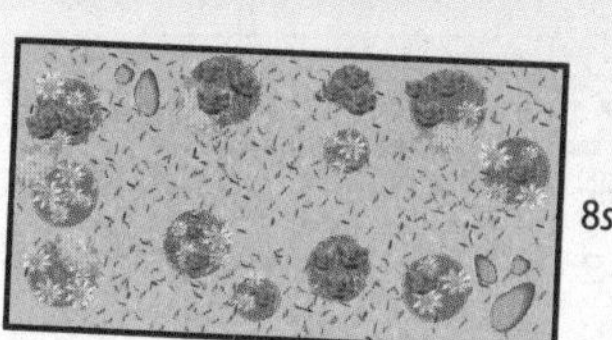

Determine the area of Mrs. Lopez's garden in simplest form.

3. Toothpicks

Hector will make the figures at the right from toothpicks.

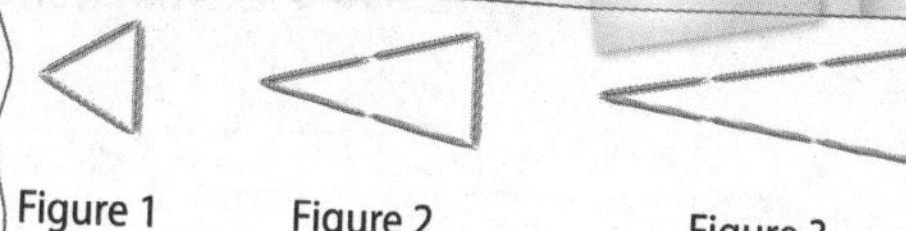

Write an expression that can find the number of toothpicks needed to make any figure. Then find the number of toothpicks needed to make the 100th figure.

4. Number Sense

Study the following sequence:

$1 - \frac{1}{2}, 1 - \frac{1}{3}, 1 - \frac{1}{4}, \ldots, 1 - \frac{1}{48}, 1 - \frac{1}{49}$, and $1 - \frac{1}{50}$

What is the product of all of the terms?

Mid-Chapter Check

Vocabulary Check

1. Write a definition of *power* in your own words using the words base and *exponent*. Then write an example of a power and label the base and exponent. TEKS Preparation for 8.2(C), 8.1(B)

Key Concept Check

2. Complete the graphic organizer on negative exponents. TEKS Preparation for 8.2(C), 8.1(E)

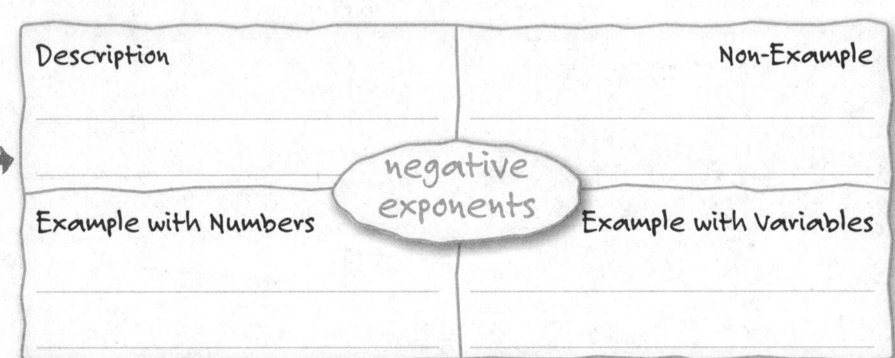

3. MP **Select Tools and Techniques** Last week, Emma took quizzes in four classes. Emma's score on each quiz is shown in the table. Express each quiz score as a decimal. Round to the nearest hundredth if necessary. TEKS Preparation for 8.2(D), 8.1(C)

Class	Correct Questions
science	8 out of 10
world languages	13 out of 15
social studies	19 out of 20
language arts	3 out of 5

Multi-Step Problem Solving

4. The distance from Earth to the Moon is 238,900 miles. Which expression is equivalent to the distance from the Moon and back? N EE MP

Ⓐ 2.389×10^{-10} mi
Ⓑ 4.778×10^{-5} mi
Ⓒ 2.389×10^{10} mi
Ⓓ 4.778×10^{5} mi

N = Number and Operations 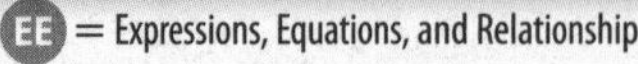 EE = Expressions, Equations, and Relationships 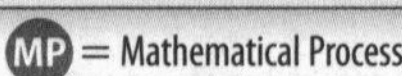 MP = Mathematical Processes

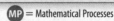

Lesson 5
Roots

Launch the Lesson: Vocabulary

A **square root** of a number is one of its two equal factors. Numbers such as 1, 4, 9, 16, and 25 are called **perfect squares** because they are squares of integers.

Complete the graphic organizer.

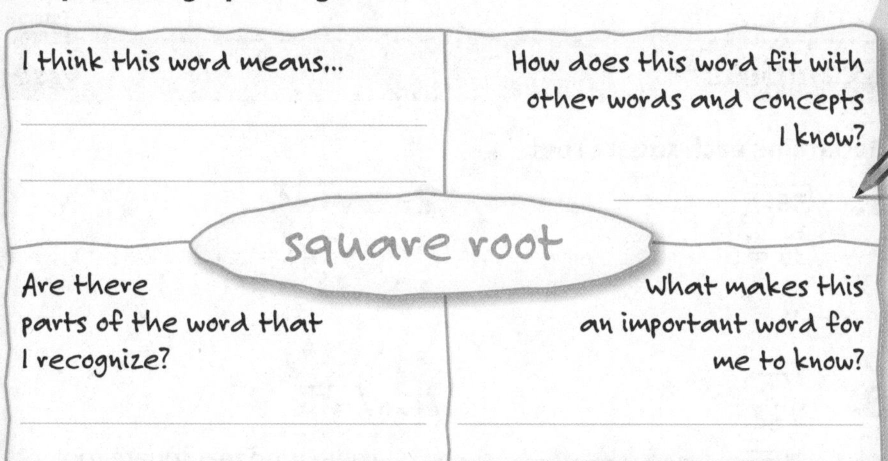

I think this word means...
How does this word fit with other words and concepts I know?
square root
Are there parts of the word that I recognize?
What makes this an important word for me to know?

Analyze What is the relationship between squaring a number and determining the square root? ______

Real-World Link

Watch 

The square base of the Great Pyramid of Giza covers almost 562,500 square feet. How could you determine the length of each side of the base? ______

Which MP Mathematical Processes did you use? Shade the circle(s) that applies.

Ⓐ Apply Math to the Real World.
Ⓑ Use a Problem-Solving Model.
Ⓒ Select Tools and Techniques.
Ⓓ Use Multiple Representations.
Ⓔ Organize Ideas.
Ⓕ Analyze Relationships.
Ⓖ Justify Arguments.

Texas Essential Knowledge and Skills

Targeted TEKS

8.2(B) Approximate the value of an irrational number, including π and square roots of numbers less than 225, and locate that rational number approximation on a number line.

Mathematical Processes

8.1(A), 8.1(B), 8.1(E), 8.1(G)

Vocab 

Vocabulary

square root
perfect square
radical sign
cube root
perfect cube

Essential Question

WHY is it helpful to write numbers in different ways?

Key Concept

Square Root

Watch

Words A square root of a number is one of its two equal factors.

Symbols If $x^2 = y$, then x is a square root of y.

Example $5^2 = 25$, so 5 is a square root of 25.

Work Zone

$\pm$

Every positive number has both a positive and negative square root. In most real-world situations, only the positive or *principal* square root is considered. A **radical sign**, $\sqrt{}$, is used to indicate the principal square root. If $n^2 = a$, then $n = \pm\sqrt{a}$.

Tutor

Examples

Determine each square root.

1. $\sqrt{36}$

$\sqrt{36} = 6$ Find the positive square root of 36; $6^2 = 36$.

2. $\pm\sqrt{1.44}$

$\pm\sqrt{1.44} = \pm 1.2$ Find both square roots of 1.44; $1.2^2 = 1.44$.

3. $-\sqrt{\frac{9}{64}}$

$-\sqrt{\frac{9}{64}} = -\frac{3}{8}$ Find the negative square root of $\frac{9}{64}$; $\left(\frac{3}{8}\right)^2 = \frac{9}{64}$.

4. $\sqrt{-16}$

There is no real square root because no number times itself is equal to −16.

Got It? Do these problems to find out.

Show your work.

a. $\sqrt{\frac{25}{36}}$ **b.** $\pm\sqrt{0.49}$ **c.** $-\sqrt{81}$ **d.** $\sqrt{-400}$

a. ____________

b. ____________

c. ____________

d. ____________

Tutor

Example

5. **Solve $m^2 = 196$.**

$m^2 = 196.$ Write the equation.

$m = \pm\sqrt{196}$ Definition of square root

$m = 14$ and -14 Check $14 \cdot 14 = 196$ and $(-14)(-14) = 196$ ✓

Got It? Do these problems to find out.

e. $169 = a^2$ **f.** $x^2 = 0.04$ **g.** $y^2 = \frac{9}{49}$

e. ____________

f. ____________

g. ____________

Cube Roots

Key Concept

Words A **cube root** of a number is one of its three equal factors.

Symbols If $x^3 = y$, then x is the cube root of y.

Numbers such as 8, 27, and 64 are **perfect cubes** because they are the cubes of integers.

$8 = 2 \cdot 2 \cdot 2$ or 2^3 $\quad 27 = 3 \cdot 3 \cdot 3$ or 3^3 $\quad 64 = 4 \cdot 4 \cdot 4$ or 4^3

The symbol $\sqrt[3]{}$ is used to indicate a cube root of a number.

If $n^3 = a$, then $n = \sqrt[3]{a}$. You can use this relationship to solve equations that involve cubes.

Tutor

Examples

Determine each cube root.

6. $\sqrt[3]{125}$

$\sqrt[3]{125} = 5$ $\quad 5^3 = 5 \cdot 5 \cdot 5$ or 125

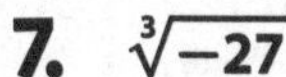

7. $\sqrt[3]{-27}$

$\sqrt[3]{-27} = -3$ $\quad (-3)^3 = (-3) \cdot (-3) \cdot (-3)$ or -27

Cube Roots

While $\sqrt{-16}$ is not a real number, $\sqrt[3]{-27}$ is a real number. $-3 \cdot -3 \cdot -3 = -27$

Got It? Do these problems to find out.

h. $\sqrt[3]{729}$ **i.** $\sqrt[3]{-64}$ **j.** $\sqrt[3]{1{,}000}$

h. ________

i. ________

j. ________

Tutor

Multi-Step Example

8. Dylan has a planter in the shape of a cube that holds 8 cubic feet of potting soil. What is the area of one side of the planter?

Step 1 Determine the side length of the planter.

Since $s^3 = 8$, the length of one side of the planter is 2 feet.

Step 2 Determine the area of one side of the planter.

$A = 2^2$ Equation for the area of a square

$A = 4$ Simplify.

The area of one side of the planter is 4 square feet.

Got It? Do these problems to find out.

k. ______________

k. An aquarium in the shape of a cube that will hold 25 gallons of water has a volume of 3.375 cubic feet. What is the area of one side of the aquarium?

Guided Practice

Determine each square root. (Examples 1–4)

1. $-\sqrt{1.69} =$ ______________

2. $\pm\sqrt{\frac{81}{121}} =$ ______________

3. $\sqrt{-1.44} =$ ______________

Show your work.

Solve each equation. Check your solution(s). (Example 5)

4. $p^2 = 225$ ______________

5. $t^2 = \frac{1}{9}$ ______________

6. $2.89 = h^2$ ______________

Determine each cube root. (Examples 6 and 7)

7. $\sqrt[3]{216} =$ ______________

8. $\sqrt[3]{-125} =$ ______________

9. $\sqrt[3]{-8} =$ ______________

10. A cube-shaped packing box can hold 729 cubic inches of packing material. Determine the area of one side of the box. (Example 8) ______________

11. **Building on the Essential Question** When would you use square roots and cube roots?

____

____

____

____

Rate Yourself!

☐ I understand how to determine square roots and cube roots.

Great! You're ready to move on!

☐ I still have questions about determining square roots and cube roots.

Find out online. Use the Self-Check Quiz.

Name ______________________ My Homework ______________________

Independent Practice

8.2(B), 8.1(F) TEKS

Determine each square root. (Examples 1–4)

1. $\sqrt{16} =$ ______

Show your work.

2. $-\sqrt{484} =$ ______

3. $\sqrt{-36} =$ ______

4. $\pm\sqrt{\frac{49}{81}} =$ ______

5. $-\sqrt{2.56} =$ ______

6. $\sqrt{-0.25} =$ ______

Solve each equation. Check your solution(s). (Example 5)

7. $v^2 = 81$ ______

8. $g^2 = \frac{64}{100}$ ______

9. $0.0169 = c^2$ ______

Determine each cube root. (Examples 6 and 7)

10. $\sqrt[3]{1,728} =$ ______

11. $\sqrt[3]{-0.125} =$ ______

12. $\sqrt[3]{\frac{27}{125}} =$ ______

13. Chloe wants to build a storage container in the shape of a cube to hold 15.625 cubic meters of hay for her horse. Determine the area of one side of the container. (Example 8)

______

14. The aspect ratio R of a hang glider is $\frac{s^2}{A}$, where s is the wingspan and A is the wing area. Adventure Sports advertises a hang glider with an aspect ratio of 1.6. If its wing area is 160 square feet, what is its wingspan?

______

MP Use a Problem Solving Model **Given the area of each square, determine the perimeter.**

15. Area = 121 square inches ______

16. Area = 25 square feet ______

17. Area = 36 square meters ______

H.O.T. Problems Higher Order Thinking

18. **Analyze** Explain why $\sqrt{-4}$ is not a real number but $\sqrt[3]{-8}$ is a real number.

______

______

______

Evaluate **Simplify each expression.**

19. $(\sqrt{36})^2 =$ ______

20. $\sqrt{n^2} =$ ______

21. $\left(\sqrt{\frac{25}{81}}\right)^2 =$ ______

22. $\left(\sqrt{\frac{a}{b}}\right)^2 =$ ______

23. **Create** Write a rule for the pattern found in Exercises 19–22.

______

______

24. **Create** Write and evaluate an expression involving a square root and a cube. The value of your expression should be greater than 100.

______

25. **Create** Write and evaluate an expression involving a cube root and a square. The value of your expression should be less than 10.

______

Name ____________________

Multi-Step Problem Solving

26. A bulletin board consists of four equal-sized cork squares arranged in a row to form a rectangle. If the total area of all four cork squares is 100 square feet, what is the length in feet of the bulletin board? N EE MP

Use a problem-solving model to solve this problem.

1 Analyze

Read the problem. Circle the information you know.
Underline what the problem is asking you to find.

2 Plan

What will you need to do to solve the problem?
Write your plan in steps.

Step 1 Determine the __________ of the area of one square.

Step 2 Multiply the answer to Step 1 by ________ .

Read to Succeed!

Use a pencil to write your answer in the boxes at the top of the grid and to fill in the correct corresponding bubble(s) below each digit.

					.		
⊕	0	0	0	0		0	0
⊖	1	1	1	1		1	1
	2	2	2	2		2	2
	3	3	3	3		3	3
	4	4	4	4		4	4
	5	5	5	5		5	5
	6	6	6	6		6	6
	7	7	7	7		7	7
	8	8	8	8		8	8
	9	9	9	9		9	9

3 Solve

Use your plan to solve the problem. Show your steps.

$100 \div 4 =$ ______ area of one square in square feet

$\sqrt{25} =$ ______ length in feet of one side of one square

$4 \cdot$ ______ $=$ ______ length in feet of entire bulletin board

The answer is ______ . Complete the grid.

4 Justify and Evaluate

How do you know your solution is accurate?

____

____

____

____

____

N = Number and Operations EE = Expressions, Equations, and Relationships MP = Mathematical Processes

More Multi-Step Problem Solving

Use a problem-solving model to solve each problem.

27. What is the difference in side length of the cubes shown below? N EE MP

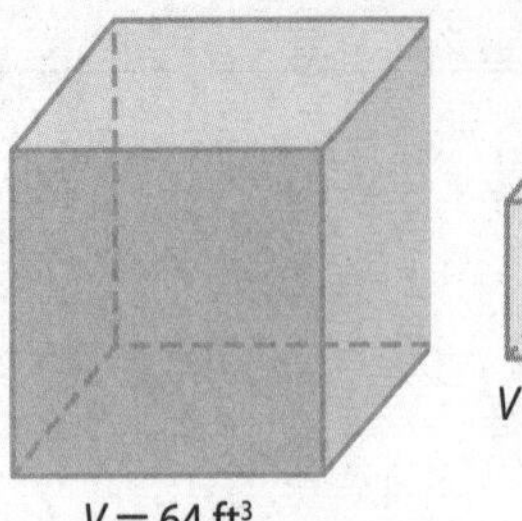

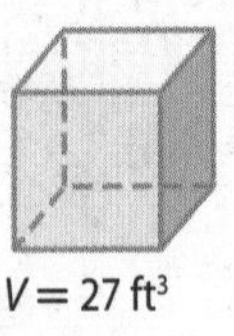

28. The area of the figure below is 300 square centimeters. What is the perimeter of the figure? N EE MP

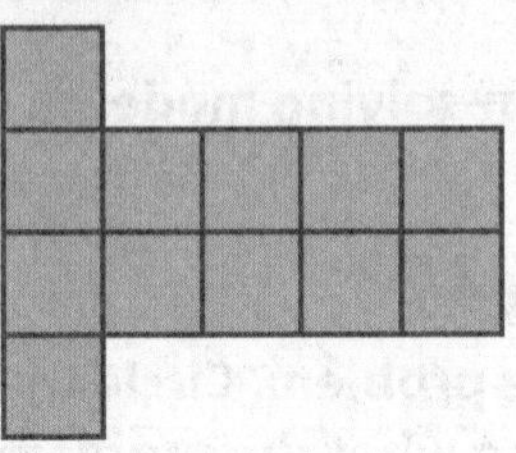

29. The volume of the rectangular prism shown is 4,320 cubic centimeters. What is the surface area of the whole prism? Explain. N EE MP

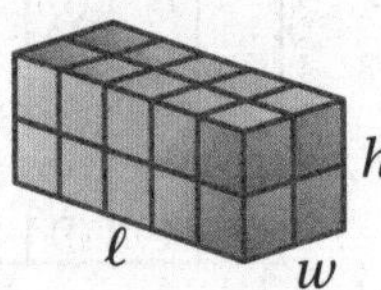

30. Dario wants to buy paper to wrap a birthday present in the cube-shaped box shown below. If an 8.3-square-foot package of wrapping paper costs $1.25, how much will Dario spend on the wrapping paper? Explain. N EE MP

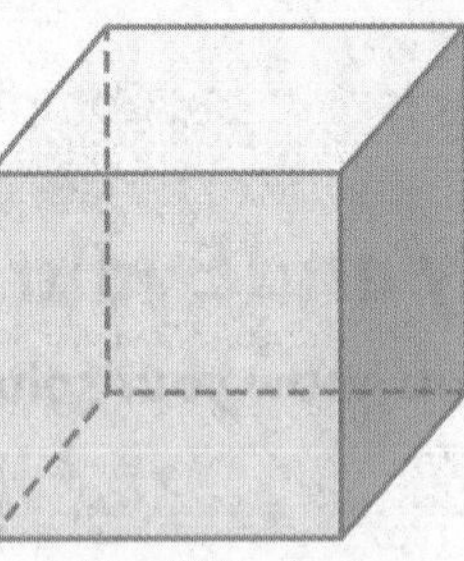

 N = Number and Operations EE = Expressions, Equations, and Relationships MP = Mathematical Processes

Hands-On Lab 6-a

Roots of Non-Perfect Squares

INQUIRY **HOW can I use multiple representations to estimate the square root of a non-perfect square number?**

Texas Essential Knowledge and Skills

Targeted TEKS

8.2(B) Approximate the value of an irrational number, including π and square roots of numbers less than 225, and locate that rational number approximation on a number line.

Mathematical Processes

8.1(C), 8.1(D), 8.1(E), 8.1(F), 8.1(G)

Mindi is making a quilting piece from a square pattern as shown. Each of the dotted lines is 6 inches. What is the approximate length of one side of the square?

What do you know? ______________________

What do you need to determine? ______________________

Hands-On Activity

Tools

Step 1 The outline of the square on dot paper is shown. Draw dotted lines connecting opposite vertices.

When you draw the lines, four triangles that are the same shape and size are formed. What are the dimensions of the triangles?

base = ☐ units height = ☐ units

The area of one triangle is ☐ square units.

The area of the square is ☐ square units.

Step 2 Copy and cut out the square in Step 1 on another sheet of paper.

Step 3 Determine the length of one side of the square. Place one side of your square on the number line. Between what two consecutive whole numbers is $\sqrt{18}$, the side length of the square, located?

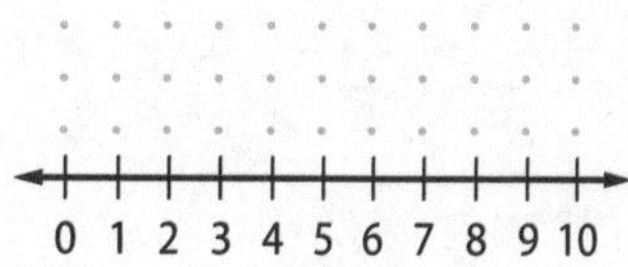

____

Estimate the length of the side of the square. ______

So, one side of the square is about ☐ units long.

Select Tools and Techniques Work with a partner. Determine the two consecutive whole numbers the side length of each square is located between using the method shown in the Activity.

1. ____________

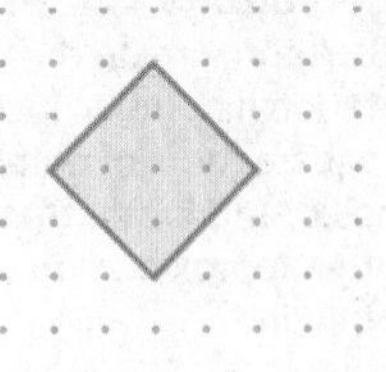

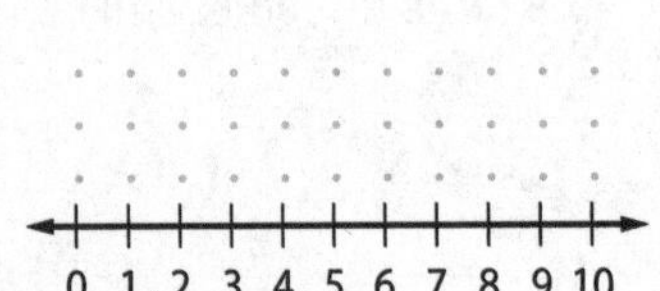

2. ____________

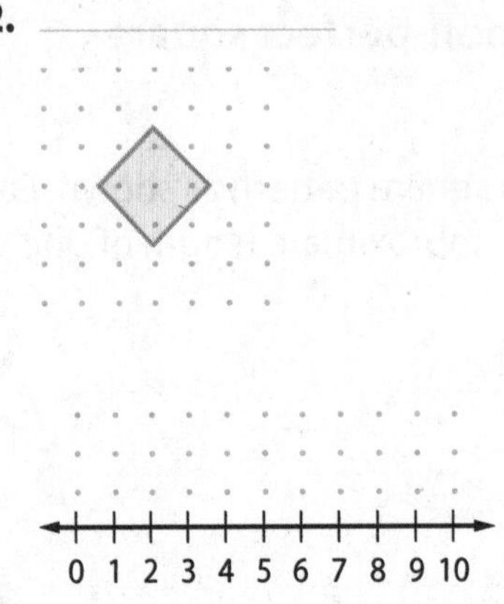

3. ____________

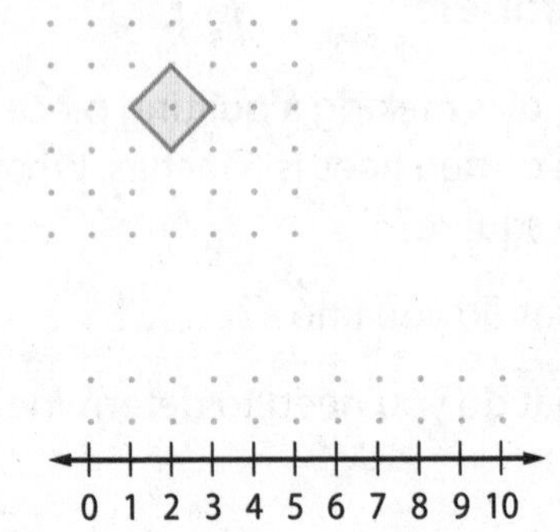

Analyze and Reflect

4. MP **Select Tools and Techniques** Estimate the side length of the square in Exercise 1. Verify your estimate by using a calculator.

Estimate ____________ Calculator ____________

5. MP **Analyze Relationships** How does the area of a square relate to the square of a number? ____________

Create

6. MP **Apply Math to the Real World** Write a real-world problem that involves estimating a square root. Use the method shown in the Activity to solve your problem.

____

____

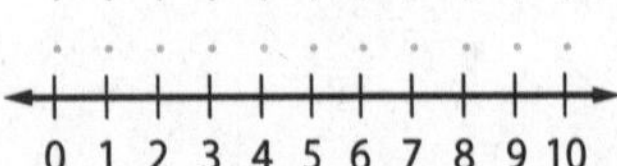

7. **INQUIRY** HOW can I use multiple representations to estimate the square root of a non-perfect square?

____

____

Lesson 6
Estimate Roots

 Launch the Lesson: Real World

Watch

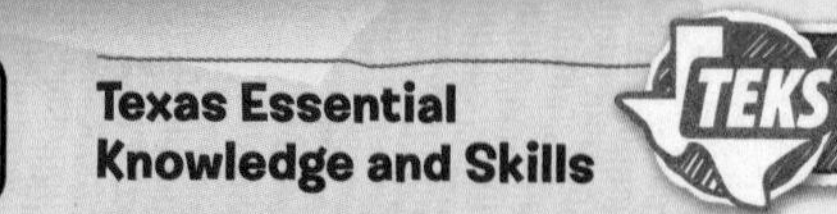

Texas Essential Knowledge and Skills

Targeted TEKS

8.2(B) Approximate the value of an irrational number, including π and square roots of numbers less than 225, and locate that rational number approximation on a number line.

Mathematical Processes

8.1(A), 8.1(B), 8.1(F), 8.1(G)

Essential Question

WHY is it helpful to write numbers in different ways?

Legend states that while sitting in his garden one day, Sir Isaac Newton was struck on the head by an apple. Suppose the apple was 25 feet above his head. The formula $t = \frac{\sqrt{h}}{4}$ can be used to find the time t in seconds it will take an object to fall from a certain height h in feet. How long did it take the apple to fall?

1. What is the square root of 25? ☐

2. How long did it take for the apple to fall?

3. Suppose another apple was 13 feet above the ground. Use the formula to write an equation representing the time it would have taken for the apple to hit the ground.

4. Can you express $\frac{\sqrt{13}}{4}$ without a radical sign? Explain.

5. Estimate $\frac{\sqrt{13}}{4}$. Explain your reasoning.

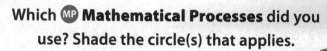

Which MP Mathematical Processes did you use? Shade the circle(s) that applies.

Ⓐ Apply Math to the Real World.
Ⓑ Use a Problem-Solving Model.
Ⓒ Select Tools and Techniques.
Ⓓ Use Multiple Representations.
Ⓔ Organize Ideas.
Ⓕ Analyze Relationships.
Ⓖ Justify Arguments.

Work Zone

Estimate Square and Cube Roots

You know that $\sqrt{8}$ is not a whole number because 8 is not a perfect square.

The number line below shows that $\sqrt{8}$ is between 2 and 3. Since 8 is closer to 9 than 4, the best whole number estimate for $\sqrt{8}$ is 3.

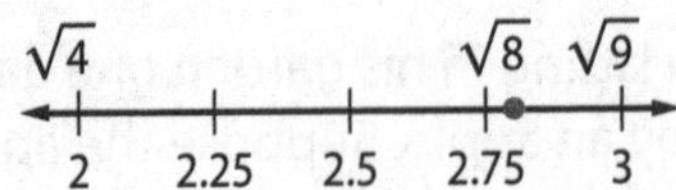

Tutor

Examples

1. Estimate $\sqrt{53}$ to the nearest integer.

- The largest perfect square less than 53 is 49. $\sqrt{49} = 7$
- The smallest perfect square greater than 53 is 64. $\sqrt{64} = 8$

Plot each square root on a number line. Then estimate $\sqrt{53}$.

√49 √53 √64

7 7.25 7.5 7.75 8

$49 < 53 < 64$ Write an inequality.

$7^2 < 53 < 8^2$ $49 = 7^2$ and $64 = 8^2$

$\sqrt{7^2} < \sqrt{53} < \sqrt{8^2}$ Find the square root of each number.

$7 < \sqrt{53} < 8$ Simplify.

Inequalities

$49 < 53 < 64$ is read 49 is less than 53, which is less than 64, or 53 is between 49 and 64.

So, $\sqrt{53}$ is between 7 and 8. Since $\sqrt{53}$ is closer to $\sqrt{49}$ than $\sqrt{64}$, the best integer estimate for $\sqrt{53}$ is 7.

2. Estimate $\sqrt[3]{320}$ to the nearest integer.

- The largest perfect cube less than 320 is 216. $\sqrt[3]{216} = 6$
- The smallest perfect cube greater than 320 is 343. $\sqrt[3]{343} = 7$

$216 < 320 < 343$ Write an inequality.

$6^3 < 320 < 7^3$ $216 = 6^3$ and $343 = 7^3$

$\sqrt[3]{6^3} < \sqrt[3]{320} < \sqrt[3]{7^3}$ Find the cube root of each number.

$6 < \sqrt[3]{320} < 7$ Simplify.

So $\sqrt[3]{320}$ is between 6 and 7. Since 320 is closer to 343 than 216, the best integer estimate for $\sqrt[3]{320}$ is 7.

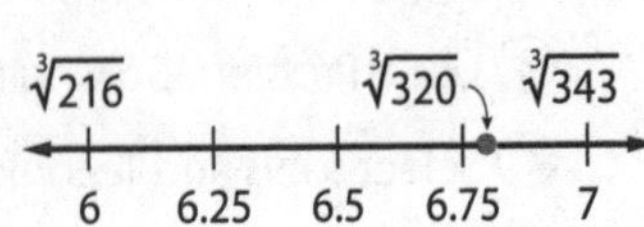

Got It? Do these problems to find out.

a. $\sqrt{35}$ **b.** $\sqrt{170}$ **c.** $\sqrt{44.8}$

d. $\sqrt[3]{62}$ **e.** $\sqrt[3]{25}$ **f.** $\sqrt[3]{129.6}$

a. ________

b. ________

c. ________

d. ________

e. ________

f. ________

Example

3. Wyatt wants to fence in a square portion of the yard to make a play area for his new puppy. The area covered is 2 square meters. How much fencing should Wyatt buy?

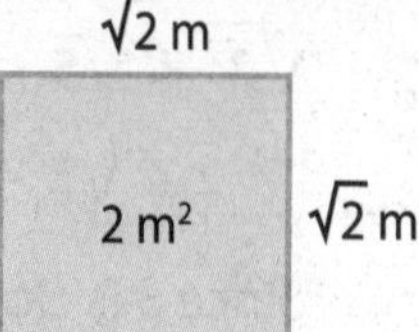

Wyatt will need $4 \cdot \sqrt{2}$ meters of fencing. The square root of 2 is between 1 and 2, so $4 \cdot \sqrt{2}$ is between 4 and 8. Is this the best approximation? You can truncate the decimal expansion of $\sqrt{2}$ to find better approximations.

Estimate $\sqrt{2}$ by truncating, or dropping, the digits after the first decimal place, then after the second decimal place, and so on until an appropriate approximation is reached.

$\sqrt{2} \approx 1.414213562$ Use a calculator.

$\sqrt{2} \approx 1.4\cancel{14213562}$ Truncate, or drop, the digits after the first decimal place. $\sqrt{2}$ is between 1.4 and 1.5.

$5.6 < 4\sqrt{2} < 6.0$ $4 \cdot 1.4 = 5.6$ and $4 \cdot 1.5 = 6.0$

To find a closer approximation, expand $\sqrt{2}$ then truncate the decimal expansion after the first two decimal places.

$\sqrt{2} \approx 1.41\cancel{4213562}$ $\sqrt{2}$ is between 1.41 and 1.42.

$5.64 < 4\sqrt{2} < 5.68$ $4 \cdot 1.41 = 5.64$ and $4 \cdot 1.42 = 5.68$

The approximations indicate that Wyatt should buy 6 meters of fencing.

STOP and Reflect

What is the difference between an exact value and an approximate value when finding square roots of numbers that are not perfect squares? Explain below.

Got It? Do this problem to find out.

g. Kelly wants to frame a square poster with an area of 120 square inches. Use the equation $s^2 = 120$ to determine three sets of approximations for the amount of molding she will need. Truncate the value of $\sqrt{120}$ to the ones, tenths, and hundredths place. Then determine how much molding she will need.

g. ________

Example

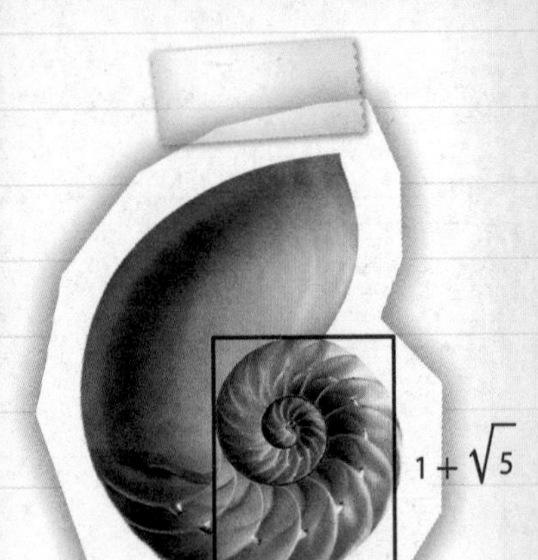

4. The *golden rectangle* is found frequently in the nautilus shell. The length of the longer side divided by the length of the shorter side is equal to $\frac{1+\sqrt{5}}{2}$. Estimate this value.

First estimate the value of $\sqrt{5}$.

$4 < 5 < 9$	4 and 9 are the closest perfect squares.
$2^2 < 5 < 3^2$	$4 = 2^2$ and $9 = 3^2$
$\sqrt{2^2} < \sqrt{5} < \sqrt{3^2}$	Find the square root of each number.
$2 < \sqrt{5} < 3$	Simplify.

Since 5 is closer to 4 than 9, the best integer estimate for $\sqrt{5}$ is 2. Use this value to evaluate the expression.

$\frac{1+\sqrt{5}}{2} \approx \frac{1+2}{2}$ or 1.5

Guided Practice

Estimate to the nearest integer. (Examples 1 and 2)

1. $\sqrt{28} \approx$ ______
2. $\sqrt{205} \approx$ ______
3. $\sqrt{122.3} \approx$ ______
4. $\sqrt[3]{51} \approx$ ______
5. $\sqrt[3]{200} \approx$ ______
6. $\sqrt[3]{95} \approx$ ______

7. **STEM** Tobias dropped a tennis ball from a height of 60 meters. The time in seconds it takes for the ball to fall 60 feet is $0.25(\sqrt{60})$. Determine three sets of approximations for the amount of time it will take. Then determine how long it will take for the ball to hit the ground. (Example 3)

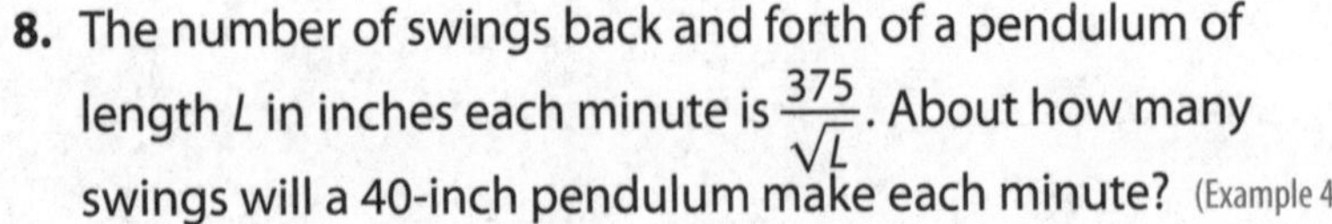

8. The number of swings back and forth of a pendulum of length L in inches each minute is $\frac{375}{\sqrt{L}}$. About how many swings will a 40-inch pendulum make each minute? (Example 4)

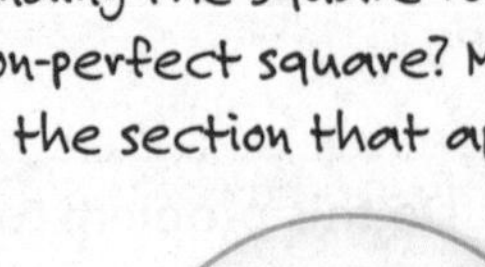

9. **Building on the Essential Question** How can I estimate the square root of a non-perfect square?

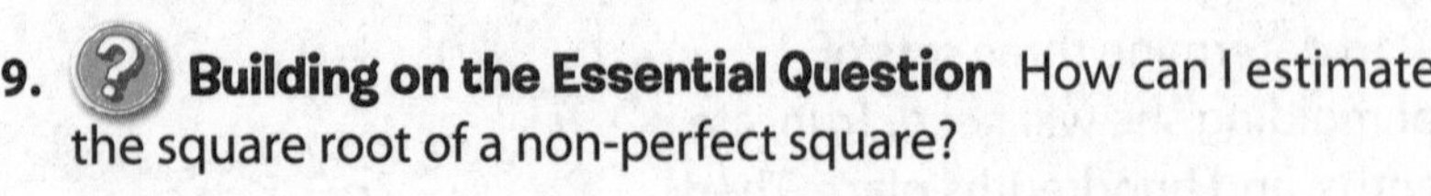

Rate Yourself!

How confident are you about finding the square root of a non-perfect square? Mark an X in the section that applies.

Find out online. Use the Self-Check Quiz.

Name ______ My Homework ______

Independent Practice

8.2(B), 8.1(F) TEKS

Estimate to the nearest integer. (Examples 1 and 2)

1. $\sqrt{23} \approx$ ______

2. $\sqrt{197} \approx$ ______

3. $\sqrt{15.6} \approx$ ______

4. $\sqrt{85.1} \approx$ ______

5. $\sqrt[3]{22} \approx$ ______

6. $\sqrt[3]{34} \approx$ ______

7. $\sqrt[3]{989} \approx$ ______

8. $\sqrt[3]{250} \approx$ ______

9. The area of Kaitlyn's square garden is 345 square feet. One side of the garden is next to a shed. She wants to put a fence around the other three sides of the garden. Determine three sets of approximations for the amount of fence it will take. Then determine how much fence she should buy. (Example 3)

______

______

10. In Little League, the bases are squares with sides of 14 inches. The expression $\sqrt{(s^2 + s^2)}$ represents the distance *diagonally across* a square of side length s. Estimate the diagonal distance across a base to the nearest inch. (Example 4)

______

11. **STEM** The formula $t = \frac{\sqrt{h}}{4}$ represents the time t in seconds that it takes an object to fall from a height of h feet. If a rock falls from a height of 125 feet, estimate how long it will take to reach the ground. (Example 4)

______

Order each set of numbers from least to greatest.

12. $\left\{7, 9, \sqrt{50}, \sqrt{85}\right\}$ ______

13. $\left\{\sqrt[3]{105}, 7, 5, \sqrt{38}\right\}$ ______

14. **Use a Problem-Solving Model** Amanda purchased a storage cube that has a volume of 4 cubic feet. She wants to put it on a bookshelf that is 12 inches tall. Will the cube fit? Explain. ______

15. Without a calculator, determine which is greater, $\sqrt{94}$ or 10. Explain your reasoning. ______

16. **Find the Error** Jasmine is estimating $\sqrt{200}$. Determine her mistake and correct it.

______

$\sqrt{200} \approx 100$

H.O.T. Problems Higher-Order Thinking

17. **Create** Find two numbers that have square roots between 7 and 8. One number should have a square root closer to 7 and the other number should have a square root closer to 8. Justify your answer.

______

18. **Evaluate** For what value(s) of p is each statement true?

$\sqrt{p} \geq 0$ ______ $\sqrt{p} = 9$ ______

$\sqrt{p} = 0$ ______ $\sqrt{-p} = 9$ ______

$\sqrt{p} < 0$ ______ $\sqrt{p} = -9$ ______

19. **Evaluate** Suppose x is a number between 1 and 10 and y is a number between 10 and 20. Determine whether the statement below is *always*, *sometimes* or *never* true. Explain your reasoning.

$$\sqrt{x} > \sqrt[3]{y}$$

______

Name ______________________________

Multi-Step Problem Solving

20. The table shows the area of four square photos. Which of the following is the order of the photos from greatest area to least area? N EE MP

Photos	Area (cm^2)
A	$\sqrt{130}$
B	$\sqrt{172}$
C	13
D	11

Ⓐ B, C, A, D
Ⓑ C, B, A, D
Ⓒ B, A, C, D
Ⓓ D, A, C, B

Use a problem-solving model to solve this problem.

1 Analyze

Read the problem. Circle the information you know.
Underline what the problem is asking you to find.

2 Plan

What will you need to do to solve the problem? Write your plan in steps.

Step 1 Estimate the ________ of photos A and B.

Step 2 Compare and order the photos from ________ according to their ________ .

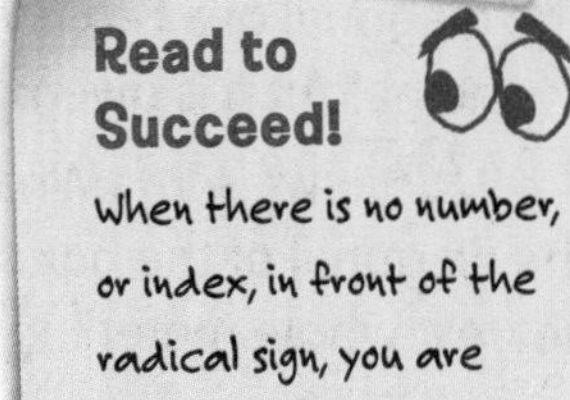

Read to Succeed!
When there is no number, or index, in front of the radical sign, you are finding a square root.

3 Solve

Use your plan to solve the problem. Show your steps.

Since $\sqrt{130}$ is a little less than halfway between ______ and ______, ______ is a good estimate for $\sqrt{130}$.

Since $\sqrt{172}$ is much closer to ______ than ______, ______ is a good estimate for $\sqrt{172}$.

Since 13.1 > 13 > 11.4 > 11, choice A is correct. Fill in that answer choice.

4 Justify and Evaluate

How do you know your solution is accurate?

____

____

____

N = Number and Operations EE = Expressions, Equations, and Relationships MP = Mathematical Processes

More Multi-Step Problem Solving

Use a problem-solving model to solve each problem.

21. The table shows the volume of four cubes. Which is the order of the volumes from least to greatest? N EE MP

Cube	Volume (cm^3)
A	$\sqrt[3]{74}$
B	3
C	$\sqrt[3]{110}$
D	5

Ⓐ $\sqrt[3]{74}, \sqrt[3]{110}, 3, 5$

Ⓑ $3, 5, \sqrt[3]{74}, \sqrt[3]{110}$

Ⓒ $3, \sqrt[3]{74}, \sqrt[3]{110}, 5$

Ⓓ $5, \sqrt[3]{110}, \sqrt[3]{74}, 3$

22. Roger made a square sign to place on his bedroom door shown below in the sketch. What is the approximate perimeter, in inches, of his sign? N EE MP

138 m^2

23. The diagonal of a box d with length ℓ, width w, and height h is given by the formula $d = \sqrt{\ell^2 + w^2 + h^2}$. What is the length of the diagonal of the box shown below to the nearest whole meter? N EE MP

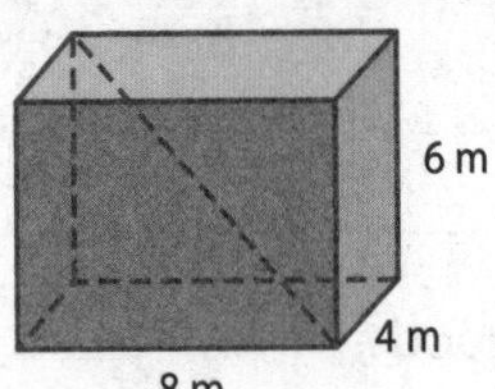

24. A circle of radius r has an area A of 214 square centimeters. Estimate the radius of the circle to the nearest whole centimeter. Use 3 as an estimate for π. Explain how you found your answer. N EE MP

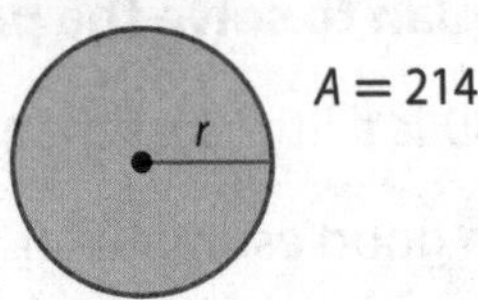

N = Number and Operations EE = Expressions, Equations, and Relationships MP = Mathematical Processes

Lesson 7

The Real Number System

Launch the Lesson: Real World

A model of a Major League diamond is shown. Are the dimensions of the model rational numbers?

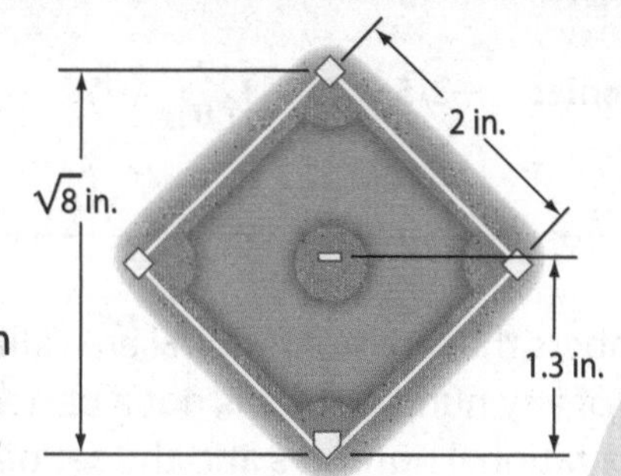

1. On the model, the distance from first base to second base is 2 inches. Is 2 a rational number? Explain.

2. On the model, the distance from the pitching mound to home plate is 1.3 inches. Is 1.3 a rational number? Explain.

3. The distance from home plate to second base is $\sqrt{8}$ inches. Using a calculator, find $\sqrt{8}$. Does it appear to terminate or repeat?

4. Use your calculator to multiply your answer to Exercise 3 by itself. Do not use the x^2 button. Is the answer 8?

5. Based on your results, can you classify $\sqrt{8}$ as a rational number? Explain.

Which MP Mathematical Processes did you use? Shade the circle(s) that applies.

- Ⓐ Apply Math to the Real World.
- Ⓑ Use a Problem-Solving Model.
- Ⓒ Select Tools and Techniques.
- Ⓓ Use Multiple Representations.
- Ⓔ Organize Ideas.
- Ⓕ Analyze Relationships.
- Ⓖ Justify Arguments.

Texas Essential Knowledge and Skills

Targeted TEKS

8.2(A) Extend previous knowledge of sets and subsets using a visual representation to describe relationships between sets of real numbers. *Also includes 8.2(B).*

Mathematical Processes

8.1(A), 8.1(B), 8.1(D), 8.1(E), 8.1(F)

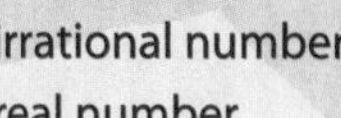

Vocabulary

irrational number

real number

Essential Question

WHY is it helpful to write numbers in different ways?

Key Concept

Real Numbers

Words	Rational Number	Irrational Number
	A rational number is a number that can be expressed as the ratio $\frac{a}{b}$, where a and b are integers and $b \neq 0$.	An **irrational number** is a number that cannot be expressed as the ratio $\frac{a}{b}$, where a and b are integers and $b \neq 0$.
Examples	$-2, 5, 3.7\overline{6}, -12\frac{7}{8}$	$\sqrt{2} \approx 1.414213562\ldots$ $\pi \approx 3.1415926535\ldots$

Work Zone

STOP and Reflect

Explain below how you know that $\sqrt{2}$ is an irrational number.

Numbers that are not rational are called irrational numbers. The square root of any number that is not a perfect square number is irrational. The set of rational numbers and the set of irrational numbers together make up the set of **real numbers**. The Venn diagram below shows the set of real numbers.

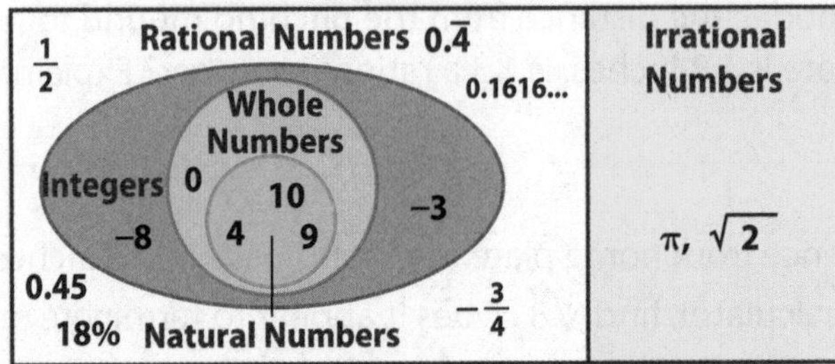

Tutor

Examples

Classify each number by determining all sets of numbers to which it belongs. Then write each number in the Venn diagram above.

1. **0.1616...** The decimal ends in a repeating pattern. It is a rational number because it is equivalent to $\frac{16}{99}$.

2. π $\pi \approx 3.1415926535\ldots$ The decimal does not terminate nor repeat, so it is an irrational number.

Show your work.

Got It? Do these problems to find out.

a. $4\frac{1}{5}$ **b.** $-\sqrt{64}$ **c.** $-\sqrt{10}$

a. ____________

b. ____________

c. ____________

Sets of Real Numbers

You can use the Venn diagram below to describe relationships between sets of real numbers.

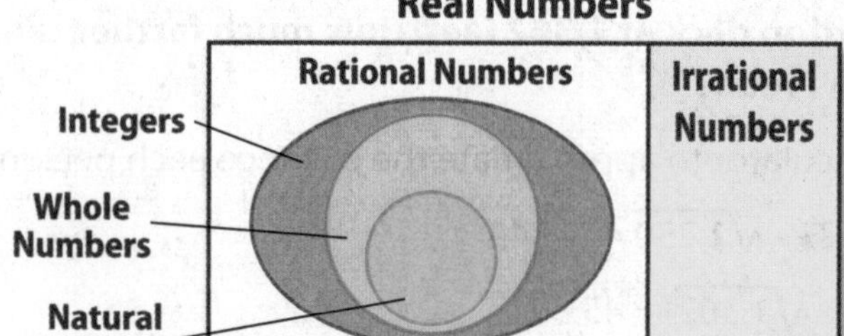

Examples

Use the Venn diagram above to determine whether each statement is *true* or *false*. If the statement is *true*, explain your reasoning. If the statement is *false*, provide *a counterexample*.

Counterexample
A counterexample is an example that shows a statement is not true.

3. All rational numbers are integers.

Integers are a subset of rational numbers. So, the statement is false. A counterexample is 0.6. The decimal 0.6 is a rational number, but not an integer.

4. All irrational numbers are real numbers.

This statement is true because irrational numbers are a subset of real numbers. For example, $\sqrt{2}$ is irrational and is real.

5. All real numbers are irrational numbers.

Real numbers can be irrational or rational. So, this statement is false. A counterexample is 2. The number 2 is a natural number, a whole numbers, an integer, a rational number, and a real number.

Got It? **Do these problems to find out.**

d. All integers are real numbers.

e. All integers are irrational numbers.

Example

6. On a clear day, the number of miles a person can see to the horizon is about $1.23\sqrt{d}$, where d is the distance from the ground in feet. Suppose Freda is at the Empire Building observation deck at 1,250 feet and Kia is at the Freedom Tower observation deck at 1,362 feet. How much farther can Kia see than Freda?

Use a calculator to approximate the distance each person can see.

Freda: $1.23 \cdot \sqrt{1{,}250} \approx 43.49$

Kia: $1.23 \cdot \sqrt{1{,}362} \approx 45.39$

$45.39 - 43.49 = 1.90$

Kia can see 1.90 miles farther than Freda.

Guided Practice

Classify each number by determining all sets of numbers to which it belongs. Write each number in the Venn diagram on the next page. (Examples 1 and 2)

1. 0.393939... ________

2. $-\sqrt{40}$ ________

3. $\sqrt{121}$ ________

Use the Venn diagram on the next page to determine whether each statement is *true* or *false*. If the statement is *true*, explain your reasoning. If the statement is *false*, provide a counterexample. (Examples 3–5)

4. All natural numbers are whole numbers.

____

5. All whole numbers are natural numbers.

____

6. The formula $A = \sqrt{s(s-a)(s-b)(s-c)}$ can be used to find the area A of a triangle. The variables a, b, and c are the side measures and s is one half the perimeter. Use the formula to find the area of a triangle with side lengths of 7 centimeters, 9 centimeters, and 10 centimeters.

(Example 6) ________

7. **Building on the Essential Question** How can you determine if a number is rational?

____

____

Rate Yourself!

How well do you understand real numbers? Circle the image that applies.

Clear

Somewhat Clear

Not So Clear

Find out online. Use the Self-Check Quiz.

Independent Practice

8.1(A), 8.2(A) TEKS

Classify each number by determining all sets of numbers to which it belongs. Then write each number in the Venn diagram below. (Examples 1 and 2)

1. $\frac{2}{3}$ ________

2. π ________

3. $7.\overline{2}$ ________

4. $\frac{12}{4}$ ________

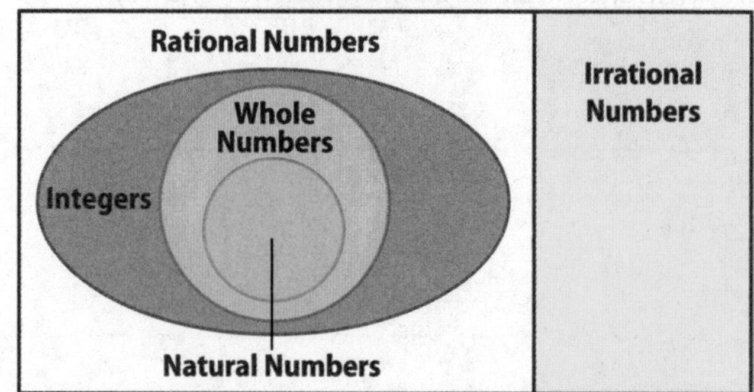

Use the Venn diagram above to determine whether each statement is *true* or *false*. If the statement is *true*, explain your reasoning. If the statement is *false*, provide a counterexample. (Examples 3–5)

5. All real numbers are natural numbers.

____

6. All rational numbers are real numbers.

____

7. An irrational number cannot be a real number.

____

8. All whole numbers are integers.

____

9. The equation $s = \sqrt{30df}$ can be used to find a car's speed s in miles per hour given the length d in feet of a skid mark and the friction factor f of the road. Police measured a skid mark of 90 feet on a dry concrete road. If the speed limit is 35 mph, was the car speeding? Explain. (Example 6)

Friction Factor		
Road	Concrete	Tar
Wet	0.4	0.5
Dry	0.8	1.0

____

10. **Organize Ideas** Write a brief description and give an example of each type of number in the graphic organizer shown.

natural	whole	integer	rational	irrational

Which One Doesn't Belong? For each set of numbers, determine the real number that does not belong with the other three. Defend your answer.

11. $\left\{\sqrt{9}, \frac{2}{3}, -6, \sqrt{3}\right\}$

12. $\left\{-\sqrt{25}, -12, -8.2\sqrt{16}\right\}$

13. $\left\{\sqrt{2}, \sqrt{1}, \sqrt{48}, \sqrt{35}\right\}$

14. **Use a Counterexample** Give a counterexample for the statement *All square roots are irrational numbers*. Explain your reasoning.

H.O.T. Problems Higher Order Thinking

Evaluate Tell whether the following statements are *always*, *sometimes*, or *never* true. If a statement is not always true, explain.

15. Integers are rational numbers.

16. Rational numbers are integers.

Create Write a number that satisfies each set of conditions.

17. an integer that is not a whole number

18. a cube root that is not rational

Name ______________________________

Multi-Step Problem Solving

19. The table shows four sets of numbers. Which set contains the most irrational numbers? N MP

Ⓐ Set A

Ⓑ Set B

Ⓒ Set C

Ⓓ Set D

Set	Numbers
A	$\sqrt{225}$, 2.252525..., $1.\bar{6}$, $\sqrt{144}$
B	$4.\overline{356}$, π, $\sqrt{100}$, 2.56
C	24, $3\frac{1}{3}\%$, 2.14351436..., $\sqrt{169}$, $1.\overline{93}$
D	$\sqrt{140}$, 3.14159..., $\sqrt{224}$, π

Use a problem-solving model to solve this problem.

1 Analyze

Read the problem. Circle the information you know.
Underline what the problem is asking you to find.

2 Plan

What will you need to do to solve the problem? Write your plan in steps.

Step 1 Determine which numbers in each set are ____________.

Step 2 Determine the set with the __________ irrational numbers.

3 Solve

Use your plan to solve the problem. Show your steps.

Determine which numbers are irrational.

Set A: ______________________________.

Set B: ______________________________.

Set C: ______________________________.

Set D: ______________________________.

Since Set D has the most irrational numbers, choice D is correct. Fill in that answer choice.

Read to Succeed!

To determine if a decimal repeats, look for repeating digits or bar notation. Ellipses (...) following a series of digits does not automatically indicate a decimal is a repeating decimal.

4 Justify and Evaluate

How do you know your solution is accurate?

____

____

____

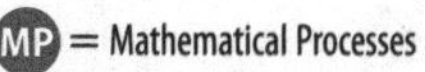
N = Number and Operations MP = Mathematical Processes

More Multi-Step Problem Solving

Use a problem-solving model to solve each problem.

20. Which set contains elements from the set of rational numbers *and* the set of irrational numbers? N MP

Ⓐ $\{3, \sqrt{25}, 1.\overline{45}, 0, -6\}$

Ⓑ $\{5, 1.\overline{23}, 0, \sqrt{225}, -7\}$

Ⓒ $\{2, \sqrt{23}, 4.\overline{6}, 0, -4\}$

Ⓓ $\{3, 1.6, 8, \sqrt{169}, -15\}$

21. The area A of an equilateral triangle with side length s is $A = \frac{s^2\sqrt{3}}{4}$. Use an integer estimate for $\sqrt{3}$ to find the sum of areas of the equilateral triangles shown below to the nearest whole square centimeter. N MP

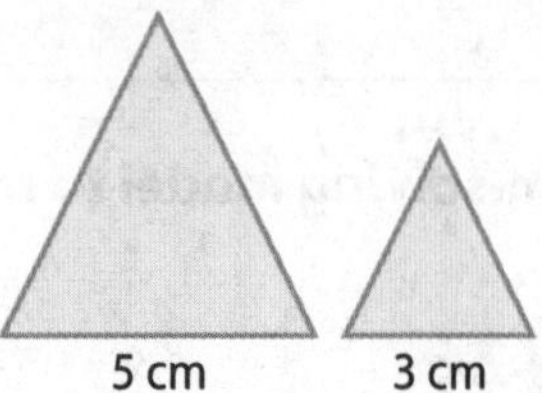

22. The areas of two squares are shown below. To the nearest whole meter, what is the difference between the side lengths of these squares? N MP

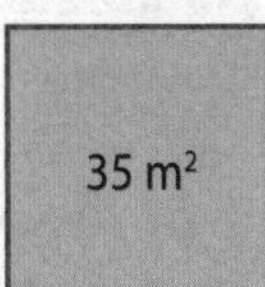

23. Label the Venn diagram with the five subsets of real numbers and examples of each subset. Then give a brief description of the set of real numbers. N MP

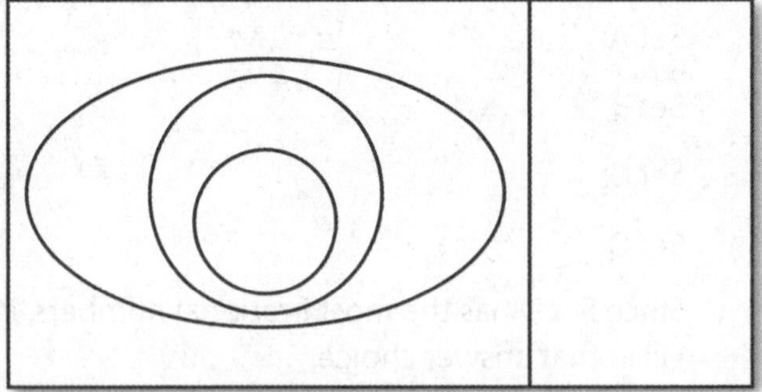

N = Number and Operations MP = Mathematical Processes

Lesson 8

Compare and Order Real Numbers

Launch the Lesson: Real World

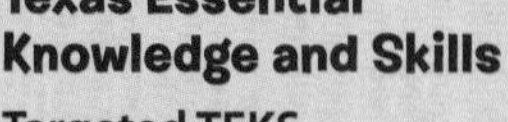

Texas Essential Knowledge and Skills

Targeted TEKS
8.2(D) Order a set of real numbers arising from mathematical and real-world contexts. *Also addresses 8.2(A) and 8.2(B).*

Mathematical Processes
8.1(A), 8.1(B), 8.1(C), 8.1(D), 8.1(E), 8.1(F)

Vocab

Essential Question
WHY is it helpful to write numbers in different ways?

The lengths of some of the smallest mammals are shown in the table. Which mammal is the smallest?

Animal	Length (cm)
Harvest Mouse	5.8
Kitti's Hog-Nosed Bat	$2\frac{9}{10}$
Masked Shrew	$4\frac{1}{2}$
Pygmy Shrew	$3\frac{3}{5}$

1. In the table, some of the lengths are written as mixed numbers. Express the mixed numbers in standard decimal notation.

____

____

2. Approximate the location of each length on the number line below. Then list the lengths in order from left to right.

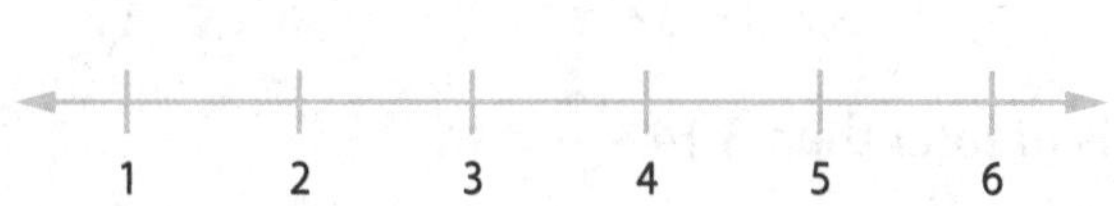

____

3. Refer to the numbers you ordered in Exercise 2. Which mammal is the smallest? ______________________________

Which MP Mathematical Processes did you use? Shade the circle(s) that applies.

Ⓐ Apply Math to the Real World.
Ⓑ Use a Problem-Solving Model.
Ⓒ Select Tools and Techniques.
Ⓓ Use Multiple Representations.
Ⓔ Organize Ideas.
Ⓕ Analyze Relationships.
Ⓖ Justify Arguments.

Work Zone

Compare Real Numbers

You can compare real numbers by expressing them in the same notation.

Tutor

Examples

Fill in each $\bigcirc$ with <, >, or = to make a true statement.

1. $\sqrt{7} \bigcirc 2\frac{2}{3}$

Express both numbers in standard decimal notation.

$\sqrt{7} \approx 2.645751311\ldots$ $\quad$ $2\frac{2}{3} = 2.666666666\ldots$

Graph both decimals on a number line. Approximate the location of each number.

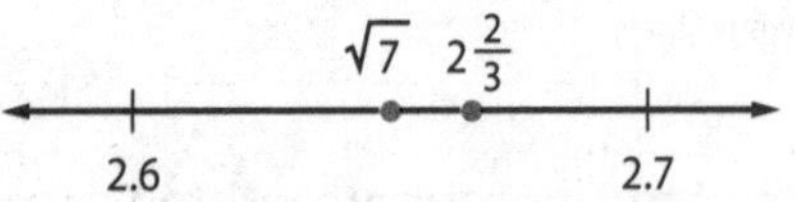

Since 2.645751311… is less than 2.66666666…, $\sqrt{7} < 2\frac{2}{3}$.

2. $\frac{18}{5} \bigcirc \pi$

$\frac{18}{5} = 3.6$ $\quad$ $\pi \approx 3.14$

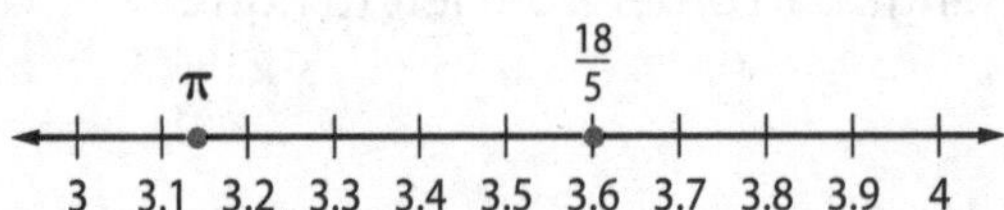

Since 3.6 is greater than 3.14, $\frac{18}{5} > \pi$.

3. $1.50 \bigcirc \sqrt{2.25}$

$1.50 = 1.5$ $\quad$ $\sqrt{2.25} = 1.5$

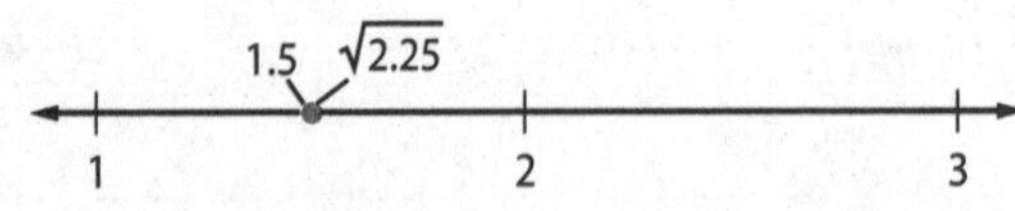

Since 1.50 and $\sqrt{2.25}$ are equal, $1.50 = \sqrt{2.25}$.

Got It? Do these problems to find out.

Fill in each $\bigcirc$ with <, >, or = to make a true statement.

a. $\sqrt{11} \bigcirc 3\frac{1}{3}$ $\quad$ **b.** $\sqrt{17} \bigcirc 4.03$ $\quad$ **c.** $\sqrt{6.25} \bigcirc 250\%$

Order Real Numbers

You can also order real numbers. To order real numbers, express the numbers in the standard decimal notation before comparing them.

Tutor

Examples

Order each set of numbers from least to greatest. Verify your answer by graphing the numbers on a number line.

4. $\left\{\sqrt{30}, 6, 5\frac{4}{5}, 5.3\overline{6}\right\}$

Express each number as a decimal. Then order the decimals.

$\sqrt{30} \approx 5.48$

$6 = 6.00$

$5\frac{4}{5} = 5.80$

$5.3\overline{6} \approx 5.37$

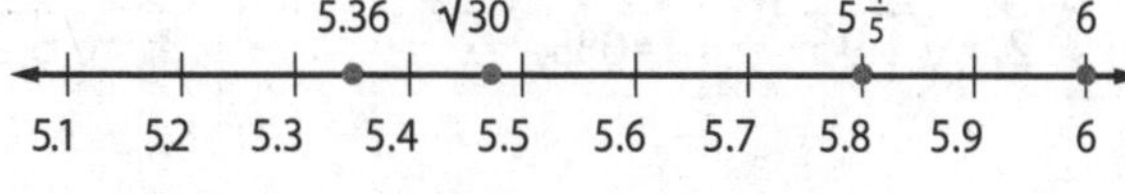

From least to greatest, the order is $5.3\overline{6}$, $\sqrt{30}$, $5\frac{4}{5}$, and 6.

5. $\left\{-\sqrt{25}, -4.\overline{5}, -4, -\frac{31}{6}\right\}$

Express each number as a decimal. Then order the decimals.

$-\sqrt{25} = -5.00$

$-4.\overline{5} \approx 4.56$

$-4 \approx -4.00$

$-\frac{31}{6} \approx -5.17$

$-\frac{31}{6}$ $-\sqrt{25}$ $-4.\overline{5}$ -4

−6 −5 −4 −3 −2

From least to greatest, the order is $-\frac{31}{6}$, $-\sqrt{25}$, $-4.\overline{5}$, and -4.

Got It? Do these problems to find out.

d. Order $\left\{-7, -\sqrt{60}, -7\frac{7}{10}, -\frac{66}{9}\right\}$ from least to greatest. Verify your answer by graphing on the number line below.

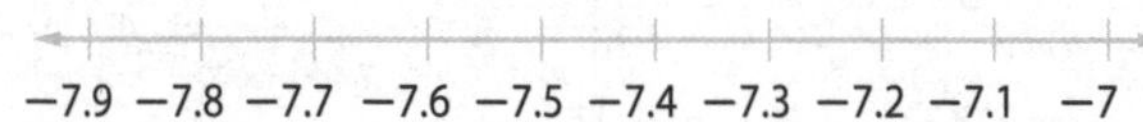

Example

6. On Wednesday, there is an $83\frac{1}{3}$% chance that it is going to rain. On Thursday, there is 90% chance of rain. On Friday, there is a 6 out of 7 chance that it will rain. On which day is there the greatest chance that it will rain?

Express each number as a decimal.

$83\frac{1}{3}\% \approx 0.83$ $\quad$ $90\% = 0.90$ $\quad$ $\frac{6}{7} \approx 0.86$

Since $0.90 > 0.86 > 0.83$, $90\% > \frac{6}{7} > 83\frac{1}{3}$.

There is the greatest chance that it will rain on Thursday.

Guided Practice

Fill in each ◯ with <, >, or = to make a true statement. (Examples 1–3)

1. $\sqrt{15}$ ◯ 3.5

2. $\sqrt{1.96}$ ◯ 140%

3. $\sqrt{6.2}$ ◯ $2.\overline{4}$

Order each set of numbers from least to greatest. Verify your answer by graphing on a number line. (Examples 4 and 5)

4. $\left\{2.\overline{71}, \sqrt{6}, \frac{5}{2}, 2\frac{3}{4}\right\}$ __________

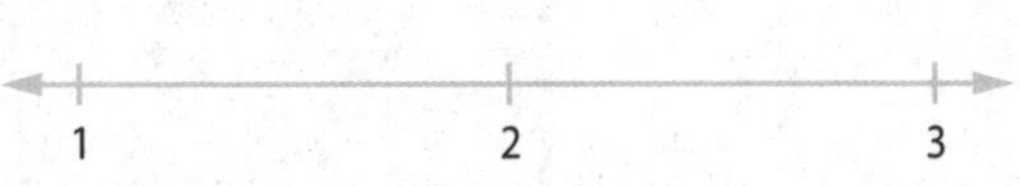

5. $\left\{-\sqrt{12}, -\frac{16}{5} -3.5, -3.\overline{3}\right\}$ __________

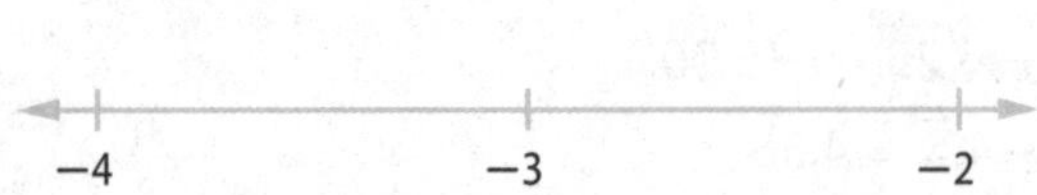

6. A teacher surveyed her students about their favorite type of pizza. Of the students in her first period, $\frac{5}{24}$ favored cheese pizza. In her second period class, 4 out of 19 favored cheese pizza. In her third period class, 20% favored cheese pizza. In which class did the greatest fraction of students favor cheese pizza? (Example 6)

____

7. **Building on the Essential Question** How can you compare and order real numbers?

____

Rate Yourself!

Are you ready to move on? Shade the section that applies.

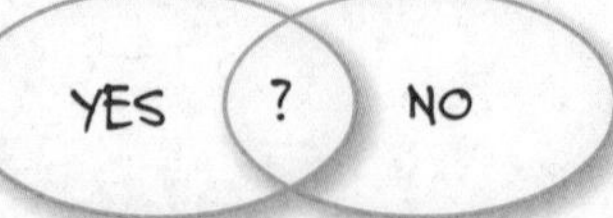

Find out online. Use the Self-Check Quiz.

Name ________________ My Homework ________________

Independent Practice

8.1(A), 8.2(D) TEKS

Fill in each ◯ with <, >, or = to make a true statement. (Examples 1–3)

1. $\sqrt{10}$ ◯ 3.2 ________

2. $5\frac{1}{6}$ ◯ $5.1\overline{6}$ ________

3. $2.\overline{21}$ ◯ $\sqrt{5.2}$ ________

Order each set of numbers from least to greatest. Verify your answer by graphing on a number line. (Examples 4 and 5)

4. $\left\{-415\%, -4.\overline{1}, -\sqrt{17}, -4.08\right\}$

____

−4.18 −4.16 −4.14 −4.12 −4.1 −4.08

5. $\left\{\frac{11}{3}, 3.26, \pi, 3.8, \sqrt{12}\right\}$

____

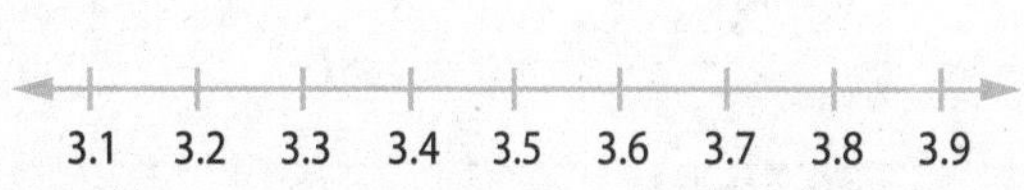

6. The table shows the on-base statistics for three players at a recent baseball tournament. Which player had the greatest on-base statistics? (Example 6)

____

Player	On-Base Statistics
1	15 out of 21
2	$\frac{14}{19}$
3	72.5%

7. Amy took four science quizzes. On her first quiz, Amy answered 21 out of 25 of the questions correctly. On the second quiz, she answered 25 out of 27 questions correctly. On the third and fourth quizzes, she answered 88% and 92% of the questions correctly, respectively. Order Amy's quiz scores from greatest to least. (Example 6)

____

8. The lengths of a shark's teeth are $\frac{9}{4}$ inches, $2\frac{1}{8}$ inches, and 2 inches. Order the length of the shark's teeth from least to greatest. Then graph the numbers on a number line.

____

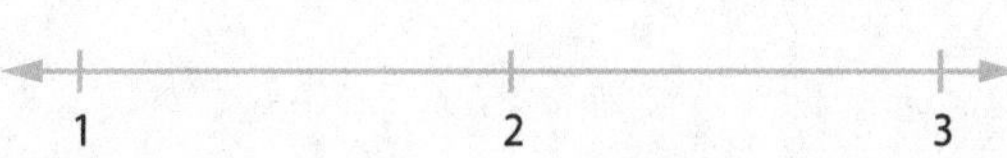

Use estimation to fill in ◯ each with <, >, or = to make a true statement.

9. 3π ◯ $\sqrt{78}$

10. π^3 ◯ $3 \cdot \sqrt{15}$

11. $\sqrt{980}$ ◯ $4\pi^2$

Analyze Relationships Write an example of each type of number.

12. a real number between $\frac{2}{9}$ and $\frac{3}{9}$

13. a real number between $-1\frac{1}{7}$ and $-1\frac{2}{7}$

14. a real number between $\sqrt{3}$ and $1\frac{3}{4}$

15. a real number between 12% and $\sqrt{0.04}$

16. Which One Doesn't Belong? Identify the number that does not have the same value as the other three. Defend your answer.

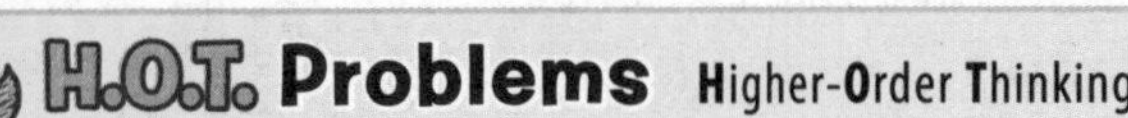

H.O.T. Problems Higher-Order Thinking

17. **Create** Write two numbers, one rational number and one irrational number, that are between 1.4 and 1.6. Include the decimal approximation of the irrational number to the nearest hundredth.

18. **Evaluate** Which real number is greater, π or $\frac{22}{7}$? Justify your answer.

19. **Evaluate** Which of the following numbers is closest to 8: $8\frac{1}{7}$, $8.\overline{14}$, or $\frac{15}{2}$? Justify your answer.

20. **Create** Write and solve a real-world problem in which you would compare rational numbers.

Name ______________________________

Multi-Step Problem Solving

21. Which number line shows {350%, π, $3.\overline{3}$, $\sqrt{14}$}? N MP

Ⓐ 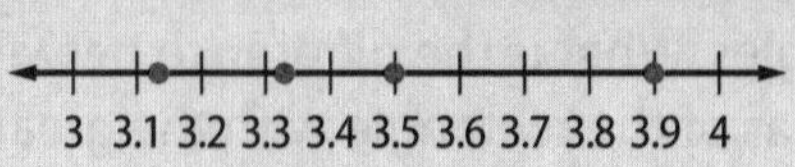

Ⓒ 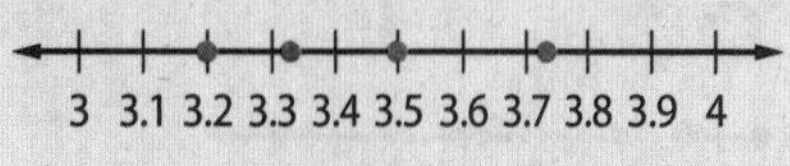

Ⓑ 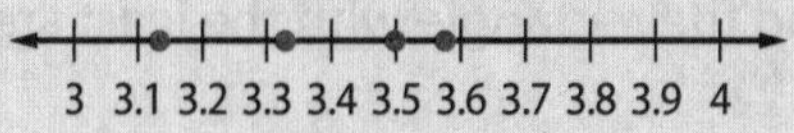

Ⓓ 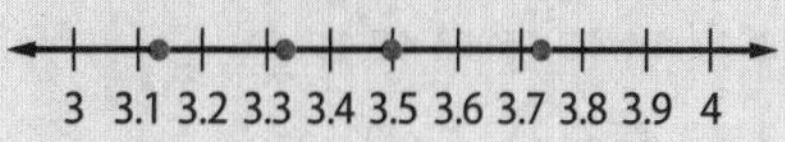

Use a problem-solving model to solve this problem.

1 Analyze

Read the problem. Circle the information you know.
Underline what the problem is asking you to find.

2 Plan

What will you need to do to solve the problem? Write your plan in steps.

Step 1 Express each number in ______________________, rounding to ____________ if necessary.

Step 2 Determine which number line shows { , , , }.

3 Solve

Use your plan to solve the problem. Show your steps.

350% = ______ $\pi \approx$ ______

$3.\overline{3} \approx$ ______ $\sqrt{14} \approx$ ______

The correct answer is ______. Fill in that answer choice.

Read to Succeed!
Consider the intervals on the number line and the locations of the points when deciding which decimal place to use in rounding.

4 Justify and Evaluate

How do you know your solution is accurate?

____

____

____

N = Number and Operations MP = Mathematical Processes

More Multi-Step Problem Solving

Use a problem-solving model to solve each problem.

22. Which list of numbers are shown on the number line? N MP

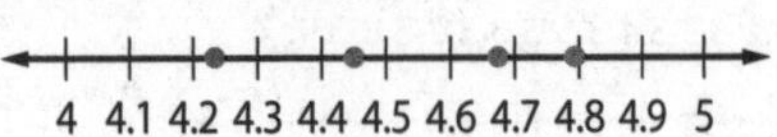

Ⓐ $4\frac{5}{11}, \sqrt{23}, 4.\overline{6}, \sqrt{18}$

Ⓑ $4\frac{5}{9}, \sqrt{23}, 4\frac{4}{11}, \sqrt{18}$

Ⓒ $4.\overline{6}, \sqrt{20}, 4\frac{4}{11}, \sqrt{18}$

Ⓓ $4\frac{5}{9}, \sqrt{23}, 4\frac{4}{9}, \sqrt{18}$

23. The table shows the dimensions of four rectangles. What is the difference between the areas of the rectangle with the greatest area and the rectangle with the least area? N EE MP

Rectangle	Width (cm)	Length (cm)
A	4	4
B	3.1	5
C	7	2.5
D	6	2.7

24. The table shows the rainfall amounts above or below normal for four three-month periods. What is the difference, expressed as a decimal, between the greatest and least amounts? N MP

Month	Amount Above or Below Normal (in.)
Jan–Mar	−3.5
Apr–Jun	$-\frac{15}{4}$
Jul–Sept	2.1
Oct–Dec	$\frac{5}{2}$

25. A square has an area of 26 square meters. An equilateral triangle has an area of 21 square meters. A cube has a volume of 710 cubic meters. To the nearest meter, what is the sum of the greatest side length and the least side length of these figures? (*Hint:* The area *A* of an equilateral triangle with side length *s* is $A = \frac{s^2\sqrt{3}}{4}$.) N MP

N = Number and Operations EE = Expressions, Equations, and Relationships MP = Mathematical Processes

21ST CENTURY CAREER

Robotics Engineer

Are you mechanically inclined? Do you like to find new ways to solve problems? If so, a career as a robotics engineer is something you should consider. Robotics engineers design and build robots to perform tasks that are difficult, dangerous, or tedious for humans. For example, a robotic insect was developed based on a real insect. Its purpose was to travel over water surfaces, take measurements, and monitor water quality.

Mathematical Process TEKS
8.1(A) Apply mathematics to problems arising in everyday life, society, and the workplace.
Targeted TEKS 8.2(C)

Is This the Career for You?

Are you interested in a career as a robotics engineer? Take some of the following courses in high school.

- Calculus
- Electro-Mechanical Systems
- Fundamentals of Robotics
- Physics

Turn the page to find out how math relates to a career in Engineering.

Explore college and careers at ccr.mcgraw-hill.com

Relying on Robots

Use the information in the table to solve each problem.

1. Express the mass of the robot in standard decimal notation. ________

2. Express the length of the robot in scientific notation. ________

3. Express the leg diameter of the robot in scientific notation. ________

4. What is the mass in milligrams? Express in standard decimal notation. ________

5. Real insects called water striders can travel 8.3 times faster than the robot. Express the speed of water striders in scientific notation.

____

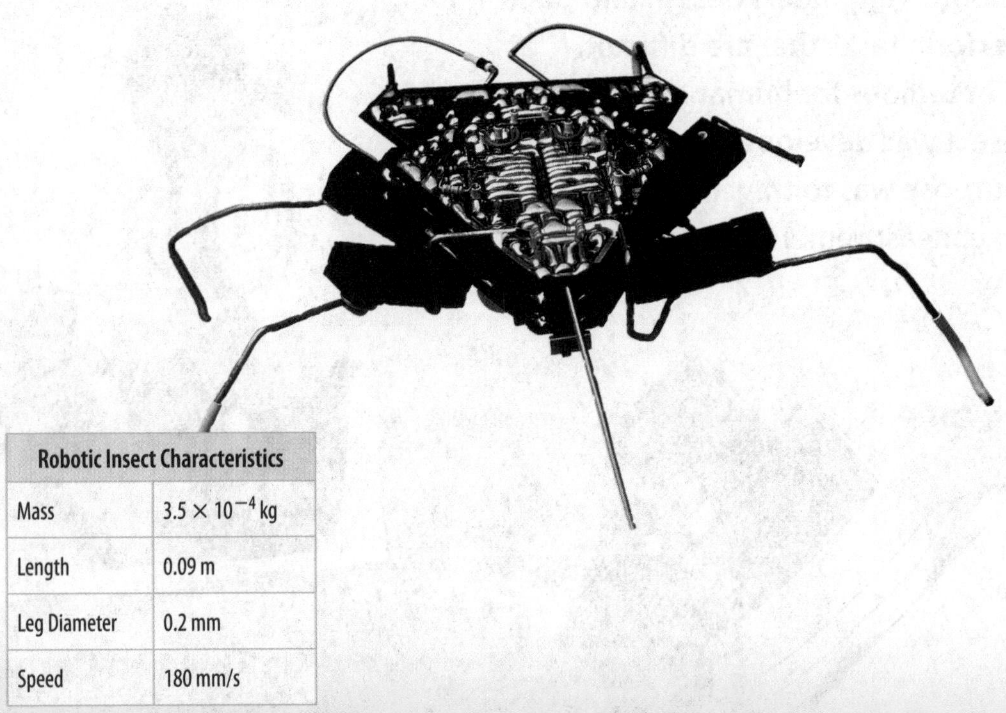

Robotic Insect Characteristics	
Mass	3.5×10^{-4} kg
Length	0.09 m
Leg Diameter	0.2 mm
Speed	180 mm/s

TEKS Career Project

It's time to update your career portfolio! Investigate the education and career requirements for a career in robotics engineering. Prepare a brief oral presentation and present it to your classmates.

What skills would you need to improve to succeed in this career?

-
-
-
-
-

Chapter Review TEKS

Vocabulary Check

Work with a partner to complete the crossword puzzle using the vocabulary list at the beginning of the chapter. Ask clarification of each item as needed.

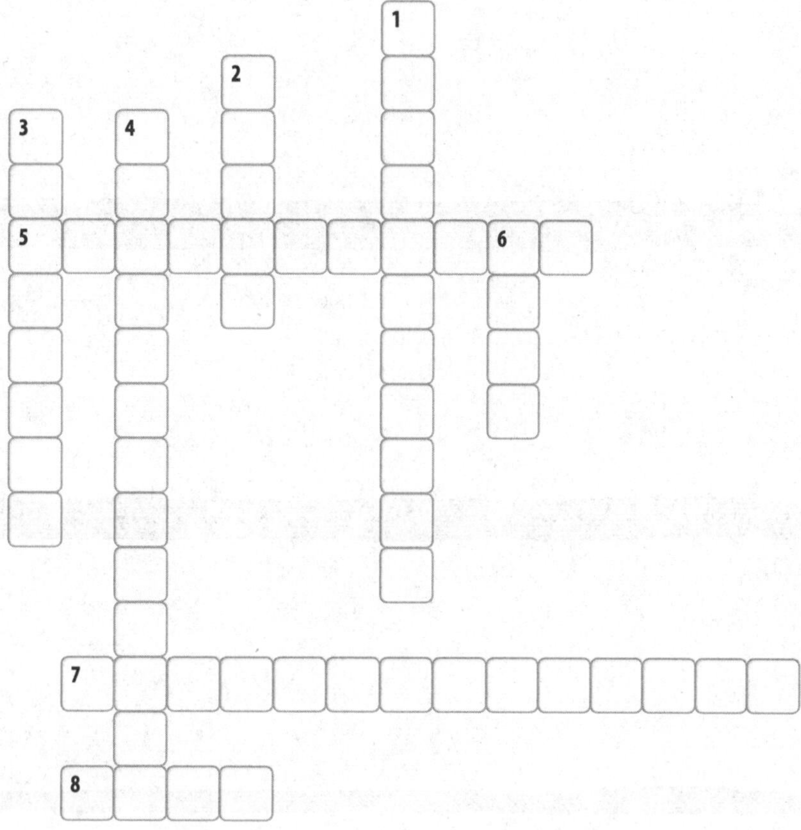

Across

5. a rational number whose cube root is a whole number

7. numbers that can be written as a comparison of two integers, expressed as a fraction

8. a number that is rational or irrational

Down

1. the symbol used to indicate a positive square root

2. a product of repeated factors using a base and exponent

3. this tells how many times a number is used as a factor

4. a rational number whose square root is a whole number

6. in a power, the number that is the common factor

Key Concept Check

Use Your FOLDABLES

Use your Foldable to help review the chapter. Share your Foldable with a partner and take turns summarizing what you learned in this chapter, while your partner listens carefully. Ask each other for help, if needed. TEKS 8.1(E)

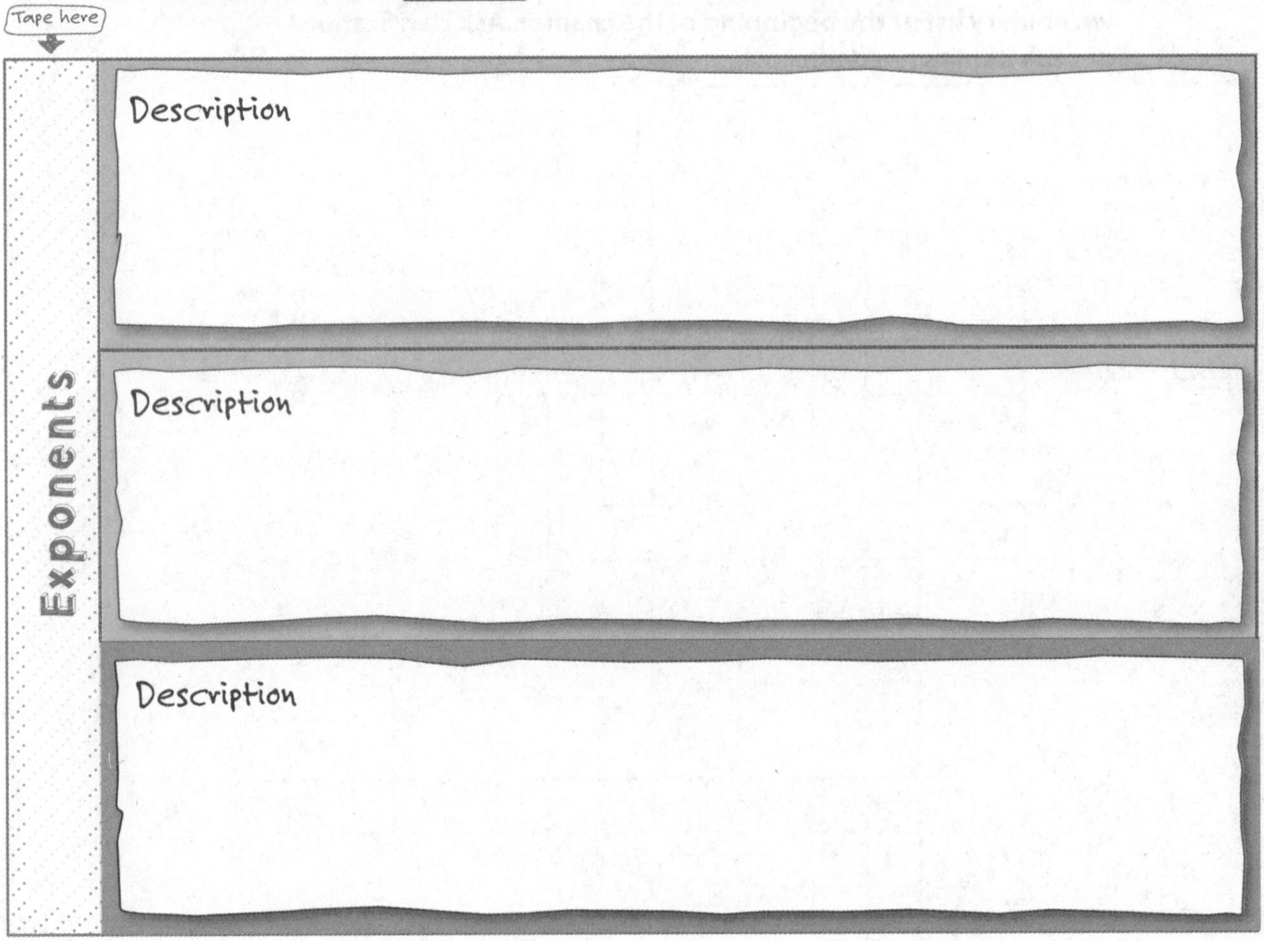

Tape here

Exponents

Description

Description

Description

Got it?

Circle the correct term or number to complete each sentence.

1. 2^3 is equal to $(2 \times 2 \times 2, 3 \times 3)$.

2. The cube root of 64 is (8, 4).

3. $\sqrt{15}\,(<, >, =)\ 4.1$.

4. 3^{-4} is equal to $\left(-81, \frac{1}{81}\right)$.

5. Scientific notation is when a number is written as a product of a power of 10 and a factor greater than or equal to 1 and (less than, less than or equal to) 10.

Multi-Step Problem Solving

6. Space probes are launched to explore other planets and the Moon. The table shows the distance from Earth to Mars and the Moon. Which total distance would be greater: a trip to and from Mars or 150 trips to and from the Moon? Show the steps you used and justify your solution using scientific notation. N EE MP

Distance from Earth	
Mars	56 million kilometers
Moon	3.84×10^5 kilometers

1 Analyze

2 Plan

3 Solve

4 Justify and Evaluate

Got it?

7. The Brown family wants to enlarge their square vegetable garden. The current side length of the garden is 5.5 feet. The table shows three options the family is considering. If the Brown family chooses the option with the greatest side length, how much more square footage will the garden have? Show your steps and justify your solution. N EE MP

Option	Side Length (ft)
Square A	$7\frac{3}{8}$
Square B	$\frac{37}{5}$
Square C	$\sqrt{54}$

N = Number and Operations EE = Expressions, Equations, and Relationships MP = Mathematical Processes

Reflect

Answering the Essential Question

Use what you learned about numbers to complete the graphic organizer. Complete each sentence in the graphic organizer. TEKS 8.1(D), 8.1(F), 8.1(G)

I use a decimal...	I use a power...
I use a fraction...	I use scientific notation...

WHY is it helpful to express numbers in different ways?

Answer the Essential Question. WHY is it helpful to express numbers in different ways? Verbally share your response with a partner, asking for help, if needed.

Chapter 2
Similarity and Dilations

Texas Essential Knowledge and Skills

Targeted TEKS

8.3 The student applies mathematical process standards to use proportional relationships to describe dilations. *Also addresses 8.8 and 8.10.*

Mathematical Processes

8.1, 8.1(A). 8.1(B), 8.1(C), 8.1(D), 8.1(E), 8.1(F), 8.1(G)

Essential Question

HOW can you determine similarity?

Math in the Real World

Models The walls of the Alamo varied in height from 9 feet to 12 feet. Suppose a model of the Alamo was built using a scale of 1 foot = 4 inches.

Use the scale to determine the least height in inches of the Alamo walls. Then convert the inches to feet.

ft

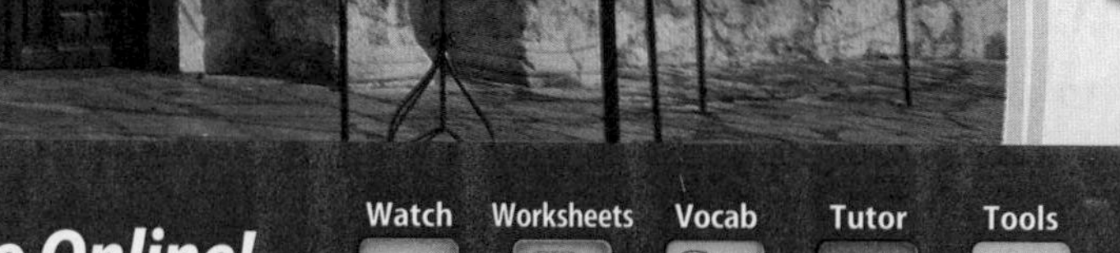

Go Online!

www.connectED.mcgraw-hill.com

Watch  Worksheets  Vocab  Tutor  Tools  Check 

What Tools Do You Need?

Vocab

Vocabulary

center of dilation | dilation | scale factor
congruent | indirect measurement | similar polygons

Use a Web

A *web* can help you understand how math concepts are related to each other. To make a web, write the major topic in the center of a piece of paper. Then, draw "arms" from the center for as many categories as you need.

Here is a partial web for the major topic of triangles. Complete the web by adding descriptions for the classifications by sides. Then add the classifications by angles. Ask your teacher or a classmate for help, if needed.

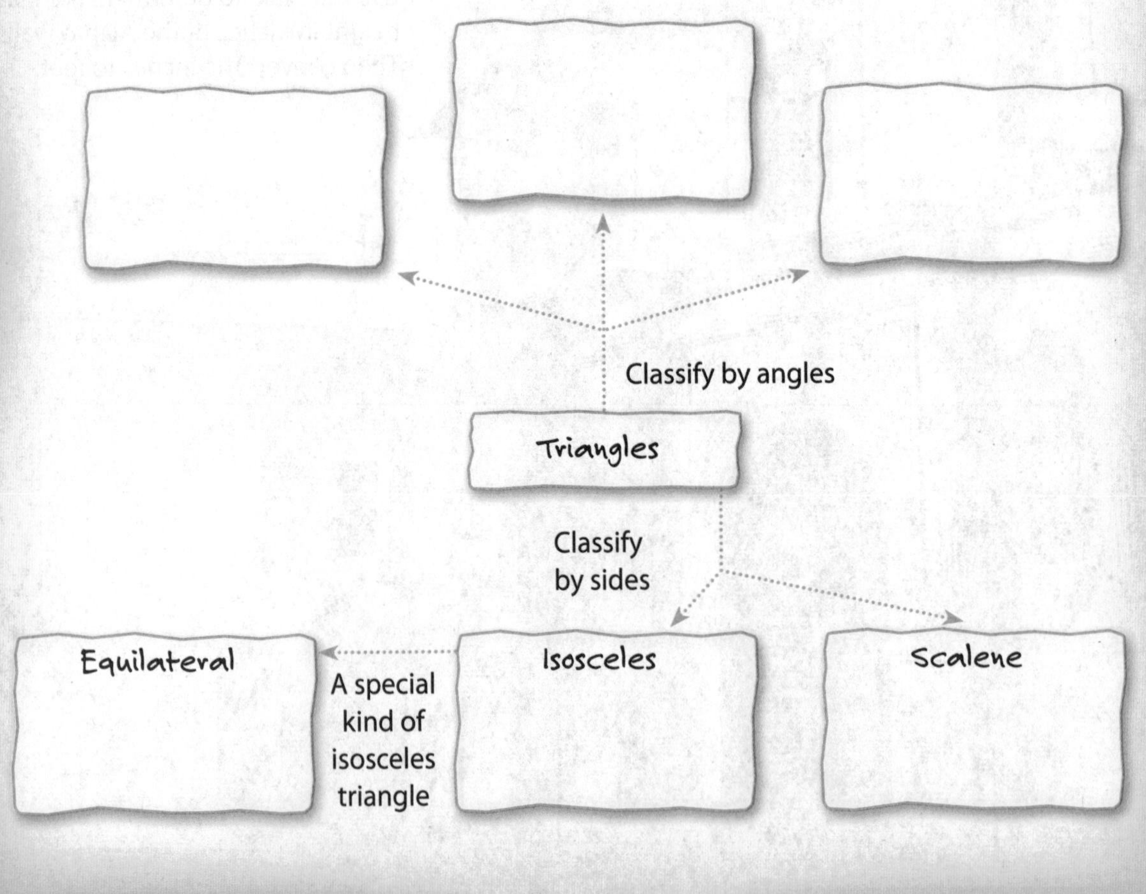

When Will You Use This?

Jasmine and Jacob in

Up, Up, and Away

Your Turn! **You will solve this problem in the chapter.**

Are You Ready?

Quick Review

Review 6.5(A), 6.6(B), 7.7(B) TEKS

Example 1

Solve $\frac{w}{12} = \frac{5}{6}$.

$\frac{w}{12} = \frac{5}{6}$	Write the proportion.
$6 \times w = 12 \times 5$	Find cross products.
$6w = 60$	Simplify.
$w = 10$	Division Property of Equality

Example 2

Write an equation that represents the relationship shown in the table.

x	1	2	3	4
y	2	4	6	8

Since each *y*-value is twice the *x*-value, the equation $y = 2x$ represents the relationship.

Quick Check

Check

Proportions **Solve each proportion.**

1. $\frac{x}{15} = \frac{7}{30}$ ______

2. $\frac{4}{9} = \frac{14}{y}$ ______

3. $\frac{12}{z} = \frac{30}{37}$ ______

4. $\frac{8}{15} = \frac{m}{21}$ ______

5. $\frac{n}{5} = \frac{18}{45}$ ______

6. $\frac{3}{7} = \frac{21}{p}$ ______

Write Equations **For each table of values, write an equation that represents the relationship.**

7.

x	1	2	3	4
y	3	6	9	12

______

8.

x	5	6	7	8
y	1	2	3	4

______

Which problems did you answer correctly in the Quick Check? Shade those exercise numbers below.

① ② ③ ④ ⑤ ⑥ ⑦ ⑧

Use the Foldable throughout this chapter to help you learn about dilations.

 cut on all dashed lines fold on all solid lines  tape to page 160

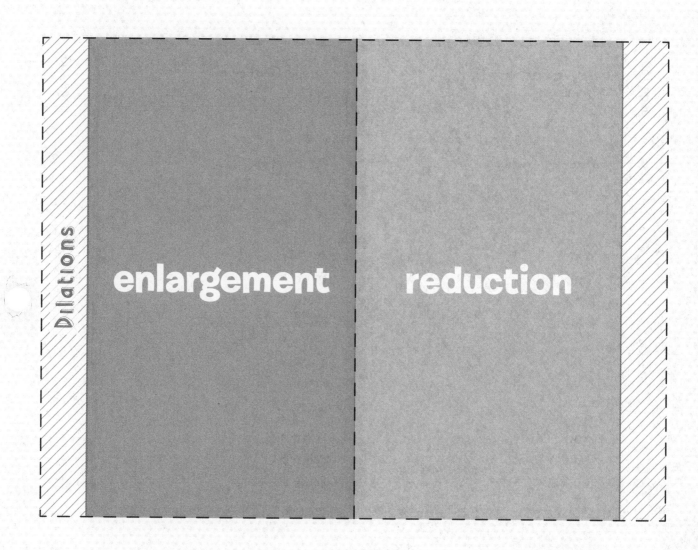

Dilations

enlargement

reduction

FOLDABLES®

Use the Foldable throughout this chapter to help you learn about dilations.

cut on all dashed lines | fold on all solid lines | 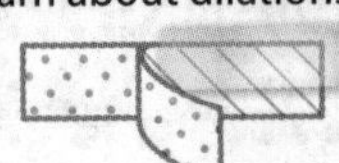 tape to page 160

page 160

Scale Factor of 3

Description

$\triangle XYZ$

Point X

Point Y

Point Z

$\triangle X'Y'Z'$

Point X'

Point Y'

Point Z'

Tab 2

Scale Factor of $\frac{1}{2}$

Description

$\triangle XYZ$

Point X

Point Y

Point Z

$\triangle X'Y'Z'$

Point X'

Point Y'

Point Z'

page 160

Tab 1

Hands-On Lab 1-a

Similar Triangles

INQUIRY **HOW can I analyze relationships between two triangles with the same shape but different sizes?**

While flying in an airplane, Ariel looked out the window and saw roads and a field like the one shown. She wondered if there was a relationship between the two triangles she saw.

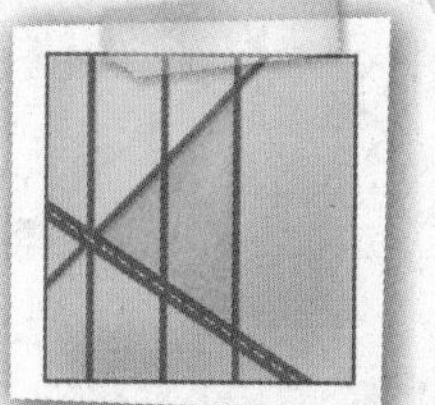

Texas Essential Knowledge and Skills TEKS

Targeted TEKS

8.3(A) Generalize that the ratio of corresponding sides of similar shapes are proportional, including a shape and its dilation.

Mathematical Processes

8.1(C), 8.1(F)

Tools

Hands-On Activity

To determine if there is a relationship between the two triangles, use the diagram shown.

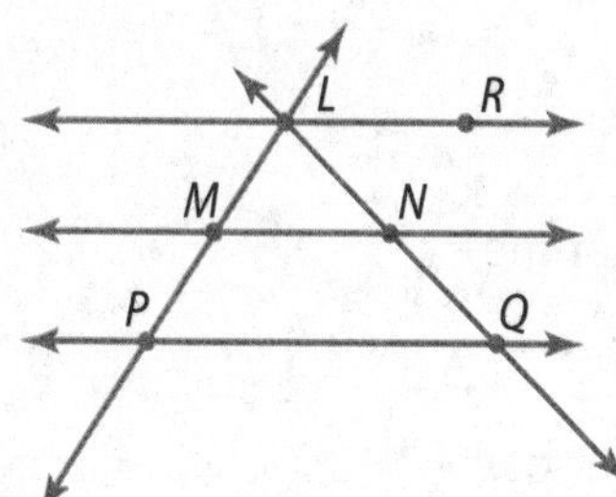

$\overleftrightarrow{LR} \parallel \overleftrightarrow{MN} \parallel \overleftrightarrow{PQ}$

Step 1 Measure and record the lengths of the line segments in millimeters and angles in degrees in the table.

△LPQ		△LMN	
LP =	m∠L = °	LM =	m∠L = °
LQ =	m∠P = °	LN =	m∠M = °
PQ =	m∠Q = °	MN =	m∠N = °

What do you notice about the measure of the corresponding angles of the triangles? ____________

Step 2 Express the lengths of the corresponding sides of the triangles as ratios.

$\frac{LP}{LM} =$ ______ $\frac{LQ}{LN} =$ ______ $\frac{PQ}{MN} =$ ______

What do you notice about the ratios of the corresponding sides of the triangles? ____________

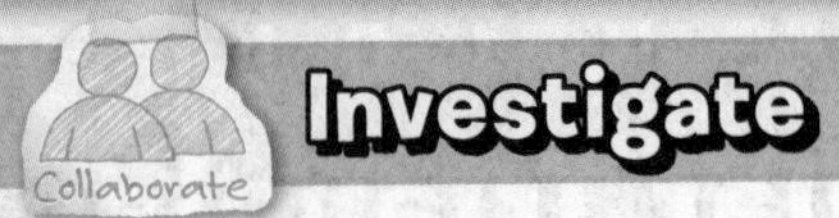

Investigate

Work with a partner.

1. **Select Tools and Techniques** Triangle *ABC* is a right triangle with $m\angle A = 53°$. On the grid, draw and label a different right triangle, triangle *XYZ*, using the given angle *X*, which also measures 53°.

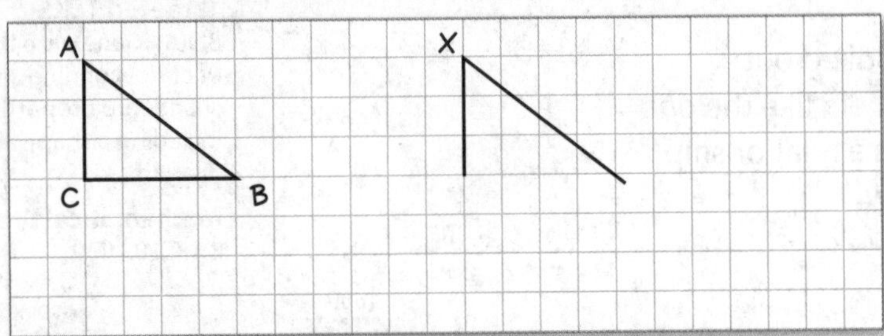

What do you notice about the shape of the triangles? ______

______

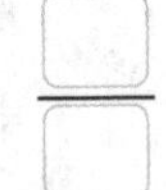

Analyze and Reflect

2. Refer to Exercise 1. What is the measure of $\angle B$? the measure of the angle that corresponds to $\angle B$ in $\triangle XYZ$? ______

3. Express the lengths of the corresponding sides of the triangles as ratios.

$\frac{AC}{\square} = \frac{\square}{\square} \quad \frac{\square}{\square} \qquad \frac{CB}{\square} = \frac{\square}{\square} \quad \frac{\square}{\square} \qquad \frac{AB}{\square} = \frac{5}{10} \quad \frac{\square}{\square}$

4. What do you notice about the ratios? ______

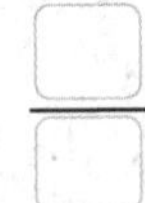

Create

5. **Analyze Relationships** The two triangles in the Activity and in Exercise 1 are called *similar triangles*. Based on your discoveries, write a sentence that describes the properties that similar triangles have.

______

______

6. **INQUIRY** HOW can I analyze relationships between two triangles with the same shape but different sizes? ______

______

______

Lesson 1

Properties of Similar Polygons

Launch the Lesson: Real World

Elsa is printing pictures at a photo kiosk in the store. She can choose between 4 × 6 prints or 5 × 7 prints. Are the side lengths of the two prints proportional? Explain. ______________________

Investigate **Follow the steps to discover how the triangles are related.**

1. Measure the sides of the two triangles in centimeters. Then, measure the angles. Write the results in the table.

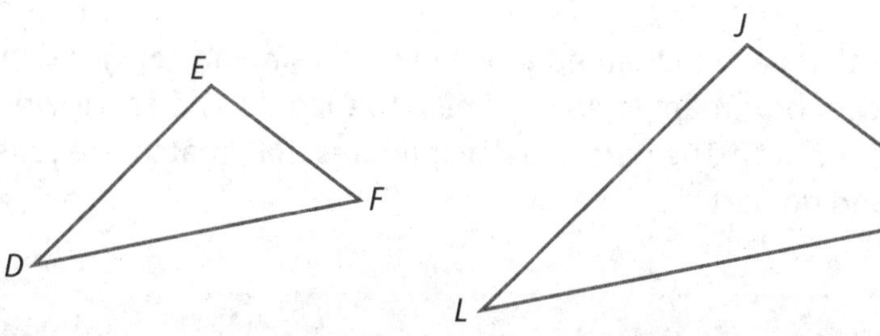

Figure	Side Length (cm)			Angle Measure (°)		
△*EFD*	DE	EF	FD	∠D	∠E	∠F
△*LJK*	LJ	JK	KL	∠L	∠J	∠K

2. What do you notice about the sides of the two triangles? the angles? ______________________

____

Which MP Mathematical Processes did you use? Shade the circle(s) that applies.

Ⓐ Apply Math to the Real World.
Ⓑ Use a Problem-Solving Model.
Ⓒ Select Tools and Techniques.
Ⓓ Use Multiple Representations.
Ⓔ Organize Ideas.
Ⓕ Analyze Relationships.
Ⓖ Justify Arguments.

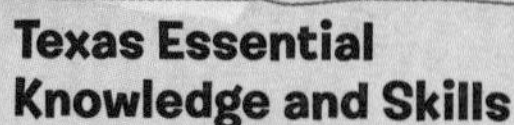

Texas Essential Knowledge and Skills

Targeted TEKS

8.3(A) Generalize that the ratio of corresponding sides of similar shapes are proportional, including a shape and its dilation.

Mathematical Processes

8.1(A), 8.1(B), 8.1(F), 8.1(G)

Vocab

Vocabulary

congruent
similar polygons
scale factor

Math Symbols

~ is similar to

Essential Question

HOW can you determine similarity?

Key Concept

Similar Polygons

Words If two polygons are similar, then

- their corresponding angles are **congruent**, or have equal measures, and
- the ratios of their corresponding sides are proportional.

The reverse is also true. If corresponding angles are congruent and ratios of corresponding sides are proportional, then the polygons are similar.

Work Zone

Model

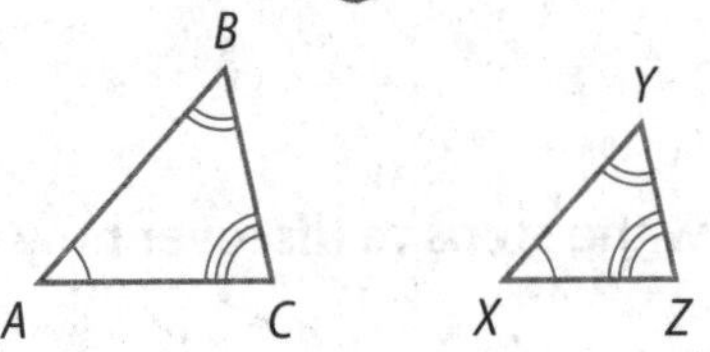

$\triangle ABC \sim \triangle XYZ$

Symbols $\angle A \cong \angle X, \angle B \cong \angle Y, \angle C \cong \angle Z$, and $\frac{AB}{XY} = \frac{BC}{YZ} = \frac{AC}{XZ}$

Polygons that have the same shape are called **similar polygons**. In the Key Concept box, triangle *ABC* is similar to triangle *XYZ*. This is written as $\triangle ABC \sim \triangle XYZ$. The parts of similar figures that "match" are called corresponding parts.

Watch Tutor

Example

1. Rectangle *JKLM* is similar to rectangle *RSTU*. What do you know about the corresponding angles and sides?

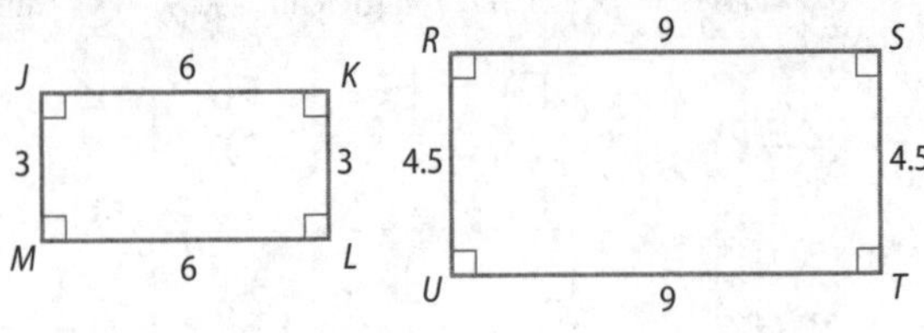

The corresponding angles are congruent. The ratios of the corresponding sides are proportional.

$$\angle J \cong \angle R, \angle K \cong \angle S, \angle L \cong \angle T, \angle M \cong \angle U$$

$$\frac{JK}{RS} = \frac{KL}{ST} = \frac{LM}{TU} = \frac{MJ}{UR}$$

Got It? Do this problem to find out.

a. Triangle *ABC* is similar to triangle *FGH*. What do you know about the corresponding angles and sides?

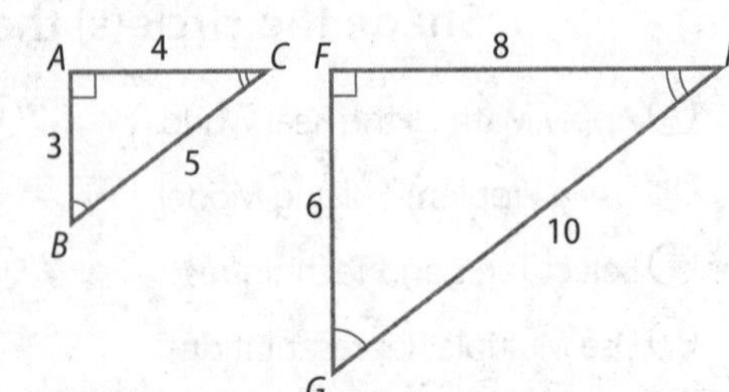

a. ____________

Determine Missing Measures

Scale factor is the ratio of the lengths of two corresponding sides of two similar polygons. You can use the scale factor of similar figures to determine missing measures.

Tutor

Example

2. Quadrilateral *UVWX* is similar to quadrilateral *DEFG*. Determine the missing measure.

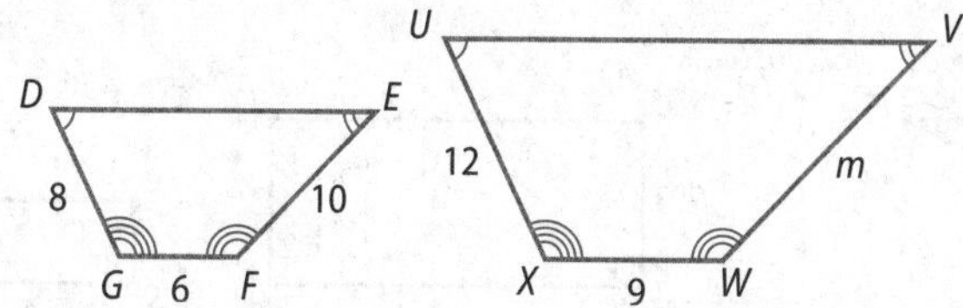

Method 1

Determine the scale factor from quadrilateral *DEFG* to quadrilateral *UVWX*.

$$\text{scale factor: } \frac{WX}{FG} = \frac{9}{6} \text{ or } \frac{3}{2}$$

So, a length on quadrilateral *UVWX* is $\frac{3}{2}$ times as long as the corresponding length on quadrilateral *DEFG*. Let *m* represent the measure of $\overline{VW}$.

$m = \frac{3}{2}(10)$ Write the equation.

$m = 15$ Multiply.

Method 2

Set up a proportion to determine the missing measure.

$\frac{VW}{EF} = \frac{WX}{FG}$ Write the proportion.

$\frac{m}{10} = \frac{9}{6}$ $VW = m, EF = 10, WX = 9, FG = 6$

$m \cdot 6 = 10 \cdot 9$ Find the cross products.

$6m = 90$ Simplify.

$m = 15$ Division Property of Equality

By either method, the missing measure is 15.

Show your work.

b. ___________

c. ___________

Got It? Do these problems to find out.

Determine each missing measure.

b. *WZ*

c. *AB*

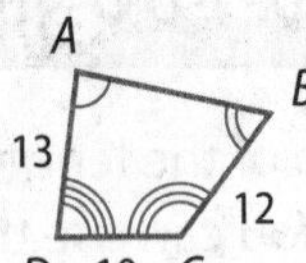

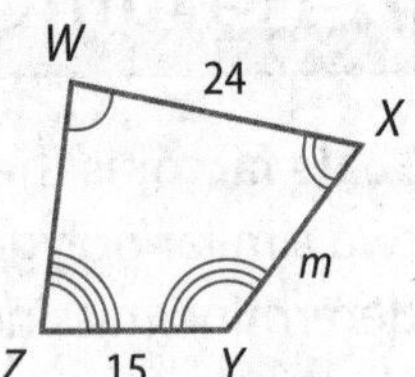

Guided Practice

Each pair of polygons is similar. What do you know about the corresponding angles and sides? (Example 1)

1.

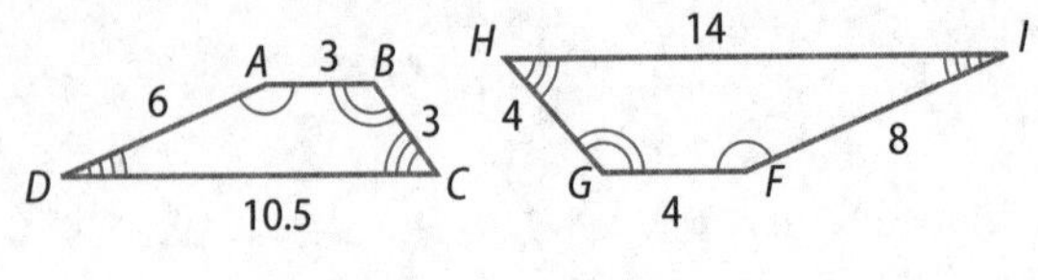

2.

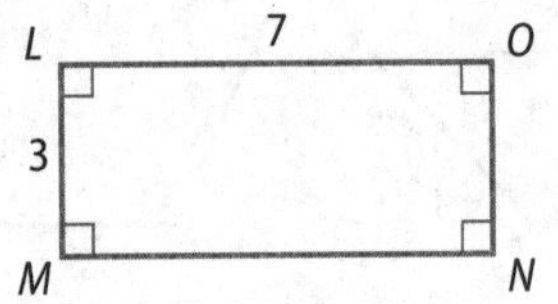

3. The two triangles are similar. Determine the missing side measures. ___________ (Example 2)

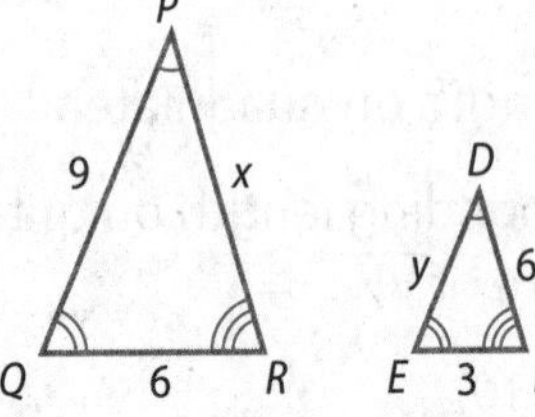

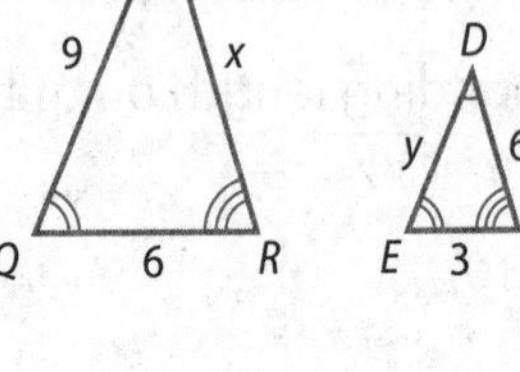

4. The two triangles are similar. Determine the missing side measure. ___________ (Example 2)

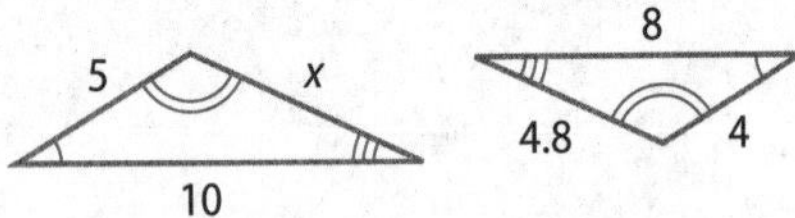

5. **Building on the Essential Question** How does the scale factor of similar figures relate to the ratio of two of the corresponding sides?

Rate Yourself!

Are you ready to move on? Shade the section that applies.

Find out online. Use the Self-Check Quiz.

Independent Practice

8.3(A), 8.1(A), 8.1(B) TEKS

Each pair of polygons is similar. What do you know about the corresponding angles and sides? (Example 1)

1.

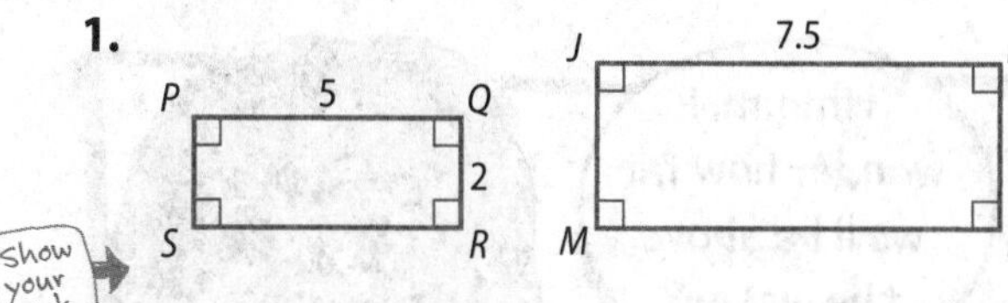

Show your work.

2.

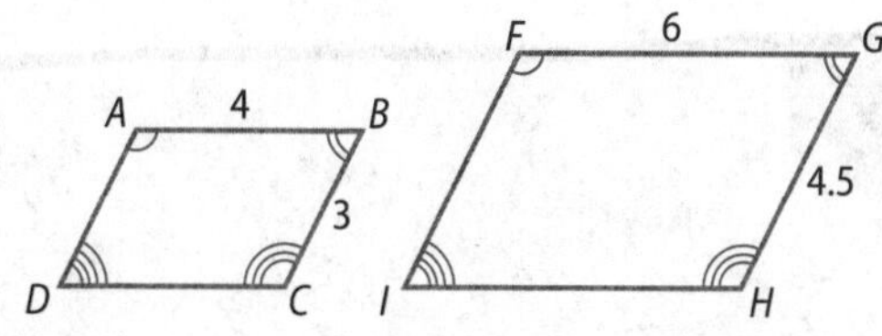

Each pair of polygons is similar. Determine the missing side measures. (Example 2)

3.

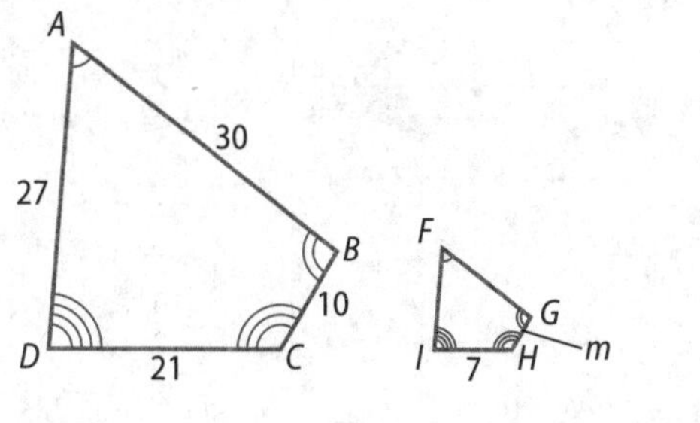

4.

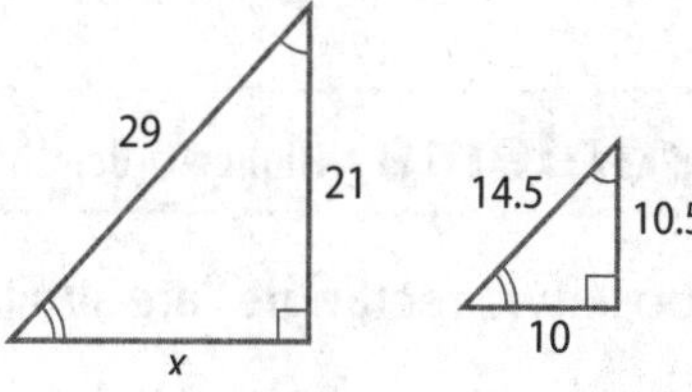

5. MP **Use a Problem-Solving Model** The figures at the right are similar.

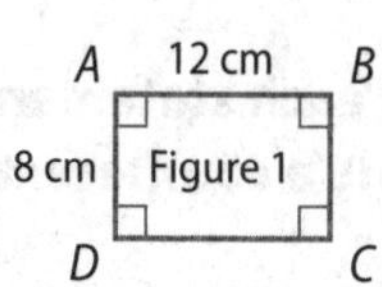

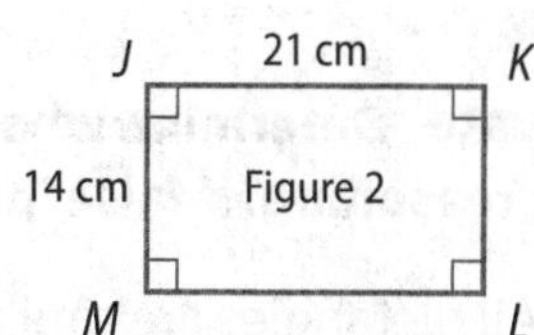

a. Determine the area of both figures.

b. Compare the scale factor of the side lengths and the ratio of the areas.

6. STEM The scale factor from the model of a human inner ear to the actual ear is 55:2. If one of the bones of the model is 8.25 centimeters long, how long is the actual bone in a human ear?

7. **MP Apply Math to the Real World** Refer to the graphic novel frame below. The brochure says that the rope is 500 feet long. Jacob drew a triangle in the sand that is similar to the actual triangle formed by a parasailer and the boat. Use the properties of similar triangles to determine the parasailer's height above the water. ______

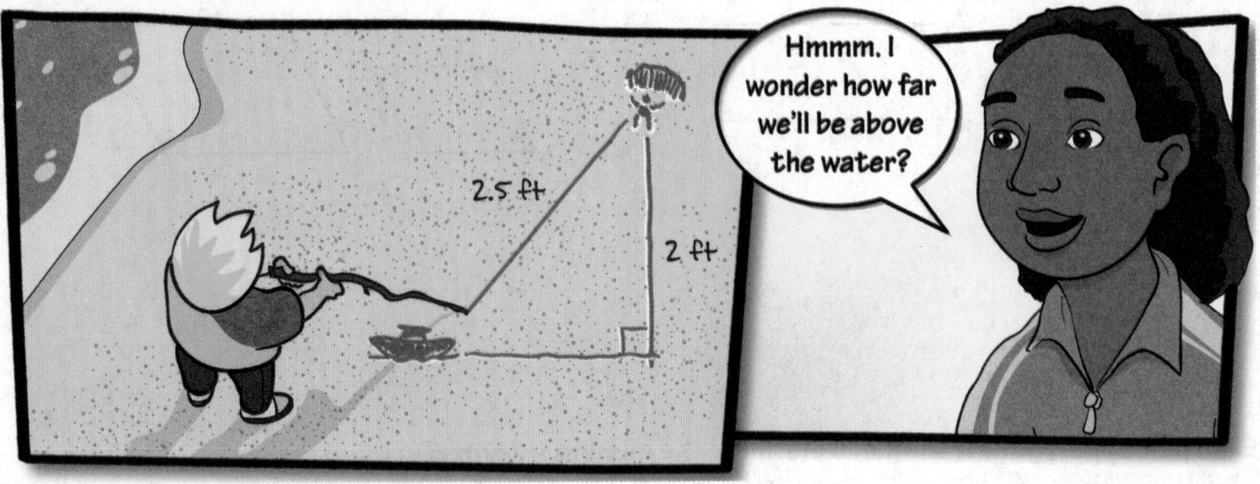

H.O.T. Problems Higher-Order Thinking

8. **Analyze** Suppose two rectangles are similar with a scale factor of 2. What is the ratio of their areas? Explain. ______

Evaluate Determine whether each statement is *true* or *false*. If true, explain your reasoning. If false, provide a counterexample.

9. All rectangles are similar.

10. All squares are similar.

11. **Create** Draw two similar polygons. Include the measures of the sides on your drawing, and identify the scale factor.

Name ____

Multi-Step Problem Solving

12. Alex used reflective tape to make the design shown on a jacket. First, he made the small polygon. Then he enlarged the small polygon to make the large polygon, using a scale factor that extended the 8-centimeter side by 2 centimeters. What total length of reflective tape did Alex use? N P MP

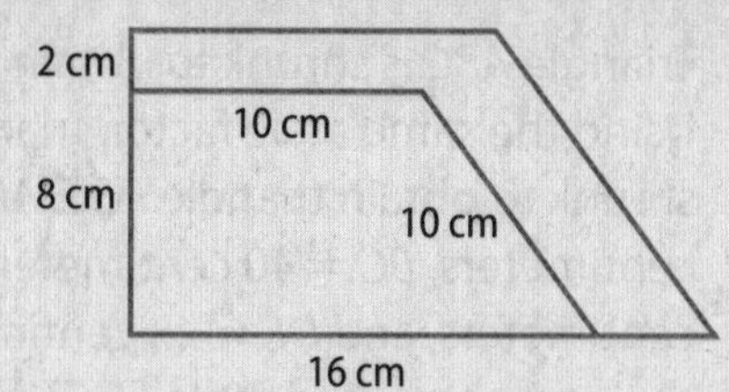

Ⓐ 44 cm Ⓒ 75 cm

Ⓑ 55 cm Ⓓ 99 cm

Use a problem-solving model to solve this problem.

1 Analyze

Read the problem. Circle the information you know. Underline what the problem is asking you to find.

2 Plan

What will you need to do to solve the problem? Write your plan in steps.

Step 1 Determine the scale factor used.

Step 2 Use the scale factor to determine the measures needed to find the total length of tape used.

3 Solve

Use your plan to solve the problem. Show your steps.

Multiply ____ and ____ by the scale factor to determine the missing measures. Add 8 + 10 + 10 + 16 + 2 + ____ + ____ + ____.

Alex used ________________ of tape. So, the correct answer is ____.

Fill in that answer choice.

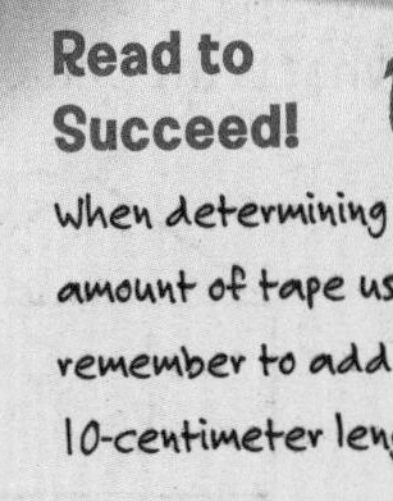

Read to Succeed!
When determining the total amount of tape used, remember to add the two 10-centimeter lengths.

4 Justify and Evaluate

How do you know your solution is accurate?

____

____

____

____

____

N = Number and Operations P = Proportionality MP = Mathematical Processes

More Multi-Step Problem Solving

Use a problem-solving model to solve each problem.

13. Triangle *ABC* is shrunk to obtain triangle *DEC*. Using the same scale factor, triangle *DEC* is shrunk to obtain triangle *FGC*. $AB = 50$ centimeters, $BC = 40$ centimeters, $CA = 40$ centimeters, and $DE = 45$ centimeters. What is the perimeter of triangle *FGC*? P N MP

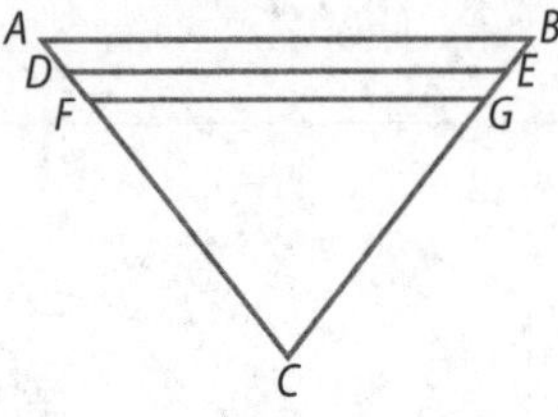

Ⓐ 87.2 cm
Ⓑ 100 cm
Ⓒ 105.3 cm
Ⓓ 117 cm

14. The rectangle shown below was used in a magazine advertisement for a digital camera. It represents the image sensor region of the camera. The actual image sensor region in the camera is a dilation of the rectangle by a scale factor of 4×10^{-2}. What is the area of the actual image sensor region, in square centimeters, rounded to the nearest hundredth? P N MP

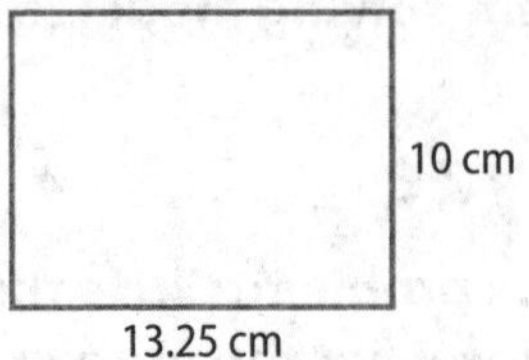

15. Abril drew the scale drawing shown below to represent the front of a garage she plans to build. The scale is 1 inch:2.5 feet. The equation $A_2 = A_1x$, where A_2 is the actual area in square feet and A_1 is the area of the drawing, represents the relationship between the areas. What is the value of x? P N MP

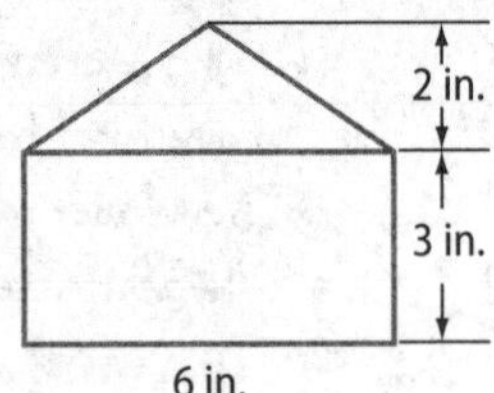

16. Triangle *ABC* is shown on the graph. Triangle *XYZ* is similar to triangle *ABC*. The *x*-coordinate of *Y* in triangle *XYZ* is 12.

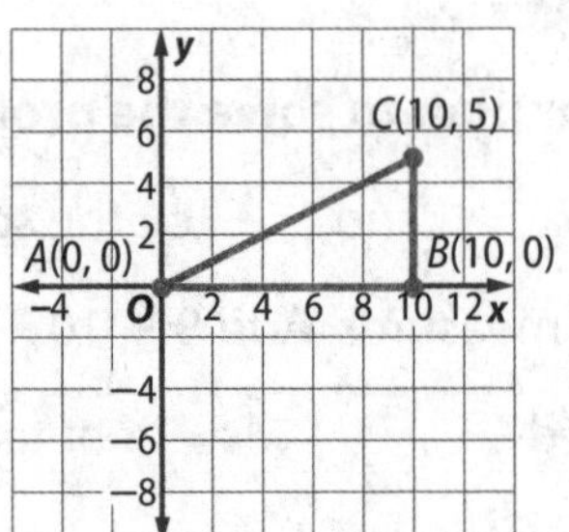

What are the coordinates of *Z*? Justify your answer. N P MP

N = Number and Operations P = Proportionality T = Two-Dimensional Shapes MP = Mathematical Processes

Lesson 2

Angle-Angle Similarity of Triangles

Launch the Lesson: Real World

Texas Essential Knowledge and Skills

Targeted TEKS

8.8(D) Use informal arguments to establish facts about the angle sum and exterior angle of triangles, the angles created when parallel lines are cut by a transversal, and the angle-angle criterion for similarity of triangles.

Mathematical Processes

8.1(A), 8.1(B), 8.1(F), 8.1(G)

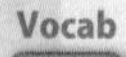

Vocabulary

indirect measurement

Essential Question

HOW can you determine similarity?

Students in the art club are cutting out similar triangles to put on a poster for the school craft fair.

Complete the steps to establish facts about how the angles of the triangles are related.

1. Using a protractor, measure angles A, B, D, and E. Write the results in the table.

$\triangle ABC = \angle A =$ 60 $\angle B =$ 60

$\triangle DEF = \angle D =$ 60 $\angle E =$ 60

2. Complete the steps below to determine the measure of the third angle in each triangle.

$\triangle ABC$	$\triangle DEF$
$m\angle A + m\angle B + m\angle C =$ 180	$m\angle D + m\angle E + m\angle F =$ 180
60 + 60 + $m\angle C =$ 180	60 + 60 + $m\angle F =$ 180
120 + $m\angle C =$ 180	120 + $m\angle F =$ 180
$m\angle C =$ 60	$m\angle F =$ 60

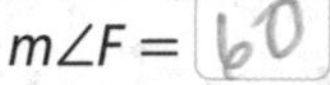

3. What do you notice about the measures of the third angle in each triangle? ________

4. **Analyze** If you know that two of the angles in one triangle are congruent to two of the angles in a second triangle, what can you conclude about the third angle? ________

Which MP **Mathematical Processes** did you use? Shade the circle(s) that applies.

Ⓐ Apply Math to the Real World.
Ⓑ Use a Problem-Solving Model.
Ⓒ Select Tools and Techniques.
Ⓓ Use Multiple Representations.
Ⓔ Organize Ideas.
Ⓕ Analyze Relationships.
Ⓖ Justify Arguments.

Key Concept

Angle-Angle (AA) Similarity

Work Zone

Words If two angles of one triangle are congruent to two angles of another triangle, then the triangles are similar.

Symbols If $\angle A \cong \angle F$ and $\angle B \cong \angle G$, then $\triangle ABC \sim \triangle FGH$.

Model

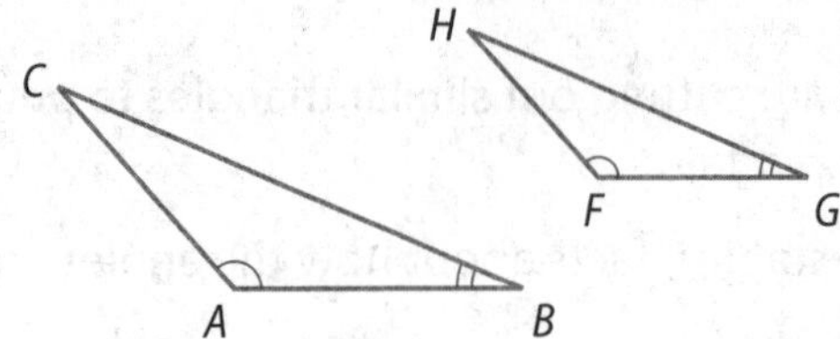

In the figure below, $\angle X \cong \angle P$ and $\angle Y \cong \angle Q$. If you extend the sides of each figure to form a triangle, you can see the two triangles are similar. So, triangle similarity can be established by showing two pairs of corresponding angles are congruent.

STOP and Reflect

What do you know about the third pair of angles in the triangles?

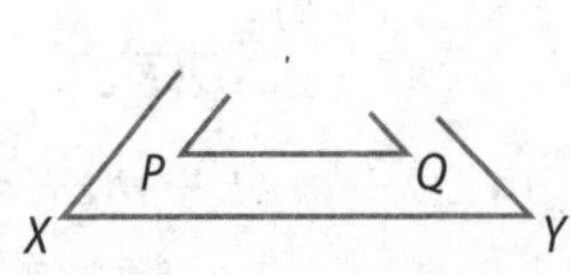

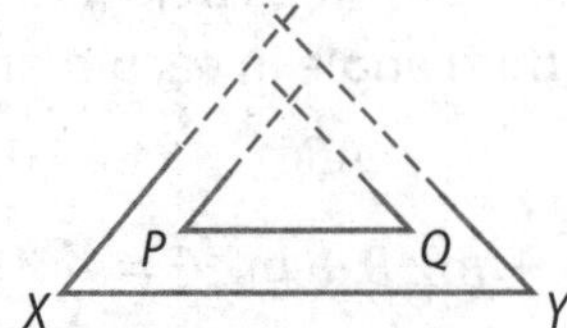

Example

1. Determine whether the triangles are similar. If so, write a similarity statement.

Angles A and E have the same measure, so they are congruent. Since $180 - 62 - 48 = 70$, $\angle G$ measures 70°. Two angles of $\triangle EFG$ are congruent to two angles of $\triangle ABC$, so $\triangle ABC \sim \triangle EFG$ by angle-angle similarity.

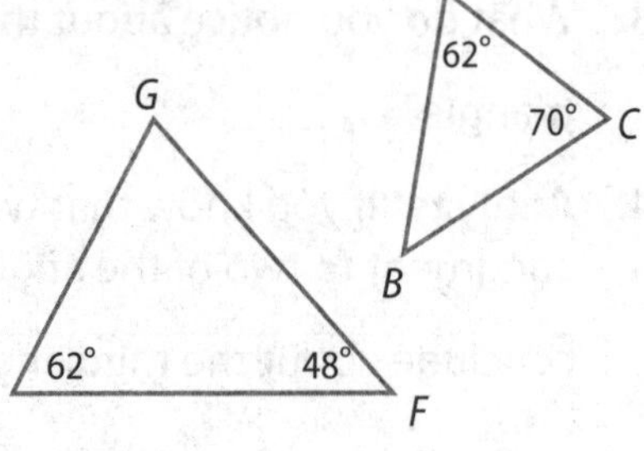

Got It? Do this problem to find out.

a.

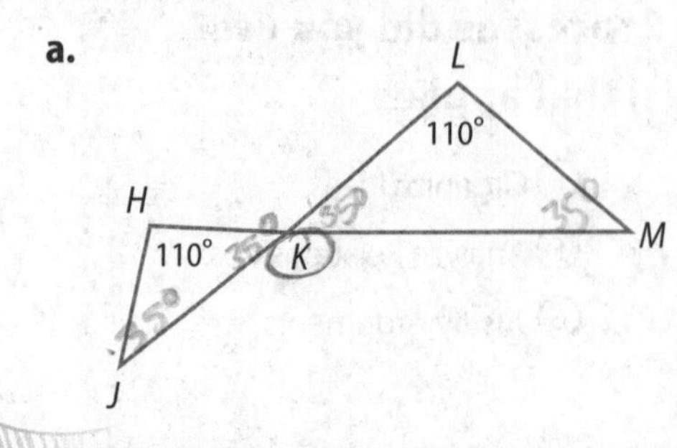

a. ______

Use Indirect Measurement

Indirect measurement allows you to use properties of similar polygons to determine distances or lengths that are difficult to measure directly.

One type of indirect measurement is *shadow reckoning*. Two objects and their shadows form two sides of right triangles.

In shadow problems, you can assume that the angles formed by the Sun's rays with two objects at the same location are congruent. Since two pairs of corresponding angles are congruent, the two right triangles are similar.

Examples

2. A fire hydrant 2.5 feet high casts a 5-foot shadow. How tall is a street light that casts a 26-foot shadow at the same time? Let *h* represent the height of the street light.

h ft
26 ft
2.5 ft
5 ft

Shadow		Height
hydrant →	$\frac{5}{26} = \frac{2.5}{h}$	← hydrant
street light →		← street light

$5h = 26 \cdot 2.5$ Find the cross products.

$5h = 65$ Multiply.

$\frac{5h}{5} = \frac{65}{5}$ Divide each side by 5.

$h = 13$

The street light is 13 feet tall.

3. In the figure at the right, triangle *DBA* is similar to triangle *ECA*. Ramon wants to know the distance across the lake.

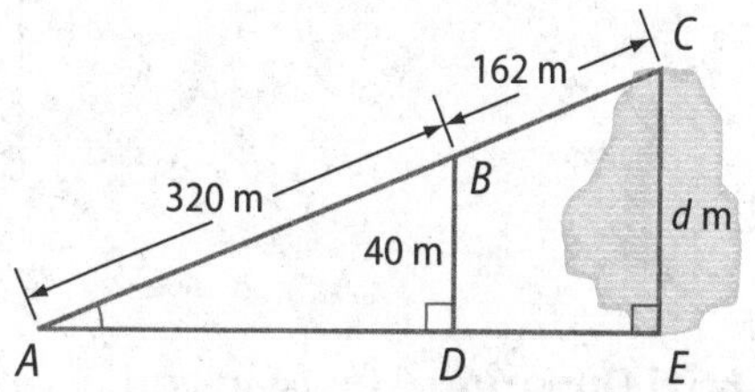

$\frac{AB}{AC} = \frac{BD}{CE}$ $\overline{AB}$ corresponds to $\overline{AC}$ and $\overline{BD}$ corresponds to $\overline{CE}$.

$\frac{320}{482} = \frac{40}{d}$ Replace *AB* with 320, *AC* with 482, and *BD* with 40.

$320d = 482 \cdot 40$ Find the cross products.

$\frac{320d}{320} = \frac{19{,}280}{320}$ Multiply. Then divide each side by 320.

$d = 60.25$

The distance across the lake is 60.25 meters.

Indirect Measurement

You can also use similar triangles that do not involve shadows to determine missing measures.

Got It? Do this problem to find out.

Show your work.

b. _______________

b. At the same time a 2-meter street sign casts a 3-meter shadow, a nearby telephone pole casts a 12.3-meter shadow. How tall is the telephone pole?

Guided Practice

For Exercises 1 and 2, determine whether the triangles are similar by angle-angle similarity. If so, write a similarity statement. (Example 1)

1.

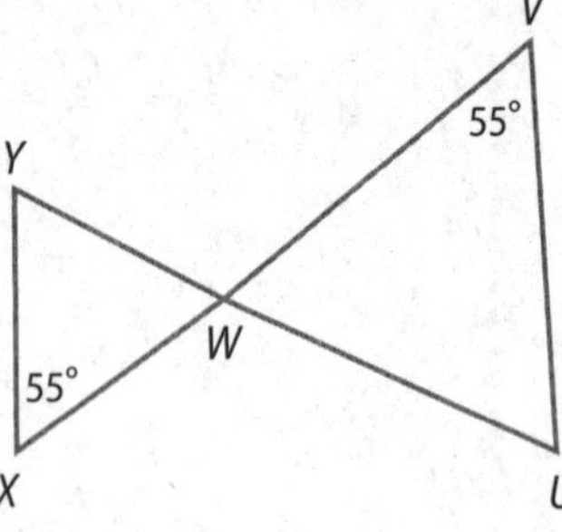

Show your work.

2.

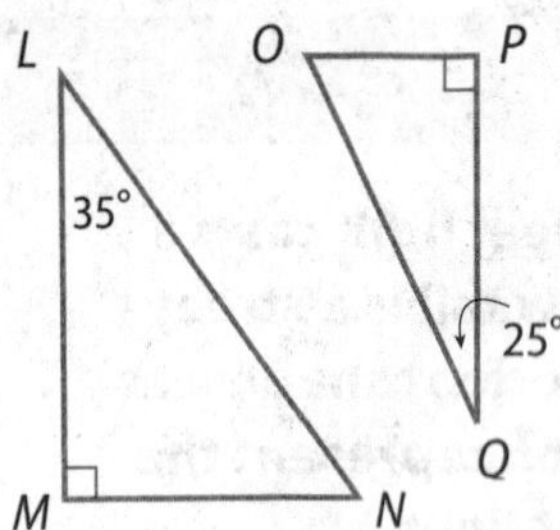

3. How tall is the tree? (Example 2) _______________

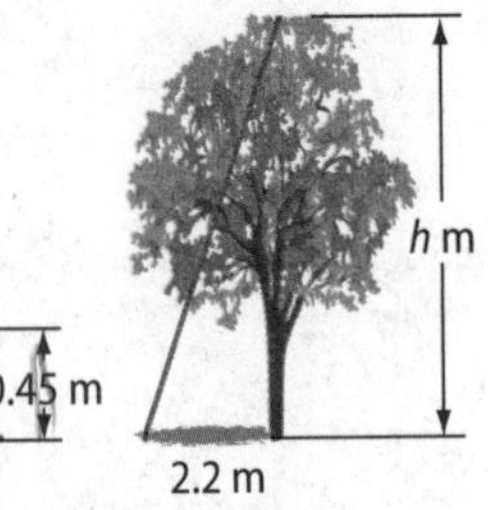

4. Determine the distance from the house to the street light. (Example 3) _______________

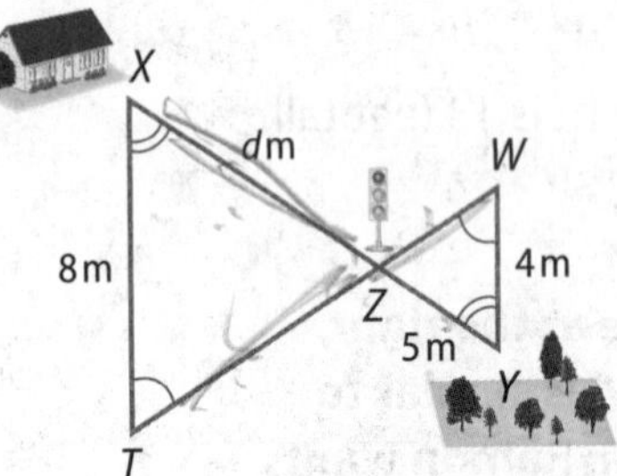

5. **Building on the Essential Question** How can you use an informal argument to establish why angle-angle similarity for triangles works?

Rate Yourself!

Are you ready to move on? Shade the section that applies.

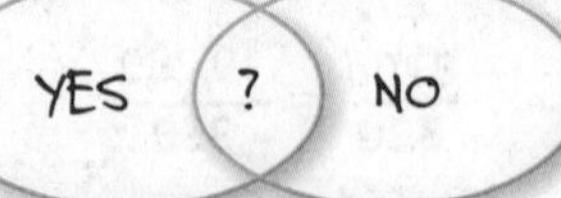

Find out online. Use the Self-Check Quiz.

Name ______________________ My Homework ______________________

Independent Practice

8.8(D), 8.1(B) TEKS

For Exercises 1 and 2, determine whether the triangles are similar. If so, write a similarity statement. (Example 1)

1.

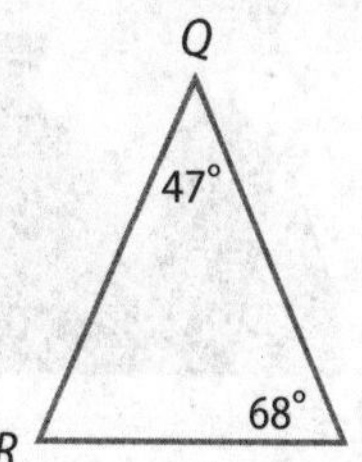

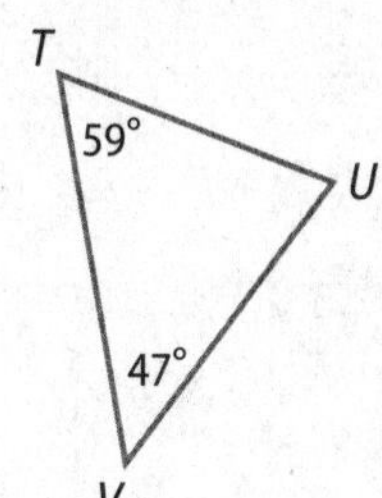

2.

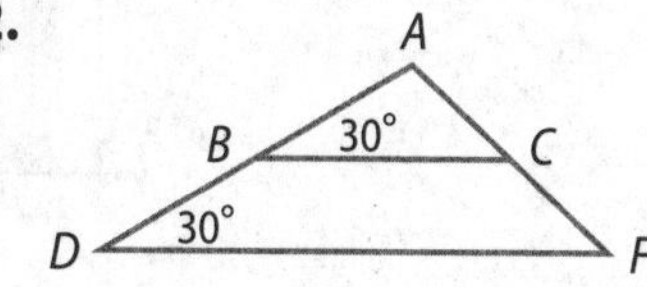

3. How tall is the taller building? (Example 2) ______

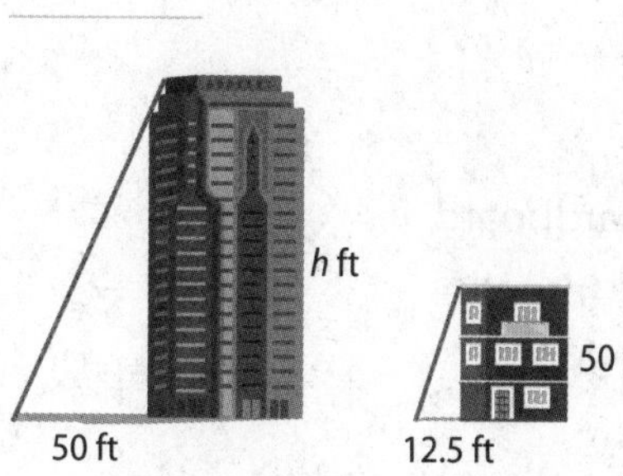

4. How tall is the taller flagpole? (Example 2) ______

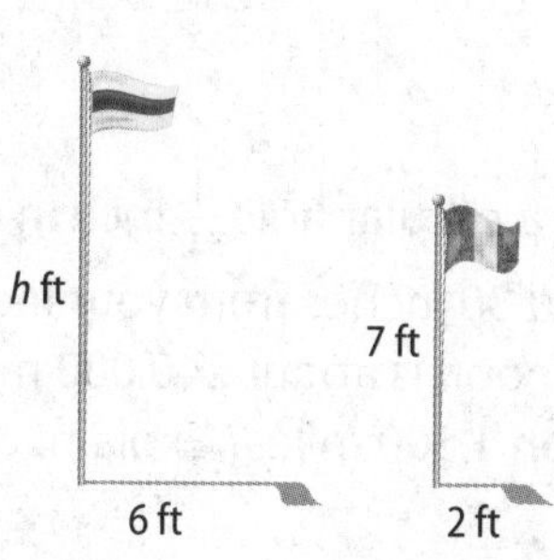

5. How far is it from the log ride to the pirate ship? (Example 3) ______

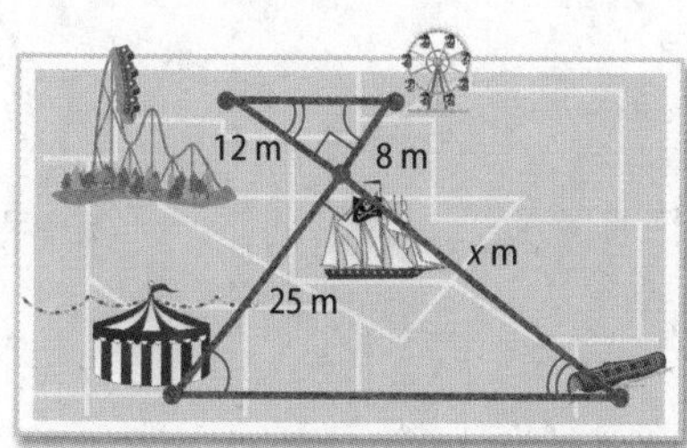

6. Determine the height of the brace. (Example 3) ______

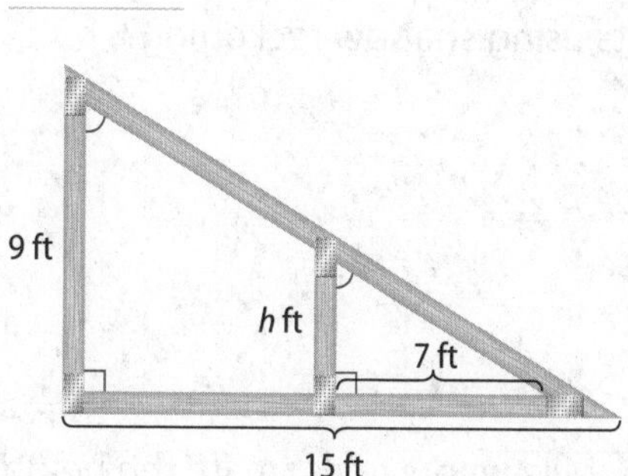

7. **MP Use a Problem-Solving Model** The Giant Wheel at Cedar Point in Ohio is one of the tallest Ferris wheels in the country at 136 feet tall. If the Giant Wheel casts a 34-foot shadow, write and solve a proportion to determine the height of a nearby man who casts an 18-inch shadow.

8. Find the Error Sara is determining the height of the lighthouse shown in the diagram. Find her mistake and correct it.

$$\frac{27}{60} = \frac{x}{90}$$
$$27 \cdot 90 = 60x$$
$$x = 40.5$$

x ft
27 ft
60 ft
90 ft

H.O.T. Problems Higher-Order Thinking

9. Create Write and solve a real-world problem involving indirect measurement.

10. Evaluate You cut a circular hole $\frac{1}{4}$-inch in diameter in a piece of cardboard. With the cardboard 30 inches from your face, the moon fits exactly into the circular hole. The moon is about 240,000 miles from Earth. Is the moon's diameter more than 1,500 miles? Explain.

11. Analyze What measures must be known in order to calculate the height of tall objects using shadow reckoning?

12. Evaluate Mila wants to estimate the height of a statue in a local park. Mila's height and both shadow lengths are shown in the diagram. Is an estimate of 15 feet reasonable for the statue's height? Justify your answer.

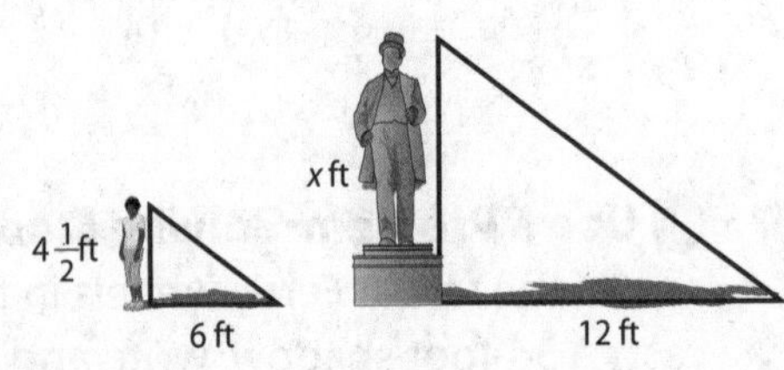

Name ________________________________

Multi-Step Problem Solving

13. Emilio is creating designs for a stained glass window. In his design, points *Q* and *R* lie on line segment *PS* and point *K* lies on line segment *JS*. Which option shows all of the similar triangles in the design, and only similar triangles? P MP

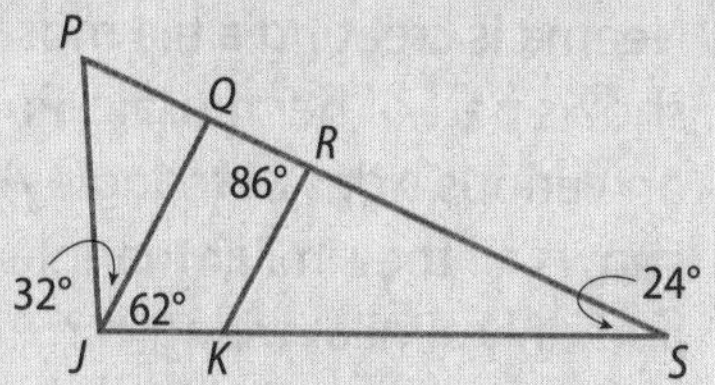

Ⓐ △SKR, △SJQ
Ⓑ △JPQ, △SKR
Ⓒ △SKR, △SJQ, △SPJ
Ⓓ △JPQ, △SJQ, △SPJ

Use a problem-solving model to solve this problem.

1 Analyze

Read the problem. Circle the information you know. Underline what the problem is asking you to find.

2 Plan

What will you need to do to solve the problem? Write your plan in steps.

Step 1 Determine the measures of the interior angles of △*SKR*, △*SJQ*, △*JPQ*, and △*SPJ*.

Step 2 Identify all of the triangles that have equal angle measures.

3 Solve

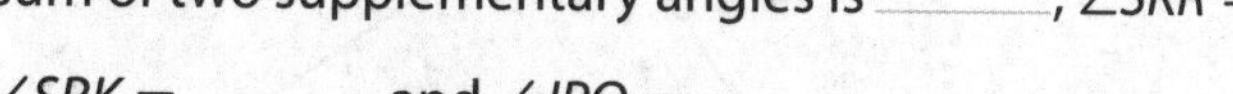

Use your plan to solve the problem. Show your steps.

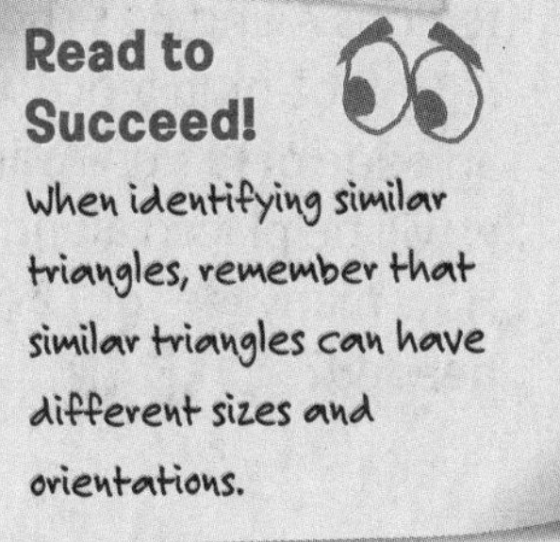

Read to Succeed!
When identifying similar triangles, remember that similar triangles can have different sizes and orientations.

Since the sum of the interior angles of a triangle is ______ and the sum of two supplementary angles is ______, ∠*SKR* = ______, ∠*SRK* = ______, and ∠*JPQ* = ______.

Since the measures of the interior angles of triangles *SKR*, *SJQ*, and *SPJ* are 24°, 94°, and 62°, the triangles are similar. So, the correct answer is ______. Fill in that answer choice.

4 Justify and Evaluate

How do you know your solution is accurate?

____

____

____

P = Proportionality MP = Mathematical Processes

More Multi-Step Problem Solving

Use a problem-solving model to solve each problem.

14. Neema is creating a tile mosaic. The diagram shows part of her mosaic. Points *B*, *D*, and *F* lie on various sides of triangle *ACE*. Which option shows all the similar triangles in the design, and only similar triangles? P EE MP

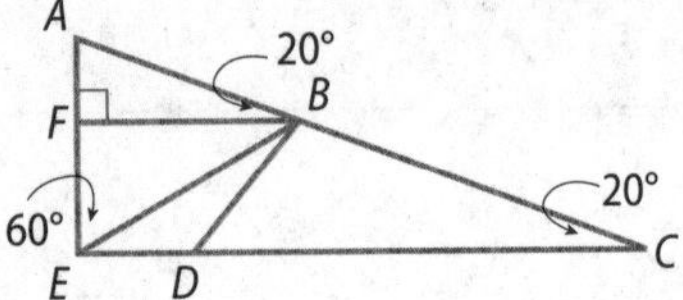

Ⓐ $\triangle AFB, \triangle AEC$

Ⓑ $\triangle AFB, \triangle BDC$

Ⓒ $\triangle AFB, \triangle AEC, \triangle BDC$

Ⓓ $\triangle AFB, \triangle BDC, \triangle ABE$

15. The diagram shows a municipal park formed by two triangular lots. A sidewalk is planned from point *P* to point *R* and from point *R* to point *S*. The shaded section from points *P* and *Q* has been paved. What is the remaining length in meters that needs to be paved?

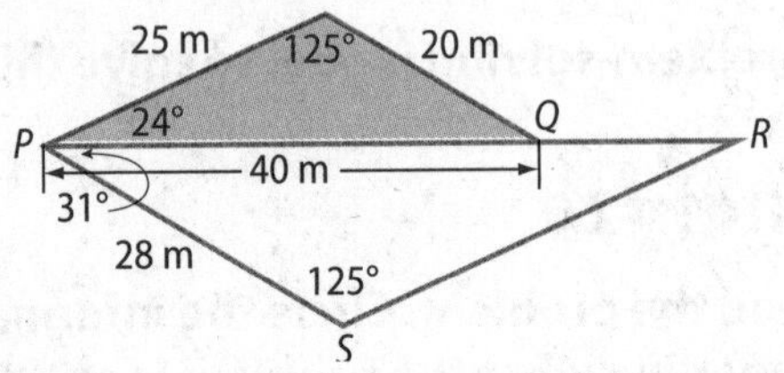

16. A triangular plot in a zoo is separated into regions A and B as shown in the diagram. A 10-foot-high fence, *x*, will be placed along an edge of region A, and a 12-foot-high fence, *y*, will be placed along an edge of region B. How many feet of 12-foot-high fence are needed? P EE MP

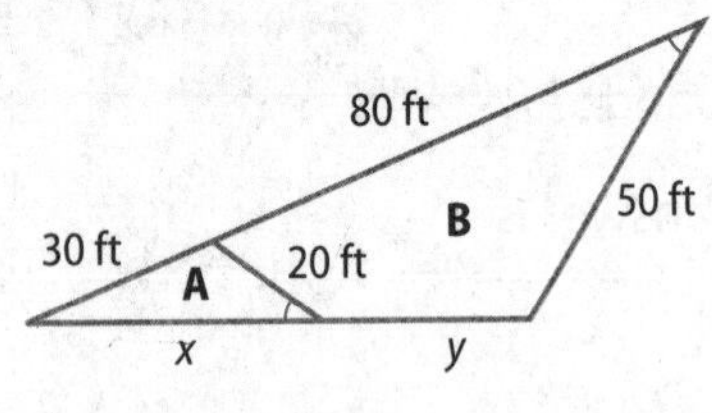

17. The length of segment *JP* is indicated by *x*. What is the value of *x* to the nearest whole number? Justify your answer. P EE N MP

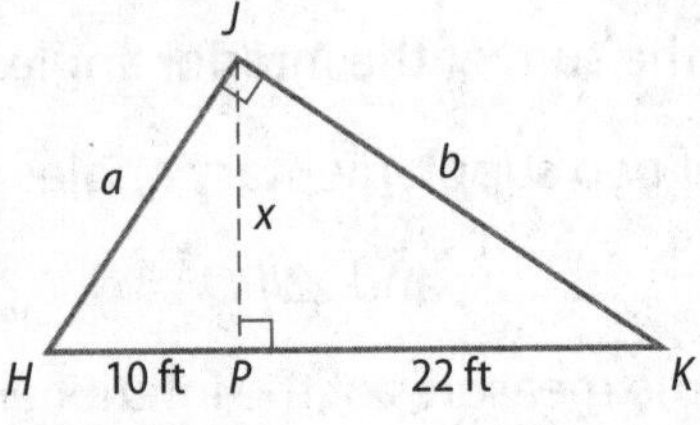

N = Number and Operations 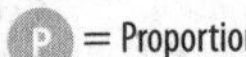 P = Proportionality EE = Expressions, Equations, and Relationships MP = Mathematical Processes

Draw a Diagram

Hammer Time

Christy wants to make shelves to store her game system and other electronics in her room. She will make brackets in the shape of right triangles to hold the shelves. Since it is a right triangle, one of the angles measures 90°.

What is the relationship between the other two angles in a right triangle?

Mathematical Process
8.1(B) Use a problem-solving model that incorporates analyzing given information, formulating a plan or strategy, determining a solution, justifying the solution, and evaluating the problem-solving process and the reasonableness of the solution.

Targeted TEKS 8.7

1 Analyze

Read the problem. Circle the information you know. Underline what the problem is asking you to find.

2 Plan

What is your strategy to solve this problem?

I will use the ______ strategy.

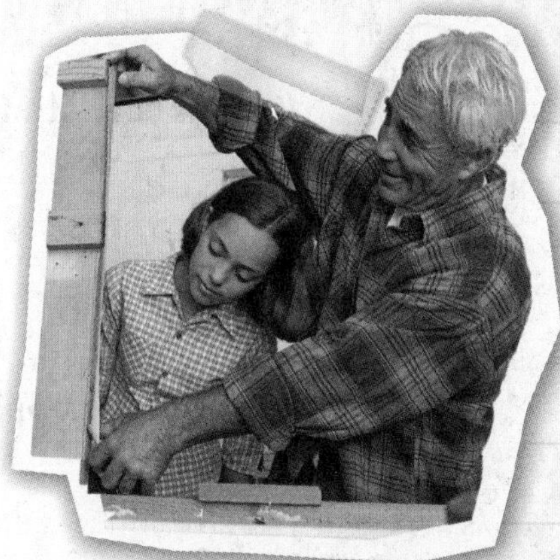

3 Solve

How can you apply the strategy?

Draw several right triangles, measure each angle, and look for a pattern.

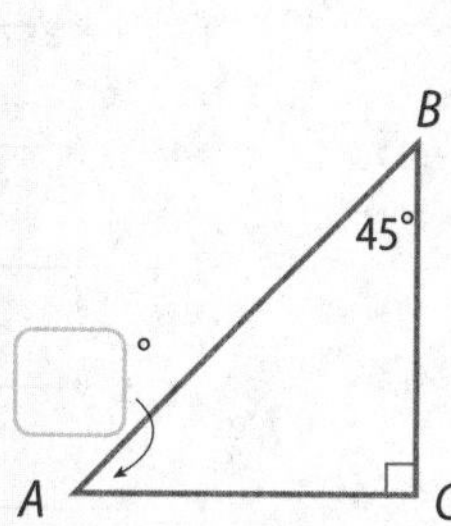

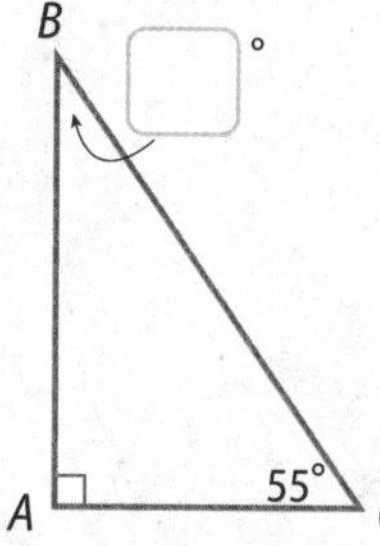

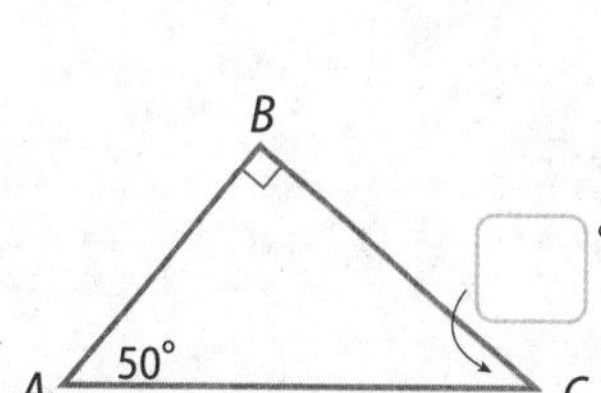

Study the pattern among the angle measures of your drawings. Make a conjecture. It appears that the sum of the measures of the acute angles of a right triangle is ____.

So, the acute angles of a right triangle are ______.

4 Justify and Evaluate

How do you know your solution is reasonable? ______

Bike-A-Thon

Jacob is participating in a biking fundraiser to the lake. After 45 miles, he is $\frac{5}{6}$ of the way there.

If he rides at an average speed of 12 miles per hour, in about how many minutes will he complete his ride?

1 Analyze

Read the problem. Circle the information you know. Underline what the problem is asking you to find.

2 Plan

What is your strategy to solve this problem?

I will use the ______________________ strategy.

3 Solve

How can you apply the strategy?

4 Justify and Evaluate

How do you know your solution is reasonable?

Multi-Step Problem Solving

Work with a small group to solve the following problems. Show your work on a separate piece of paper.

1. Dance

Ms. Samson's dance class is evenly shaped in a circle.

If the sixth person is directly opposite the sixteenth person, how many people are in the circle?

2. Stadium Seating

A section of the baseball stadium is set up so that each row has the same number of seats. Kyleigh is seated in the seventh row from the back and the eighth row from the front of this section. Her seat is the fourth one from the right and the seventh from the left.

How many seats are in this section of the baseball stadium?

3. Scrapbooks

A scrapbook page measures 12 inches long by 12 inches wide.

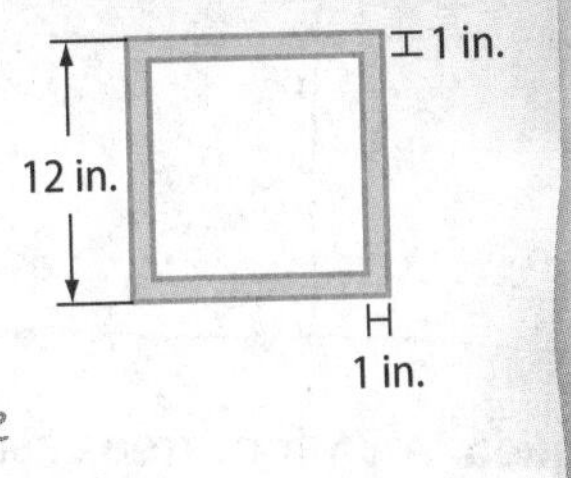

How many 3-inch by 5-inch horizontal photographs can be placed on the page if $\frac{1}{2}$ inch is placed between each photo and at least 1 inch is left as a margin on all four sides?

4. Geometry

The sides of a right triangle are in the ratio 3:4:5. The perimeter of the triangle is 84 feet.

What is the area of the triangle?

294

Vocabulary Check

1. Complete the following sentence. TEKS 8.8(D), 8.1(D)

If two angles of one triangle are congruent to two angles of another triangle, ______________________.

Key Concept Check

2. Complete the graphic organizer on similar polygons. TEKS 8.3(A), 8.1(E)

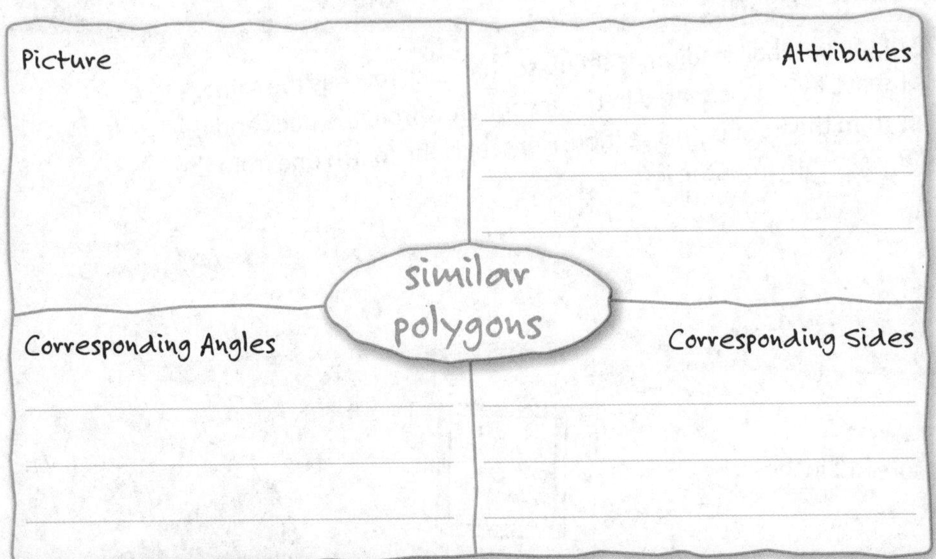

3. MP **Select Tools and Techniques** A 36-foot tree casts a 9-foot shadow at the same time a building casts a 15-foot shadow. How tall is the building? TEKS 8.3(A), 8.1(C)

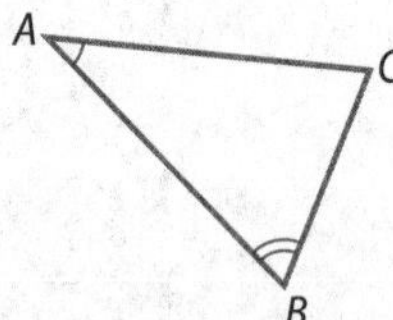

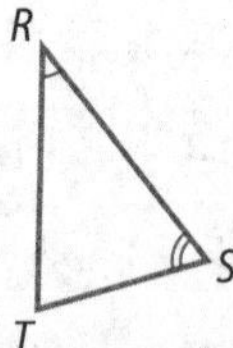

Multi-Step Problem Solving

4. Elijah is making copies of old photographs for a photo album. He enlarges several 4-inch by 6-inch photographs by a scale factor of 1.5. If a photo album page is 12 inches by 12 inches, what is the maximum number of enlarged photos that will fit on the page? P N MP

Ⓐ 1 photo
Ⓑ 2 photos
Ⓒ 3 photos
Ⓓ 4 photos

P = Proportionality N = Number and Operations MP = Mathematical Processes

Hands-On Lab 3-a

Model Dilations

INQUIRY **How can I analyze relationships to connect attributes of similarity to dilations?**

One way to create murals on a wall is to use a drawing grid method. Artists draw a grid on the artwork to be copied and draw a similar grid on the wall. By transferring sections of the artwork, the mural is the same shape as the artwork, but a different size. Follow the steps to enlarge a triangle.

Texas Essential Knowledge and Skills TEKS

Targeted TEKS
8.3(A) Generalize that the ratio of corresponding sides of similar shapes are proportional, including a shape and its dilation.

Mathematical Processes
8.1(C), 8.1(F), 8.1(G)

Vocab

Vocabulary
dilation
center of dilation

Hands-On Activity 1

Use grid paper to enlarge $\triangle ABC$ by a *scale factor* of 2. Point A will be the center point for the enlargement. Prime symbols can be used to indicate corresponding vertices. In this Activity, use A', B', and C'.

Step 1 On the grid shown below, $\overrightarrow{AB}$ is drawn to the edge of the grid. Draw $\overrightarrow{AC}$ in the same way.

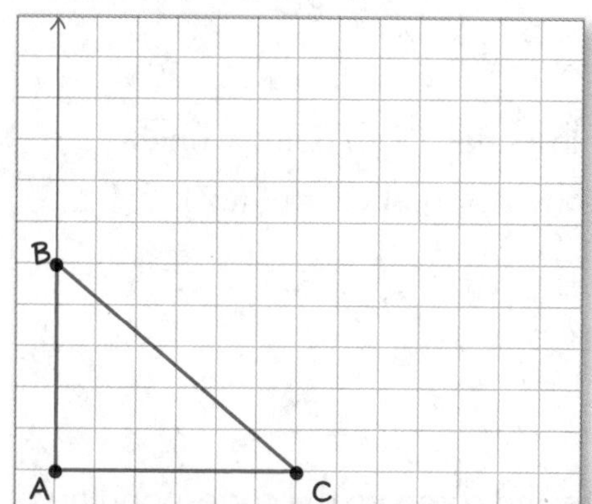

Step 2 Draw point B' on $\overrightarrow{AB}$ so that $AB' = 2(AB)$. Draw point C' on $\overrightarrow{AC}$ so that $AC' = 2(AC)$.

Step 3 Draw $\overline{B'C'}$ to complete $\triangle AB'C'$.

1. What is the ratio of the length of $\overline{AB}$ to the length of $\overline{AB'}$? ________
2. What is the ratio of the length of $\overline{AC}$ to the length of $\overline{AC'}$? ________
3. What is the ratio of the length of $\overline{BC}$ to the length of $\overline{B'C'}$? ________
4. What do you notice about the ratios of corresponding sides? Is $\triangle ABC$ similar to $\triangle A'B'C'$? ________

Hands-On Activity 2

In Activity 1, you used a dilation to transform $\triangle ABC$ by a scale factor of 2. A **dilation** is a transformation, or mapping, that enlarges or reduces a figure by a scale factor relative to a center point. That point is called the **center of dilation.**

In this Activity, you will draw the image of $\triangle XYZ$ after a dilation with a scale factor of $\frac{1}{2}$. Point C will be the center of dilation.

Step 1 Triangle XYZ is shown below. Using a ruler, draw line segments connecting point C to each of the vertices of the triangle. $\overline{CY}$ is done for you.

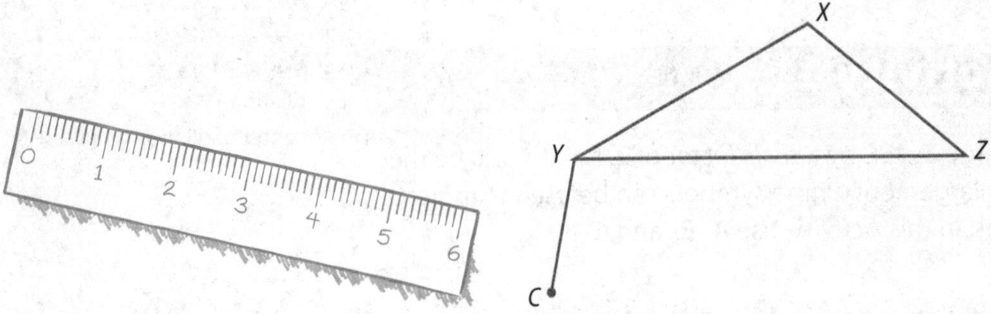

Step 2 Measure $\overline{CY}$. Draw point Y' on $\overline{CY}$ so that $CY' = \frac{1}{2}(CY)$.

Step 3 Repeat Step 2 for the two remaining sides. Draw point X' on $\overline{CX}$ so that $CX' = \frac{1}{2}(CX)$ and point Z' on $\overline{CZ}$ so that $CZ' = \frac{1}{2}(CZ)$.

Step 4 Draw $\triangle X'Y'Z'$.

5. MP **Select Tools and Techniques** Measure and compare the corresponding lengths on the original and new triangles. Describe the relationship between these measurements. ______________________________

____

6. MP **Select Tools and Techniques** Measure and compare the corresponding angles on the original and new triangles. Describe the relationship between these measurements. ______________________________

____

7. Is $\triangle X'Y'Z'$ similar to $\triangle XYZ$? ______________________________

Work with a partner. Draw the image after a dilation with the given scale factor. Point *A* is the center of dilation.

8. scale factor: 3

Show your work.

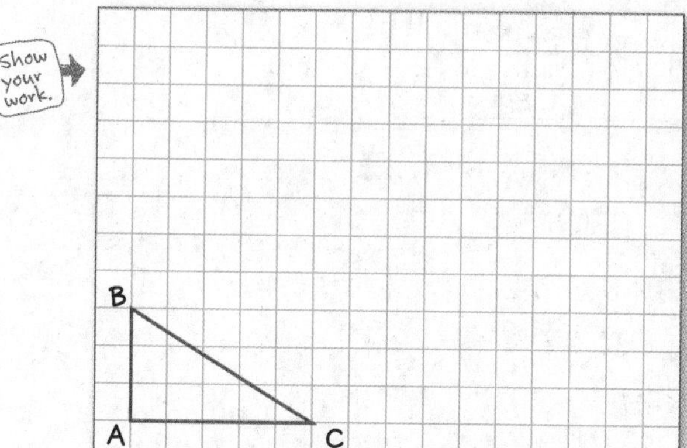

9. scale factor: $\frac{1}{3}$

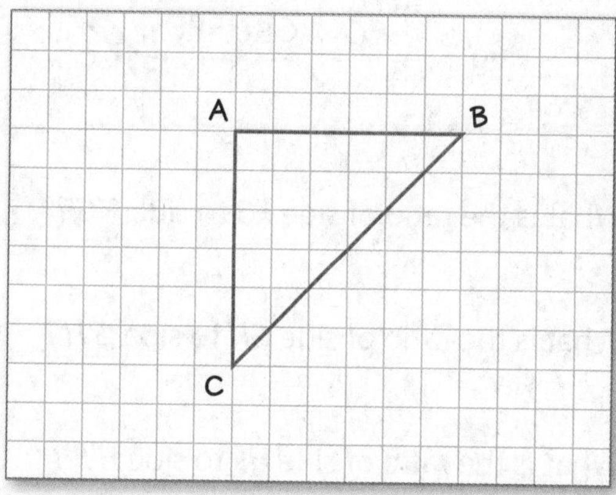

Work with a partner. Draw the image after a dilation with the given scale factor. Point *C* is the center of dilation.

10. scale factor: 3

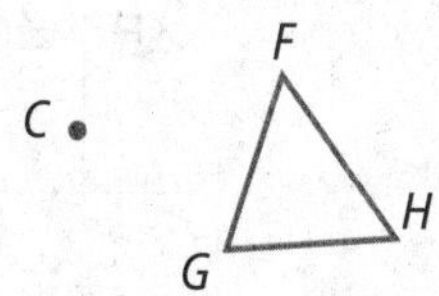

11. scale factor: $\frac{1}{5}$

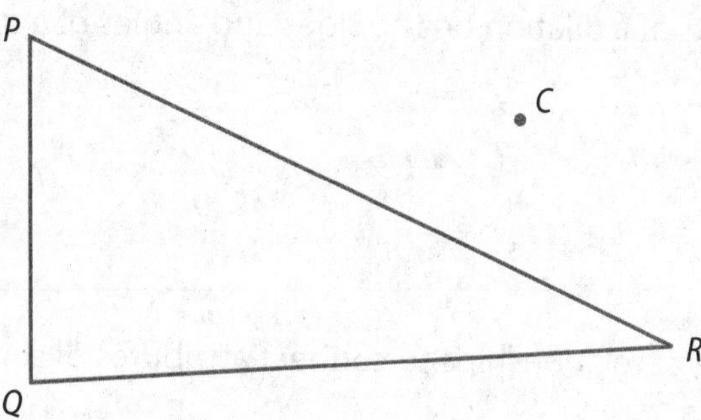

Analyze and Reflect

MP Select Tools and Techniques For each figure from Exercise 10, measure the given side lengths in millimeters. Complete the table.

12.

Original Figure	Side Lengths (mm)		
△FGH	FG	GH	HF

13.

Dilated Figure	Side Lengths (mm)		
△F′G′H′	F′G′	G′H′	H′F′

14. What is the ratio of side *FG* to side *F′G′*? ______

15. What is the ratio of side *GH* to side *G′H′*? ______

16. What is the ratio of side *HF* to side *H′F′*? ______

17. MP **Organize Ideas** How do corresponding sides compare between the original figure and its dilation? ______

18. MP **Select Tools and Techniques** Find the measures of the angles of △*FGH* and △*F′G′H′* in Exercise 10. Describe the relationship between the corresponding angles.

______

Angle Measure (°)		
∠F	∠G	∠H
∠F′	∠G′	∠H′

Create

19. MP **Analyze Relationships** Based on the Activities and Exercises, write a conjecture about the effects of a dilation on the sides and angles of a triangle.

______

20. **INQUIRY** How can I analyze relationships to connect attributes of similarity to dilations?

______

Lesson 3 Dilations

Launch the Lesson: Vocabulary

A dilation uses a scale factor to enlarge or reduce a figure.

Scan the lesson and complete the graphic organizer.

Dilation

Things that are like this	Characteristics	Things I've already learned that I can use for this

Texas Essential Knowledge and Skills

Targeted TEKS

8.3(B) Compare and contrast the attributes of a shape and its dilation(s) on a coordinate plane. *Also addresses 8.3(C).*

Mathematical Processes

8.1(A), 8.1(B), 8.1(D), 8.1(E), 8.1(F), 8.1(G)

Math Symbols

$(x, y) \longrightarrow (kx, ky)$

Essential Question

HOW can you determine similarity?

Real-World Link

Watch

Necie wants to insert a photo of her dog on her blog. The current size of the photo is 480 pixels by 640 pixels.

1. Suppose she wants to reduce the photo to 120 pixels by 160 pixels. Compare and contrast the original photo and the reduction.

2. What is the scale factor from the original to the reduction? ______

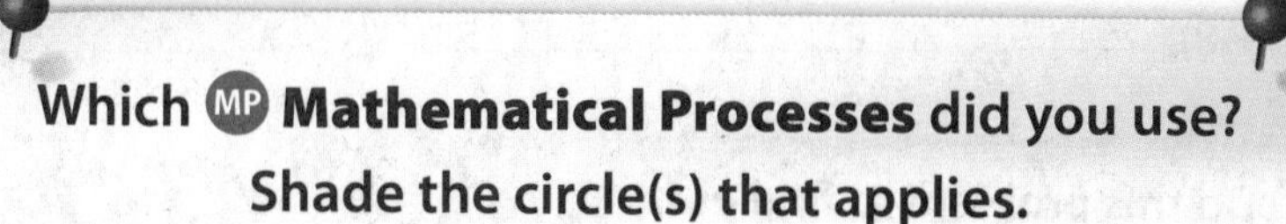

Which MP Mathematical Processes did you use? Shade the circle(s) that applies.

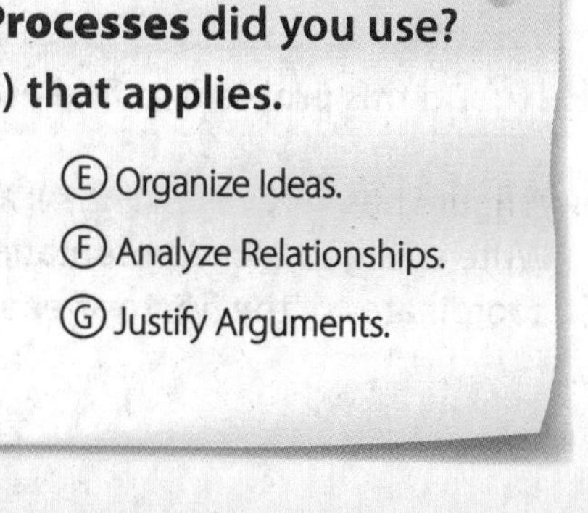

Ⓐ Apply Math to the Real World.
Ⓑ Use a Problem-Solving Model.
Ⓒ Select Tools and Techniques.
Ⓓ Use Multiple Representations.
Ⓔ Organize Ideas.
Ⓕ Analyze Relationships.
Ⓖ Justify Arguments.

Key Concept

Dilations in the Coordinate Plane

Work Zone

Words A dilation with a scale factor of k will be:

- an enlargement, or an image larger than the original, if $k > 1$,
- a reduction, or an image smaller than the original, if $0 < k < 1$,
- the same as the original figure if $k = 1$.

Model

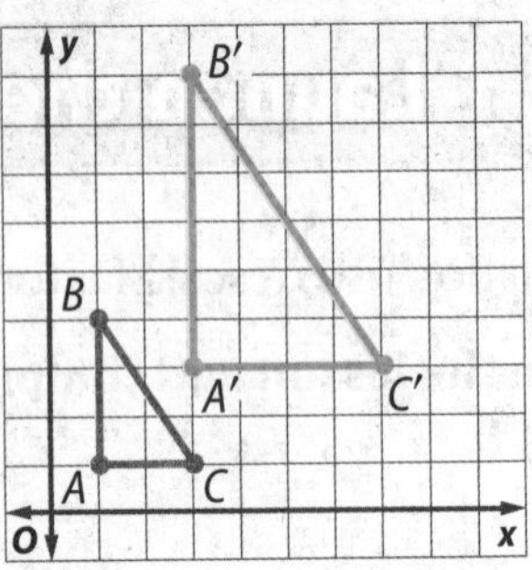

When the center of dilation in the coordinate plane is the origin, each coordinate of the preimage is multiplied by the scale factor k to find the coordinates of the image.

Symbols $(x, y) \rightarrow (kx, ky)$

You can compare and contrast a shape and its dilation. The preimage and the image are the same shape but not necessarily the same size since the figure is enlarged or reduced by a scale factor. The preimage and image are not congruent.

Tutor

Example

Center of Dilation

In this lesson, the origin is the center of dilation.

1. A triangle has vertices $A(0, 0)$, $B(8, 0)$, and $C(3, -2)$. Write an algebraic representation for the dilation. Determine the coordinates of the triangle after a dilation with a scale factor of 4.

The dilation is $(x, y) \rightarrow (4x, 4y)$. Multiply the coordinates of each vertex by 4.

$A(0, 0) \rightarrow (4 \cdot 0, 4 \cdot 0) \rightarrow (0, 0)$
$B(8, 0) \rightarrow (4 \cdot 8, 4 \cdot 0) \rightarrow (32, 0)$
$C(3, -2) \rightarrow [4 \cdot 3, 4 \cdot (-2)] \rightarrow (12, -8)$

So, the coordinates after the dilation are $A'(0, 0)$, $B'(32, 0)$, and $C'(12, -8)$.

Show your work.

Got It? Do this problem to find out.

a. A figure has vertices $W(-2, 4)$, $X(1, 4)$, $Y(3, -1)$, and $Z(-3, -1)$. Write an algebraic representation for the dilation. Determine the coordinates of the figure after a dilation with a scale factor of 2.

a. ________

Example

2. A figure has vertices $X(10, 2)$, $Y(10, 8)$, and $Z(6, 5)$. Graph the figure and the image of the figure after a dilation with a scale factor of $\frac{1}{2}$. Compare and contrast the figures.

The dilation is $(x, y) \rightarrow \left(\frac{1}{2}x, \frac{1}{2}y\right)$. Multiply the coordinates of each vertex by $\frac{1}{2}$. Then graph both figures on the coordinate plane.

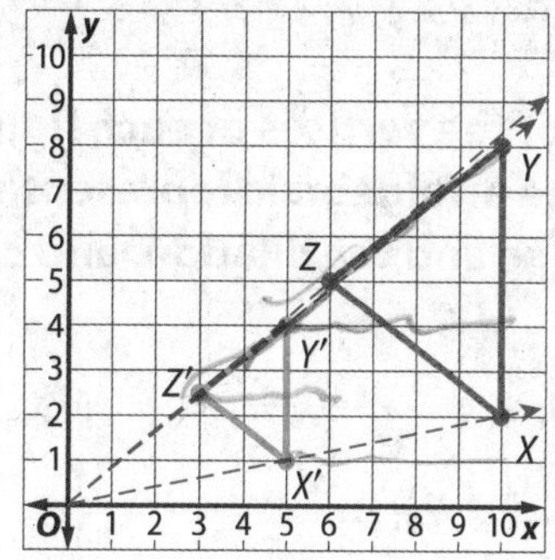

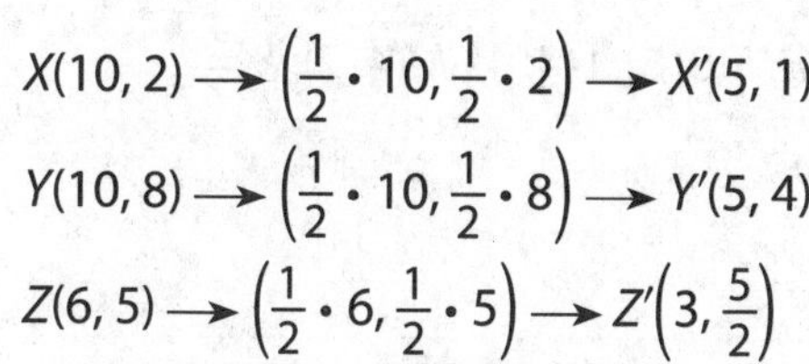

$X(10, 2) \rightarrow \left(\frac{1}{2} \cdot 10, \frac{1}{2} \cdot 2\right) \rightarrow X'(5, 1)$

$Y(10, 8) \rightarrow \left(\frac{1}{2} \cdot 10, \frac{1}{2} \cdot 8\right) \rightarrow Y'(5, 4)$

$Z(6, 5) \rightarrow \left(\frac{1}{2} \cdot 6, \frac{1}{2} \cdot 5\right) \rightarrow Z'\left(3, \frac{5}{2}\right)$

The figures are similar, so they have the same shape. The dilation is smaller than the original figure because the scale factor is between 0 and 1.

Check

Draw lines through the origin and each of the vertices of the original figure. The vertices of the dilation should lie on those same lines.

Got It? Do this problem to find out.

b. A figure has vertices $F(-1, 1)$, $G(1, 1)$, $H(2, -1)$, and $I(-1, -1)$. Graph the figure and the image of the figure after a dilation with a scale factor of 3. Compare and contrast the figures.

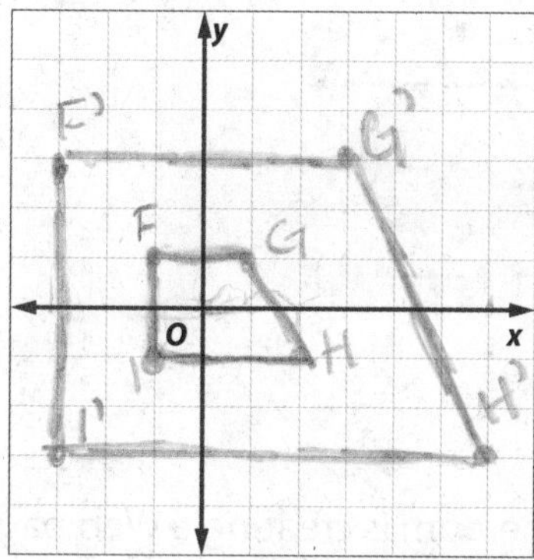

b. ______________

Example

3. Through a microscope, the image of a grain of sand with a 0.25-millimeter diameter appears to have a diameter of 11.25 millimeters. What is the scale factor of the dilation?

Write a ratio comparing the diameters of the two images.

$$\frac{\text{diameter in dilation}}{\text{diameter in original}} = \frac{11.25}{0.25}$$

$$= 45$$

So, the scale factor of the dilation is 45.

and Reflect

Explain below how you can determine if a dilation is a reduction or an enlargement based on the scale factor.

If the scale factor is more then one it's an enlargement. If it is less than one it gets smaller.

Got It? Do this problem to find out.

c. ________

c. Lucas wants to enlarge a 3- by 5-inch photo to a $7\frac{1}{2}$- by $12\frac{1}{2}$-inch photo. What is the scale factor of the dilation?

Guided Practice

Determine the coordinates of the vertices of each figure after a dilation with the given scale factor *k*. Write an algebraic representation for the dilation. Then graph the original image and the dilation, and compare and contrast the figures. (Examples 1 and 2)

Show your work.

1. $A(3, 5)$, $B(0, 4)$, $C(-2, -2)$; $k = 2$

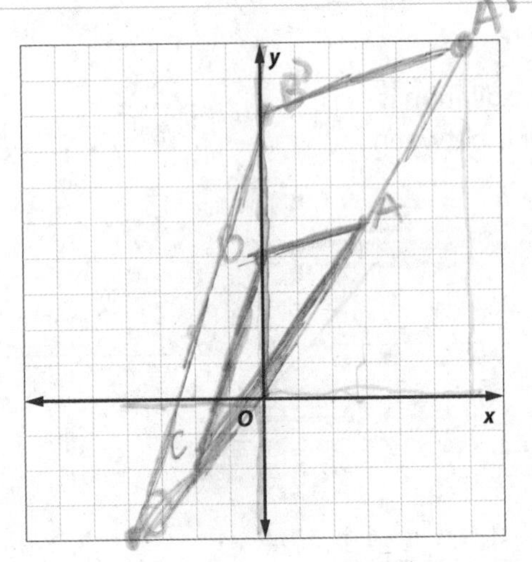

2. $J(0, -4)$, $K(0, 6)$, $L(4, 4)$, $M(4, 2)$; $k = \frac{1}{4}$

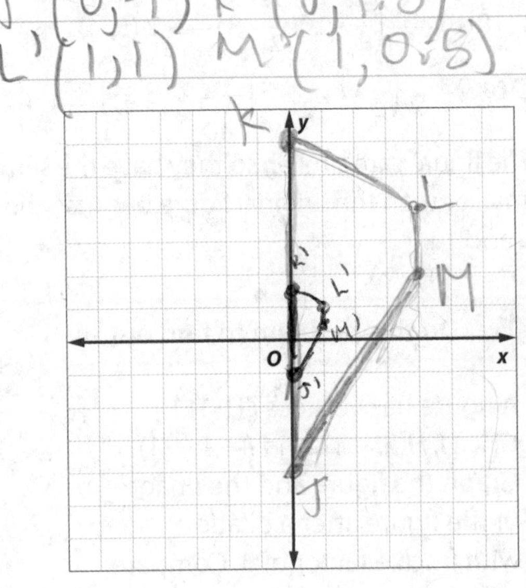

3. **STEM** Mrs. Bowen's homeroom is creating a Web page for their school's Intranet site. They need to reduce a scanned photograph so it is 720 pixels by 320 pixels. If the scanned photograph is 1,080 pixels by 480 pixels, what is the scale factor of the dilation? (Example 3) ________

4. **Building on the Essential Question** How are dilations similar to scale drawings?

Rate Yourself!

How confident are you about how to dilate a figure? Check the box that applies.

Find out online. Use the Self-Check Quiz.

FOLDABLES Time to update your Foldable!

Name _______________ My Homework _______________

Independent Practice

8.3(B), 8.3(C), 8.1(E), 8.1(F) TEKS

Determine the coordinates of the vertices of each figure after a dilation with the given scale factor *k*. Then graph the original image and the dilation. (Examples 1 and 2)

1. $C(1, 4), A(2, 2), T(5, 5); k = 2$

____

____

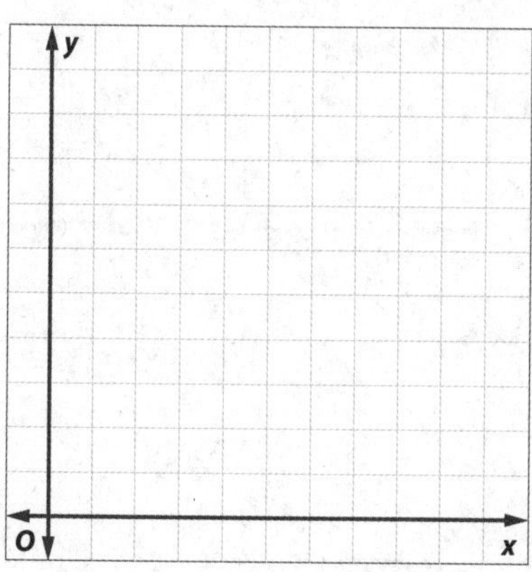

2. $R(1, 1), S(1, 7), T(5, 7), U(5, 1); k = \frac{3}{4}$

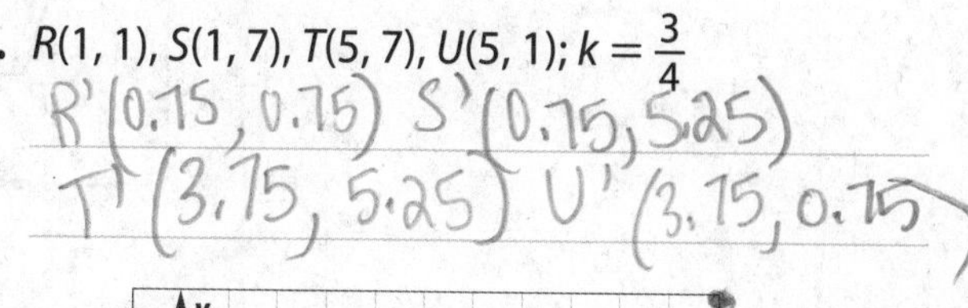

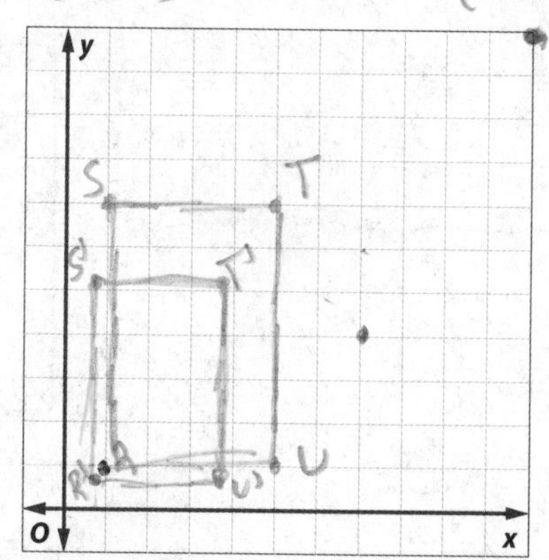

3. Refer to Exercises 1 and 2. Write an algebraic representation for each dilation. (Example 1)

Exercise 1: _______________ Exercise 2: _______________

4. Refer to Exercises 1 and 2. Compare and contrast each pair of figures. Are the figures congruent? Explain. (Example 2)

____

____

5. A graphic designer created a logo on $8\frac{1}{2}$- by 11-inch paper. In order to be placed on a business card, the logo needs to be $1\frac{7}{10}$ inches by $2\frac{1}{5}$ inches. What is the scale factor of the dilation? (Example 3)

____

6. Darian wants to build a regulation-size pool table that is 9 feet in length. The plans he ordered are 18 by 36 inches. What is the scale factor of the dilation he must use to build the regulation pool table? (Example 3) _______________

7. **MP Organize Ideas** In each part of the graphic organizer, sketch an image of pentagon *MNOPQ* after a dilation within the given parameters.

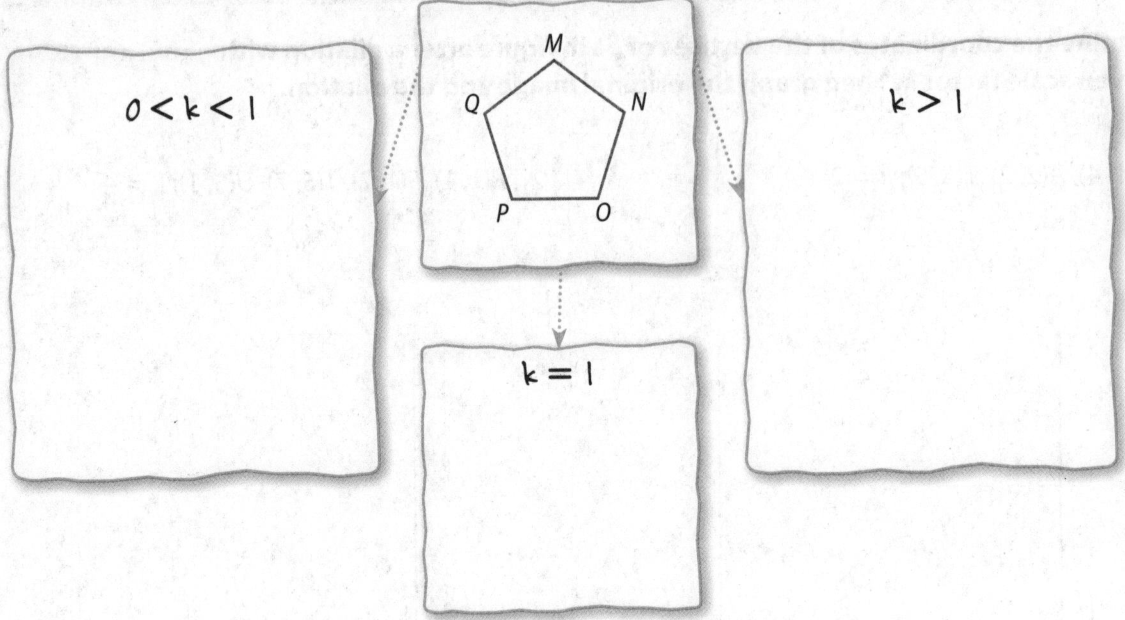

H.O.T. Problems Higher-Order Thinking

8. **Analyze** The *orientation* of a figure describes its position relative to another figure. For example, the triangles in Example 2 on page 139 have the same orientation, but they are not congruent. Study the dilations you graphed on pages 140–141. Then tell whether the following statements are *always, sometimes,* or *never* true about dilations on a coordinate plane. If a statement is not always true, explain your reasoning.

   a. In a dilation, the image and preimage are congruent. ______________

   b. In a dilation, the image and preimage have the same orientation.

9. **Evaluate** The coordinates of two triangles are shown in the table. Is $\triangle WXY$ a dilation of $\triangle ABC$? Explain.

WXY		ABC	
W	(a, b)	A	(4a, 2b)
X	(a, c)	B	(4a, 2c)
Y	(d, b)	C	(4d, 2b)

10. **Analyze** The algebraic representation of a dilation is $(x, y) \rightarrow \left(\frac{1}{a}x, \frac{1}{a}y\right)$. If the dilation is an enlargement, write three possible values of *a*.

Name ____________________

Multi-Step Problem Solving

11. Malik uses a dilation in a perspective drawing. Using the origin as the center of the dilation, he dilates Rectangle I to obtain Rectangle II. Which option describes the change in perimeter, using the following variables?

P_I = perimeter of Rectangle I

P_{II} = perimeter of Rectangle II

SF = scale factor of the dilation

Ⓐ $P_I = SF \times P_{II}$

Ⓑ $P_I = (SF)^2 \times P_{II}$

Ⓒ $P_{II} = SF \times P_I$

Ⓓ $P_{II} = (SF)^2 \times P_I$

Use a problem-solving model to solve this problem.

1 Analyze

Read the problem. Circle the information you know.
Underline what the problem is asking you to find.

2 Plan

What will you need to do to solve the problem? Write your plan in steps.

Step 1 Determine which equations model the relationship between scale factor and __________ when dilating a figure.

Step 2 Determine which equation models the dilation of __________ to obtain __________.

3 Solve

Use your plan to solve the problem. Show your steps.

Answer choices ____ and ____ show the relationship between scale factor and perimeter.

Of these two choices, ____ shows the dilation of __________ to obtain __________. So, the correct answer is ____. Fill in that answer choice.

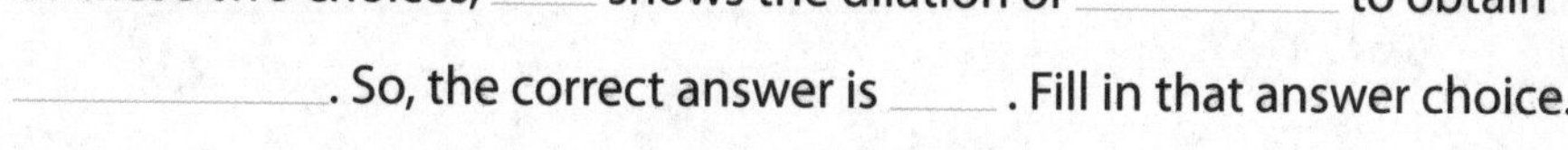

Read to Succeed!
Remember that perimeter uses linear units of measure, while area uses square units of measure.

4 Justify and Evaluate

How do you know your solution is accurate?

____

____

P = Proportionality MP = Mathematical Processes

More Multi-Step Problem Solving

Use a problem-solving model to solve each problem.

12. Fina is an architect. She drew quadrilateral *ABCD* to represent a window. Then, using the origin as the center, she dilated it to obtain the larger quadrilateral *A′B′C′D′*. Which statement is true? P N MP

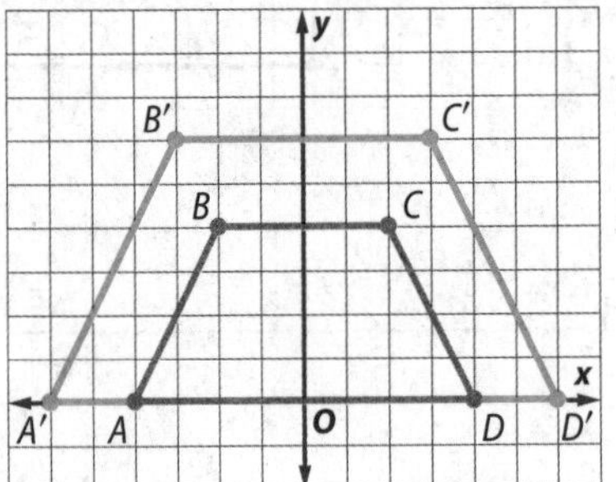

Ⓐ $m\angle A' = 1.5 \times m\angle A$

Ⓑ $m\angle A' = 2.25 \times m\angle A$

Ⓒ area of $A'B'C'D' = 1.5 \times$ area of $ABCD$

Ⓓ area of $A'B'C'D' = 2.25 \times$ area of $ABCD$

13. Aponi is a structural engineer. She drew $\triangle PQR$ to represent a roof truss. Using point *P* as the center, she dilated $\triangle PQR$ by a scale factor of 2 and then dilated the resulting image by a scale factor of 1.1 to obtain a final image. The area of the final image, A'', is related to the original area *A* by the equation $A'' = x \cdot A$. What is the value of *x*? P N MP

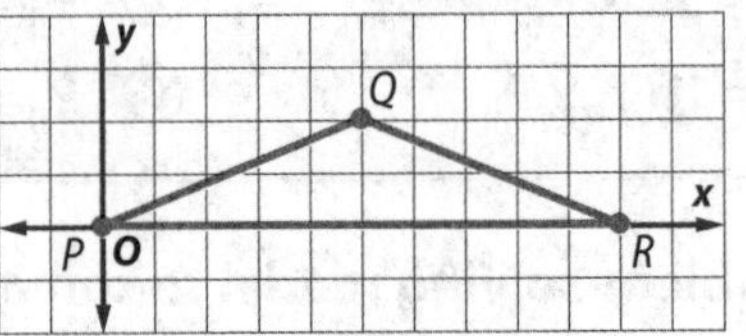

14. The rectangle below is dilated, increasing both dimensions by 20%. Then the image is dilated, decreasing both dimensions by 20%. The origin is the center of both dilations. The perimeter of the final image, P'', is related to the original perimeter *P* by the equation $P' = x \cdot P$. What is the value of *x*? P N MP

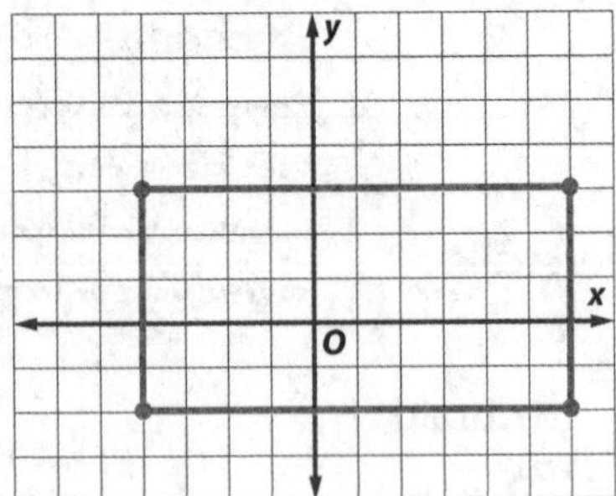

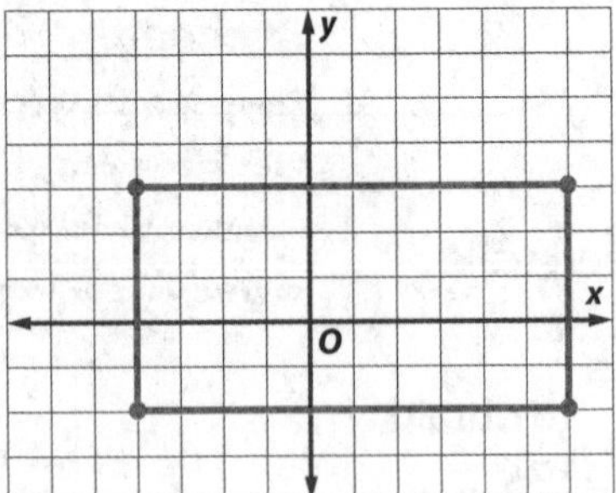

15. Polygon *PQRS* has vertices $P(-4, -2)$, $Q(3, -2)$, $R(3, 6)$, and $S(-4, 6)$. Polygon *PQRS* is dilated, using the origin as the center of the dilation. The image is polygon $P'Q'R'S'$, and P' has coordinates $(-10, -5)$. What is the perimeter of polygon $P'Q'R'S'$? Support your answer. P T MP

N = Number and Operations P = Proportionality T = Two-Dimensional Shapes MP = Mathematical Processes

Hands-On Lab 4-a

Changes in Dimensions

INQUIRY **HOW can I select tools and techniques to analyze the effect of enlarging or reducing a figure by a scale factor on its perimeter and area?**

Texas Essential Knowledge and Skills TEKS

Targeted TEKS
8.10(D) Model the effect on linear and area measurements of dilated two-dimensional shapes. *Also addresses 8.3(A).*

Mathematical Processes
8.1(C), 8.1(D), 8.1(E), 8.1(F), 8.1(G)

A middle school parking lot is 400 feet long and 200 feet wide. The school board wants to double the dimensions of the parking lot. How will the perimeter and area of the enlarged parking lot compare to the perimeter and area of the current parking lot?

Hands-On Activity 1

Step 1 Draw the current parking lot on the grid paper where each unit represents 100 feet.

Step 2 Determine the perimeter and area of the current parking lot.

perimeter: ______________________________

area: ______________________________

Step 3 On the same grid paper, draw the new parking lot.

Step 4 Determine the perimeter and area of the new parking lot.

perimeter: ______________________________

area: ______________________________

Refer to Steps 2 and 4.

1. Describe the relationship between the perimeters of the two parking lots.

____

____

2. Describe the relationship between the areas of the two parking lots.

____

____

On a park map, a picnic area is represented by a rectangle with the coordinates (0, 0), (0, 4), (6, 4), and (6, 0). The park is going to be renovated and the picnic area will be half its current size. How will this affect the area and the perimeter of the picnic area on the map?

Hands-On Activity 2

Step 1 On the coordinate grid, draw a rectangle that represents the current picnic area.

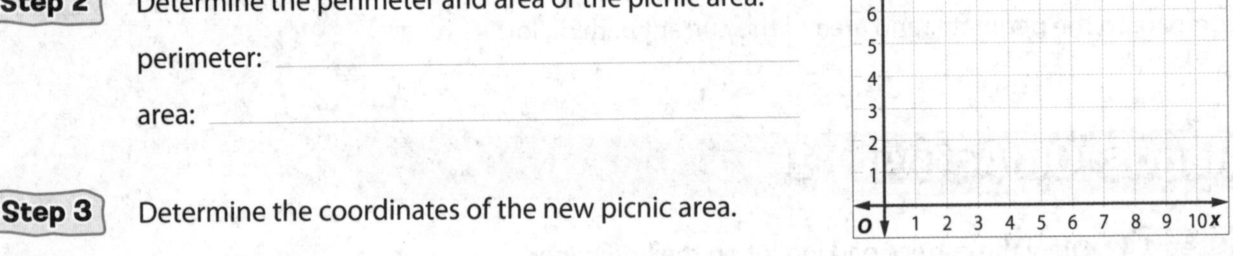

Step 2 Determine the perimeter and area of the picnic area.

perimeter: ______________________

area: ______________________

Step 3 Determine the coordinates of the new picnic area.

____

Step 4 On the same coordinate grid, draw the rectangle that represents the new picnic area.

Step 5 Determine the perimeter and area of the new picnic area.

perimeter: ______________________

area: ______________________

Refer to Steps 2 and 5.

3. Describe the relationship between the perimeters of the two picnic areas.

____

____

4. Describe the relationship between the areas of the two picnic areas.

____

____

Work with a partner. For each situation, draw the original figure and the new figure. Then complete the table.

5. The side length of a square is 3 inches. The side length of a similar square is three times that of the original square.

	Original Figure	New Figure
Perimeter		
Area		

6. The length of a rectangle is 12 inches and the width of the rectangle is 9 inches. A similar rectangle has dimensions that are one third the original rectangle.

	Original Figure	New Figure
Perimeter		
Area		

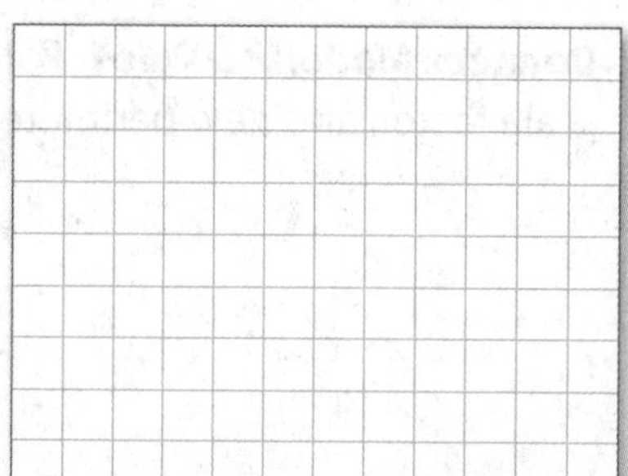

7. The coordinates of a figure are $A(2, 1)$, $B(2, 4)$, $C(6, 4)$, and $D(6, 1)$. Graph the figure and the image of the figure after dilation with a scale factor of 1.5.

	Original Figure	Dilation
Perimeter		
Area		

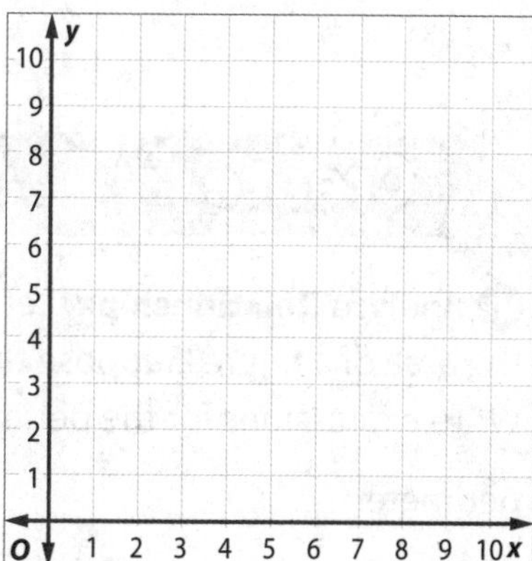

Analyze and Reflect

Work with a partner.

8. Refer to the Activities and Exercises to complete the table.

Figure	Original Perimeter	Original Area	Scale Factor	New Perimeter	New Area
Activity 1					
Activity 2					
Exercise 5					
Exercise 6					
Exercise 7					

9. Connect Models to Rules For each figure, look at the original perimeter, scale factor, and new perimeter. What pattern do you notice?

10. Connect Models to Rules For each figure, look at the original area, scale factor, and new area. What pattern do you notice?

On Your Own

Create

11. MP **Analyze Relationships** Let P represent the perimeter and A represent the area of a figure. Suppose the figure is dilated by a scale factor of $\frac{3}{2}$. Write expressions for the perimeter and area of the dilated figure.

perimeter: ______________ area: ______________

12. INQUIRY HOW can I select tools and techniques to analyze the effect of enlarging or reducing a figure by a scale factor on its perimeter and area?

Lesson 4

Area and Perimeter of Similar Figures

Launch the Lesson: Real World

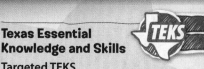

Texas Essential Knowledge and Skills

Targeted TEKS
8.10(D) Model the effect on linear and area measurements of dilated two-dimensional shapes.
Also addresses 8.3(A).

Mathematical Processes
8.1(A), 8.1(B), 8.1(F), 8.1(G)

Essential Question
HOW can you determine similarity?

Investigate The sponsors of a rectangular community garden plan to double the dimensions of the garden. Complete the steps to discover how changes in the garden's dimensions will affect its perimeter and area.

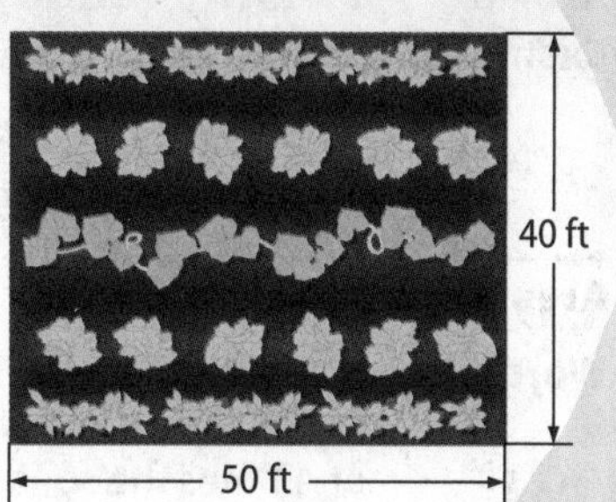

1. Use $P = \ell + w + \ell + w$ to determine the perimeter of each garden.

   $P =$ ______ $P =$ ______

   $=$ ______ $=$ ______

2. Use $A = \ell w$ to determine the area of each garden.

   $A =$ ______ $A =$ ______

   $=$ ______ $=$ ______

3. **Analyze** How does a scale factor of 2 affect the perimeter? the area?

   ______

4. **Analyze** Suppose the sponsors wanted to triple the dimensions. How does a scale factor of 3 affect the perimeter and area?

   ______

5. **Create** Write a conjecture that explains how changes in dimensions affect the perimeter and area.

   ______

   ______

Which MP Mathematical Processes did you use? Shade the circle(s) that applies.

Ⓐ Apply Math to the Real World.
Ⓑ Use a Problem-Solving Model.
Ⓒ Select Tools and Techniques.
Ⓓ Use Multiple Representations.
Ⓔ Organize Ideas.
Ⓕ Analyze Relationships.
Ⓖ Justify Arguments.

Key Concept

Perimeter and Area of Similar Figures

Work Zone

Perimeter

Words If figure B is similar to figure A by a scale factor, then the perimeter of B is equal to the perimeter of A times the scale factor.

Examples perimeter of figure B = perimeter of figure A • scale factor

$$4\ell + 4w = (2\ell + 2w) \cdot 2$$

Area

Words If figure B is similar to figure A by a scale factor, then the area of B is equal to the area of A times the square of the scale factor.

Examples area of figure B = area of figure A • (scale factor)^2

$$4\ell w = (\ell w) \cdot 2^2$$

Models

ℓ, w

Figure A

2ℓ, $2w$

Figure B

In similar, or dilated figures, the perimeters are related by the scale factor, k. The area of one similar figure is equal to the area of the other similar figure times the *square* of the scale factor, or k^2.

Tutor

Example

1. Two rectangles are similar. One has a length of 6 inches and a perimeter of 24 inches. The other has a length of 7 inches. What is the perimeter of this rectangle?

The scale factor is $\frac{7}{6}$. The perimeter of the original is 24 inches.

$x = 24\left(\frac{7}{6}\right)$ Multiply by the scale factor.

$x = \frac{\overset{4}{\cancel{24}}}{1}\left(\frac{7}{\underset{1}{\cancel{6}}}\right)$ Divide out common factors.

$x = 28$ Simplify.

So, the perimeter of the new rectangle is 28 inches.

Got It? **Do this problem to find out.**

Show your work.

a. Triangle LMN is similar to triangle PQR. If the perimeter of $\triangle LMN$ is 64 meters, what is the perimeter of $\triangle PQR$?

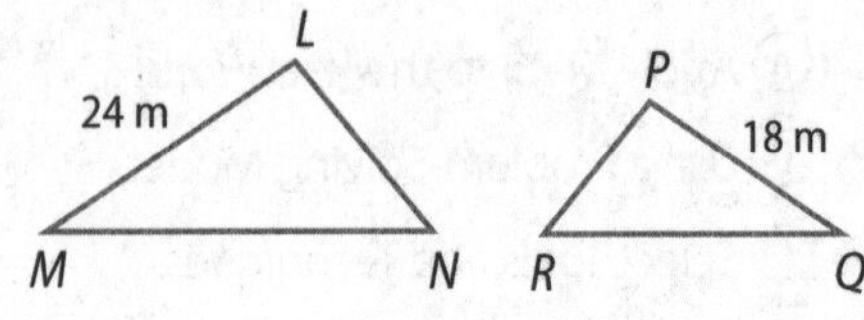

a. ________

Multi-Step Example

2. In a scale drawing, the perimeter of the garden is 64 inches. The actual length of $\overline{AB}$ is 18 feet. What is the perimeter of the actual garden?

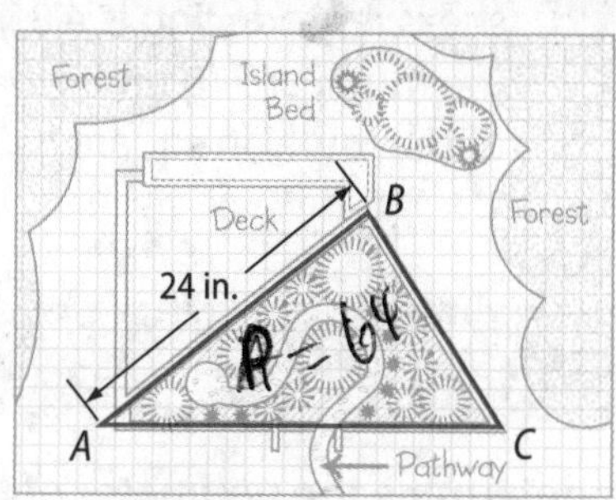

Step 1 The actual length is proportional to the length in the drawing with a ratio of $\frac{18 \text{ ft}}{24 \text{ in.}}$. Find the scale factor.

$\frac{18 \text{ ft}}{24 \text{ in.}} = \frac{216 \text{ in.}}{24 \text{ in.}}$ or $\frac{9}{1}$ Convert feet to inches and divide out units.

Step 2 Find the perimeter of the actual garden.

perimeter of garden = perimeter of drawing • scale factor

$P = 64 \cdot 9$ or 576 Substitute. Then simplify.

The perimeter of the actual garden is 576 inches or 48 feet.

> **Scale Factor**
>
> When determining the scale factor from one figure to another, the units must be the same.

Got It? Do this problem to find out.

b. Two quilting squares are shown. The scale factor is 3:2. What is the perimeter of square *TUVW*?

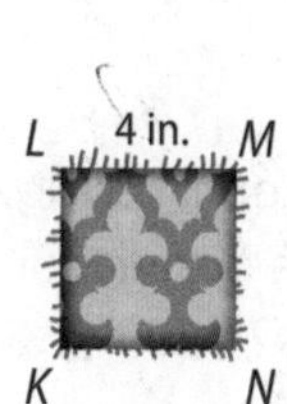

b. ______________

Example

3. The Eddingtons have a 5-foot by 8-foot porch on the front of their house. They are building a similar porch on the back with double the dimensions. Determine the area of the back porch.

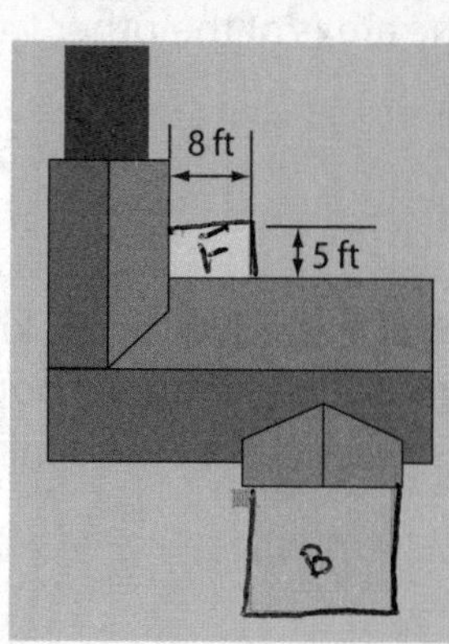

The scale factor is 2.

The area of the front porch is (5)(8) or 40 square feet.

$x = 40(2)^2$ Multiply by the square of the scale factor.

$x = 40(4)$ or 160 Evaluate the power.

The back porch will have an area of 160 square feet.

Got It? Do this problem to find out.

c. Malia is painting a mural on her bedroom wall. The image she is reproducing is 4.8 inches by 7.2 inches. If the dimensions of the mural are 10 times the dimensions of the image, find the area of the mural in square inches.

c. ______________

Guided Practice

For each pair of similar figures, determine the perimeter of the second figure. (Example 1)

1.

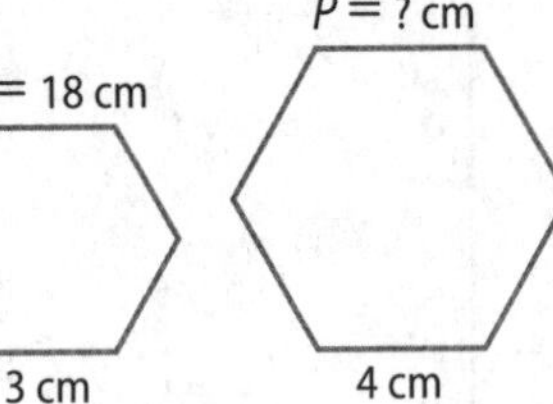

2.

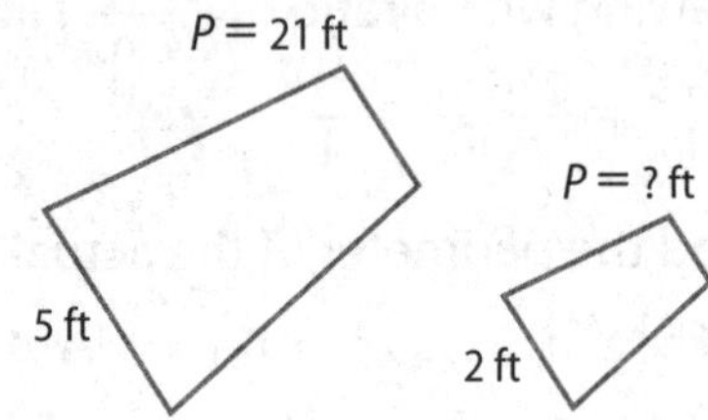

3. Julie is enlarging a digital photograph on her computer. The original photograph is 5 inches by 7 inches. If she enlarges the dimensions 1.5 times, what will be the perimeter and area of the new image? (Examples 2 and 3)

4. Logan is flying a kite that is made up of three similar rectangles. The sides of the three rectangles are in the ratio 1:2:3. If the area of the smallest rectangle is 72 square inches, what are the areas of the other two rectangles? (Example 3) ______________

5. **Building on the Essential Question** If you know two figures are similar and you are given the area of both figures, how can you determine the scale factor of the similarity?

Rate Yourself!

How well do you understand how to find the perimeter and area of similar figures? Circle the image that applies.

Clear | Somewhat Clear | Not So Clear

Find out online. Use the Self-Check Quiz.

Independent Practice

8.10(D), 8.3(A), 8.1(E), 8.1(F), 8.1(G) TEKS

For each pair of similar figures, determine the perimeter of the second figure. (Example 1)

1.

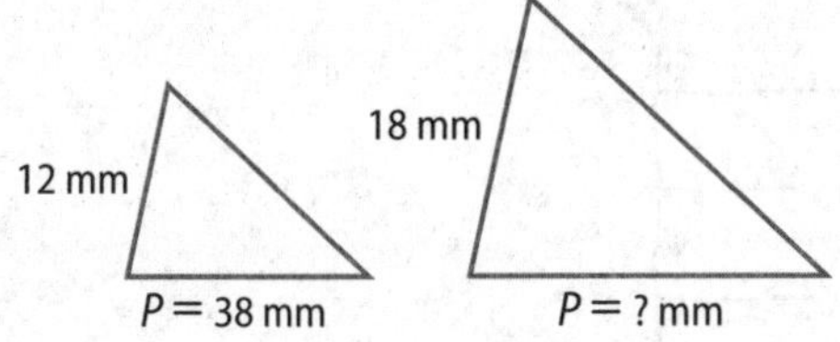

2.

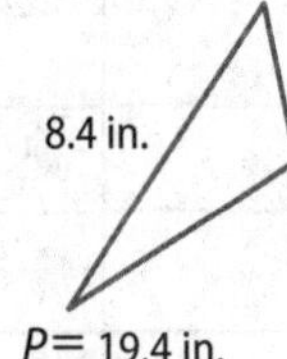

3. The city of Brice is planning to build a skate park. An architect designed the area shown at the right. In the plan, the perimeter of the park is 80 inches. If the actual length of $\overline{WX}$ is 50 feet, what will be the perimeter of the actual skate park? (Example 2) ______

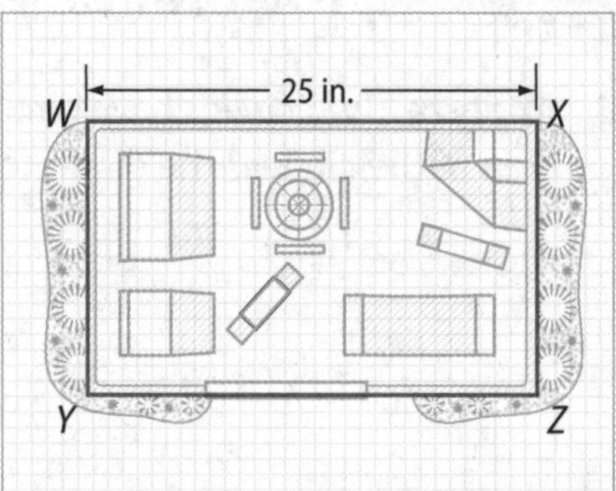

4. A child's desk is made so that the dimensions are two-thirds the dimensions of a full-size adult desk. Suppose the top of the full-size desk measures 54 inches long by 36 inches wide. What is the perimeter and area of the top of the child's desk? (Examples 2 and 3)

5. Theo is constructing a miniature putting green in his backyard. He wants it to be similar to a putting green at the local golf course, but one third the dimensions. The area of the putting green at the golf course is 1,134 square feet. What will be the area of the putting green Theo constructs?

6. Craig is making a model version of his neighborhood that uses model trains. The ratio of the model train to the actual train is 1:64. His neighborhood covers an area of 200,704 square feet. What will be the area of the model neighborhood?

7. **MP Organize Ideas** Complete the graphic organizer to compare how the scale factor affects the side lengths, perimeter, and area of dilated rectangles.

If the scale factor is...	Multiply the ...			
	Length by	Width by	Perimeter by	Area by
2				
4				
0.5				
$\frac{2}{3}$				
k				

H.O.T. Problems Higher-Order Thinking

8. **Analyze** Two circles have circumferences of π and 3π. What is the ratio of the area of the circles? the diameters? the radii?

9. **Evaluate** A company wants to reduce the dimensions of its logo from 6 inches by 4 inches to 3 inches by 2 inches to use on business cards. Robert thinks that the new logo is $\frac{1}{4}$ the size of the original logo. Denise thinks that is $\frac{1}{2}$ of the original size. Explain their thinking.

10. **Create** Use the coordinate plane to draw a rectangle. Dilate the rectangle and draw the dilation. Then determine the perimeter and area of each rectangle to model the effect of the dilation.

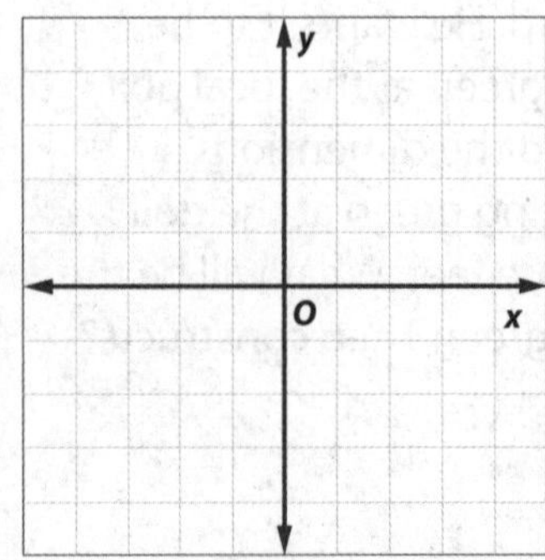

Name ______________________________

Multi-Step Problem Solving

11. Ella is painting two walls that have the shape of the figure at the right. The first wall has an area of 720 square feet. The second wall is a dilation of the first wall with a scale factor of 1.2. One gallon of paint will cover 300 square feet. If paint costs $25.00 per gallon, how much will Ella spend to paint both walls? P MP

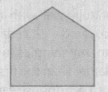

Use a problem-solving model to solve this problem.

1 Analyze

Read the problem. Circle the information you know. Underline what the problem is asking you to find.

2 Plan

What will you need to do to solve the problem? Write your plan in steps.

Step 1 Determine the total area of both walls.

Step 2 Determine the cost of the total number of gallons needed to paint both walls.

Read to Succeed!

Remember that perimeter uses linear units of measure, while area uses square units of measure.

3 Solve

Use your plan to solve the problem. Show your steps.

The area of the larger wall is ________ square feet. So, the total area is 720 + ________ or ________ square feet.

To find the number of gallons needed, divide ________ by ________ and round to the nearest whole number. To find the total cost, multiply ___ gallons by ________.

Ella will spend ________ to paint both walls. Complete the grid.

					.		
⊕	0	0	0	0		0	0
⊖	1	1	1	1		1	1
	2	2	2	2		2	2
	3	3	3	3		3	3
	4	4	4	4		4	4
	5	5	5	5		5	5
	6	6	6	6		6	6
	7	7	7	7		7	7
	8	8	8	8		8	8
	9	9	9	9		9	9

4 Justify and Evaluate

How do you know your solution is accurate?

____

____

____

P = Proportionality MP = Mathematical Processes

More Multi-Step Problem Solving

Use a problem-solving model to solve each problem.

12. A rectangular wall with an area of 300 square feet is covered with cedar shingles. Hugo needs to buy shingles to cover another wall that is larger than the first wall by a scale factor of 1.5. Suppose each shingle costs $120, and one shingle covers 100 square feet. How much will Hugo spend on shingles to cover the second wall? P T EE MP

13. The "T" shape is a target on a square board at a carnival game. It is formed by two rectangles that are each 40 centimeters long and 10 centimeters wide. The game operator wants to make the target smaller. He dilates the target by a scale factor of $\frac{1}{2}$ and replaces the target on the square board. What is the area of the new target? P T MP EE

14. The diagram shown below represents a rectangular painting. The artist wants to create another painting of the same shape by dilating the rectangle by a scale factor of 1.4. She needs to buy canvas for the painting surface and molding for the frame. Suppose canvas costs $1.00 per square foot and molding costs $4.10 per foot. If molding is sold by the foot and canvas is sold by the square foot, what will be the total cost of the materials for the new painting? P T MP

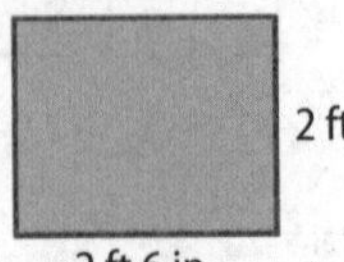

15. The table provides information about three shapes and their dilated images. Which shape was dilated by the greatest scale factor? Support your answer. P T MP EE N

Shapes and Dilated Images
A rectangle has a width of 10 cm and an area of 200 cm^2. The perimeter of the dilated figure is 90 cm.
A circle has a radius of 10 cm. The area of the dilated figure is 628 cm^2.
A trapezoid has an area of 150 cm^2 and parallel side lengths of 10 cm and 20 cm. The height of the dilated figure is 20 cm.

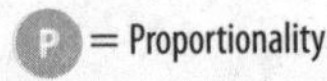 N = Number and Operations 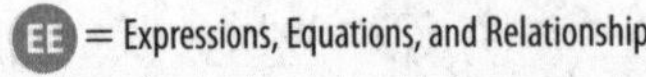 P = Proportionality EE = Expressions, Equations, and Relationships  T = Two-Dimensional Shapes 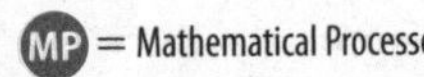 MP = Mathematical Processes

21ST CENTURY CAREER

Car Designer

Do you like drawing? Are you technical and precise in your drawings? You should consider a career as a car designer. Car designers use Computer Aided Design to create technical drawings that are used in manufacturing and construction. Information from architects and engineers is used to create highly specialized drawings that show how to construct everything from a nightstand to the space shuttle.

Mathematical Process TEKS
8.1(A) Apply mathematics to problems arising in everyday life, society, and the workplace.
Targeted TEKS 8.3(A)

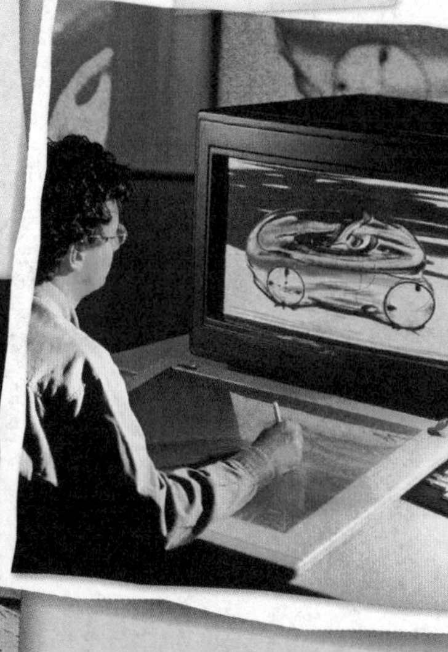

Is This the Career for You?

Are you interested in a career as a car designer? Take some of the following courses in high school.

- Geometry
- Mechanical Drawing
- Computer Graphics
- Design

Turn the page to find out how math relates to a career in Car Design.

Explore college and careers at ccr.mcgraw-hill.com

Drive Yourself to Success

Use the information on the drawing to solve each problem.

1. Are the views of the drawing of the car similar to views of the actual car? Explain.

2. Is the drawing a dilation of the actual car? Explain.

3. If the scale factor is $\frac{1}{25}$, find the following:
   a. the length of the actual car
   b. the distance from the front wheel to the rear wheel of the actual car

4. If the scale factor is $\frac{1}{25}$ and the actual height of the car is 60 inches, what is y?

5. If the scale factor is $\frac{1}{25}$ and $x = 2\frac{4}{5}$ inches, what is the actual distance between the tires on the car?

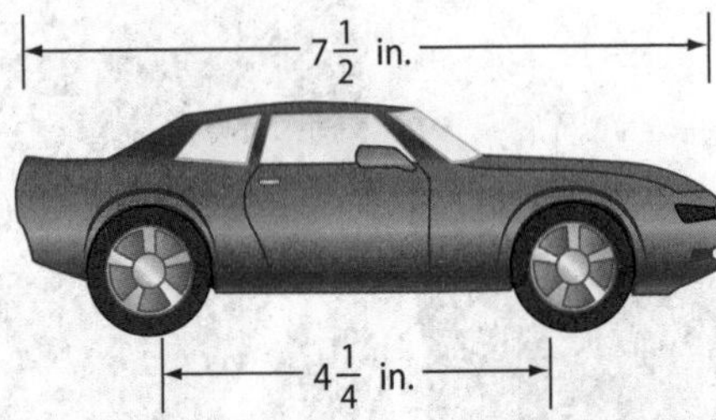

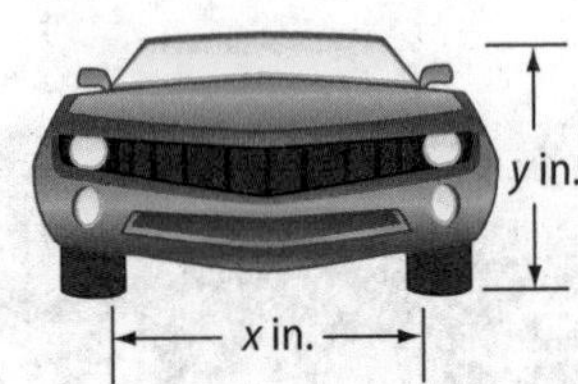

TEKS Career Project

Prepare a brief oral presentation about the features that you would include in a new car design and present it to your classmates. As others are presenting, listen carefully to their presentations. A the end, ask any clarifying questions.

List several challenges associated with this career.

-
-
-
-
-

Chapter Review

Vocabulary Check

Work with a partner to complete the puzzle by unscrambling the letters below each column to complete the definition of a word from the vocabulary list at the beginning of the chapter. Seek clarification of each vocabulary terms as needed.

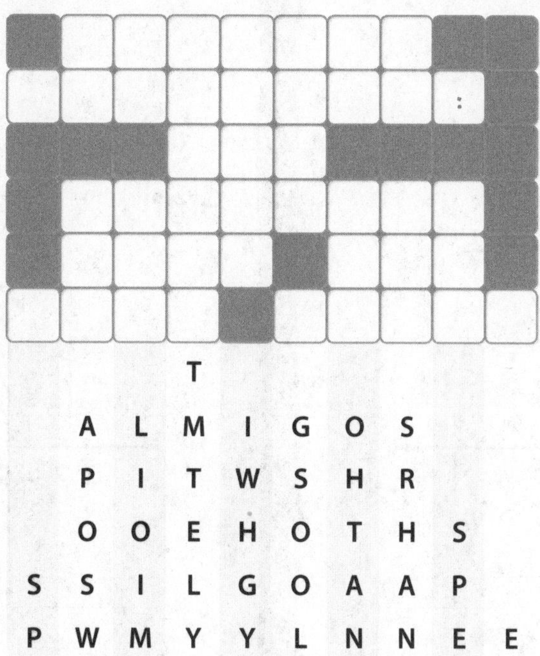

Complete each sentence using vocabulary from the chapter. Take turns saying each sentence aloud while your partner listens carefully.

1. Figures with congruent angles and proportional sides are similar.

2. In the algebraic representation $(x, y) \rightarrow (kx, kx)$, k is the Scale factor.

3. A(n) dilation is a transformation, or mapping, that involves enlarging or reducing a figure.

4. Indirect Measure uses properties of similar polygons to find distances or lengths that are difficult to measure directly.

Key Concept Check

Use Your FOLDABLES

Use your Foldable to help review the chapter. Share your Foldable with a partner and take turns summarizing what you learned in this chapter, while your partner listens carefully. Ask for clarification of any concepts, as needed. TEKS 8.1(E)

Tape here

Tab 1 Dilations

Algebraic Representation

Graph

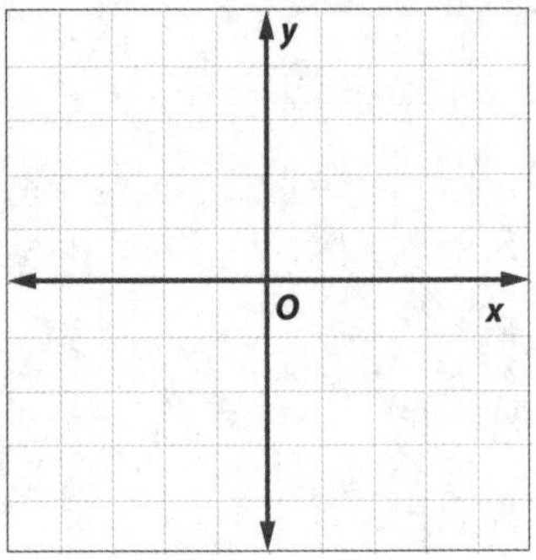

y
O
x

Algebraic Representation

Graph

y
O
x

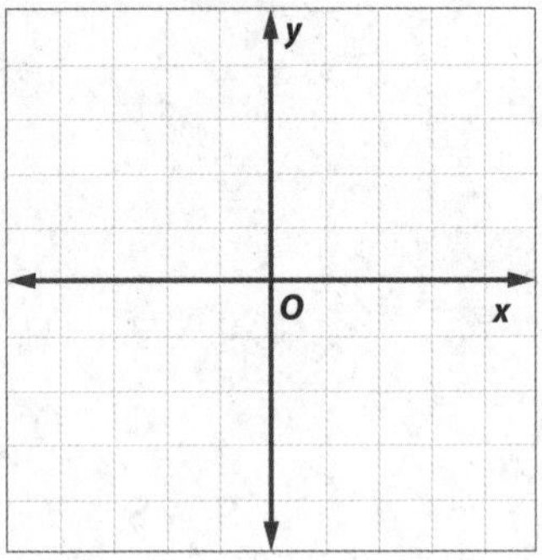

Tab 2

Got it?

Circle the correct term or number to complete each sentence.

TEKS 8.3(A), 8.8(D), 8.10(D)

1. A dilation with a scale factor of 3 is a(n) (enlargement, reduction).
2. If quadrilateral *ABCD* is similar to quadrilateral *RSTU*, angle *A* is (congruent, proportional) to angle *R*.
3. When two angles of one triangle are equal to two angles of another triangle, the two triangles must be (congruent, similar).
4. If parallelogram *X* is similar to parallelogram *Y* by a scale factor of 2, the area of *X* is (2, 4) times the area of *Y*.

Multi-Step Problem Solving

5. In the scale drawing at the right, the perimeter of a picnic area is 90 inches. The actual length of $\overline{AB}$ is 10 feet. What is the perimeter in feet and the area in square feet of the actual picnic area? Show your work and justify your solution. P MP

1 Analyze

2 Plan

3 Solve

4 Justify and Evaluate

Got it?

6. The diagram represents the rug in the Coughlin's family room. Mrs. Coughlin wants a rug that is half the size of the current rug. What will be the area of the new rug in square inches? Show your work and justify your solution. P MP

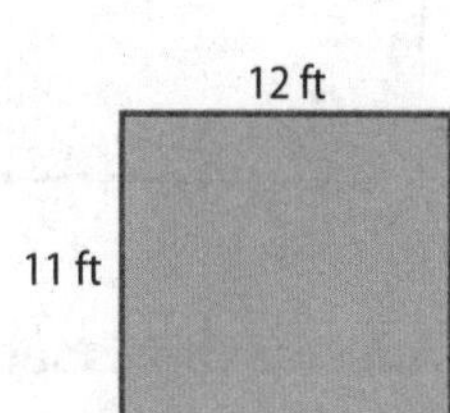

P = Proportionality MP = Mathematical Processes

Reflect

Answering the Essential Question

Use what you learned about similarity and dilations to complete the graphic organizer. Describe how you would show similarity using measurements and dilations. TEKS 8.1(D), 8.1(E), 8.1(G)

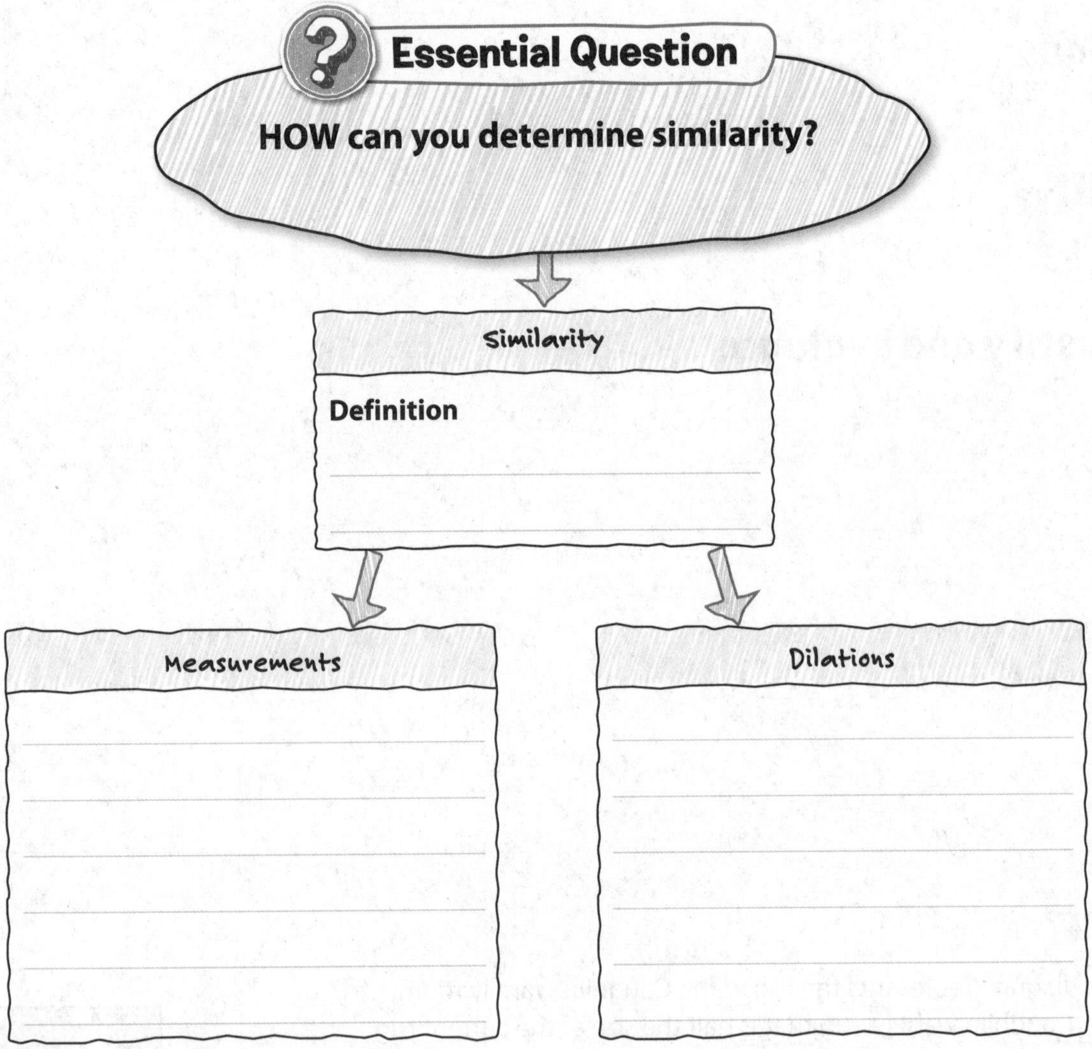

Essential Question

HOW can you determine similarity?

Similarity

Definition

Measurements

Dilations

Answer the Essential Question. HOW can you determine similarity? Verbally share your response with a partner, seeking and providing clarification as needed.

Chapter 3

Proportional Relationships and Slope

Texas Essential Knowledge and Skills

Targeted TEKS

8.4 The student applies mathematical process standards to explain proportional and non-proportional relationships involving slope.

Mathematical Processes

8.1, 8.1(A), 8.1(B), 8.1(C), 8.1(D), 8.1(E), 8.1(F), 8.1(G)

Essential Question

WHY are graphs helpful?

Math in the Real World

Battleships The Battleship Texas State Historic Site is located in La Porte, Texas. Monique drew a coordinate grid to model the location of the Battleship Texas. She placed the ship between I—5 and I—10. Circle the ship that represents the location of the Battleship Texas.

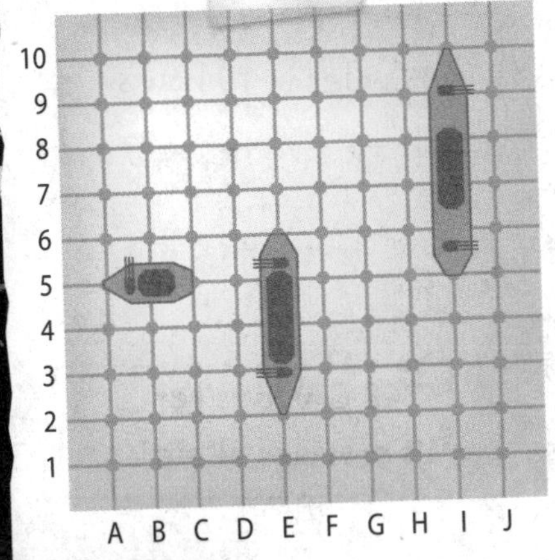

Go Online!
www.connectED.mcgraw-hill.com

Watch  Worksheets  Vocab  Tutor  Tools  Check 

What Tools Do You Need?

Vocabulary

constant of proportionality
constant of variation
constant rate of change
direct variation
linear relationship
point-slope form
rise
run
slope
slope-intercept form
standard form
x-intercept
y-intercept

Review Vocabulary

Rates A rate is a ratio that compares two quantities with different kinds of units. Some common rates are $\frac{\text{miles}}{\text{hour}}$, $\frac{\text{price}}{\text{ounce}}$, and $\frac{\text{meters}}{\text{second}}$.

Unit Rates A rate is a unit rate when it has a denominator of 1 unit. You can find the unit rate by writing a ratio, then dividing the numerator by the denominator.

Circle the correct answer for each unit rate.

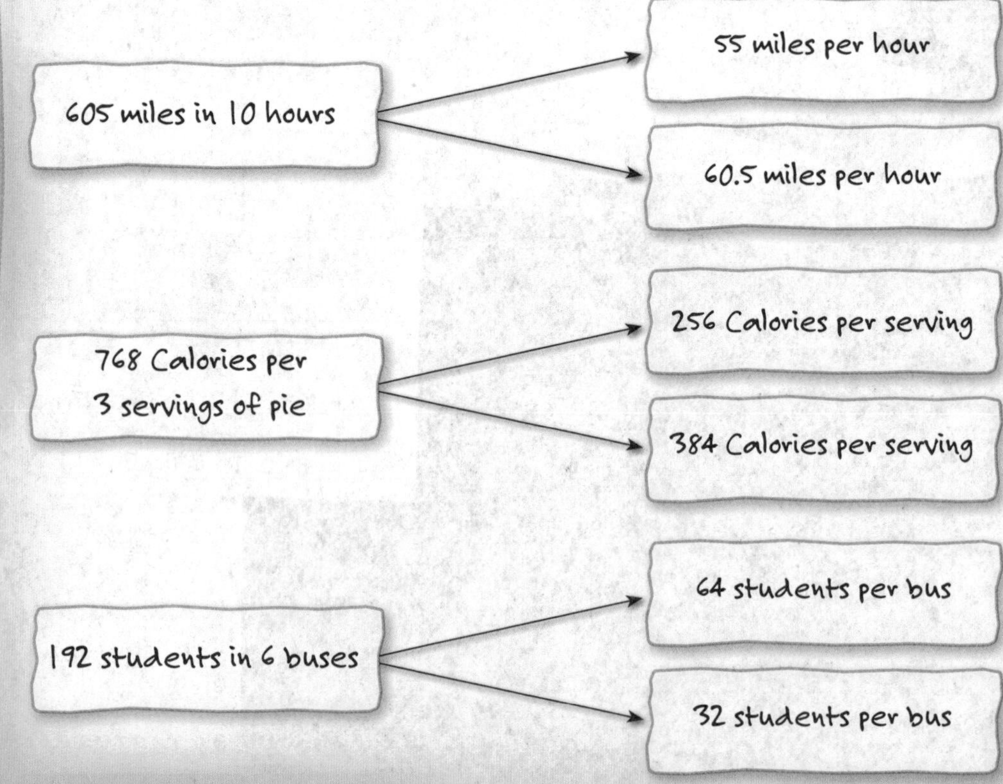

When Will You Use This?

Hana and Enrique in

A Fair Deal

Your Turn! **You will solve this problem in the chapter.**

Are You Ready?

Quick Review

Example 1

Find −15 − 8.

$-15 - 8 = -15 + (-8)$ To subtract 8, add −8.

$= -23$ Simplify.

Example 2

Evaluate $\frac{11+4}{9-4}$.

$\frac{11+4}{9-4} = \frac{15}{5}$ Simplify the numerator and denominator.

$= 3$ Simplify.

Quick Check

Subtract Integers **Find each difference.**

1. $5 - (-4) =$ ______

2. $10 - 8 =$ ______

Show your work.

3. $-4 - 3 =$ ______

4. $-6 - (-2) =$ ______

5. $12 - 6 =$ ______

6. $-5 - (-3) =$ ______

Numerical Expressions **Evaluate each expression.**

7. $\frac{6-2}{5+5} =$ ______

8. $\frac{7-4}{8-4} =$ ______

9. $\frac{3-1}{1+9} =$ ______

10. $\frac{5+7}{8-6} =$ ______

11. $\frac{2-4}{3+2} =$ ______

12. $\frac{1-5}{8-2} =$ ______

How Did You Do?

Which problems did you answer correctly in the Quick Check? Shade those exercise numbers below.

① ② ③ ④ ⑤ ⑥ ⑦ ⑧ ⑨ ⑩ ⑪ ⑫

FOLDABLES®

Use the Foldable throughout this chapter to help you learn about proportional and non-proportional relationships.

cut on all dashed lines   fold on all solid lines   tape to page 248

Linear Proportional Relationships

$y = mx$

$y = mx + b$

Linear Non-Proportional Relationships

Use the Foldable throughout this chapter to learn about proportional and non-proportional relationships.

 cut on all dashed lines 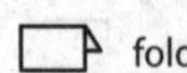 fold on all solid lines  tape to page 248

page 248

Description

Table

x						
y						

Tab 2

Description

Table

x						
y						

page 248

Tab 1

Lesson 1

Constant Rate of Change

Launch the Lesson: Real World

The time to download songs from the Internet is shown in the table. At this rate, how long would it take to download 9 songs?

Time (minutes), x	0	1	2	3	4
Number of Songs, y	0	2	4	6	8

1. What is the rate of change? Explain.

0.5

2. Graph the ordered pairs from the table on the graph shown. Label the axes. Use the graph to determine the time needed to download 9 songs.

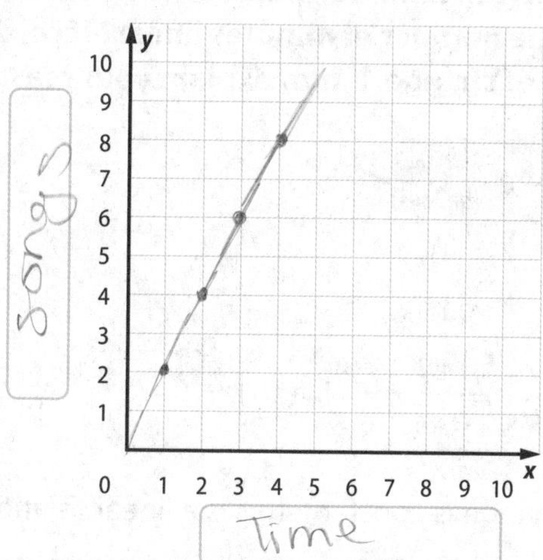

Texas Essential Knowledge and Skills

Targeted TEKS

8.4(C) Use data from a table or graph to determine the rate of change or slope and y-intercept in mathematical and real-world problems. *Also addresses 8.4(B), 8.5(F).*

Mathematical Processes

8.1(A), 8.1(B), 8.1(F)

Vocabulary

linear relationship

constant rate of change

Essential Question

WHY are graphs helpful?

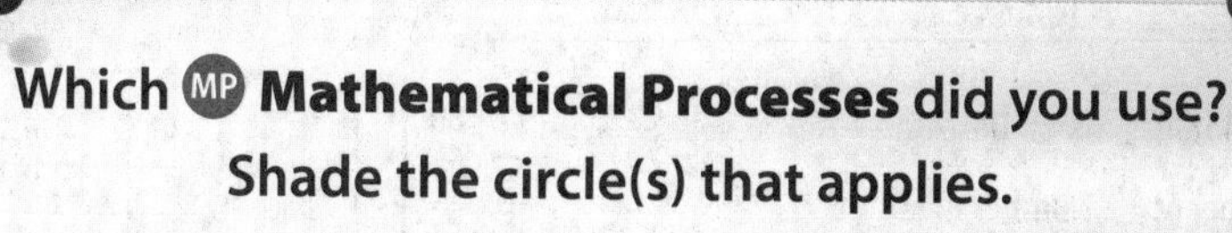

Which MP Mathematical Processes did you use? Shade the circle(s) that applies.

Ⓐ Apply Math to the Real World.

Ⓑ Use a Problem-Solving Model.

Ⓒ Select Tools and Techniques.

Ⓓ Use Multiple Representations.

Ⓔ Organize Ideas.

Ⓕ Analyze Relationships.

Ⓖ Justify Arguments.

Work Zone

Linear Relationships

Relationships that have straight-line graphs, like the one on the previous page, are called **linear relationships**. Notice that as the number of songs increases by 2, the time in minutes increases by 1. The unit rate is 2 songs per minute.

	Time (minutes), x	Number of Songs, y	
	0	0	
+1	1	2	+2
+1	2	4	+2
+1	3	6	+2

Rate of Change

$\frac{2}{1} = 2$ songs per minute

The rate of change between any two points in a linear relationship is the same or *constant*. A linear relationship has a **constant rate of change.**

Tutor

Example

Unit Rate

Since the number of gallons of water in the fish tank decreases by 16 gallons every 2 minutes, the unit rate is −8 gallons per minute.

1. The number of gallons of water remaining in a fish tank over time is shown. Is the relationship between the number of gallons and the number of minutes linear? If so, determine the constant rate of change. If not, explain your reasoning.

	Time (minutes)	Water (gallons)	
	2	134	
+2	4	118	−16
+2	6	102	−16
+2	8	86	−16

As the number of minutes increases by 2, the number of gallons in the fish tank decreases by 16 gallons.

Show your work.

Since the rate of change is constant, this is a linear relationship. The constant rate of change is $-\frac{16}{2}$ or −8 gallons per minute. This means that 8 gallons of water is draining from the fish tank each minute.

Got It? Do these problems to find out.

a.

Hot Air Balloon Descent	
Number of Seconds	Number of Meters Above Sea Level
10	165
20	143
30	123
40	99

b.

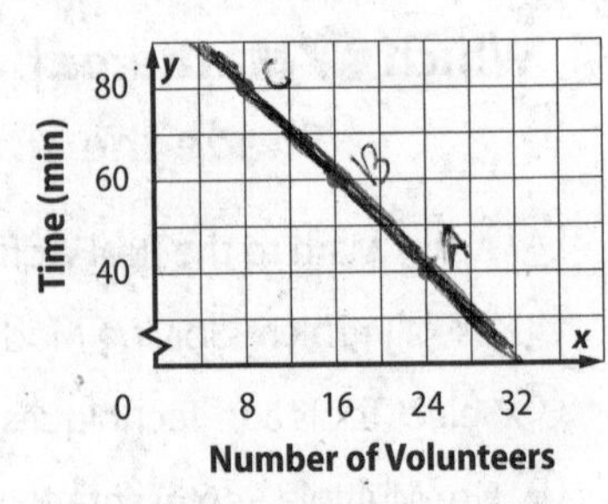

a. ______

b. ______

Proportional Linear Relationships

Words Two quantities *a* and *b* have a proportional linear relationship if they have a constant ratio and a constant rate of change.

Symbols $\frac{b}{a}$ is constant and $\frac{\text{change in } b}{\text{change in } a}$ is constant.

To determine if two quantities are proportional, compare the ratio $\frac{b}{a}$ for several pairs of points to determine if there is a constant ratio.

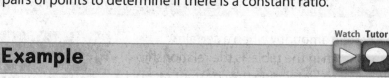

Example

Watch Tutor

2. Determine if there is a proportional linear relationship between the number of hours you rent a cotton candy machine and the total cost of renting the machine. Explain your reasoning.

Method 1 Make a table.

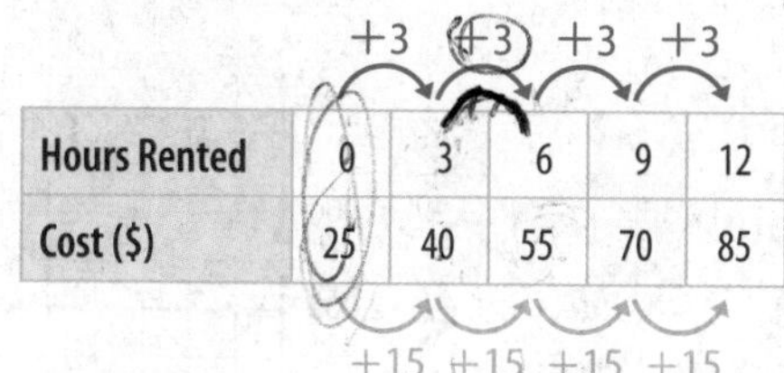

Hours Rented	0	3	6	9	12
Cost ($)	25	40	55	70	85

+3 +3 +3 +3

+15 +15 +15 +15

Constant Rate of Change

$$\frac{\text{change in cost}}{\text{change in hours}} = \frac{15}{3} \text{ or } 5$$

Proportional Relationships

Two quantities are proportional if they have a constant ratio.

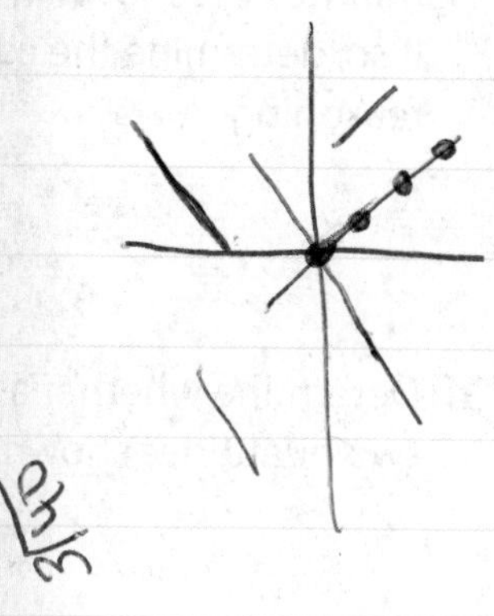

The rate of change is constant. This is a linear relationship.

To determine if the two quantities are proportional, express the relationship between the cost and the number of hours for several columns as a ratio.

$$\frac{\text{cost}}{\text{number of hours}} \longrightarrow \frac{40}{3} \approx 13.3 \qquad \frac{55}{6} \approx 9.2 \qquad \frac{70}{9} \approx 7.8$$

The ratios are not the same. The relationship is not proportional.

Method 2 Make a graph.

Graph the points on the coordinate plane. Then connect them with a line.

Since the points appear to fall in a straight line, this is a linear relationship.

Since the line connecting the points does not pass through the origin, the relationship between the number of hours you rent the cotton candy machine and the cost is *not* proportional.

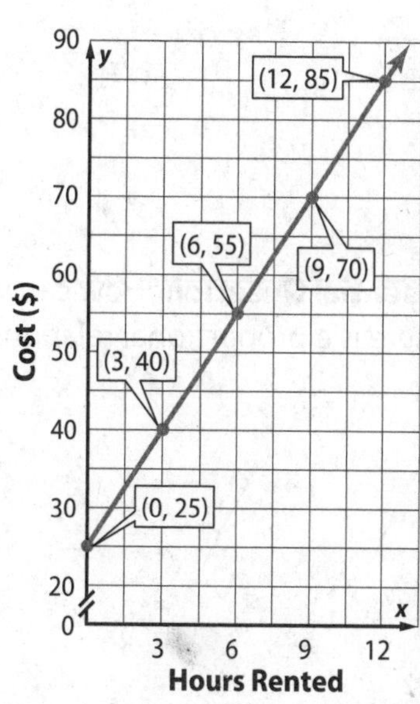

Got It? Do this problem to find out.

c. ______________

c. Use the table to determine if there is a proportional linear relationship between mass of an object in kilograms and the weight of the object in pounds. Explain your reasoning.

Weight (lb)	20	40	60	80
Mass (kg)	9	18	27	36

Guided Practice

1. The length a spring stretches a certain amount y when a certain amount of weight x is applied as shown in the table. Is the relationship between the two quantities linear? If so, determine the constant rate of change. If not, explain your reasoning. (Example 1)

Show your work.

ROC = 1/4

Physical Science	
Weight Applied (oz), x	Spring Stretch Length (in.), y
8	2
12	3
16	4

+4 +1

2. The altitude y of a certain airplane after a certain number of minutes x is shown in the graph. Is the relationship linear? If so, determine the constant rate of change. If not, explain your reasoning. (Example 1)

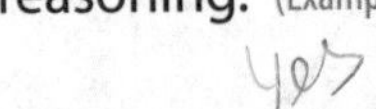
yes

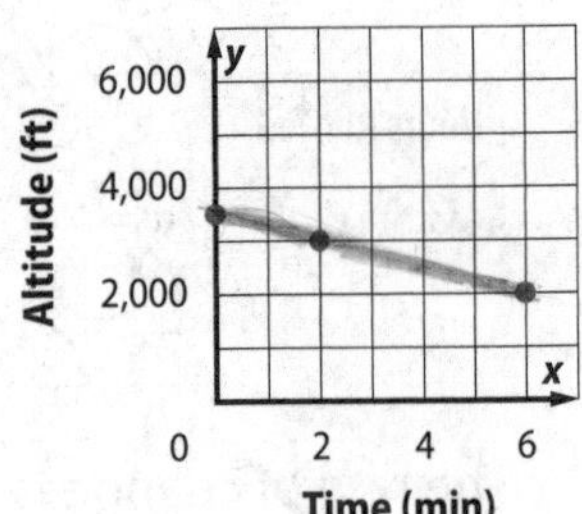

3. Determine whether a proportional relationship exists between the two quantities shown in Exercise 1. Explain your reasoning. (Example 2)

4. **Building on the Essential Question** How can you use a table to determine if there is a proportional relationship between two quantities? It goes through (0,0) and is linear

Rate Yourself!

Are you ready to move on? Shade the section that applies.

YES ? NO

Find out online. Use the Self-Check Quiz.

Name ______________________ My Homework ______________________

Independent Practice

8.4(C), 8.4(B), 8.1(F) TEKS

Determine whether the relationship between the two quantities shown in each table or graph is linear. If so, determine the constant rate of change. If not, explain your reasoning. (Example 1)

1.

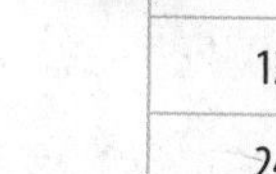

Cost of Electricity to Run Personal Computer	
Time (h)	Cost (¢)
5	15
8	24
12	36
24	72

yes

2.

Filling a Swimming Pool				
Time (min)	2	4	6	8
Water (gal)	6	12	24	32

yes

3.

+2 +2 +2

Italian Dressing Recipe				
Oil (c)	2	4	6	8
Vinegar (c)	$\frac{3}{4}$	$1\frac{1}{2}$	$2\frac{1}{4}$	3

+3/4 +3/4 +3/4

Proportional Linear Relationship

4.

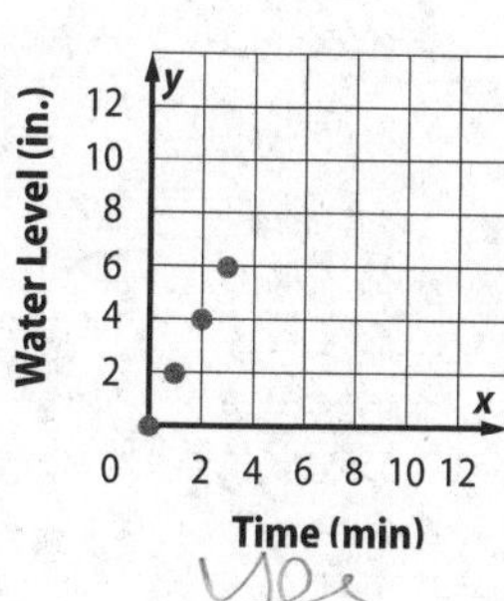

yes

5.

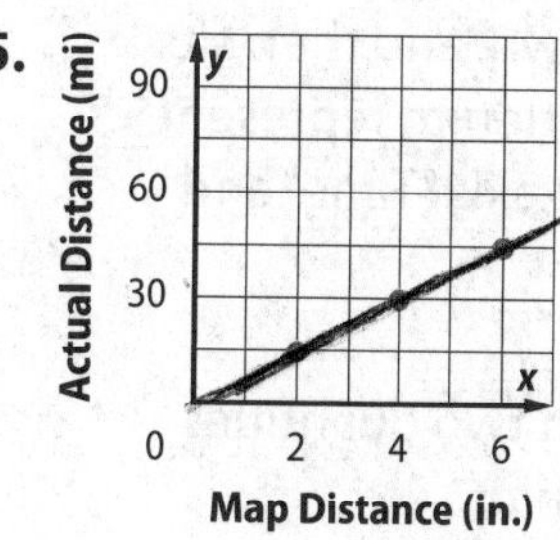

yes

6.

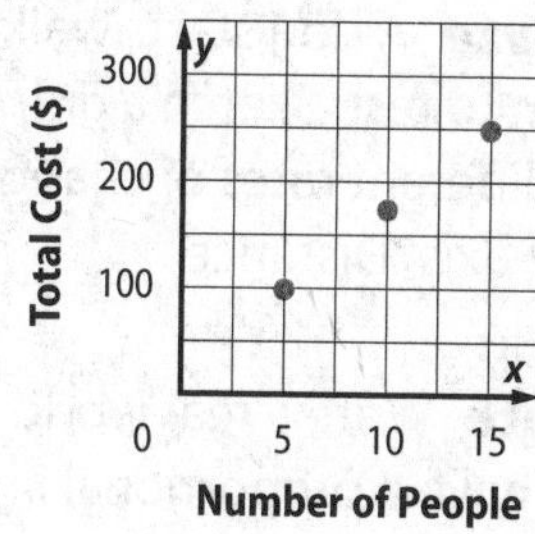

yes

Determine whether a proportional relationship exists between the two quantities shown in Exercises 7–9. Explain your reasoning. (Example 2)

7. Exercise 1

8. Exercise 3

9. Exercise 5

10. MP **Analyze Relationships** Match the table with its rate of change, or unit rate.

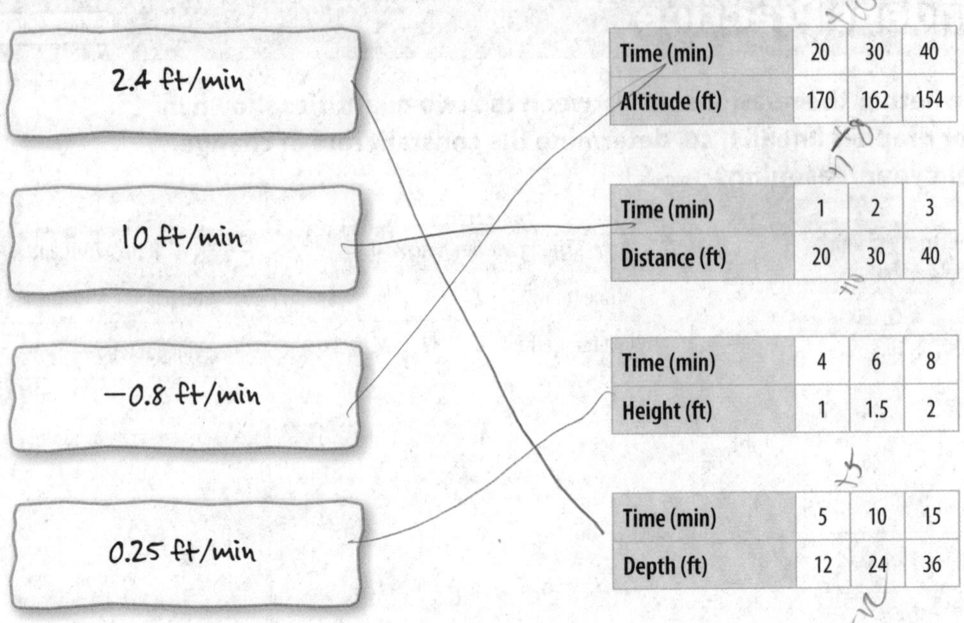

Time (min)	20	30	40
Altitude (ft)	170	162	154

Time (min)	1	2	3
Distance (ft)	20	30	40

Time (min)	4	6	8
Height (ft)	1	1.5	2

Time (min)	5	10	15
Depth (ft)	12	24	36

H.O.T. Problems Higher-Order Thinking

11. Analyze A dog starts walking, slows down, and then sits down to rest. Sketch a graph of the situation to represent the different rates of change. Label the *x*-axis "Time" and the *y*-axis "Distance".

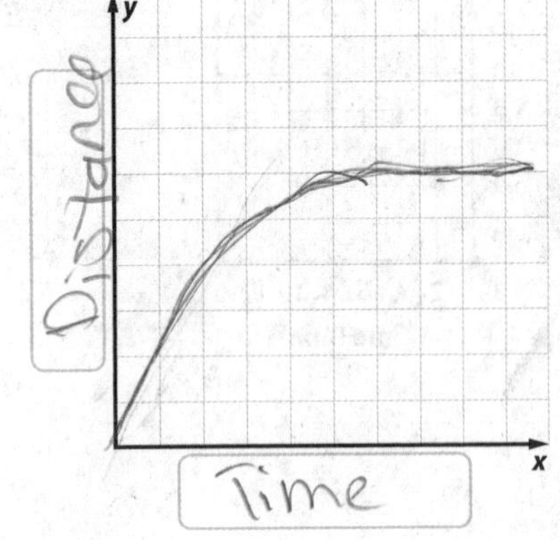

12. Create Write a real-world situation with two quantities that have a proportional linear relationship.

13. Analyze Refer to Exercise 2. Is the relationship proportional? Justify your reasoning.

14. Evaluate Each table shows a relationship with a constant rate of change. Is each relationship proportional? Justify your reasoning.

a.

Cost of Play Tickets ($)				
t	1	2	3	4
c	3.50	4.00	4.50	5.00

b.

Cost of Play Tickets ($)				
t	1	2	3	4
c	2.50	5.00	7.50	10.00

Name ____________________

Multi-Step Problem Solving

15. The graph shows the relationship between the length of the side of a square and the perimeter of the square. Which statement describes the relationship? P MP

Ⓐ It is a proportional linear relationship with a unit rate of 8.
Ⓑ It is a proportional linear relationship with a unit rate of 4.
Ⓒ It is a non-proportional linear relationship.
Ⓓ It is a non-linear relationship.

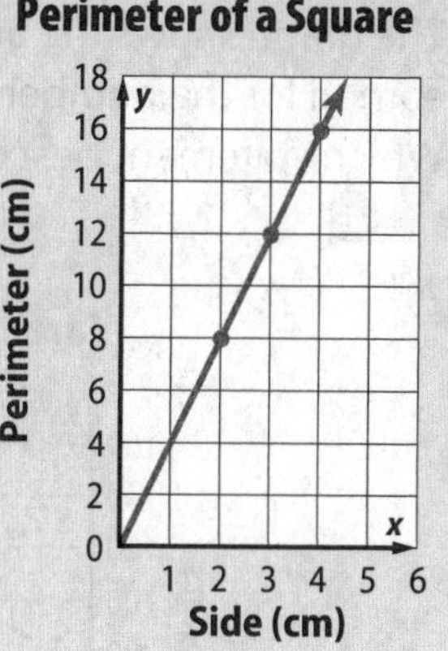

Use a problem-solving model to solve this problem.

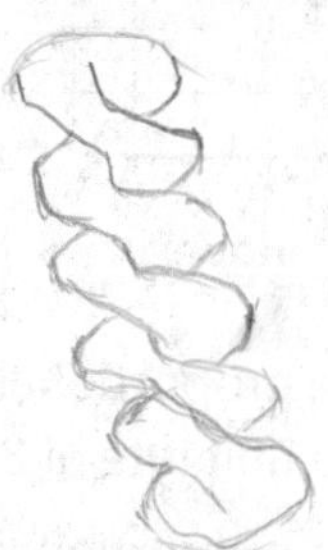

1 Analyze

Read the problem. Circle the information you know. Underline what the problem is asking you to find.

2 Plan

What will you need to do to solve the problem? Write your plan in steps.

Step 1 Connect the points to see if they form a line passing through the origin.

Step 2 If the relationship is linear, determine if the ________ of the pairs of points equal ____ or ____.

3 Solve

Use your plan to solve the problem. Show your steps.

The points form a ________ that passes through the ________.

Since there is a vertical distance of ____ units and a horizontal distance of ____ unit between points, the unit rate is ________ or ____.

So, the relationship is a ____________________ with a unit rate of ____. The correct answer is ____.

Read to Succeed!
When finding a unit rate from a graph, count the units up or down and then the right or left.

4 Justify and Evaluate

How do you know your solution is accurate?

____

____

P = Proportionality MP = Mathematical Processes

More Multi-Step Problem Solving

Use a problem-solving model to solve each problem.

16. The graph shows the amount of pay Jared earned for the number of hours he worked. Which statement best describes the graph?

P MP

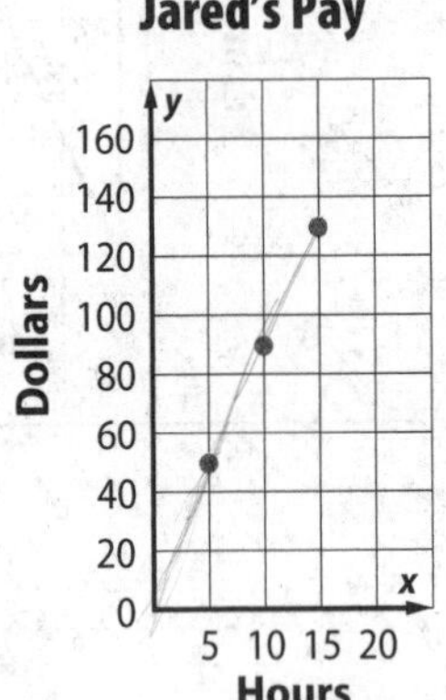

Ⓐ The graph shows a proportional linear relationship with a unit rate of 8.

Ⓑ The graph shows a proportional linear relationship with a unit rate of 10.

Ⓒ The graph shows a non-proportional linear relationship.

Ⓓ The graph shows a non-linear relationship.

17. The table below shows the print speed for color paper of an office computer. How many pages can the printer print in one hour?

P N MP

Minutes	Pages per Minute
2	32
3	48
4	64

18. The table below shows the amount of dog food needed each day based on a dog's weight. How many pounds of dog food are needed to feed a 28-pound dog for 1 week? Round your answer to the nearest pound.

P N MP

Weight (lb)	Daily Amount of Food (oz)
5	1.6
15	4.8
20	6.4

19. The table below shows a linear relationship. What is the value of k? Support your answer.

x	y
3	9
7	k
9	21

N = Number and Operations 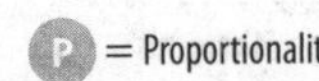 P = Proportionality EE = Expressions, Equations, and Relationships MP = Mathematical Processes

Graphing Technology Lab 1-b

Graphing Technology: Rate of Change

INQUIRY **HOW can I select tools and techniques to determine the rate of change?**

Texas Essential Knowledge and Skills TEKS

Targeted TEKS
8.4(B) Graph proportional relationships, interpreting the unit rate as the slope of the line that models the relationship. *Also addresses 8.4(C).*

Mathematical Processes
8.1 (C)

At the school store, tickets to the football game are sold for \$5 each. The equation $y = 5x$ can be used to find the total cost y of any number of tickets x. Find the rate of change.

What do you know?

____

What do you need to find?

____

Hands-On Activity

Recall that a rate of change is a rate that describes how one quantity changes in relation to another.

Step 1 Enter the equation. Press [Y=] 5 [X,T,θ,n].

Step 2 Graph the equation in the standard viewing window. Press [Zoom] 6.

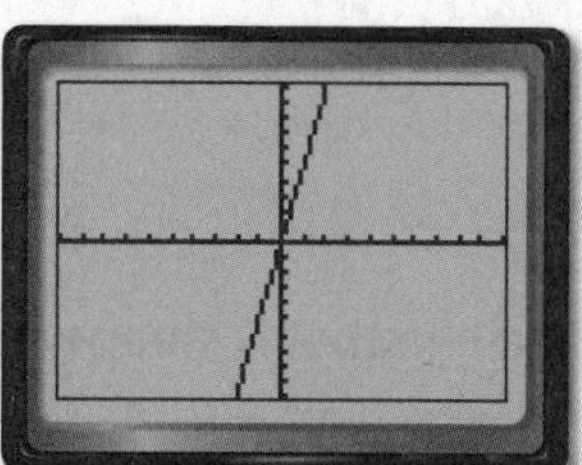

Step 3 Press [2nd] [TblSet] [▼] [▼] [ENTER] [▼] [ENTER] to generate the table automatically. Press [2nd] [TABLE] to access the table. Choose any two points on the line and find the rate of change.

$$\frac{\text{change in total cost}}{\text{change in number of tickets}} = \frac{\$(\square - \square)}{(\square - \square)\text{ tickets}}$$

$$= \frac{\square}{\square \text{ ticket}}$$

So, the rate of change, or unit rate, is _______________.

Investigate

Work with a partner. School T-shirts are sold for $10 each and packages of markers are sold for $2.50 each.

1. For each item, write an equation that can be used to find the total cost y of x items. ____________

2. Graph the equations in the same window as the equation from the Activity. Copy your calculator screen on the blank screen shown at the right.

Analyze and Reflect

3. Refer to Exercises 1 and 2. Determine each rate of change. Is there a relationship between the steepness of the lines on the graph and the rates of change? Explain.

Create

4. **Create** Without graphing, write an equation for a line that is steeper than $y = \frac{1}{3}x$. Support your answer.

5. **INQUIRY** HOW can I select tools and techniques to determine the rate of change?

Lesson 2
Slope

Launch the Lesson: Vocabulary

The term slope is used to describe the steepness of a straight line. **Slope** is the ratio of the **rise**, or vertical change, to the **run** or horizontal change.

Complete the graphic organizer.

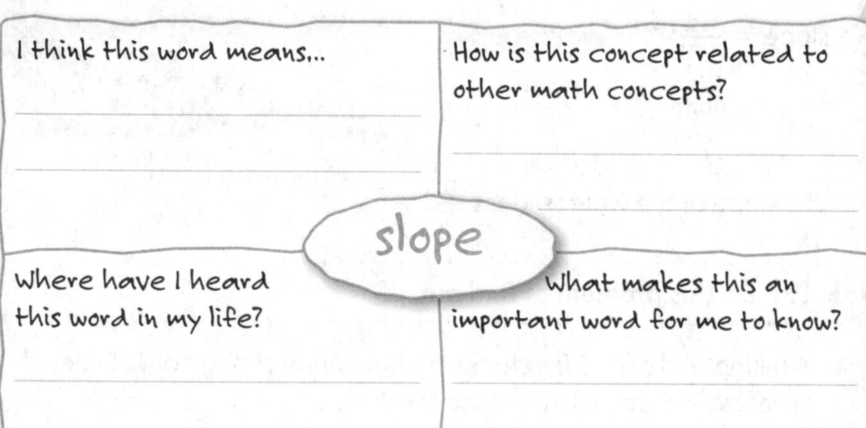

I think this word means...
How is this concept related to other math concepts?
slope
Where have I heard this word in my life?
What makes this an important word for me to know?

Texas Essential Knowledge and Skills

Targeted TEKS
8.4(C) Use data from a table or graph to determine the rate of change or slope and y-intercept in mathematical and real-world problems. *Also addresses 8.4(A), 8.4(B).*

Mathematical Processes
8.1(A), 8.1(B)

Vocab

Vocabulary
slope
rise
run

Essential Question
WHY are graphs helpful?

Real-World Link

A ride at an amusement park rises 8 feet every horizontal change of 2 feet. How could you determine the slope of the ride?

Which MP Mathematical Processes did you use? Shade the circle(s) that applies.

Ⓐ Apply Math to the Real World.
Ⓑ Use a Problem-Solving Model.
Ⓒ Select Tools and Techniques.
Ⓓ Use Multiple Representations.
Ⓔ Organize Ideas.
Ⓕ Analyze Relationships.
Ⓖ Justify Arguments.

Work Zone

Find Slope Using a Graph or Table

Slope is a rate of change. It can be positive (slanting upward) or negative (slanting downward).

$$\text{slope} = \frac{\text{rise}}{\text{run}}$$

rise ← vertical change between any two points

run ← horizontal change between the same two points

Tutor

Example

1. Determine the slope of the water slide.

$\text{slope} = \frac{\text{rise}}{\text{run}}$ Definition of slope.

$= \frac{18 \text{ ft}}{40 \text{ ft}}$ rise = 18 ft, run = 40 ft

$= \frac{9}{20}$ Simplify.

The slope of the water slide is $\frac{9}{20}$.

18 ft

40 ft

Got It? Do this problem to find out.

a. __________

a. A hiking trail rises 6 feet for every horizontal change of 100 feet. What is the slope of the hiking trail?

Tutor

Examples

Translating Rise and Run

up → positive
down → negative
right → positive
left → negative

2. The graph shows the cost of muffins at a bake sale. Determine the constant rate of change. Then determine the slope and compare it to the constant rate of change.

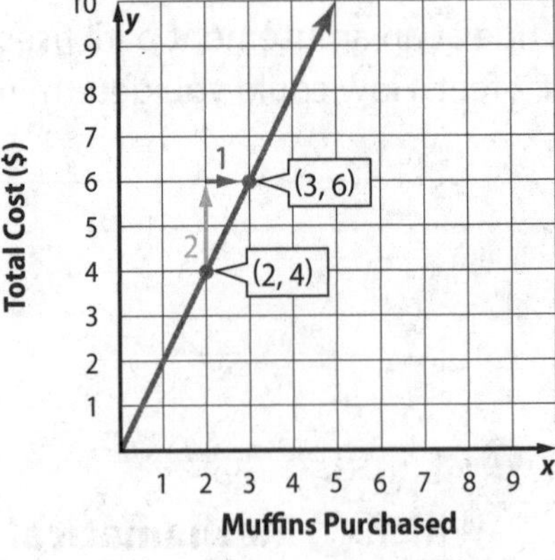

Choose two points on the line. The vertical change is 2 units and the horizontal change is 1 unit. So, the constant rate of change is $\frac{2}{1}$ or 2. Find the slope.

$\text{slope} = \frac{\text{rise}}{\text{run}}$ Definition of slope

$= \frac{2}{1}$ rise = 2, run = 1

The slope of the line is $\frac{2}{1}$ or 2. This means the unit cost is $2 per muffin. The slope is equivalent to the constant rate of change.

3. The table shows the number of pages Garrett has left to read after a certain number of minutes. The points lie on a line. Determine the slope of the line.

Time (min), x	Pages left, y
1	12
3	9
5	6
7	3

Choose any two points from the table to find the changes in the x- and y-values.

$$\text{slope} = \frac{\text{change in } y}{\text{change in } x} \quad \text{Definition of slope}$$

$$= \frac{9 - 12}{3 - 1} \quad \text{Use the points (1, 12) and (3, 9).}$$

$$= \frac{-3}{2} \text{ or } -\frac{3}{2} \quad \text{Simplify.}$$

So, the slope is $\frac{-3}{2}$. This means the unit rate is $\frac{-3}{2}$ pages per minute, or 3 less pages remain every 2 minutes.

To check, choose two different points from the table and find the slope.

Check $\text{slope} = \frac{\text{change in } y}{\text{change in } x}$

$$= \frac{3 - 6}{7 - 5}$$

$$= \frac{-3}{2} \text{ or } -\frac{3}{2} \checkmark$$

Slope

In linear relationships, no matter which two points you choose, the slope, or rate of change, of the line is always constant.

Got It? **Do these problems to find out.**

Determine the slope of each line.

b.

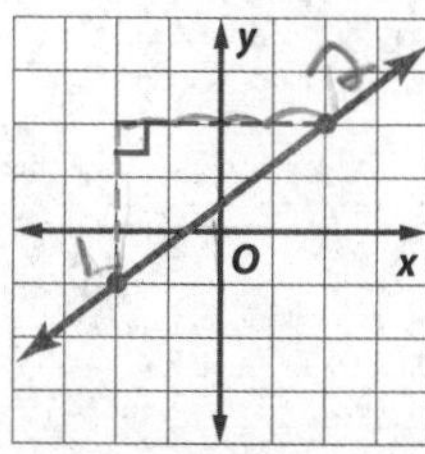

c.

Time (min) x	0	4	8	12
Depth (ft) y	−2	−1	0	1

b. 3/4

c. 4

Slope Formula

Key Concept

Words The slope m of a line passing through points (x_1, y_1) and (x_2, y_2) is the ratio of the difference in the y-coordinates to the corresponding difference in the x-coordinates.

Symbols $m = \frac{y_2 - y_1}{x_2 - x_1}$, where $x_2 \neq x_1$

Model

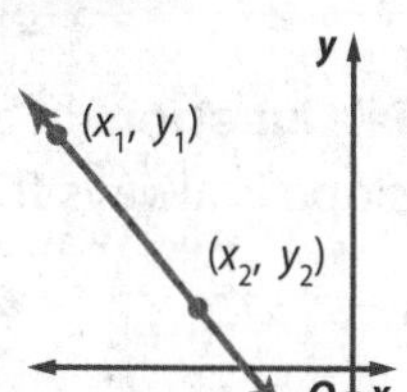

It does not matter which point you define as (x_1, y_1) and (x_2, y_2). However the coordinates of both points must be used in the same order.

Using the Slope Formula

To check Example 4, let $(x_1, y_1) = (-4, 3)$ and $(x_2, y_2) = (1, 2)$. Then find the slope.

d. ____________

e. ____________

Watch Tutor

Example

4. Determine the slope of the line that passes through $R(1, 2)$, $S(-4, 3)$.

$m = \dfrac{y_2 - y_1}{x_2 - x_1}$ Slope formula

$m = \dfrac{3 - 2}{-4 - 1}$ $(x_1, y_1) = (1, 2)$ $(x_2, y_2) = (-4, 3)$

$m = \dfrac{1}{-5}$ or $-\dfrac{1}{5}$ Simplify.

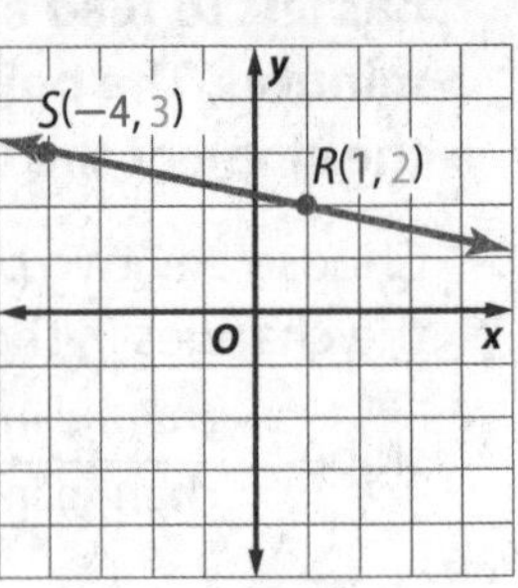

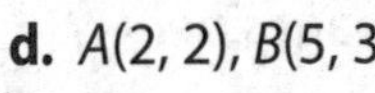

Got It? Do these problems to find out.

d. $A(2, 2)$, $B(5, 3)$

e. $J(-7, -4)$, $K(-3, -2)$

Guided Practice

1. Determine the slope of the toy race track. (Example 1)

____

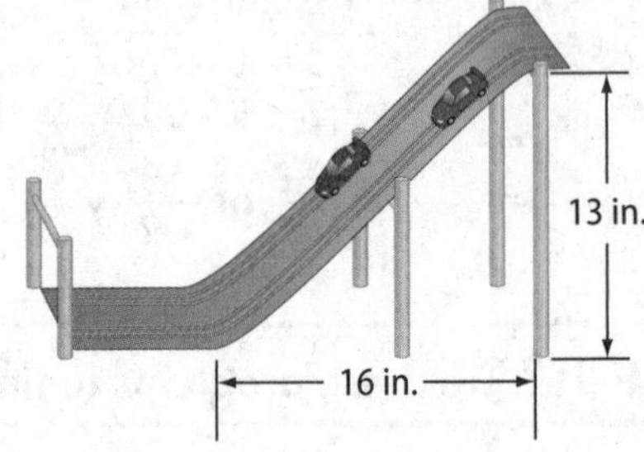

Determine the slope of each line. (Examples 2 and 3)

2. ____________

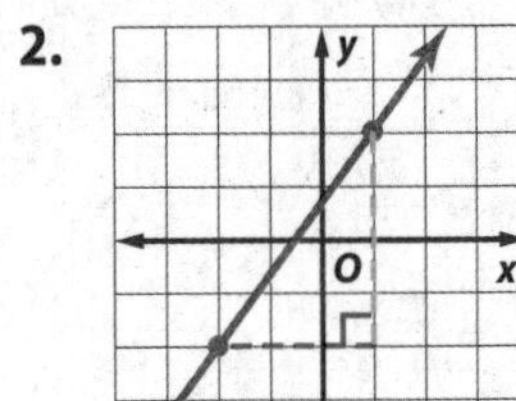

3. ____________

x	0	1	2	3
y	1	3	5	7

Determine the slope of the line that passes through each pair of points. (Example 4)

4. $A(-3, -2)$, $B(5, 4)$ ____________

5. $E(-6, 5)$, $F(3, -3)$ ____________

x_1 y_1 x_2 y_2

$\dfrac{y_2 - y_1}{x_2 - x_1} = m$

$\dfrac{-3-5}{3-(-6)} = \dfrac{-8}{9} = -\dfrac{8}{9}$

$3+6$

6. **Building on the Essential Question** In any linear relationship, explain why the slope is always the same.

____

____

____

Rate Yourself!

How well do you understand slope? Circle the image that applies.

Clear Somewhat Clear Not So Clear

Find out online. Use the Self-Check Quiz.

Name ______________________ My Homework ______________________

Independent Practice

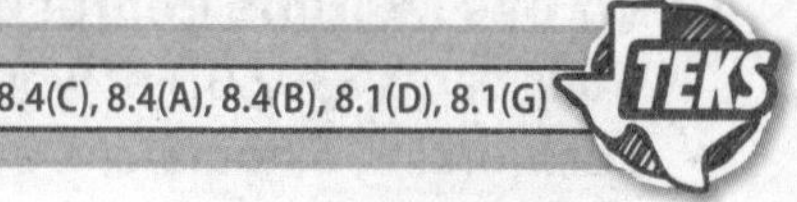

1. Determine the slope of a dirt bike hill that descends 12 feet for every horizontal change of 18 feet.

2/3

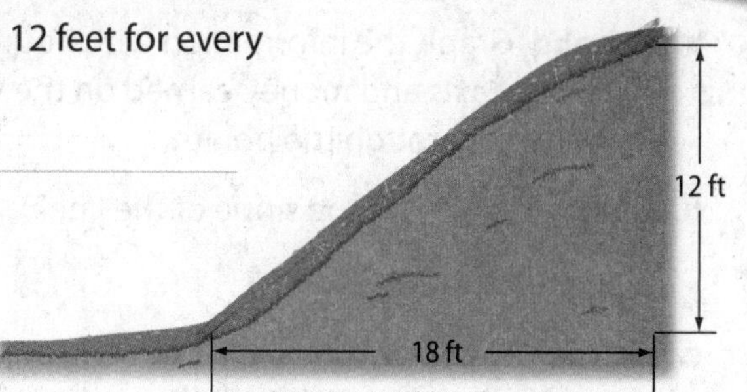

Determine the slope of each line. (Example 2)

2.

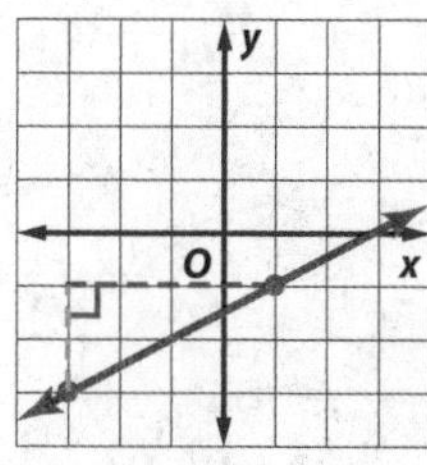

1/2

3.

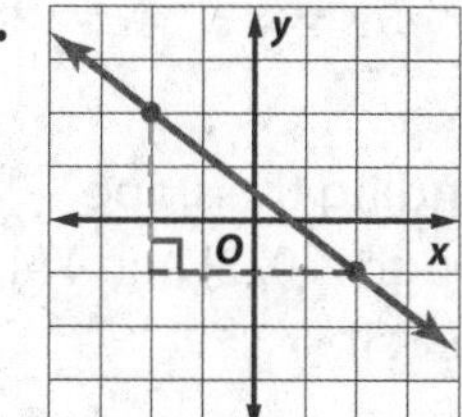

3/4

The points given in the table lie on a line. Determine the slope of each line. (Example 3)

4. -2/5

x	0	2	4	6
y	9	4	−1	−6

5.

x	0	1	2	3
y	3	5	7	9

Determine the slope of the line that passes through each pair of points. (Example 4)

6. $A(0, 1)$, $B(2, 7)$ 

7. $C(2, 5)$, $D(3, 1)$ 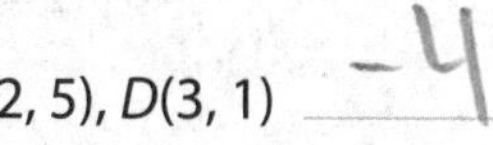

8. $E(1, 2)$, $F(4, 7)$ 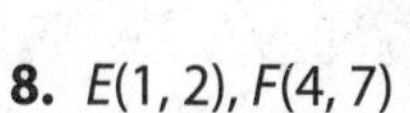 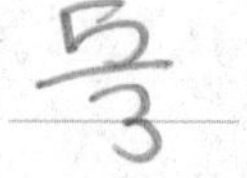

9. MP **Justify Arguments** Wheelchair ramps for access to public buildings are allowed a maximum of one inch of vertical increase for every one foot of horizontal distance. Would a ramp that is 10 feet long and 8 inches tall meet this guideline? Explain your reasoning to a classmate.

10. MP **Use Multiple Representations** For working 3 hours, Sofia earns $30.60. For working 5 hours, she earns $51. For working 6 hours, she earns $61.20.

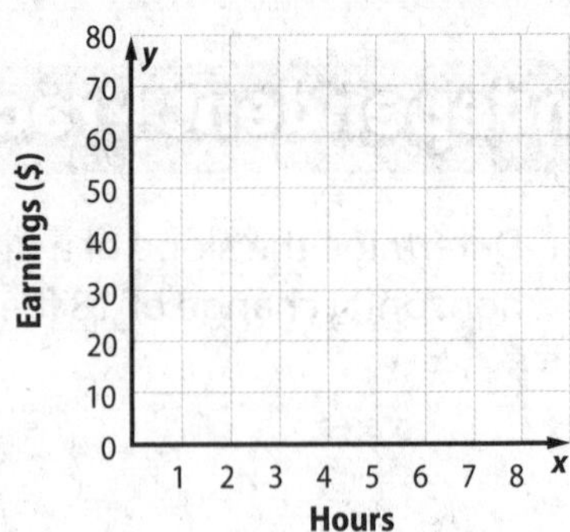

a. **Graphs** Graph the information with hours on the horizontal axis and money earned on the vertical axis. Draw a line through the points.

b. **Numbers** What is the slope of the line?

c. **Words** What does the slope of the line represent? How does the slope relate to the unit rate?

11. Find the Error Jacob is finding the slope of the line that passes through $X(0, 2)$ and $Y(4, 3)$. Circle his mistake and correct it.

H.O.T. Problems Higher-Order Thinking

12. Evaluate Two lines that are parallel have the same slope. Determine whether quadrilateral $ABCD$ is a parallelogram. Support your answer.

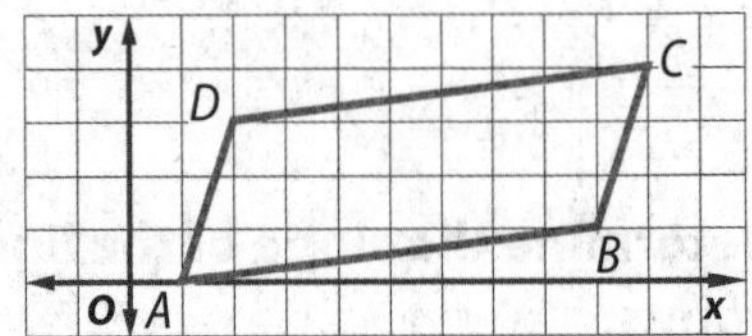

13. Create Give three points that lie on the lines with the following slopes.

a. 5

b. $\frac{1}{5}$

c. −5

Name ______________________________

Multi-Step Problem Solving

14. The table shows the coordinates of two points on a line. If the slope of the line is $-\frac{3}{4}$, what is the value of k? P EE MP

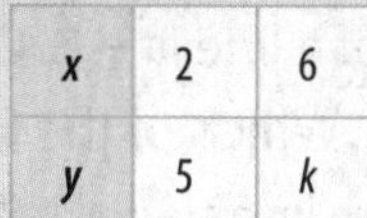

x	2	6
y	5	k

Ⓐ -8

Ⓑ -2

Ⓒ 2

Ⓓ 8

Use a problem-solving model to solve this problem.

1 Analyze

Read the problem. Circle the information you know.
Underline what the problem is asking you to find.

2 Plan

What will you need to do to solve the problem? Write your plan in steps.

Step 1 Replace known values for the variables in the slope formula.

Step 2 Solve the equation for k.

3 Solve

Use your plan to solve the problem. Show your steps.

Replace m with $-\frac{3}{4}$, y_2 with ______, y_1 with ______, x_2 with ______, and x_1 with ______.
Solve for k.

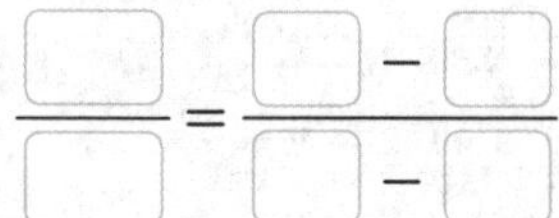

Since $k =$ ______, the correct answer is ______.

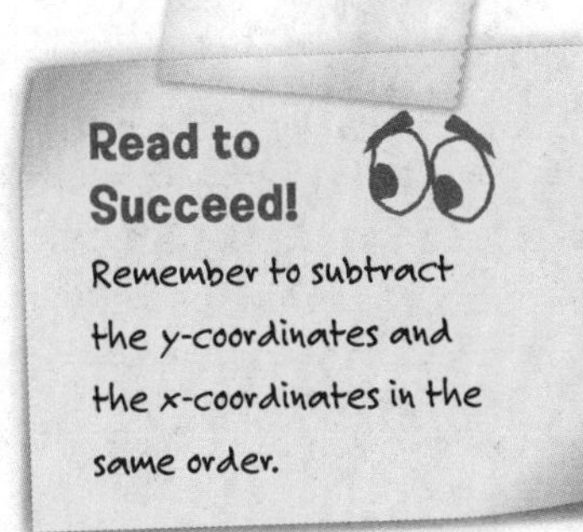

Read to Succeed!
Remember to subtract the y-coordinates and the x-coordinates in the same order.

4 Justify and Evaluate

How do you know your solution is accurate?

____

____

____

P = Proportionality EE = Expressions, Equations, and Relationships MP = Mathematical Processes

More Multi-Step Problem Solving

Use a problem-solving model to solve each problem.

15. The slope of a line is $-\frac{2}{3}$. One point on the line is (4, 3). Which of the following is another point on the line? P N MP

Ⓐ (10, 7)

Ⓑ (10, −1)

Ⓒ (0, 9)

Ⓓ (8, 9)

16. The table below shows the times, called split times, for each mile in a 5-mile race. What is the average rate of change for the entire race in miles per minute? P N MP

5-Mile Race Splits

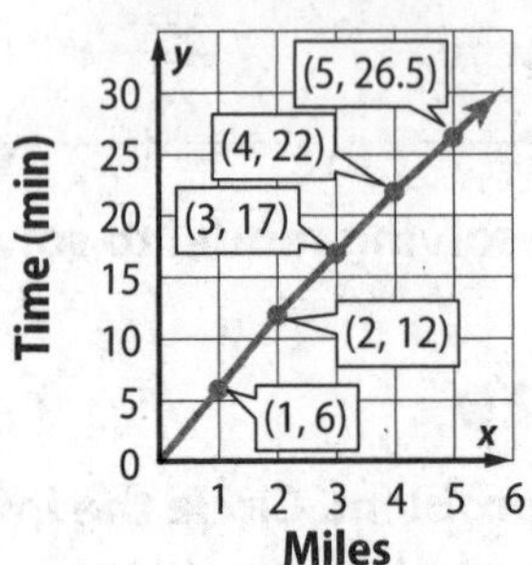

17. The points in the table below lie on a line. What is the value of y when x is 10?

P N EE MP

x	−1	1	3
y	−87	3	93

18. The vertices of parallelogram $ABCD$ are $A(11, 5)$, $B(8, 1)$, $C(2, 3)$, and $D(x, 7)$. What is the value of x? Justify your answer. P N EE MP

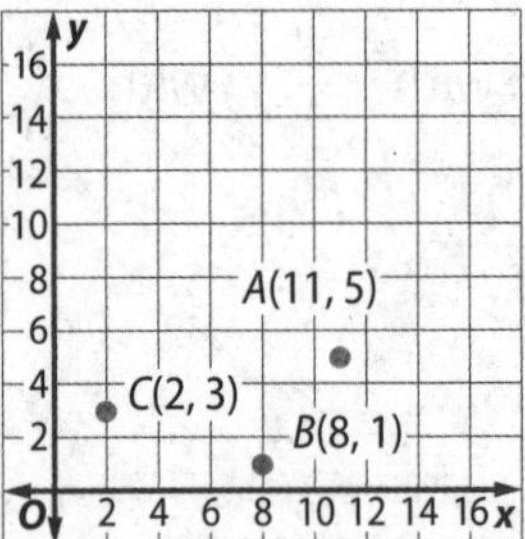

N = Number and Operations 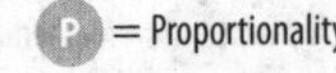 P = Proportionality EE = Expressions, Equations, and Relationships MP = Mathematical Processes

Lesson 3

Slope and Similar Triangles

Launch the Lesson: Real World

In an experiment using a coiled spring toy, Zoe and Jack determined they needed to raise one side of a 5-foot board 3 feet for the toy to move. Find the slope of the board.

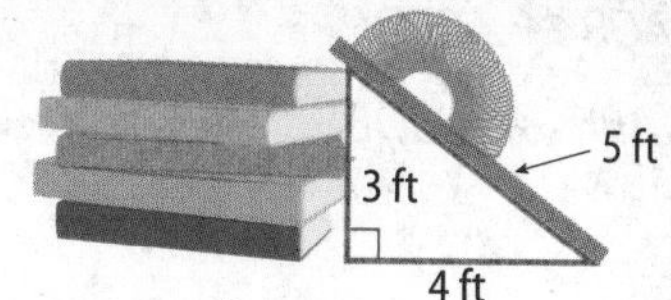

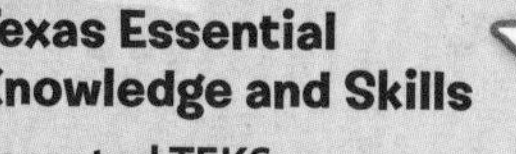

Texas Essential Knowledge and Skills

Targeted TEKS

8.4(A) Use similar right triangles to develop an understanding that slope, m, given as the rate comparing the change in y-values to the change in x-values, $\frac{(y_2 - y_1)}{(x_2 - x_1)}$, is the same for any two points (x_1, y_1) and (x_2, y_2) on the same line. *Also addresses 8.4(C).*

Mathematical Processes

8.1(A), 8.1(B), 8.1(C), 8.1(D), 8.1(F)

Essential Question

WHY are graphs helpful?

Collaborate

Investigate Work with a partner. Use the graph to discover how slope triangles are related.

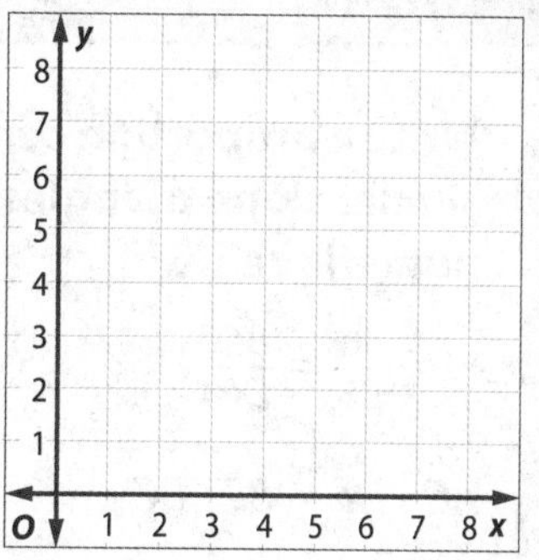

1. Draw the triangle formed by $A(0, 2)$, $B(0, 4)$, and $C(3, 4)$. What kind of triangle did you draw? ____________

2. Draw the triangle formed by $D(6, 6)$, $F(6, 8)$, and $G(9, 8)$. How is $\triangle DFG$ related to $\triangle ABC$? ____________

3. Draw the triangle formed by $A(0,2)$, $K(0, 6)$, and $D(6, 6)$. How is $\triangle AKD$ related to $\triangle ABC$? ____________

4. What is true about $\overline{AC}$, $\overline{DG}$, and $\overline{AD}$? ____________

Which MP Mathematical Processes did you use? Shade the circle(s) that applies.

Ⓐ Apply Math to the Real World.
Ⓑ Use a Problem-Solving Model.
Ⓒ Select Tools and Techniques.
Ⓓ Use Multiple Representations.
Ⓔ Organize Ideas.
Ⓕ Analyze Relationships.
Ⓖ Justify Arguments.

Work Zone

Similar Triangles and the Coordinate Plane

In the figure shown, $\triangle ABC$ and $\triangle BDE$ are slope triangles. Slope triangles are similar.

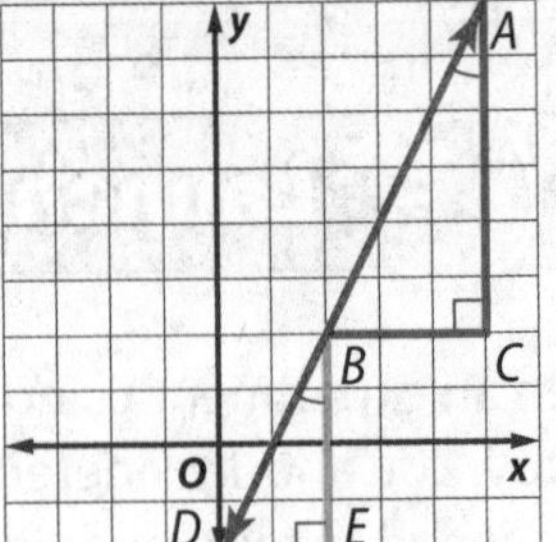

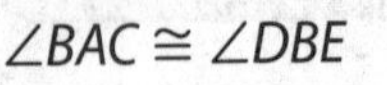

$\angle BAC \cong \angle DBE$	Given
$\angle ACB \cong \angle BED$	Given
$\triangle ABC \sim \triangle BDE$	Angle-Angle Similarity

You can use the properties of similar triangles to show the ratios of the rise to the run for each right triangle are equal.

Example

Tutor

1. Write a proportion comparing the rise to the run for each of the similar slope triangles shown above. Then determine the numeric value.

$\frac{AC}{BE} = \frac{BC}{DE}$	Corresponding sides of similar triangles are proportional.
$AC \cdot DE = BE \cdot BC$	Find the cross products.
$\frac{AC \cdot DE}{BC \cdot DE} = \frac{BE \cdot BC}{BC \cdot DE}$	Division Property of Equality
$\frac{AC}{BC} = \frac{BE}{DE}$	Simplify.
$\frac{6}{3} = \frac{4}{2}$	$AC = 6, BC = 3, BE = 4, DE = 2$

So, $\frac{AC}{BC} = \frac{BE}{DE}$, or $\frac{6}{3} = \frac{4}{2}$. Notice that this is the same value as the slope, $\frac{4}{2}$ or 2.

Got It? Do this problem to find out.

a. Graph $\triangle MNO$ with vertices $M(3, 1)$, $N(1, 0)$, and $O(3, 0)$, and $\triangle PQR$ with vertices $P(5, 2)$, $Q(-1, -1)$, and $R(5, -1)$. Then write a proportion comparing the rise to the run for each of the similar slope triangles and determine the numeric value.

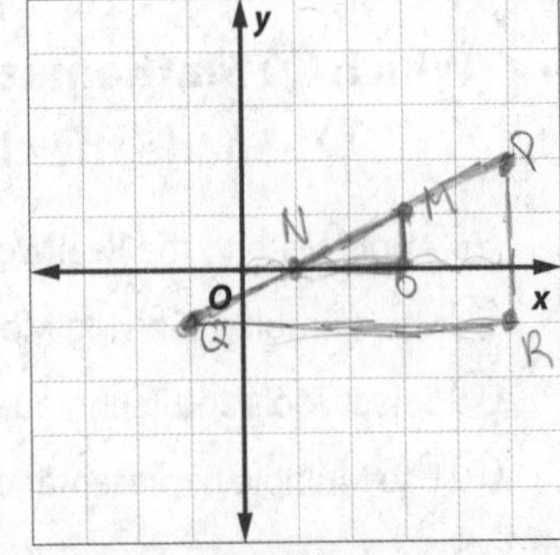

Show your work.

a. $\frac{1}{2}$

Similar Triangles and Slope

Key Concept

Words The ratio of the rise to the run of two slope triangles formed by a line is equal to the slope of the line.

Example

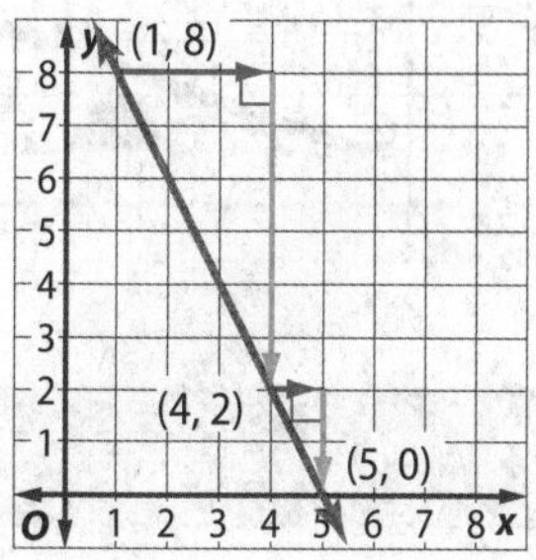

Larger Triangle

$\frac{\text{rise}}{\text{run}} = \frac{6}{-3}$, or -2

Smaller Triangle

$\frac{\text{rise}}{\text{run}} = \frac{2}{-1}$, or -2

slope $= \frac{-2}{1}$, or -2

The ratios of the rise to the run of the two similar slope triangles in Example 1 are the same as the slope of the line. Since the ratios are equal, the slope m of a line is the same between any two distinct points on a non-vertical line in the coordinate plane.

Example

2. The pitch of a roof refers to the slope of the roof line. Choose two points on the roof and determine the pitch of the roof shown. Then verify that the pitch is the same by choosing a different set of points.

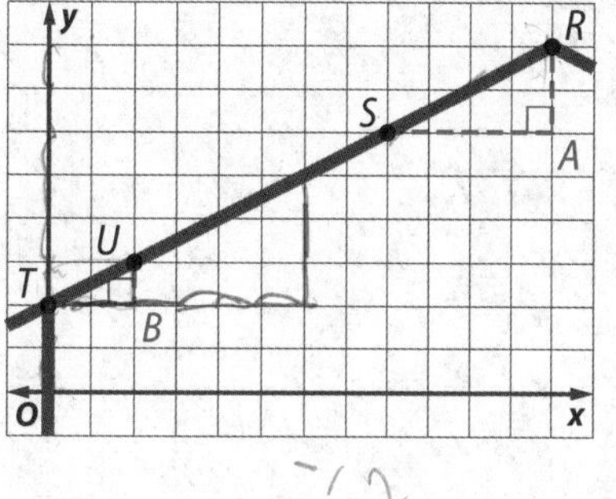

$m = \frac{y_2 - y_1}{x_2 - x_1}$ Formula for slope

$m = \frac{8 - 6}{12 - 8}$ Use the points S and R. $(x_1, y_1) = (8, 6)$ and $(x_2, y_2) = (12, 8)$

$m = \frac{2}{4}$ or $\frac{1}{2}$ Simplify.

The pitch of the roof is $\frac{1}{2}$. Verify that the pitch is the same using two other points.

$m = \frac{y_2 - y_1}{x_2 - x_1}$ Formula for slope

$m = \frac{2 - 3}{0 - 2}$ Use the points U and T. $(x_1, y_1) = (2, 3)$ and $(x_2, y_2) = (0, 2)$

$m = \frac{-1}{-2}$ or $\frac{1}{2}$ Simplify. The pitch is the same.

Is the statement $\triangle RAS \sim \triangle UBT$ true? Explain below.

Got It? Do this problem to find out.

b. The plans for a teeter-totter are shown at the right. Using points *G* and *L*, determine the slope of the teeter-totter. Then verify that the slope is the same at a different location by choosing a different set of points.

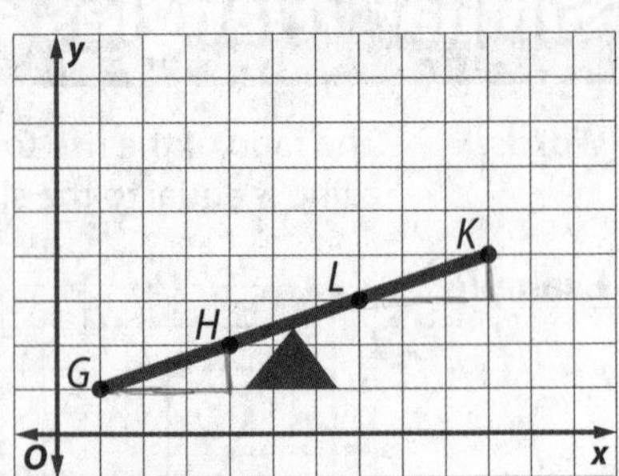

Guided Practice

1. Graph $\triangle ACG$ with vertices $A(1, 4)$, $C(3, -2)$, and $G(1, -2)$, and $\triangle BCF$ with vertices $B(2, 1)$, $C(3, -2)$, and $F(2, -2)$. Then write a proportion comparing the rise to the run for each of the similar slope triangles and determine the numeric value. (Example 1)

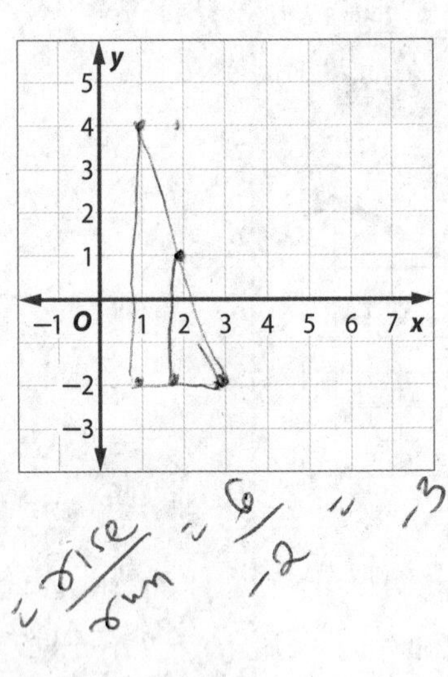

2. The plans for a set of stairs are shown below. Using points *X* and *Z*, determine the slope of the line down the stairs. Then verify that the slope is the same at a different location by choosing a different set of points. (Example 2)

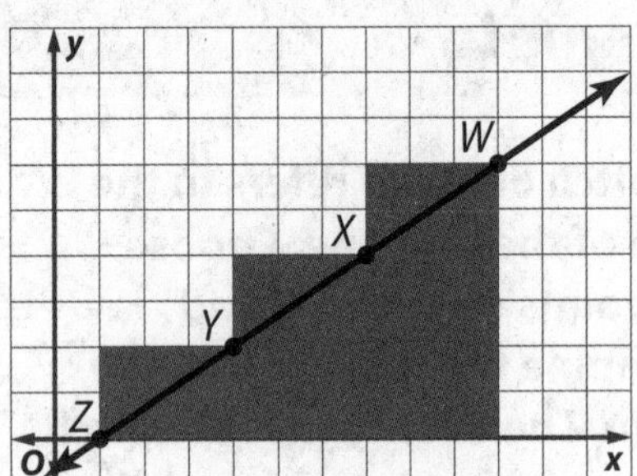

3. Building on the Essential Question How is the slope of a line related to the similar slope triangles formed by the line?

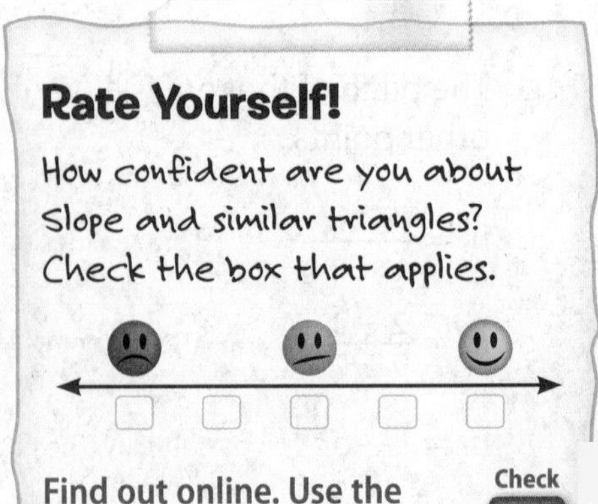

Rate Yourself!
How confident are you about Slope and similar triangles? Check the box that applies.
Find out online. Use the Self-Check Quiz.

Name ______________________ My Homework ______________________

Independent Practice

8.4(A), 8.4(C), 8.1(C), 8.1(F) TEKS

Graph each pair of similar triangles. Then write a proportion comparing the rise to the run for each of the similar slope triangles and determine the numeric value. (Example 1)

1. $\triangle ABC$ with vertices $A(-6, -1)$, $B(-4, -1)$, and $C(-6, -3)$; $\triangle NLM$ with vertices $N(-3, 3)$, $L(0, 3)$, and $M(-3, 0)$

Show your work.

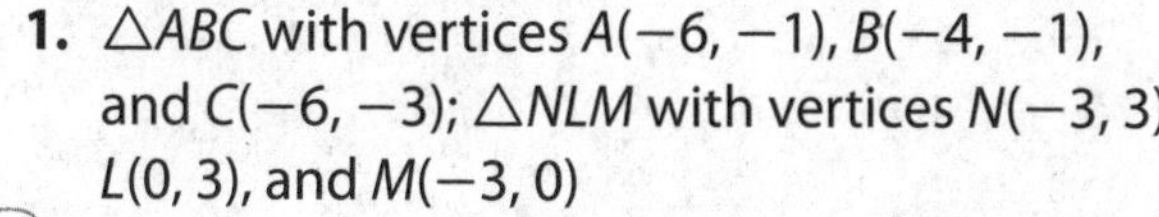

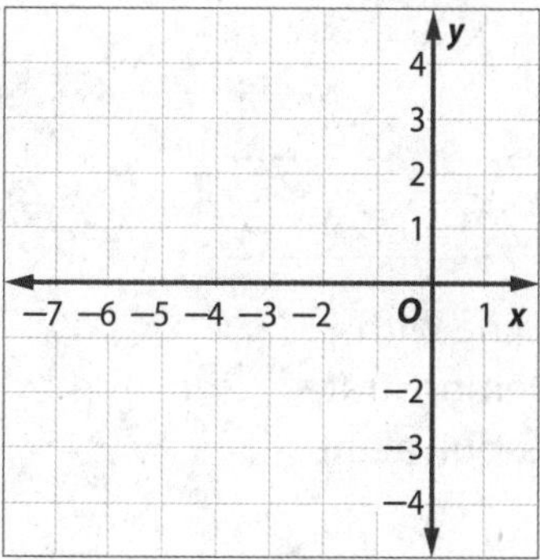

2. $\triangle FGH$ with vertices $F(2, 3)$, $G(2, -1)$, and $H(-6, 3)$; $\triangle JKL$ with vertices $J(0, 2)$, $K(0, 0)$, and $L(-4, 2)$

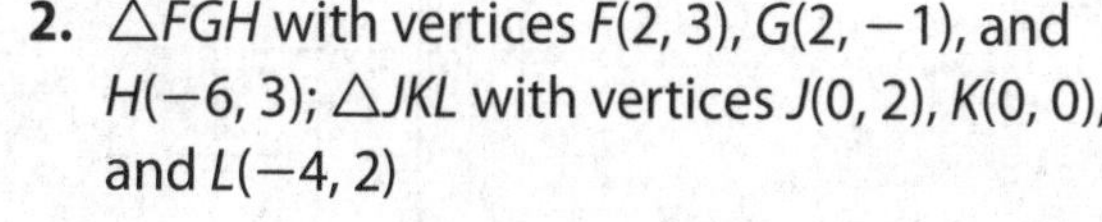

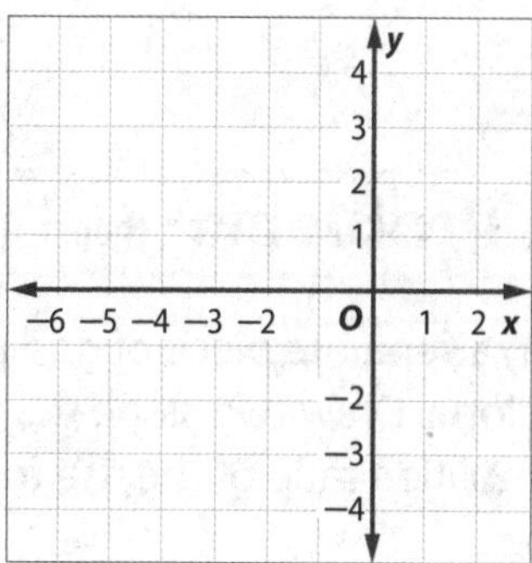

3. The plans for a skateboard ramp are shown. Use two points to determine the slope of the ramp. Then verify that the slope is the same at a different location by choosing a different set of points. (Example 2)

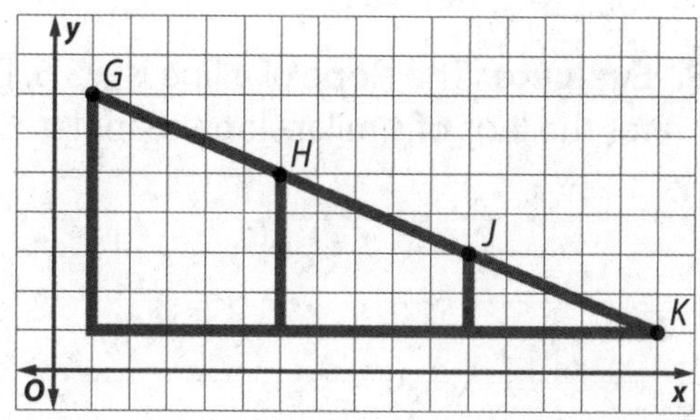

4. A ladder is leaning up against the side of a house. Use two points to determine the slope of the ladder. Then verify that the slope is the same at a different location by choosing a different set of points. (Example 2)

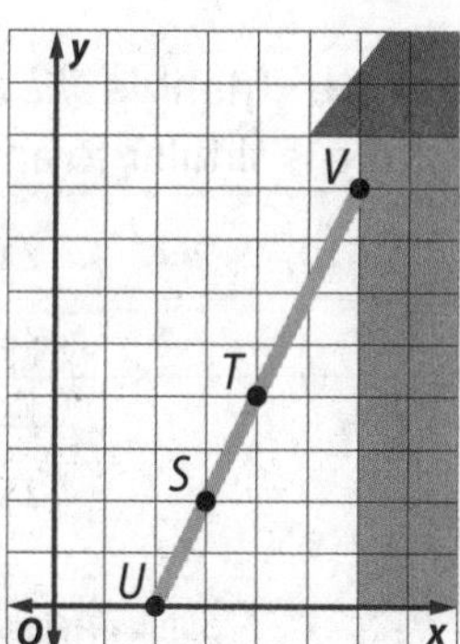

5. **MP Analyze Relationships** Triangle XYZ has vertices $X(0, 0)$, $Y(10, 0)$, and $Z(0, 6)$. Triangle MYP has vertices $M(5, 0)$, $Y(10, 0)$, and $P(x, y)$. Determine the missing coordinates for P if $\triangle MYP \sim \triangle XYZ$.

6. **Select Tools and Techniques** Use a graph to determine the missing coordinates of point Z if $\triangle MNP \sim \triangle XYZ$.

$M(0, 0)$, $N(1, 0)$, $P(1, 2)$, $X(1, 2)$, $Y(3, 2)$

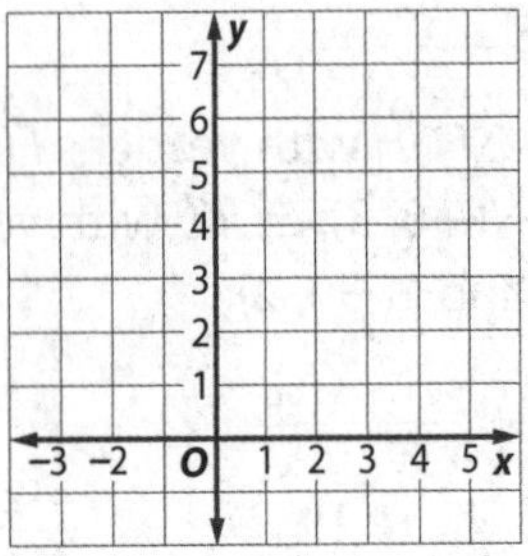

H.O.T. Problems Higher-Order Thinking

7. **Create** On a separate piece of grid paper, draw the graph of a line with a positive slope. Draw two slope triangles formed by the line. Demonstrate that the simplified ratio of the rise to the run of each triangle is equivalent to the slope.

8. **Evaluate** The slope of a line is -3.5. Determine two possible measurements for the legs of similar slope triangles. Support your answer.

9. **Analyze** Triangle JKL has vertices $J(0, 0)$, $K(1, 0)$, and $L(1, 2)$. Determine if each triangle is similar to and/or a slope triangle with $\triangle JKL$.

$\triangle ABC$: $A(1, 2)$, $B(1, 6)$, $C(3, 6)$
$\triangle MNP$: $M(3, 1)$, $N(6, 1)$, $P(6, 6)$
$\triangle RST$: $R(1, 2)$, $S(4, 2)$, $T(4, 5)$
$\triangle WXY$: $W(0, 0)$, $X(-1, -2)$, $Y(0, -2)$

Similar Triangles	Slope Triangles	Neither

Name ______________________________

Multi-Step Problem Solving

10. The graph shows a line and a slope triangle *RST* for the line. Which of the following are the coordinates of another slope triangle for the line? P N MP

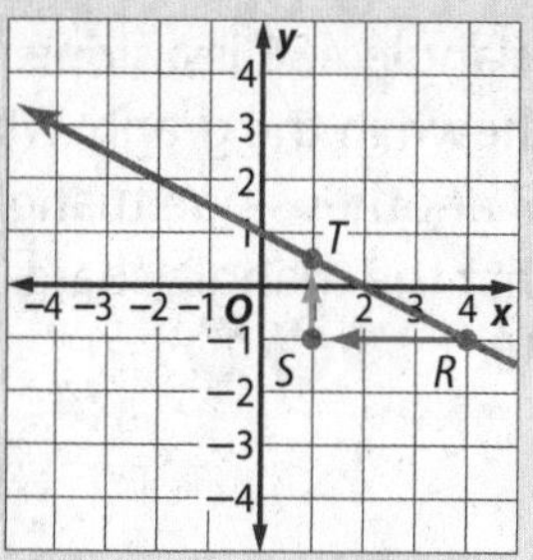

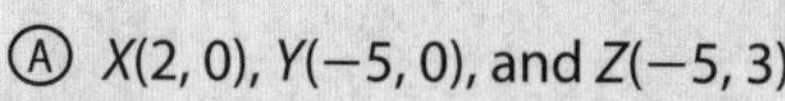

Ⓐ $X(2, 0)$, $Y(-5, 0)$, and $Z(-5, 3)$

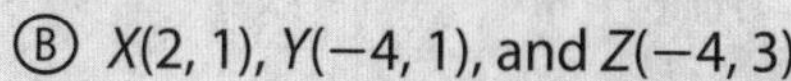

Ⓑ $X(2, 1)$, $Y(-4, 1)$, and $Z(-4, 3)$

Ⓒ $X(2, -1)$, $Y(-5, -1)$, and $Z(-5, 3)$

Ⓓ $X(2, 0)$, $Y(-4, 0)$, and $Z(-4, 3)$

Use a problem-solving model to solve this problem.

1 Analyze

Read the problem. Circle the information you know. Underline what the problem is asking you to find.

2 Plan

What will you need to do to solve the problem? Write your plan in steps.

Step 1 Graph each set of vertices. Determine which triangles have two ________ that lie on ____.

Step 2 Determine the slopes of the triangles with two ________ on line ____.

3 Solve

Use your plan to solve the problem. Show your steps.

The vertices of choices ____ and ____ form triangles with two ________ that lie on line ____.

The slope of *RT* is ______. Count units to determine that only the line *XZ* formed by the triangle with vertices at (__, __), (____, __), and (____, __) has the same slope. Fill in that answer choice ____.

Read to Succeed!

While triangles may appear to be similar, you need to determine slopes to establish similarity.

4 Justify and Evaluate

How do you know your solution is accurate?

____

____

____

N = Number and Operations P = Proportionality MP = Mathematical Processes

More Multi-Step Problem Solving

Use a problem-solving model to solve each problem.

11. Triangle *ABC* is a slope triangle for the line shown in the graph. What are the coordinates of another slope triangle for the line, given that the triangle shares a vertex with triangle *ABC*? P N MP

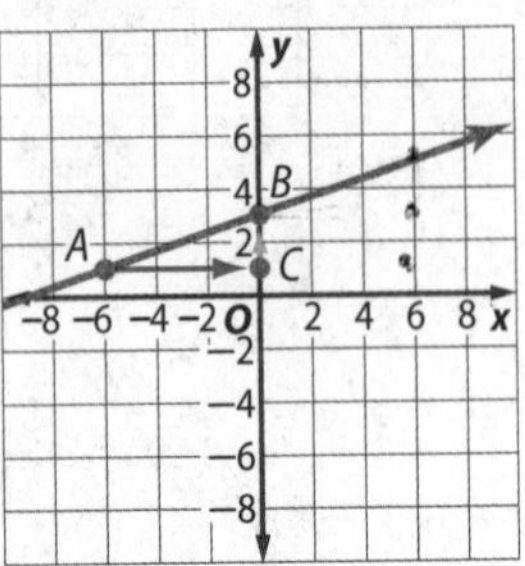

Ⓐ D(6, 5), E(6,3), and *A*

Ⓑ D(6, 5), E(6, 1), and *C*

Ⓒ D(6, 5), E(6, 3), and *B*

Ⓓ D(6, 5), E(6, 1), and *B*

12. The tables show the coordinates of two slope triangles for a line. What is the slope of the line? P N MP

Point	*R*	*S*	*T*
x	−3	−1	−1
y	−10	−10	−4

Point	*U*	*V*	*W*
x	1	2	2
y	2	2	5

13. Xavier is making a wooden box frame formed by an 8-inch square and two connecting triangles. What is the total amount of wood, in inches, needed to make the frame? Explain.

P N MP

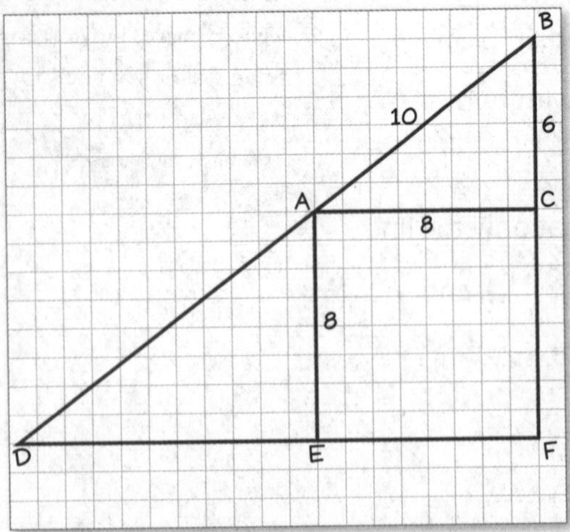

N = Number and Operations   P = Proportionality   MP = Mathematical Processes

Lesson 4

Equations in $y = mx$ Form

Launch the Lesson: Real World

For a bike-a-thon, David can raise \$20 for 2 hours of cycling, \$40 for 4 hours of cycling, and \$60 for 6 hours of cycling. Let's investigate the relationship between biking time and money raised.

1. Is the relationship in the table a proportional relationship? Explain.

____

2. Complete the steps below to derive the equation for a proportional linear relationship.

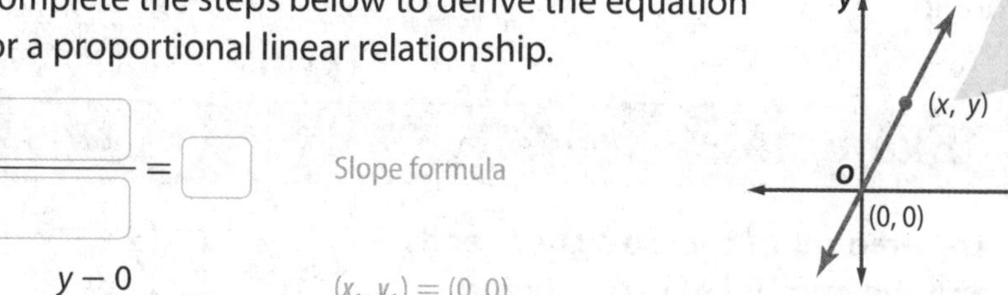

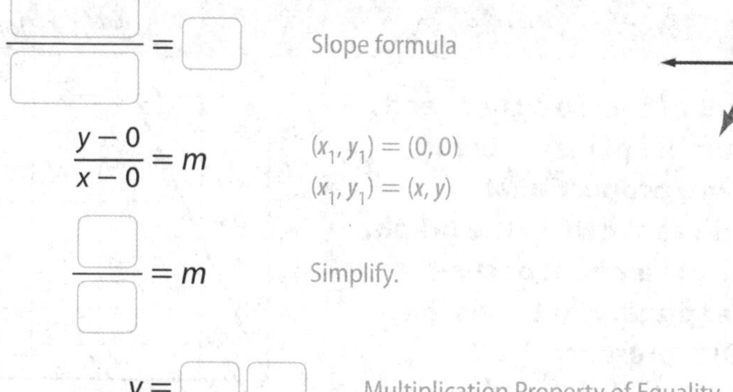

$\frac{\square}{\square} = \square$ Slope formula

$\frac{y - 0}{x - 0} = m$ $(x_1, y_1) = (0, 0)$; $(x_1, y_1) = (x, y)$

$\frac{\square}{\square} = m$ Simplify.

$y = \square\,\square$ Multiplication Property of Equality

↑ constant ratio

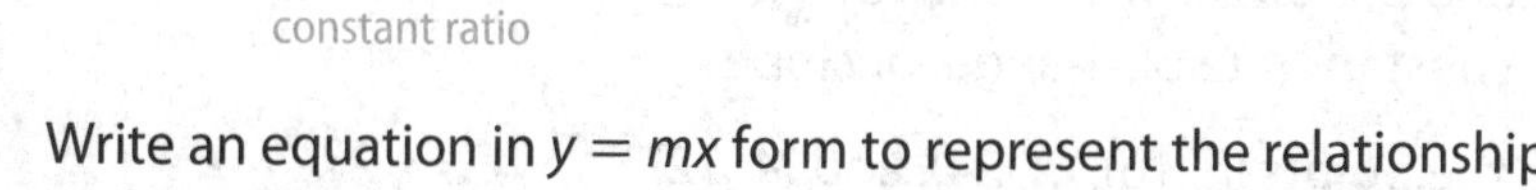

3. Write an equation in $y = mx$ form to represent the relationship in the table. ______________________________

4. The point (1, 10) represents the unit rate 10. Use the slope formula to determine the slope of the line between (0, 0) and (1, 10). What do you notice? ______________________________

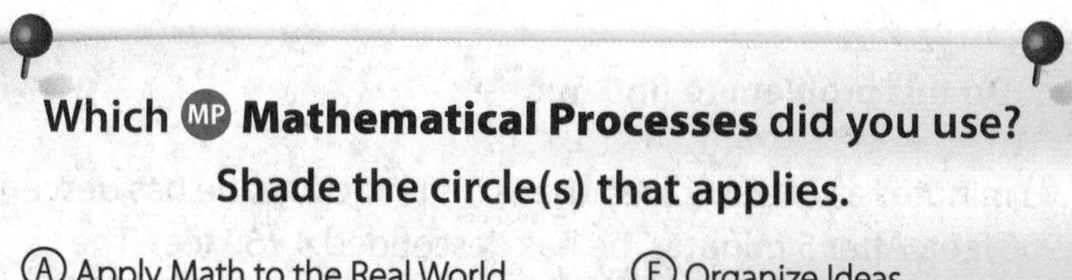

Which MP Mathematical Processes did you use? Shade the circle(s) that applies.

Ⓐ Apply Math to the Real World.
Ⓑ Use a Problem-Solving Model.
Ⓒ Select Tools and Techniques.
Ⓓ Use Multiple Representations.
Ⓔ Organize Ideas.
Ⓕ Analyze Relationships.
Ⓖ Justify Arguments.

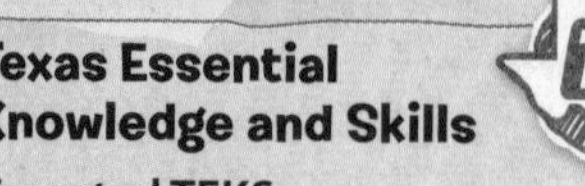

Texas Essential Knowledge and Skills

Targeted TEKS

8.5(A) Represent linear proportional situations with tables, graphs, and equations in the form of $y = kx$. *Also addresses 8.4(B), 8.4(C).*

Mathematical Processes

8.1(A), 8.1(B), 8.1(D), 8.1(E), 8.1(F)

Essential Question

WHY are graphs helpful?

Key Concept

Proportional Linear Relationships

Work Zone

Words A linear relationship is proportional when the ratio of y to x is a constant, m.

Symbols $y = mx$, where m is the slope and $m \neq 0$

Example $y = 3x$

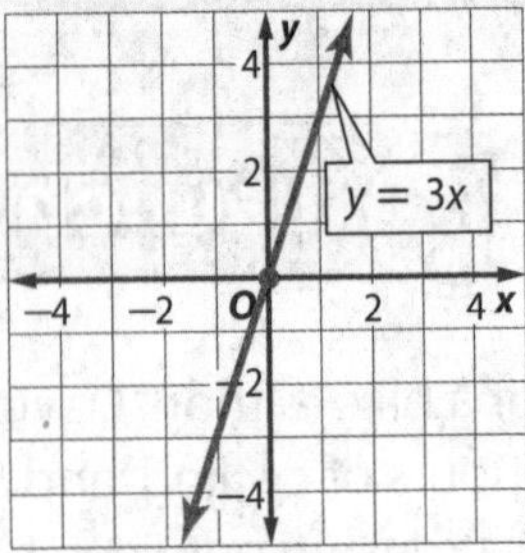

The slope of the graph of $y = mx$ is m. Since (0, 0) is one solution of $y = mx$, the graph of a proportional linear relationship passes through the origin.

Tutor

Example

1. The amount of cheese a chef needs and the number of pizzas being made are in a proportional relationship as shown in the graph. Determine the amount of cheese needed per pizza. What does the point (0, 0) represent?

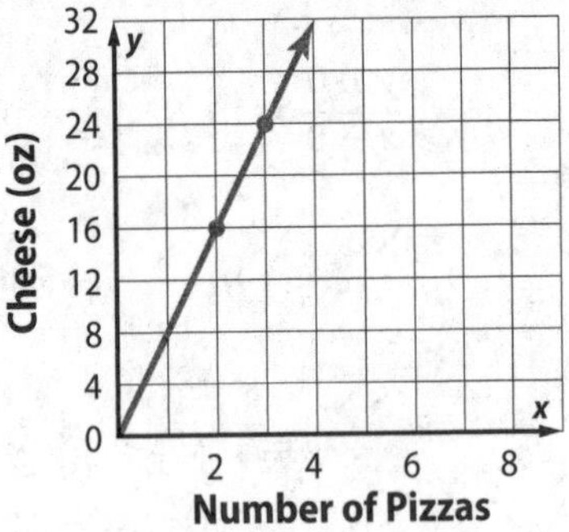

To determine the amount of cheese needed per pizza, or the unit rate, find the constant rate of change, or slope.

Use the points (2, 16), (3, 24), and (4, 32).

$\frac{\text{amount of cheese}}{\text{number of pizzas}} \rightarrow \frac{16}{2} \text{ or } \frac{8}{1} \qquad \frac{24}{3} \text{ or } \frac{8}{1} \qquad \frac{32}{4} \text{ or } \frac{8}{1}$

So, 8 ounces of cheese is needed per pizza. The unit rate of 8 ounces of cheese per pizza is also the slope of the line.

The point (0, 0) means that 0 ounces of cheese are needed for 0 pizzas.

Got It? Do this problem to find out.

a. Two minutes after a skydiver opens his parachute, he has descended 1,900 feet. After 5 minutes, he has descended 4,750 feet. The relationship between the distance he has descended and the time in minutes is a proportional linear relationship. Determine the number of feet the skydiver has descended per minute.

950

Example

2. A cyclist can ride 3 miles in 0.25 hour. The distance ridden in miles *y* and the time in hours *x* are in a proportional linear relationship. This situation can be represented by $y = 12x$. Graph the equation. Determine and interpret the slope.

Make a table of values. Then graph the equation $y = 12x$. In the equation of a proportional linear relationship, *m* represents the slope. In the table, the slope is the constant rate of change or unit rate.

So, the slope of the line is $\frac{12}{1}$.

Hours, x	$y = 12x$	Miles, y
0	$y = 12(0)$	0
1	$y = 12(1)$	12
2	$y = 12(2)$	24

(+1, +1 between rows of Hours; +12, +12 between rows of Miles)

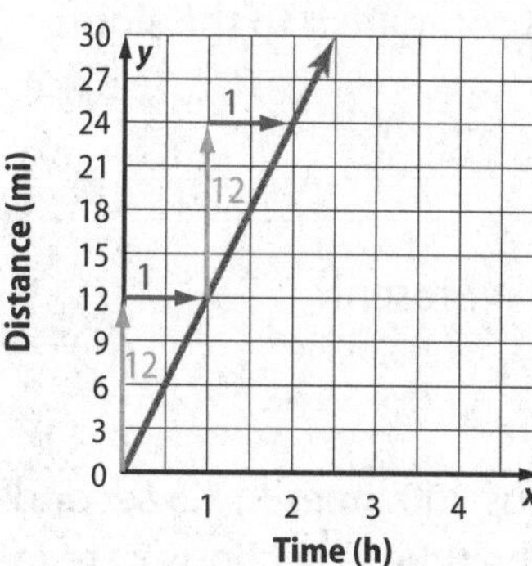

So, the cyclist can ride 12 miles per hour.

Got It? **Do this problem to find out.**

b. A grocery store sells 6 oranges for \$2. The cost of the oranges and the number of oranges are in a proportional linear relationship. This situation can be represented by $y = \frac{1}{3}x$. Graph the equation. Determine and interpret the slope.

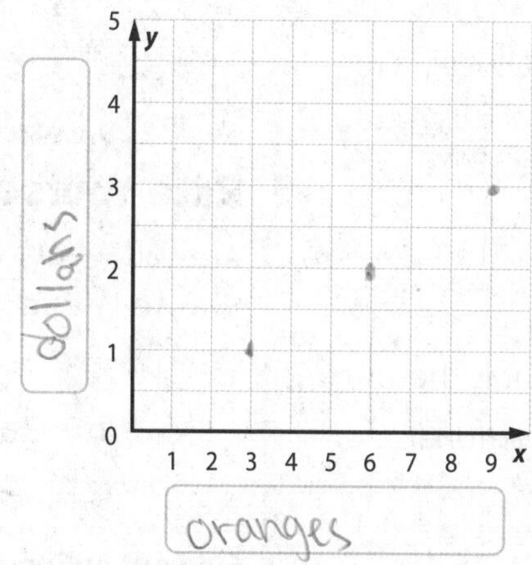

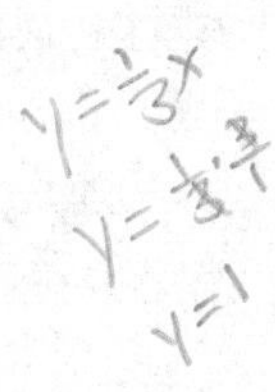

Guided Practice

1. A color printer can print 36 pages in 3 minutes and 108 pages in 9 minutes. If the number of pages and the time are in a proportional linear relationship, at what rate is the color printer printing? (Example 1)

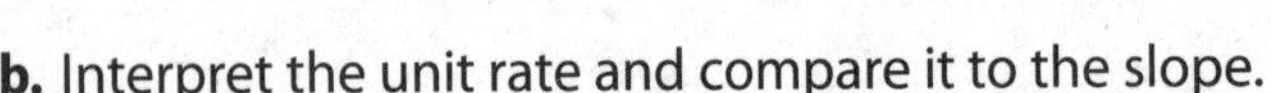

2. The number of miles a whale can swim and the time in minutes are in a proportional linear relationship as shown in the graph at right. (Example 1)

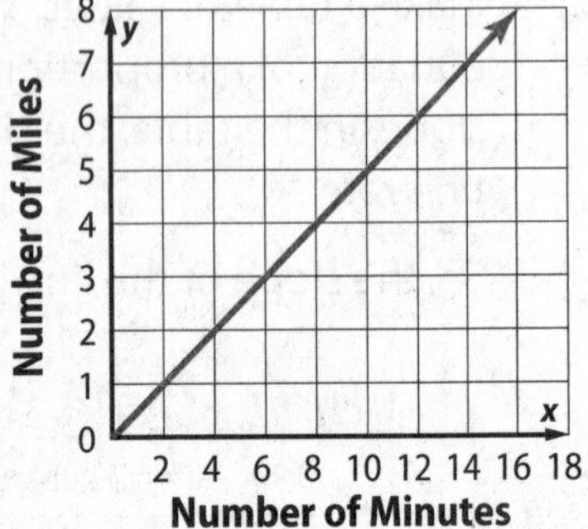

a. Determine and interpret the slope.

$\frac{1}{2}$

b. Interpret the unit rate and compare it to the slope.

UR = $\frac{1}{2}$ = Slope

c. What does the point (0, 0) represent?

Origin

3. A honeybee can beat its wings 300 times in 1.5 seconds. The number of beats y and the time in seconds x are in a proportional linear relationship. This situation can be represented by $y = 200x$. (Example 2)

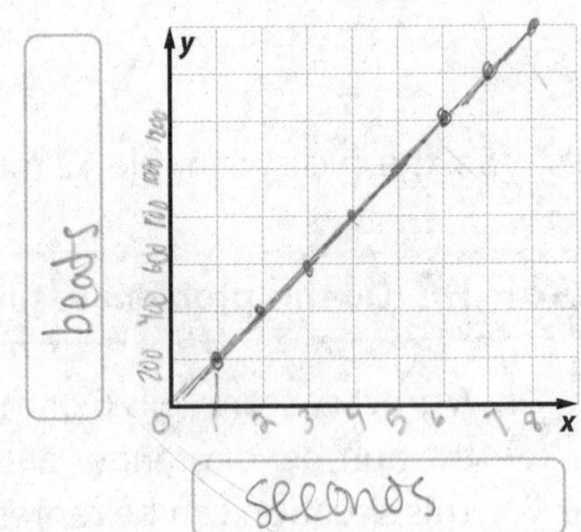

a. Graph the equation on the coordinate plane.

b. Determine and interpret the slope.

200

c. Interpret the unit rate and compare it to the slope.

Unit Rate = Slope

d. Explain how the graph shows a proportional linear relationship.

(0, 0) Straight

4. **Building on the Essential Question** What is the significance of the slope of the graph of a proportional linear relationship?

Rate Yourself!

Are you ready to move on? Shade the section that applies.

YES ? NO

Find out online. Use the Self-Check Quiz. Check

FOLDABLES Time to update your Foldable!

Name ______________________ My Homework ______________

Independent Practice

8.5(A), 8.4(B), 8.4(C), 8.1(D), 8.1(F), 8.1(G) TEKS

1. The total cost of an ice cream sundae and the number of scoops of ice cream ordered are in a proportional linear relationship. The relationship is shown in the graph. (Example 1)

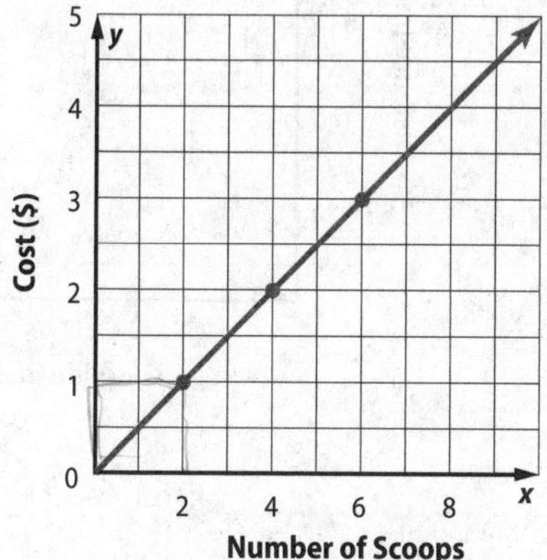

   a. Determine and interpret the slope.

   b. Interpret the unit rate and compare it to the slope.

   c. What does the point (0, 0) represent?

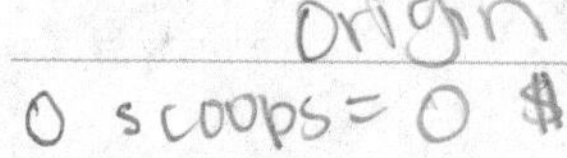

2. The amount of money Jake earns and the number of dogs he walks are in a proportional linear relationship as shown in the graph. (Example 1)

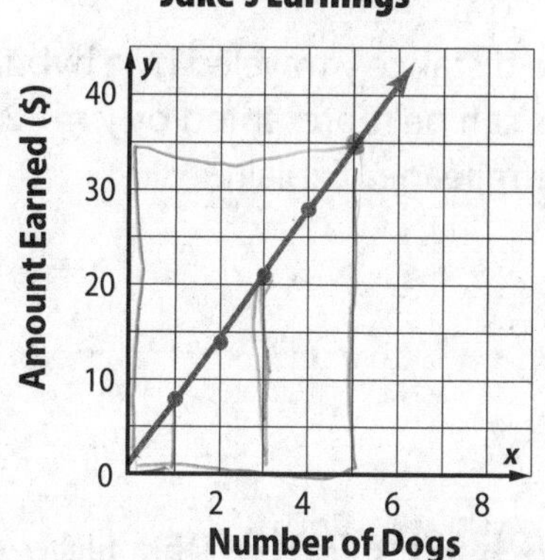

   a. Determine and interpret the slope.

   b. Interpret the unit rate and compare it to the slope.

   c. What does the point (0, 0) represent?

3. The average cat's heart beats 60 times in 30 seconds. The number of heartbeats y and the time in seconds x are in a proportional linear relationship. This situation can be represented by $y = 2x$. (Example 2)

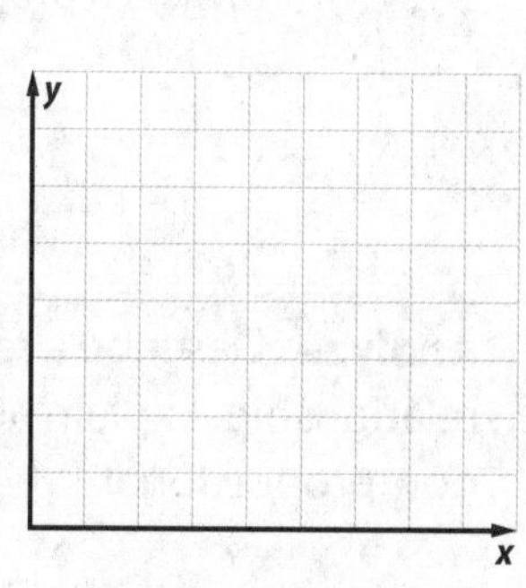

   a. Graph the equation on the coordinate plane.

   b. Determine and interpret the slope.

   c. Interpret the unit rate and compare it to the slope.

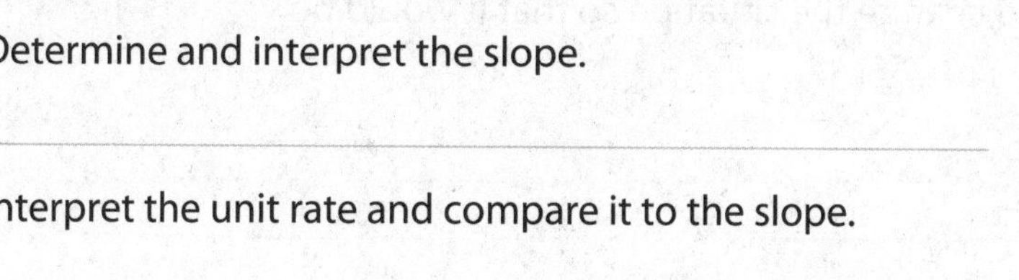

   d. Explain how the graph shows a proportional linear relationship.

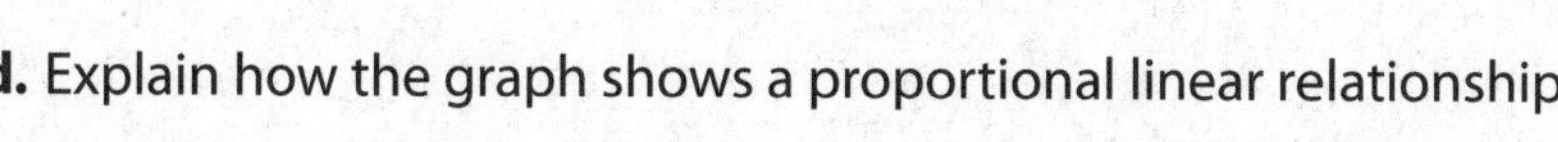

4. **MP Use Multiple Representations** A new compact car can travel 288 miles on nine gallons of gasoline. The distance driven in miles y and the number of gallons of gasoline x are in a proportional linear relationship. This situation can be represented by the equation $y = 32x$.

a. Graph the equation on the coordinate plane.

b. How many miles per gallon does the car get?

c. The distance y traveled by a hybrid car using x gallons of gas can be represented by $y = 42x$. Which car gets better gas mileage? Explain.

Distance (mi)
350
280
210
140
70
0
2 4 6 8
Gasoline (gal)

H.O.T. Problems Higher-Order Thinking

5. **Create** Describe a real-world proportional linear relationship whose graph would show a line with a 2.5-unit increase in y for every 1-unit increase in x. Graph the relationship and then interpret the unit rate.

6. **Evaluate** Explain whether the following statement is *true* or *false*.

A linear relationship that has a constant rate of change is always a proportional relationship.

7. **Analyze** Describe a real-world situation that is a proportional linear relationship. Explain how you could change the situation so that it would be non-proportional.

Name ____

Multi-Step Problem Solving

8. Trevor burns 40 Calories when he cycles for 5 minutes and 80 Calories when he cycles for 10 minutes. The equation $y = 3.25x$ represents the number of Calories he burns when walking. How many more Calories does Trevor burn by cycling for 20 minutes than by walking for 20 minutes? P N MP

Use a problem-solving model to solve this problem.

1 Analyze

Read the problem. Circle the information you know. Underline what the problem is asking you to find.

2 Plan

What will you need to do to solve the problem? Write your plan in steps.

Read to Succeed!
When writing an equation for Calories burned by cycling, find the unit rate of Calories burned per minute.

Step 1 Write an equation to represent the Calories burned when ________.

Step 2 Replace ________ in both equations with ________ and determine the number of Calories burned by ________ each of cycling and walking.

3 Solve

Use your plan to solve the problem. Show your steps.

The equation ________ represents the Calories burned when ________.

Trevor burns ____(____) or ____ Calories when cycling and ____(____) or ____ Calories when walking. Since ____ − ____ = ____, ____ more Calories are burned by cycling.

Complete the grid.

					.		
+	0	0	0	0		0	0
−	1	1	1	1		1	1
	2	2	2	2		2	2
	3	3	3	3		3	3
	4	4	4	4		4	4
	5	5	5	5		5	5
	6	6	6	6		6	6
	7	7	7	7		7	7
	8	8	8	8		8	8
	9	9	9	9		9	9

4 Justify and Evaluate

How do you know your solution is accurate?

____

____

P = Proportionality N = Number and Operations MP = Mathematical Processes

More Multi-Step Problem Solving

Use a problem-solving model to solve each problem.

9. The table below shows the number of words Luz types over different periods of time. Deepak's typing speed is represented by the equation $w = 34t$. If each student types for 5 minutes at a constant rate, who types more words? how many more? P N MP

Number of Words (w)	Time in Minutes (t)
84	3
168	6
224	8

10. The table below shows the number of rectangular tiles needed to cover square-shaped floors with certain side lengths. If the number of tiles is proportional to the area of the floor, how many tiles would be needed for a square-shaped floor with a side length of 9 feet? P N EE MP

Number of Tiles	Side Length of Floor (ft)
147	7
432	12
675	15

11. Denzel and Maria played a game and recorded their scores after each turn as ordered pairs. Denzel's ordered pairs included (1, 4), (3, 12), and (4, 16). Maria's ordered pairs included (1, 5), (5, 25), and (6, 30). Each player made a graph using the ordered pairs. Assuming each player's score is proportional, what is the difference between the slope of Denzel's graph and the slope of Maria's graph? P N MP

12. Refer to the graph below. What is the value of x when $y = 125$? Explain. P EE MP

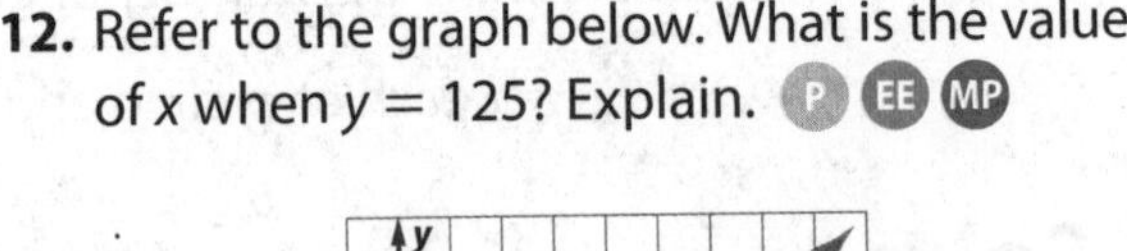

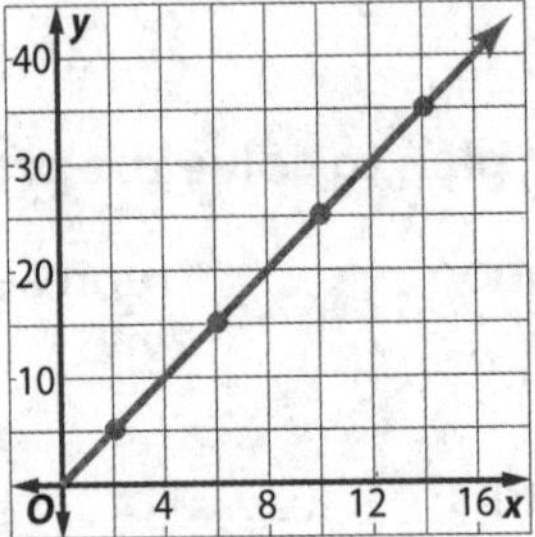

N = Number and Operations P = Proportionality EE = Expressions, Equations, and Relationships MP = Mathematical Processes

Lesson 5

Direct Variation

Launch the Lesson: Real World

Texas Essential Knowledge and Skills

Targeted TEKS
8.5(E) Solve problems involving direct variation. *Also addresses 8.5(A), 8.4(B), and 8.4(C).*

Mathematical Processes
8.1(A), 8.1(B), 8.1(D), 8.1(F)

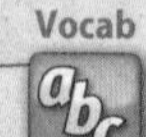

Vocabulary
direct variation
constant of variation
constant of proportionality

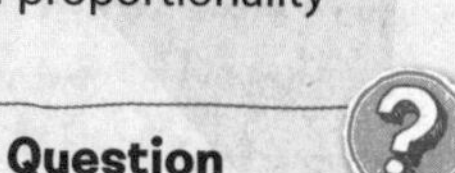

Essential Question
WHY are graphs helpful?

The heart of a blue whale can weigh up to 4,000 pounds. The table shows the number of gallons of blood a blue whale's heart pumps. Use the table to find the constant rate of change.

Number of Beats	Blood Pumped (gallons)
3	180
6	360
9	540
12	720

1. Write an equation in $y = mx$ form to represent the situation.

2. Graph the equation on the coordinate plane below.

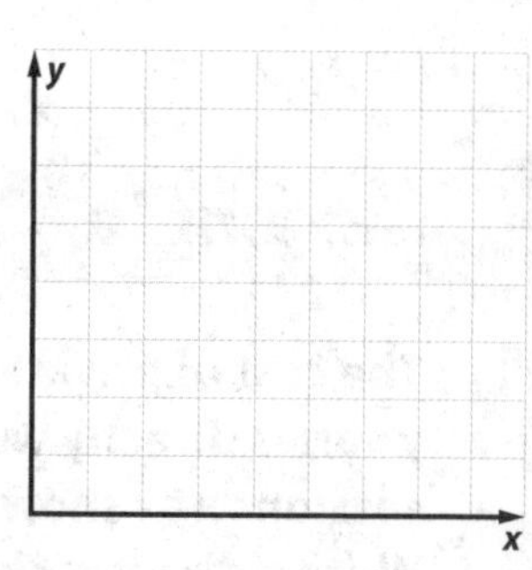

3. Determine the slope of the line and interpret its meaning.

4. Is there a proportional linear relationship between these two quantities? Why or Why not?

Which MP Mathematical Processes did you use? Shade the circle(s) that applies.

Ⓐ Apply Math to the Real World.
Ⓑ Use a Problem-Solving Model.
Ⓒ Select Tools and Techniques.
Ⓓ Use Multiple Representations.
Ⓔ Organize Ideas.
Ⓕ Analyze Relationships.
Ⓖ Justify Arguments.

Key Concept — Direct Variation

Words A **direct variation** is a linear relationship in which the ratio of y to x is a constant, m. We say y varies directly with x.

Symbols $m = \frac{y}{x}$ or $y = mx$, where m is the **constant of variation** and $m \neq 0$

Example $y = 2x$

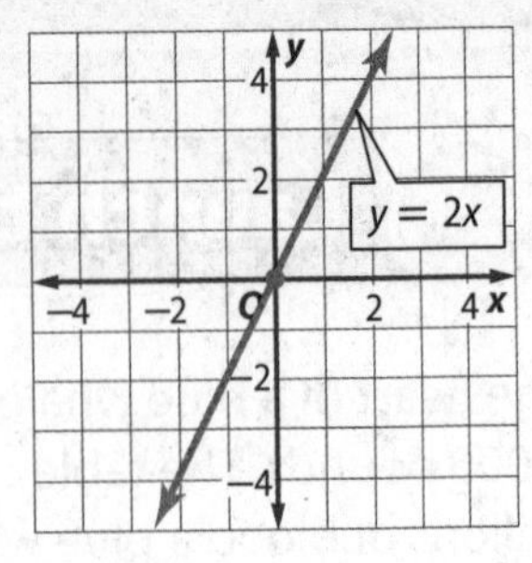

Work Zone

$y = mx$ or $y = kx$

A direct variation can be represented by the equations $y = mx$ or $y = kx$, where m and k represent the constant of variation, the constant of proportionality, the slope, and the unit rate.

In the last lesson, you learned that when the ratio of two variable quantities is constant, a proportional linear relationship exists. This proportional linear relationship is called a direct variation. The constant ratio is also called the constant of variation or **constant of proportionality**.

Example

1. The cost of private gymnastic lessons y varies directly with the number of sessions x as shown in the graph. Write a direct variation equation. Identify the constant of variation and interpret its meaning.

Cost ($) — Number of Sessions; points (1, 10) and (2, 20); rise 10, run 1

To write the equation, first find the slope using the graph.

$$\text{slope} = \frac{\text{rise}}{\text{run}} = \frac{10}{1} \text{ or } 10$$

Now write the equation.

$y = mx$ Direct variation

$y = 10x$ Replace m with 10.

The direct variation equation is $y = 10x$.

The constant of variation is equal to the slope. So, the constant of variation is $\frac{10}{1}$ or 10. This means that the unit rate, or cost per session, is $10.

Multi-Step Example

2. A 3-year-old cat is often considered to be 15 in human years. Assume that the equivalent age in human years y varies directly with its age as a cat x. Write and solve a direct variation equation to determine the human-year age of a cat that is 6 years old.

Step 1 Write a direct variation equation.

Let x represent the cat's actual age and let y represent the human-equivalent age.

$y = mx$	Direct variation
$15 = m(3)$	$y = 15, x = 3$
$5 = m$	Simplify.
$y = 5x$	Replace m with 5.

Step 2 Determine the human-year age of the cat.

You want to know the human-year age, or y-value, when the cat is 6 years old.

$y = 5x$	Write the equation.
$y = 5 \cdot 6$	$x = 6$
$y = 30$	Simplify.

So, when a cat is 6 years old, the equivalent age in human years is 30.

Check

Graph the equation $y = 5x$.

The y-value when $x = 6$ is 30.

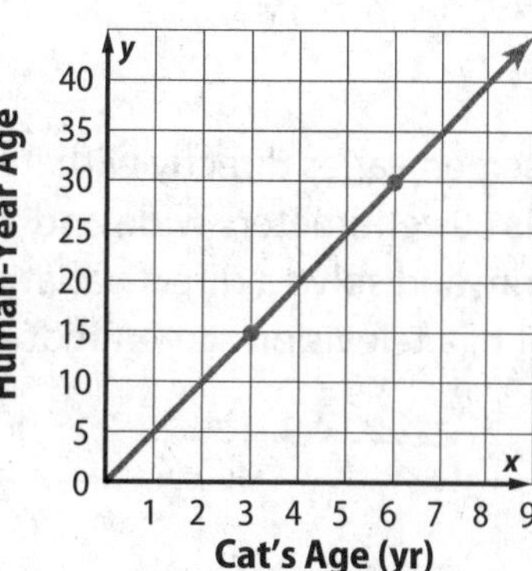

Got It? Do this problem to find out.

a. A Monarch butterfly can fly 93 miles in 15 hours. Assume the distance traveled is directly proportional to the time traveled. Write and solve a direct variation equation to determine how far the Monarch butterfly will travel in 24 hours.

a. 148.8

Tutor

Example

3. The distance *d* in miles covered by a rabbit in *t* hours can be represented by the equation $d = 35t$. The distance covered by a grizzly bear is shown in the table. Which animal is faster? Explain.

Time (h)	Distance (mi)
1	30
2	60
3	90
4	120

Rabbit $d = 35t$

The slope or unit rate is 35 mph.

Grizzly Bear Find the rate of change.

rate of change $= \frac{30}{1}$ or 30

Since $35 > 30$, the rabbit is the faster animal.

Guided Practice

1. A grocery store is having a sale on ears of corn. The cost of the corn *y* varies directly with the number of ears of corn *x* as shown in the graph. (Examples 1 and 3)

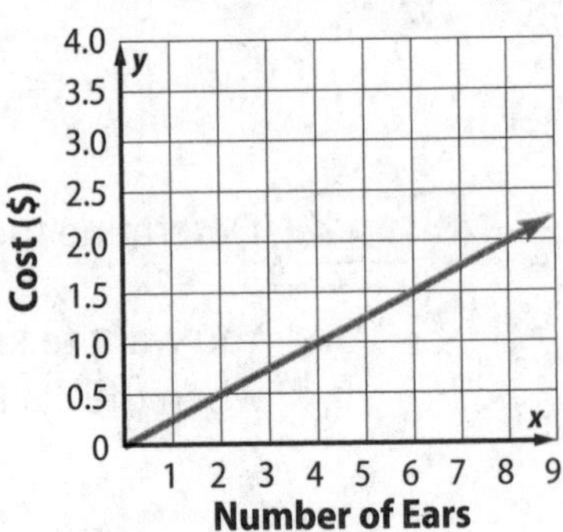

   a. Write a direct variation equation. Identify the constant of variation and interpret its meaning.

   b. At another store, the cost of the corn *y* varies directly with the number of ears of corn *x* is represented by $y = \frac{1}{5}x$. Which store is having a better sale on corn? Explain.

2. The height of a television screen varies directly with its width. A television screen is 60 centimeters wide and 33.75 centimeters high. Write and solve a direct variation equation to find the height of a television screen that is 90 centimeters wide. (Example 2)

3. **Building on the Essential Question** What are four mathematical representations that are equivalent to the slope in a direct variation?

Rate Yourself!

How well do you understand direct variation? Circle the image that applies.

Clear | Somewhat Clear | Not So Clear

Find out online. Use the Self-Check Quiz.

Check

FOLDABLES Time to update your Foldable!

Name ______________________ My Homework ______________________

Independent Practice

8.5(E), 8.5(A), 8.4(B), 8.4(C), 8.1(D), 8.1(F) TEKS

1. The time it takes you to hear thunder y varies directly with your distance from the lightning x as shown in the graph. Write a direct variation equation. Identify the constant of variation and interpret its meaning. (Example 1)

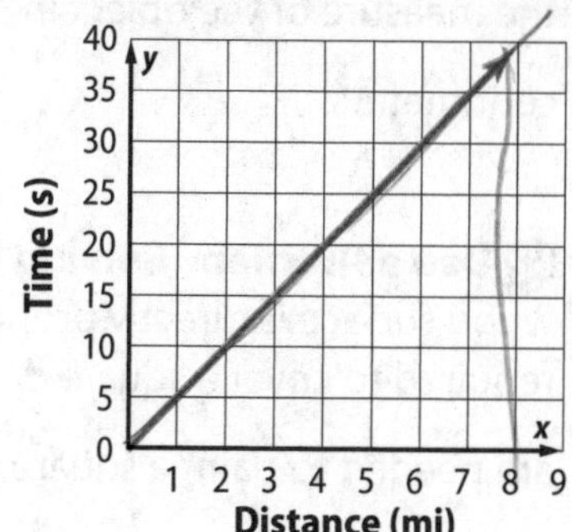

2. The weight of an object on Mars varies directly with its weight on Earth. An object that weighs 50 pounds on Mars weighs 150 pounds on Earth. Suppose an object weighs 120 pounds on Earth. Write and solve a direct variation equation to find how much an object would weigh on Mars. (Example 2)

3. The cost y for computer repairs at Computer Access for x hours is shown in the graph. The cost at Computers R Us can be represented by the equation $y = 23.5x$. Which company has the lower repair cost? Explain. (Example 3)

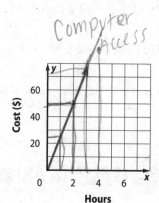

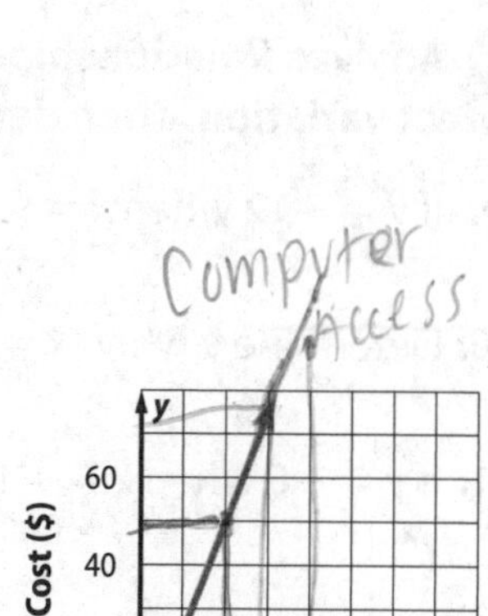

4. **Financial Literacy** Damon's earnings for four weeks from a part time job are shown in the table. Assume that his earnings vary directly with the number of hours worked.

Time Worked (h)	15	12	22	9
Total Pays ($)	112.50	90.00	165.00	67.50

Damon has been offered a job that will pay him $7.35 per hour worked. Which job has the better pay? Explain. (Example 3)

Determine whether each linear function is a direct variation. If so, determine the constant of variation. If not, explain why not.

5.

Pictures, x	5	6	7	8
Profit, y	20	24	28	32

6.

Age, x	10	11	12	13
Grade, y	5	6	7	8

7. The number of centimeters varies directly with the number of inches. If an object is 5 inches long, find the measure of the object in centimeters. ____________

Inches, x	6	9	12	15
Centimeters, y	15.24	22.86	30.48	38.10

8. **MP Use a Problem-Solving Model** The amount of stain needed to cover a wood surface is directly proportional to the area of the surface. If 3 pints are required to cover a square deck with a side of 7 feet, how many pints of stain are needed to paint a square deck with a side of 10 feet 6 inches? ____________

MP Analyze Relationships If y varies directly with x, write an equation for the direct variation. Then determine each value.

9. If $y = -12$ when $x = 9$, determine y when $x = -4$. ____________

10. Determine y when $x = 10$ if $y = 8$ when $x = 20$. ____________

11. If $y = -6$ when $x = -14$, determine x when $y = -4$. ____________

H.O.T. Problems Higher-Order Thinking

12. **Create** Write three ordered pairs for a direct variation relationship where $y = 12$ when $x = 16$.

13. **Analyze** Explain how the constant of variation affects the appearance of the graph of a direct variation equation.

Evaluate Determine whether the following statements are *true* or *false*. Explain your reasoning.

14. Every linear relationship is a direct variation.

15. Every direct variation is a linear relationship.

Name ____

Multi-Step Problem Solving

16. Cody and Jira processed mail items for a marketing campaign. Each person processed at a constant rate. Cody began at 9:00 A.M., and Jira began at 9:20 A.M. What was the total number of items processed by 10:40 A.M.? P MP

Time	Number of Items Processed	
	Cody	Jira
9:00 A.M.	0	–
9:20 A.M.	30	0
9:48 A.M.	72	35

Ⓐ 250 items
Ⓑ 270 items
Ⓒ 275 items
Ⓓ 360 items

Use a problem-solving model to solve this problem.

1 Analyze

Read the problem. Circle the information you know.
Underline what the problem is asking you to find.

2 Plan

What will you need to do to solve the problem? Write your plan in steps.

Step 1 Determine the ____________ processed ____________ by each worker.

Step 2 Use each unit rate to find the ____________ processed by each worker and the ____________ processed by ____.

3 Solve

Use your plan to solve the problem. Show your steps.

Read to Succeed!
When determining the number of minutes worked, remember there are 60 minutes in an hour.

Cody processed 72 items in ____ minutes, or ____ items per minute.

Jira processed 35 items in ____ minutes, or ____ items per minute.

By 10:40, Cody had worked ____ minutes and Jira had worked ____ minutes.

So, Cody processed ____(____) or ____ items and Jira processed ____(____) or ____ items. Together, they processed ____ + ____ or ____ items. The correct answer is ____. Fill in that answer.

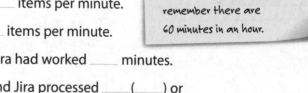

4 Justify and Evaluate

How do you know your solution is accurate?

____

____

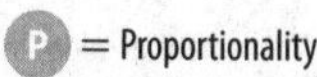 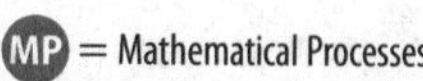

P = Proportionality MP = Mathematical Processes

More Multi-Step Problem Solving

Use a problem-solving model to solve each problem.

17. Jamal and Arturo are shoveling snow from a 120-foot-long driveway, each working at a constant rate. Jamal began at 1:30 P.M., and Arturo began at 1:42 P.M. What is the total number of feet both workers will have shoveled by 2:15 P.M.? P MP

Time	Feet of Snow Shoveled	
	Jamal	Arturo
1:30 P.M.	0	–
1:42 P.M.	16	0
2:00 P.M.	40	36

Ⓐ 104 feet

Ⓑ 114 feet

Ⓒ 126 feet

Ⓓ 136 feet

18. The amount of money Ciana earns varies directly with the amount of time she works, as shown in the graph. Gloria earns $1.20 per hour more than Ciana earns. Gloria's earnings can be represented by the equation $y = mx$, where y is the number of dollars earned and x is the number of hours worked. What is the value of m? P MP

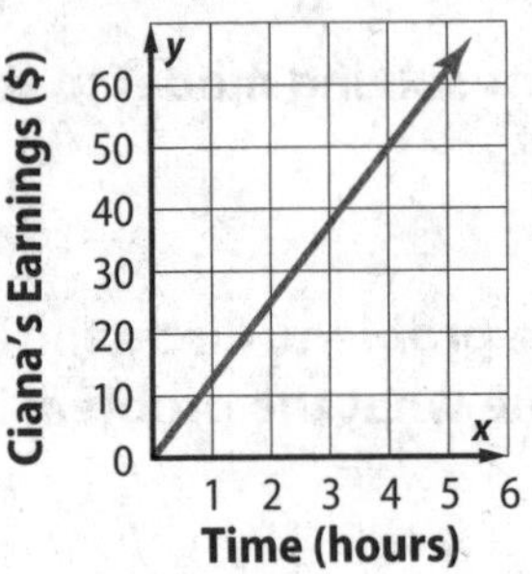

19. Ian travels 75 feet when he walks 30 paces. He travels 100 feet when he walks 40 paces. He writes and graphs an equation of the form $y = mx$ that represents the relationship between the number of paces x and the number of feet traveled y. If the graph passes through the point $(4, y_1)$, what is the value of y_1? P MP

20. Three students have part-time jobs. For each student, the amount earned varies directly with the amount of time worked. Jada earns $510 by working 50 hours and then gets a raise of $0.50 per hour. Kami earns $606 by working 60 hours and then gets a 5% raise. Tyrell earns $9.90 per hour and then gets a 10% raise. Who has the highest hourly rate after the raises? Justify your answer. P MP

P = Proportionality MP = Mathematical Processes

Focus on Mathematical Processes
Guess, Check, and Revise

Polar Plunge

Adrienne's class is going to the zoo to see a polar bear exhibit. Student admission is \$6.50 and adult admission is \$11.50. They spent \$210 on 30 tickets.

How many students and adults are going to the zoo?

Mathematical Process
8.1(B) Use a problem-solving model that incorporates analyzing given information, formulating a plan or strategy, determining a solution, justifying the solution, and evaluating the problem-solving process and the reasonableness of the answer.

Targeted TEKS 8..8

Analyze

What are the facts?

The student cost is \$6.50 and the adult cost is \$11.50. There are 30 people on the trip.

Plan

What is your strategy to solve this problem?

Make a guess and check to see if your guess is correct.

Solve

How can you apply the strategy?

Make a table.

Students → s; Adults → a

s	a	$6.50s + 11.50a$	Check
26	4	$6.50(26) + 11.50(4) = 215$	too high
29	1	$6.50(29) + 11.50(1) = 200$	too low
28	2	$6.50(28) + 11.50(2) =$ ☐	
27	3	$6.50(27) + 11.50(3) =$ ☐	

So, 27 students and 3 adults are going to the zoo.

Justify and Evaluate

Does the answer make sense?

$27 + 3 = 30$ and $6.50(27) + 11.50(3) = 210$; the guess is correct. ✓

Coins

Gerardo has $2.50 in quarters, dimes, and nickels.

If he has 18 coins, how many of each coin does he have?

Analyze

Read the problem. Circle the information you know.
Underline what the problem is asking you to find.

Plan

Choose a problem-solving strategy.

I will use the ______________________________ strategy.

Solve

Use your problem-solving strategy to solve the problem.

Justify and Evaluate

How do you know your solution is accurate?

____

____

Multi-Step Problem Solving

Work with a small group to solve the following problems. Show your work on a separate piece of paper.

1. Sport Trading Cards

Baseball cards come in packages of 8 and 12. Brighton bought some of each type for a total of 72 baseball cards.

How many of each package did he buy?

2. Family

Five siblings have a combined age of 195 years. The oldest is 13 years older than the youngest, Marc. The middle child, Anna, is five years younger than Josie. The other two siblings are 6 years apart.

If the second oldest child is 42, what are the ages of the siblings?

3. Wrap it Up

Shya works part-time at a gift-wrapping store. The store sells wrapping paper rolls and square packages of wrapping paper. There are a total of 125 rolls and packages. Each roll costs \$3.50, and each package costs \$2.25. The total cost of all of the rolls and packages is \$347.50.

How many rolls of wrapping paper are there?

4. Future Careers

Number of Students	Speaker
15	all three
20	nurse and firefighter
30	Webmaster and nurse
12	firefighter only

One hundred fifteen students could sign up to hear three different speakers for career day. Seventy students heard the nurse speak, 52 heard the firefighter, and 78 heard the Webmaster. Some students heard more than one speaker. The results are shown in the table above.

How many students signed up only to hear the Webmaster?

Mid-Chapter Check

Vocabulary Check

Vocab

1. Define *slope*. Explain how to find the slope of a line. TEKS 8.4(C), 8.1(D)

Key Concept Check

2. Cross out the relationship that does not belong in the organizer. Support your answer. TEKS 8.5(A), 8.1(E)

Number of Pizzas	1	2	3	4
Cost ($)	8	16	24	32

$c = 6.75n$

The cost for pizzas varies directly with the number of pizzas ordered.

Number of Pizzas	1	2	3	4
Cost ($)	10	18	26	34

3. MP **Select Tools and Techniques** Ernesto baked 3 cakes in $2\frac{1}{2}$ hours. Assume that the number of cakes baked varies directly with the number of hours. Write and solve a direct variation equation to find how many cakes can he bake in $7\frac{1}{2}$ hours.

TEKS 8.5(E), 8.1(C)

Multi-Step Problem Solving

4. A club logo has four concentric circles. Suppose you graph the circumference versus the diameter. Which of the following is the slope of the resulting line? P N MP

Ⓐ πr^2

Ⓑ $2\pi r$

Ⓒ πd

Ⓓ π

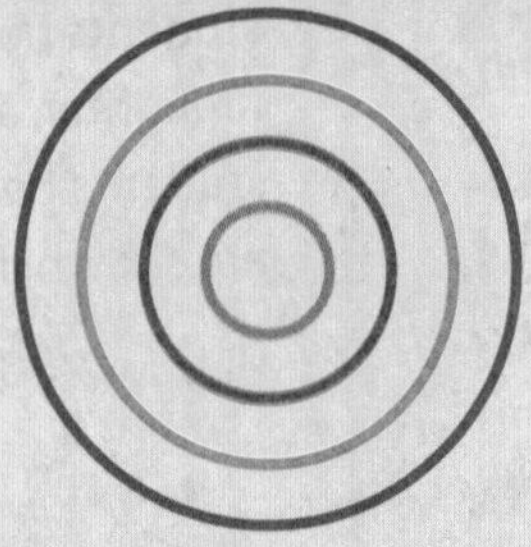

P = Proportionality N = Number and Operations MP = Mathematical Processes

Hands-On Lab 6-a

Proportional and Non-Proportional Relationships

INQUIRY HOW can I use multiple representations to distinguish between proportional linear relationships and non-proportional linear relationships?

The total cost of 3 cups of hot chocolate at a local coffee shop is \$8.25. Assume that the total cost of cups of hot chocolate y varies directly with the number of cups of hot chocolate ordered x. What is the cost of one hot chocolate?

Texas Essential Knowledge and Skills TEKS

Targeted TEKS
8.5(F) Distinguish between proportional and non-proportional situations using tables, graphs, and equations in the form $y = kx$ or $y = mx + b$, where $b \neq 0$.

Mathematical Processes
8.1(C), 8.1(D), 8.1(E), 8.1(F),

Hands-On Activity 1

Step 1 Complete the table for 0, 1, 2, and 3 cups of hot chocolate. Assign the variables x and y.

Cups of Hot Chocolate, ___	Cost (\$) ___

Step 2 Graph the ordered pairs on the coordinate plane below. Then connect the points with a straight line.

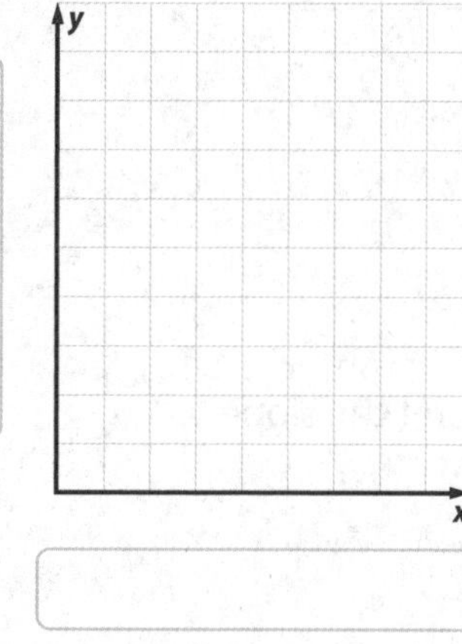

1. Write an equation in $y = mx$ form that represents this relationship. ______
2. Determine and interpret the slope.
3. The *y-intercept* of a line is the y-coordinate of the point where the line crosses the y-axis. Determine and interpret the y-intercept.
4. Determine if this is a proportional or non-proportional relationship. Explain.
5. Is the relationship a direct variation? Why or why not?

The relationship in Activity 1 is linear proportional. The graph of a linear proportional relationship is a straight line that passes through the origin. The quantities in its table have a constant ratio.

Suppose a company charges $10 for a golf shirt and $2 for each word embroidered on the shirt. Let's investigate this relationship.

Hands-On Activity 2

Step 1 Complete the table for 0, 1, 2, and 3 words embroidered. Assign the variables *x* and *y*.

Words Embroidered,	Cost ($)

Step 2 Graph the ordered pairs on the coordinate plane shown. Then connect the points with a straight line.

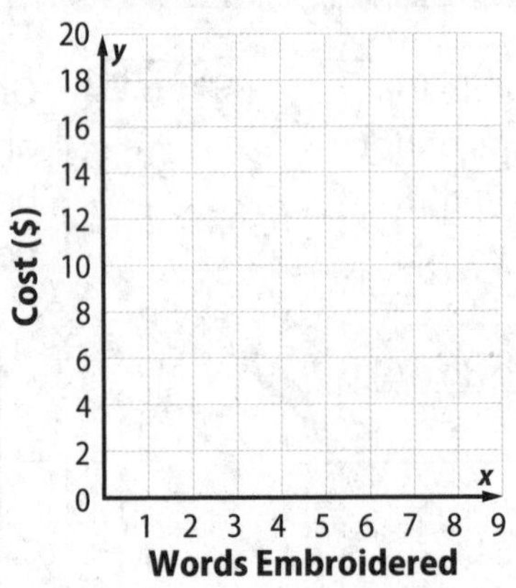

6. Determine and interpret the slope.

7. Determine and interpret the *y*-intercept.

8. Determine if this is a proportional or non-proportional relationship. Explain.

9. Can the equation be written in $y = mx$ form? Explain.

Work with a partner. For each linear relationship, determine the slope and *y*-intercept. Then determine if the relationship is proportional or non-proportional. Justify your response.

10. The graph below shows the linear relationship between the number of pizza toppings ordered and the cost.

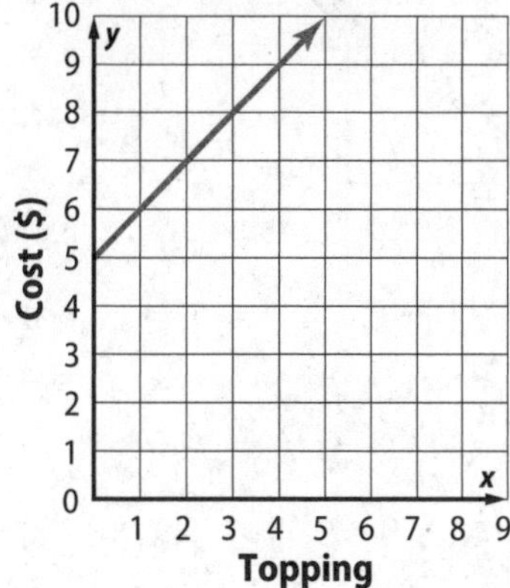

slope: ____ *y*-intercept: ____

11. The graph below shows the linear relationship between the number of pages read and the number of days.

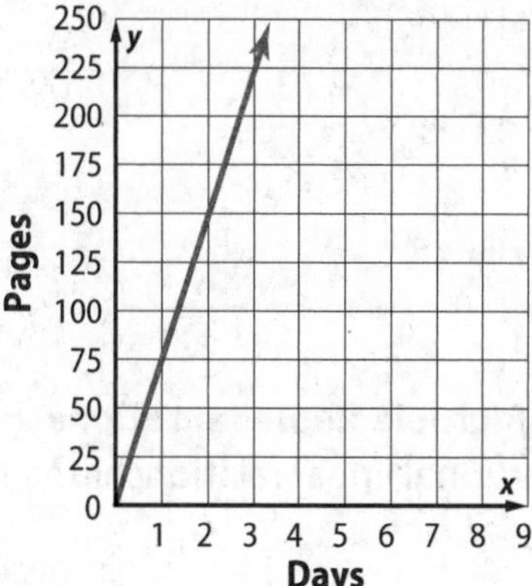

slope: ____ *y*-intercept: ____

12.

Time (min), *x*	Cupcakes Iced, *y*
10	20
20	40
30	60
40	80

slope: ____ *y*-intercept: ____

13.

Time (months), *x*	Savings ($), *y*
10	450
20	650
30	850
40	1,050

slope: ____ *y*-intercept: ____

Analyze and Reflect

MP Organize Ideas **Refer to Exercises 10–13. Work with a partner to complete the table. The first one is done for you.**

	Exercise	y-intercept	Is the relationship a direct variation?	Can the equation be written in $y = mx$ form?
14.	10	5	no	no
15.	11			
16.	12			
17.	13			

18. **MP Use Multiple Representations** How does a graph represent a proportional linear relationship? a table?

19. **MP Use Multiple Representations** How does a graph represent a non-proportional linear relationship? a table?

20. **MP Analyze Relationships** If you know the *y*-intercept of a linear relationship, how can you determine whether the relationship is a direct variation?

Create

21. Write the equations for two relationships, one proportional and one non-proportional.

22. **INQUIRY** HOW can I use multiple representations to distinguish between proportional linear relationships and non-proportional linear relationships?

Lesson 6

Equations in $y = mx + b$ Form

Launch the Lesson: Real World

Watch

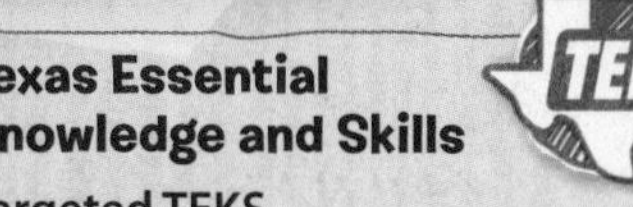

Texas Essential Knowledge and Skills

Targeted TEKS

8.5(I) Write an equation in the form $y = mx + b$ to model a linear relationship between two quantities using verbal, numerical, tabular, and graphical representations. *Also addresses 8.4(C), 8.5(B).*

Mathematical Processes

8.1(A), 8.1(B), 8.1(D), 8.1(G)

Vocab

Vocabulary

y-intercept

slope-intercept form

Essential Question

WHY are graphs helpful?

An interception in football is when a defensive player catches a pass made by an offensive player.

In a nonproportional linear relationship, the graph passes through the point (0, *b*) or the *y*-intercept. The **y-intercept** of a line is the *y*-coordinate of the point where the line crosses the *y*-axis.

Complete the steps to derive the equation for a non-proportional linear relationship by using the slope formula.

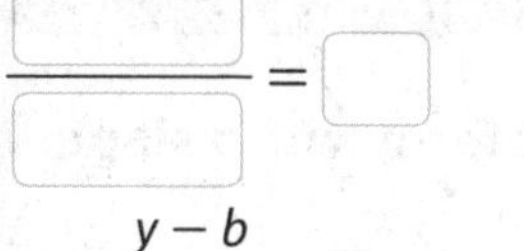

$\frac{\square}{\square} = \square$ Slope formula

$\frac{y - b}{x - 0} = m$ $(x_1, y_1) = (0, b)$

$(x_2, y_2) = (x, y)$

$\frac{\square}{\square} = m$ Simplify.

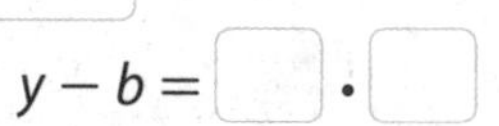

$y - b = \square \cdot \square$ Multiplication Property of Equality

$y = \square + \square$ Addition Property of Equality

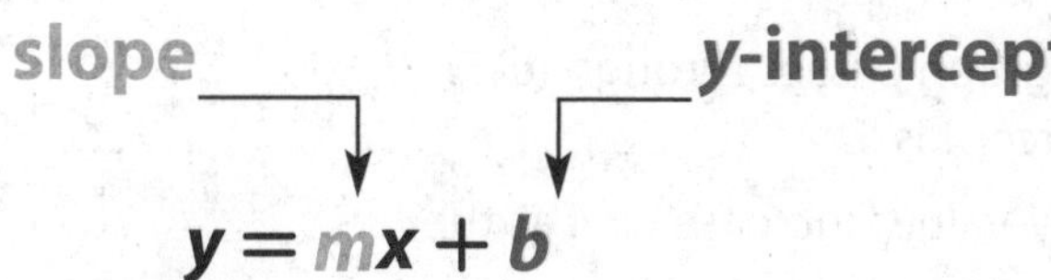

How can knowing about an interception in football help you remember the definition of *y*-intercept?

____

____

Which MP **Mathematical Processes** did you use? **Shade the circle(s) that applies.**

Ⓐ Apply Math to the Real World.
Ⓑ Use a Problem-Solving Model.
Ⓒ Select Tools and Techniques.
Ⓓ Use Multiple Representations.
Ⓔ Organize Ideas.
Ⓕ Analyze Relationships.
Ⓖ Justify Arguments.

Work Zone

Slope-Intercept Form of a Line

Proportional linear relationships can be written in the form $y = mx$. Non-proportional linear relationships can be written in the form $y = mx + b$, where $b \neq 0$. This is called the **slope-intercept form.** When an equation is written in this form, m is the slope and b is the y-intercept.

slope: $\frac{2}{3}$

$$y = \frac{2}{3}x - 4$$

y-intercept: -4

Tutor

Examples

1. Write an equation of a line in slope-intercept form with a slope of −3 and a y-intercept of −4.

$y = mx + b$ — Slope-intercept form

$y = -3x + (-4)$ — Replace m with -3 and b with -4.

$y = -3x - 4$ — Simplify.

2. Write an equation in slope-intercept form for the relationship shown in the table.

Since the graph passes through (0, 5), the y-intercept is 5.

Since the y-values increase by 4 as the x-values increase by 2, the slope is $\frac{4}{2}$ or 2.

x	0	2	4	6
y	5	9	13	17

+2 +2 +2 (x-values); +4 +4 +4 (y-values)

$y = mx + b$ — Slope-intercept form

$y = 2x + 5$ — Replace m with 2 and b with 5.

3. Write an equation in slope-intercept form for the graph shown.

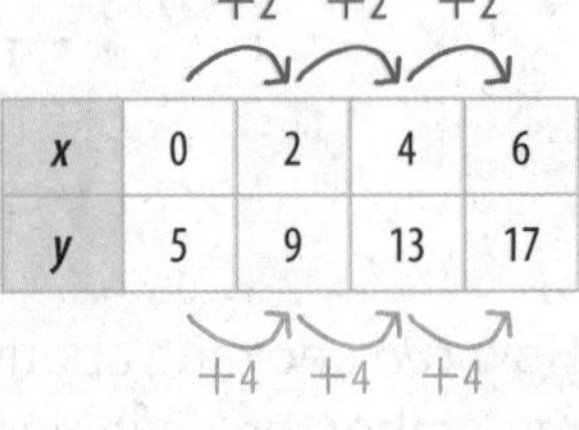

The y-intercept is 4. From (0, 4), you move down 1 unit and right 2 units to another point on the line.

So, the slope is $-\frac{1}{2}$.

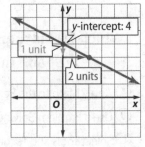

$y = mx + b$ — Slope-intercept form

$y = -\frac{1}{2}x + 4$ — Replace m with $-\frac{1}{2}$ and b with 4.

Got It? Do these problems to find out.

a. Write an equation of a line in slope-intercept form with a slope of $\frac{3}{4}$ and a y-intercept of -3.

b. Write an equation of a line in slope-intercept form for the table.

x	0	−2	−4	−6	−8
y	8	12	16	20	24

c. Write an equation in slope-intercept form for the graph shown.

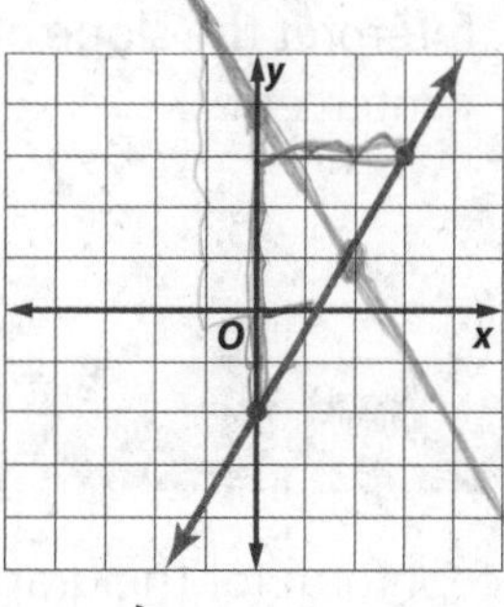

a. $y=\frac{3}{4}x-3$

b. $y=-2(x)+8$

c. $y=\frac{5}{3}x+2$

Interpret the Slope and the Y - Intercept

When an equation in slope-intercept form applies to a real-world situation, the slope represents the rate of change and the y-intercept represents the initial value.

Examples

4. Student Council is selling T-shirts during spirit week. It costs \$20 for the design and \$5 to print each shirt. The cost y to print x shirts is given by $y = 5x + 20$. Graph $y = 5x + 20$ using the slope and y-intercept.

Step 1 Determine the slope and y-intercept.
$y = 5x + 20$

slope = 5
y-intercept = 20

Step 2 Graph the y-intercept (0, 20).

Step 3 Write the slope 5 as $\frac{5}{1}$. Use it to locate a second point on the line. Go up 5 units and right 1 unit. Then draw a line through the points.

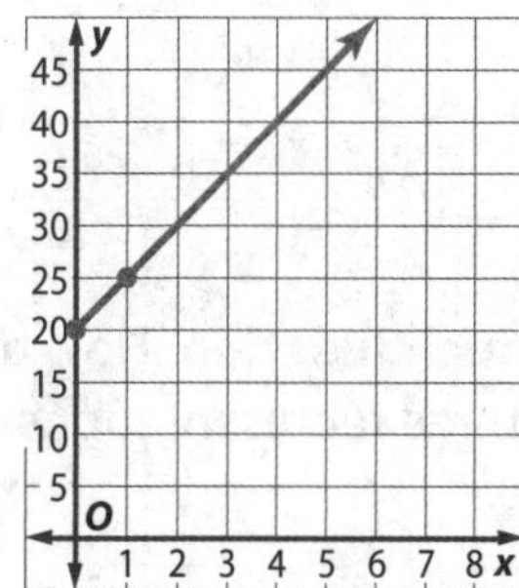

5. Interpret the slope and the y-intercept.

The slope 5 represents the cost in dollars per T-shirt. The y-intercept 20 is the one-time charge in dollars for the design.

e. ______________

Got It? Do these problems to find out.

A taxi fare in dollars y can be determined by the equation $y = 0.75x + 2.50$, where x is the number of miles traveled.

d. Graph the equation.

e. Interpret the slope and the y-intercept.

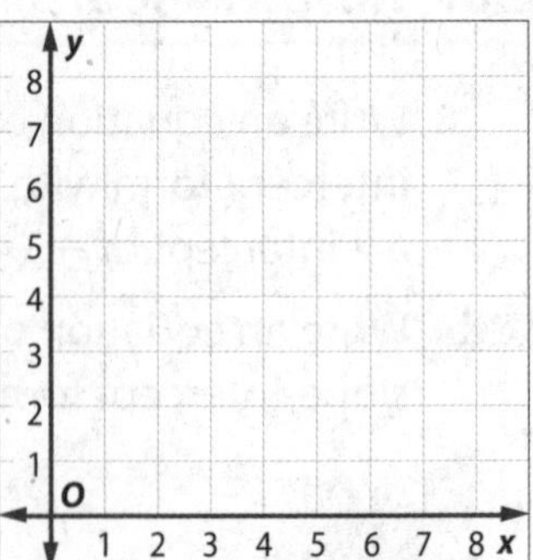

Guided Practice

1. Write an equation in slope-intercept form for the graph shown. (Examples 1 and 4) y=mx+b

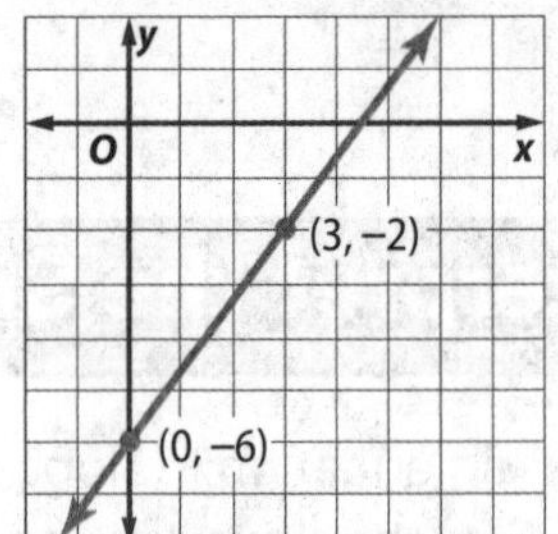

2. Write an equation in slope-intercept form for the table. (Example 2)

x	8	4	0	−4
y	2	4	6	8

____

3. Liam is reading a 254-page book for school. He can read 40 pages in one hour. The equation for the number of pages he has left to read is $y = 254 - 40x$, where x is the number of hours he reads. (Examples 3, 4, and 5)

a. Graph the equation.

b. Interpret what the slope and the y-intercept represent.

____

____

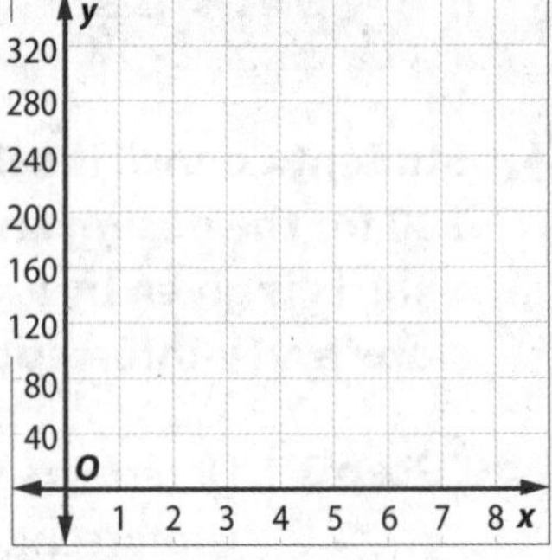

4. **Building on the Essential Question** How does the y-intercept appear in these three representations: table, equation, and graph? ______________

____

____

____

____

Rate Yourself!

How confident are you about equations in slope-intercept form? Check the box that applies.

Check

Find out online. Use the Self-Check Quiz.

FOLDABLES Time to update your Foldable!

Name ______________________ My Homework ______________________

Independent Practice

8.5(I), 8.5(B), 8.4(C), 8.1(A), 8.1(D), 8.1(G) **TEKS**

Write an equation of a line in slope-intercept form with the given slope and *y*-intercept. (Example 1)

1. slope: $-\frac{3}{4}$, *y*-intercept: -2

$y = mx + b$

$y = -\frac{3}{4}x - 2$

2. slope: $\frac{5}{6}$, *y*-intercept: 8

$y = mx + b$

$y = \frac{5}{6}x + 8$

Write an equation in slope-intercept form for each table. (Example 2)

3.

x	0	3	6	9
y	10	14	18	22

$y = \frac{4}{3}x + 10$

4.

x	8	6	4	2
y	2	3	4	5

Write an equation in slope-intercept form for each graph shown. (Example 3)

5.

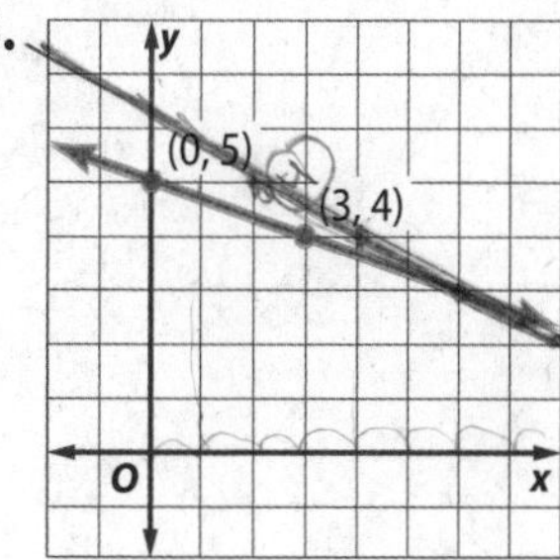

6.

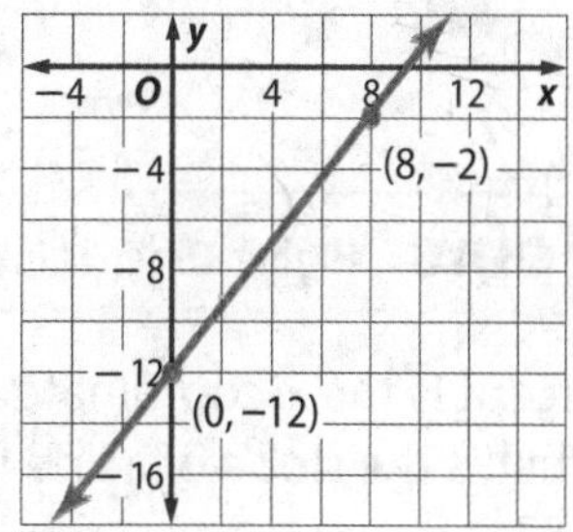

7. MP **Use Multiple Representations** The Viera family is traveling from Philadelphia to Orlando for vacation. The equation $y = 1{,}000 - 65x$ represents the distance in miles remaining in their trip after *x* hours. (Examples 4 and 5)

a. Graph the equation.

b. Interpret the slope and the *y*-intercept. 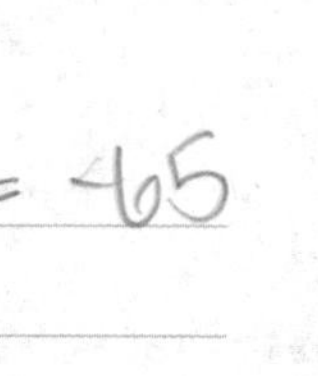

y-intercept = 1000

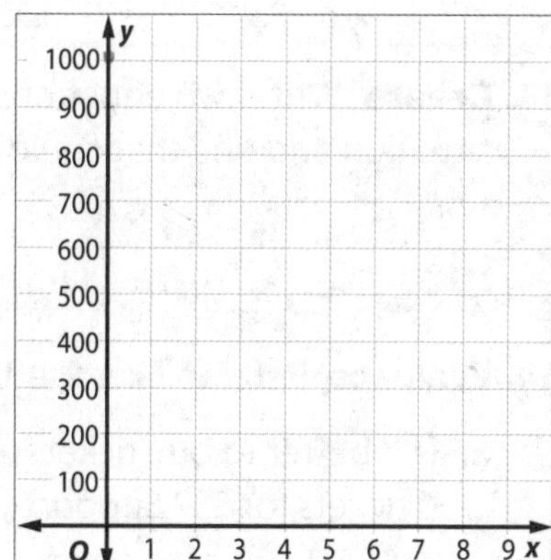

Copy and Solve Graph each equation on a separate piece of grid paper.

8. $y = \frac{1}{3}x - 5$

9. $y = -x + \frac{3}{2}$

10. $y = -\frac{4}{3}x + 1$

11. MP **Apply Math to the Real World** Refer to the graphic novel frame below for Exercises a–b.

Suppose admission to the fair is $3.

a. Write an equation in slope-intercept form for the total cost of admission and any number of tickets at the rate of 6 tickets for $5. ______

b. Write an equation in slope-intercept form for the total cost of admission and any number of tickets at the rate of 12 tickets for $8. ______

H.O.T. Problems Higher-Order Thinking

12. Analyze The x-intercept is the x-coordinate of the point where a graph crosses the x-axis. What is the slope of a line that has a y-intercept but no x-intercept? Explain. ______

13. Create Write two equations, one that could represent a proportional linear situation and one that could represent a non-proportional linear situation

______

14. Evaluate Refer to Exercise 11.

a. Is it better to buy tickets at the rate of 12 tickets for $8 or at the rate of 6 tickets for $5? Support your answer.

______

Name ____________________

Multi-Step Problem Solving

15. The table shown at the right represents the online cost of a specific number of tickets, including a \$2 handling fee, at a movie theater last week. Next week, the movie theater will increase the online ticket price by \$1 each. Which equation represents the new online cost of movie theater tickets, including the \$2 handling fee? P MP

Number of Tickets	Cost (\$)
0	2
1	11
2	20
3	29

Ⓐ $y = 9x$

Ⓑ $y = 9x + 2$

Ⓒ $y = 10x$

Ⓓ $y = 10x + 2$

Use a problem-solving model to solve this problem.

1 Analyze

Read the problem. Circle the information you know. Underline what the problem is asking you to find.

2 Plan

What will you need to do to solve the problem? Write your plan in steps.

Step 1 Write an ________ that represents ____________.

Step 2 Revise the ________ to represent ____________.

3 Solve

Use your plan to solve the problem. Show your steps.

Last week, the cost per ticket was $\frac{\square - \square}{\square - \square} = \$\square$.

The equation ________ represents the cost of x number of tickets last week. So, the equation ________ represents the new cost. The correct answer is ____.

Read to Succeed!
When writing an equation in slope-intercept form, ask yourself what the slope will represent and what the y-intercept will represent.

4 Justify and Evaluate

How do you know your solution is accurate?

____

____

____

P = Proportionality MP = Mathematical Processes

More Multi-Step Problem Solving

Use a problem-solving model to solve each problem.

16. The table shown below shows the number of pizzas ordered from a local pizza shop and the total cost in dollars. The cost includes a \$2 delivery fee. Next week, the shop is going to decrease the price of a pizza by \$1.50. Which equation represents the new relationship? P MP

Number of Pizzas	Total Cost (\$)
1	13
2	24
3	35
4	46

Ⓐ $y = 9.50x + 2$

Ⓑ $y = 9.50x$

Ⓒ $y = 12.50x + 2$

Ⓓ $y = 12.50x$

17. Davina is comparing cell phone plans. The first plan has a flat fee of \$10 per month plus \$0.04 per text message. The second plan has a flat fee of \$5 per month plus \$0.12 per text message. What is the difference in dollars of the two plans for sending 15 text messages each month for six months? N MP

18. A puppy grows at a constant rate of 1.25 pounds per week. After 4 weeks, he weighs 8 pounds. How many pounds will he weigh after 6 weeks if he continues to grow at the same rate? P N MP

19. If the given line is slid right 4 and up 2 grid spaces, what will be the equation of the line? P N MP

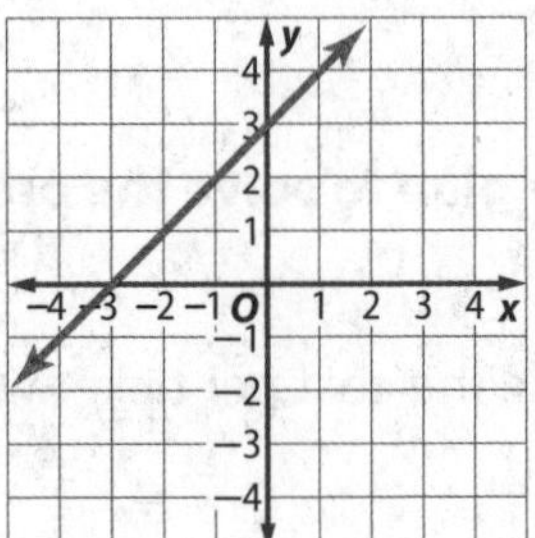

N = Number and Operations P = Proportionality MP = Mathematical Processes

Lesson 7

Graph a Line Using Intercepts

Launch the Lesson: Real World

Watch 

Alonso's classmates spent \$48 on an order of nachos and popcorn. Each serving of nachos costs \$3 and each serving of popcorn costs \$2. The equation $2x + 3y = 48$ represents this situation. On the graph of the equation, what does the point (24, 0) represent?

1. Complete the steps to write the equation in slope-intercept form.

$$2x + 3y = 48$$

$$\underline{\square = \square}$$

$$\frac{3y}{\square} = \frac{48 - 2x}{\square}$$

$$y = 16 - \frac{2}{3}x$$

$$y = \frac{\square}{\square}x + \square$$

slope ↑ ↑ ***y*-intercept**

2. Graph the equation. What does the point (24, 0) represent?

____

____

____

____

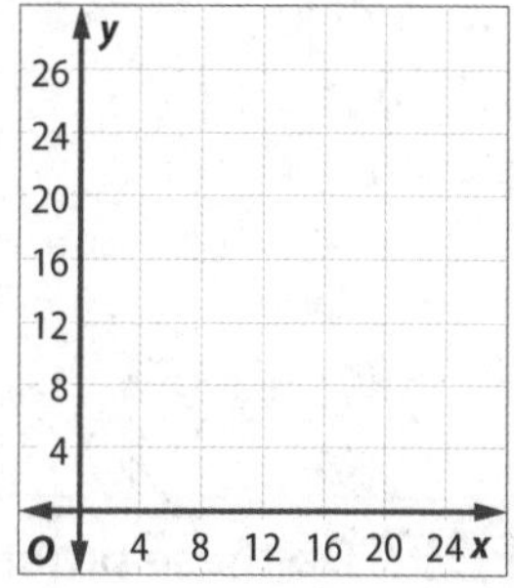

Texas Essential Knowledge and Skills

TEKS

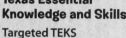

Targeted TEKS

8.5(B) Represent linear non-proportional situations with tables, graphs, and equations in the form $y = mx + b$ where $b \neq 0$. *Also addresses 8.4(C).*

Mathematical Processes

8.1 (A), 8.1 (B), 8.1 (F)

Vocab

Vocabulary

x-intercept

standard form

Essential Question

WHY are graphs helpful?

nachos?

Which MP Mathematical Processes did you use? Shade the circle(s) that applies.

Ⓐ Apply Math to the Real World.

Ⓑ Use a Problem-Solving Model.

Ⓒ Select Tools and Techniques.

Ⓓ Use Multiple Representations.

Ⓔ Organize Ideas.

Ⓕ Analyze Relationships.

Ⓖ Justify Arguments.

Work Zone

a. 15

b.

Slope-Intercept Form

The **x-intercept** of a line is the x-coordinate of the point where the graph crosses the x-axis. Since any linear equation can be graphed using two points, you can use the x- and y-intercepts to graph an equation.

Tutor

Example

1. Determine the x- and y-intercepts of $y = 1.5x - 9$. Then use the intercepts to graph the equation.

Step 1 First determine the y-intercept.

$y = 1.5x + (-9)$ — Write the equation in the form $y = mx + b$.

$b = -9$

Step 2 To determine the x-intercept, let $y = 0$ and solve for x.

$0 = 1.5x - 9$ — Write the equation. Let $y = 0$.

$9 = 1.5x$ — Addtion Property of Equality

$\frac{9}{1.5} = \frac{1.5x}{1.5}$ — Division Property of Equality

$6 = x$ — Simplify.

Step 3 Graph the points (6, 0) and (0, −9) on a coordinate plane. Then connect the points.

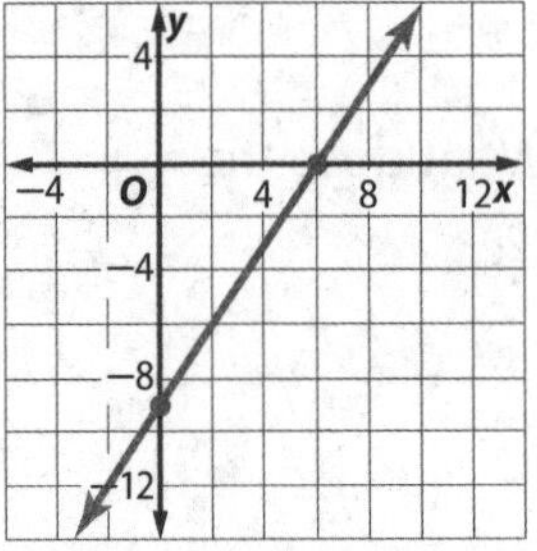

Got It? Do these problems to find out.

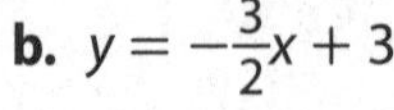

a. $y = -\frac{1}{3}x + 5$

b. $y = -\frac{3}{2}x + 3$

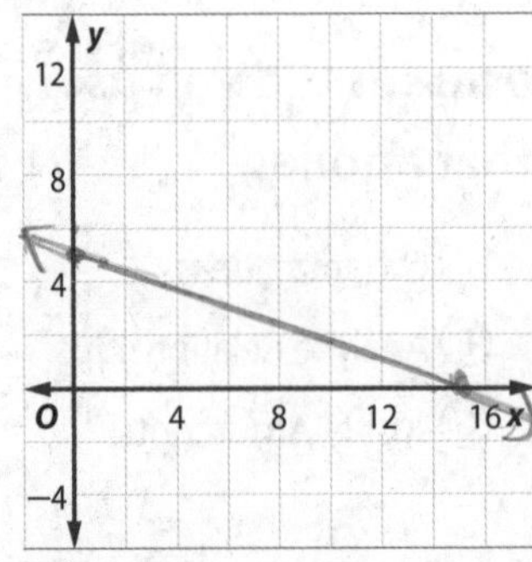

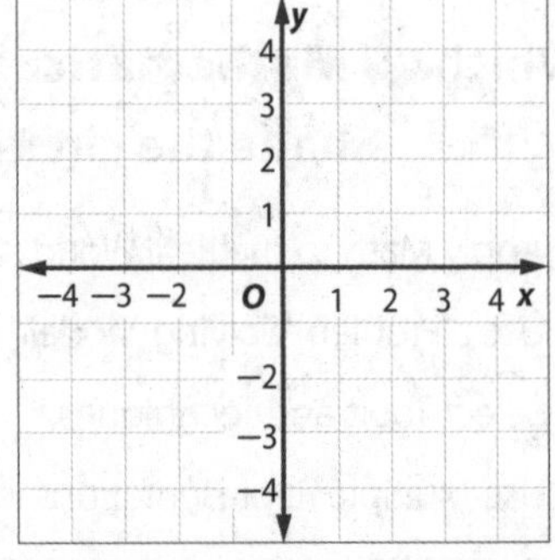

Standard Form

When an equation is written in the form $Ax + By = C$, where $A \geq 0$, and A, B, and C are integers, it is written in **standard form**.

Describe below two different methods for graphing a line.

Examples

Tutor

Mauldin Middle School wants to make \$4,740 from yearbooks. Print yearbooks x cost \$60 and digital yearbooks y cost \$15. This can be represented by the equation $60x + 15y = 4{,}740$.

2. Use the x- and y-intercepts to graph the equation.

To find the x-intercept, let $y = 0$. To find the y-intercept, let $x = 0$.

$$60x + 15y = 4{,}740 \qquad 60x + 15y = 4{,}740$$
$$60x + 15(0) = 4{,}740 \qquad 60(0) + 15y = 4{,}740$$
$$60x = 4{,}740 \qquad 15y = 4{,}740$$
$$x = 79 \qquad y = 316$$

3. Interpret the x- and y-intercepts.

The x-intercept is at the point (79, 0). This means they can sell 79 print yearbooks and 0 digital yearbooks to earn \$4,740.

The y-intercept is at the point (0, 316). This means they can sell 0 print yearbooks and 316 digital yearbooks to earn \$4,740.

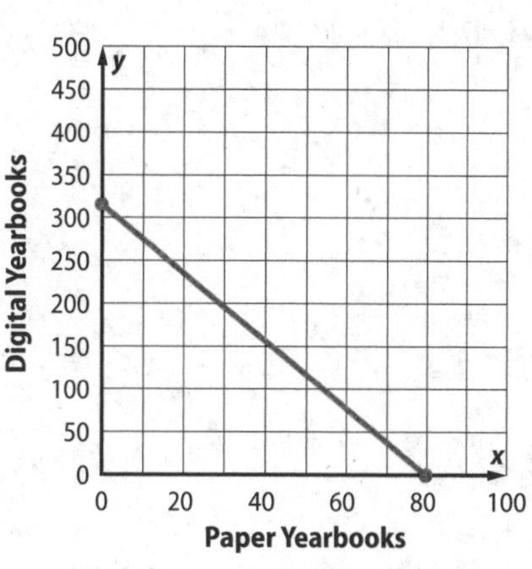

y-intercept

When an equation is written in slope-intercept form, $y = mx + b$, the y-intercept is equal to b.

Got It? Do this problem to find out.

c. Mr. Davies spent \$230 on lunch for his class. Sandwiches x cost \$6 and drinks y cost \$2. This can be represented by the equation $6x + 2y = 230$. Use the x- and y-intercepts to graph the equation. Then interpret the intercepts.

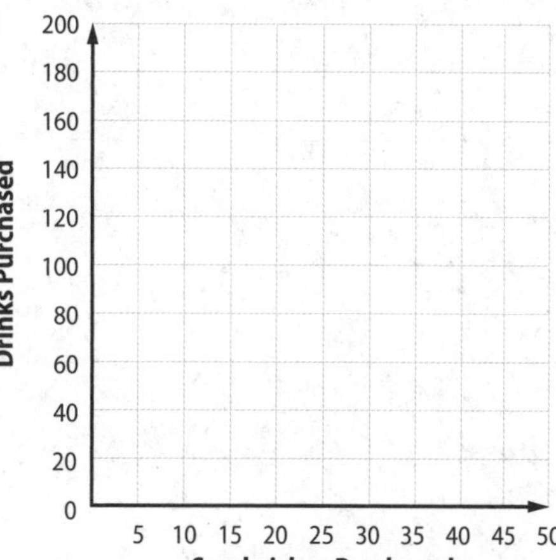

c. ______________

Guided Practice

Determine the *x*- and *y*-intercepts of each equation. Then use the intercepts to graph the equation. (Example 1)

1. $y = 3x - 9$ ____________

Show your work.

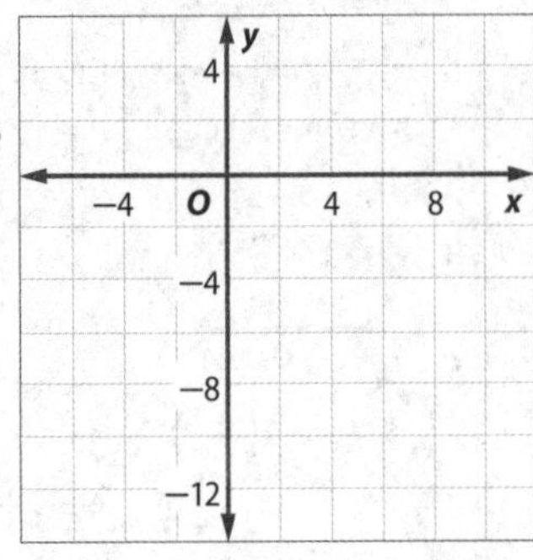

2. $y = \frac{1}{2}x + 2$ ____________

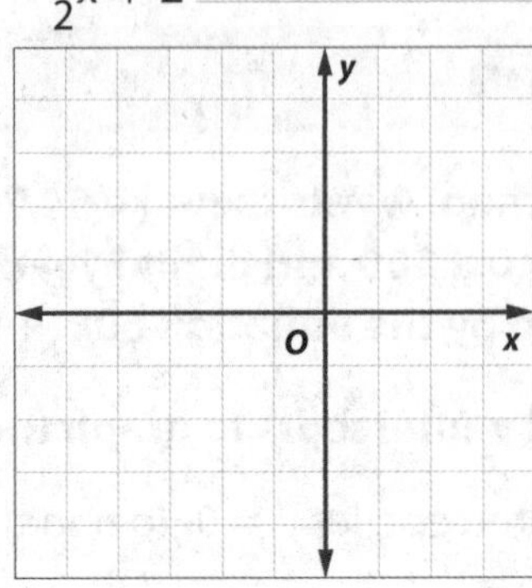

3. A store sells juice boxes in packages of 6 boxes and 8 boxes. They have 288 total juice boxes. This is represented by the function $6x + 8y = 288$. Use the *x*- and *y*-intercepts to graph the equation. Then interpret the *x*- and *y*-intercepts. (Examples 2 and 3)

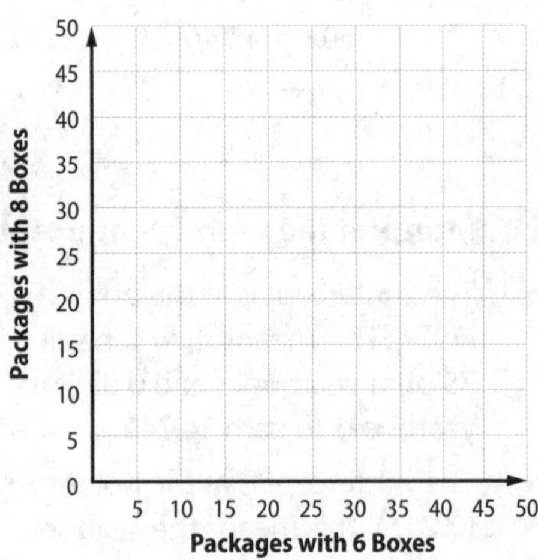
Packages with 8 Boxes
Packages with 6 Boxes

4. **Building on the Essential Question** How can the *x*-intercept and *y*-intercept be used to graph a linear equation? ____________

Rate Yourself!

Are you ready to move on? Shade the section that applies.

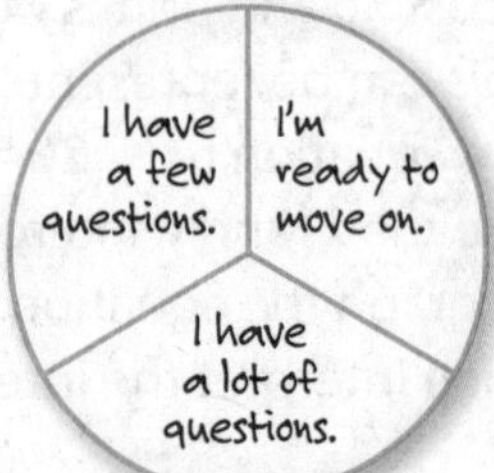
I have a few questions.
I'm ready to move on.
I have a lot of questions.

Find out online. Use the Self-Check Quiz.

Check

Name ________________________________ My Homework ________________________________

Independent Practice

8.5(B), 8.4(C), 8.1(D) TEKS

Determine the *x*- and *y*-intercepts of each equation. Then use the intercepts to graph the equation. (Example 1)

1. $y = -2x + 7$

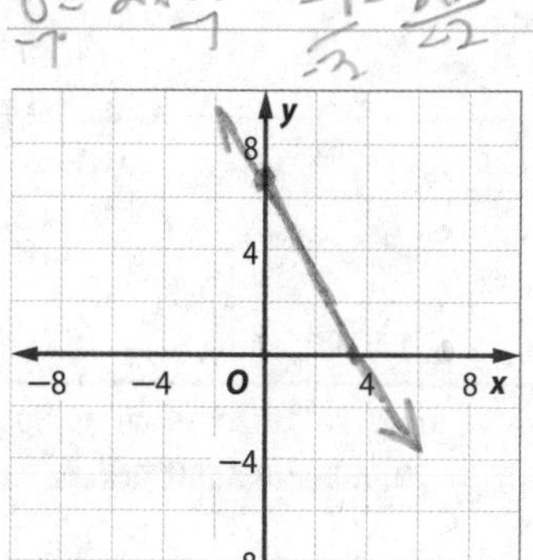

2. $y = \frac{3}{4}x + 3$

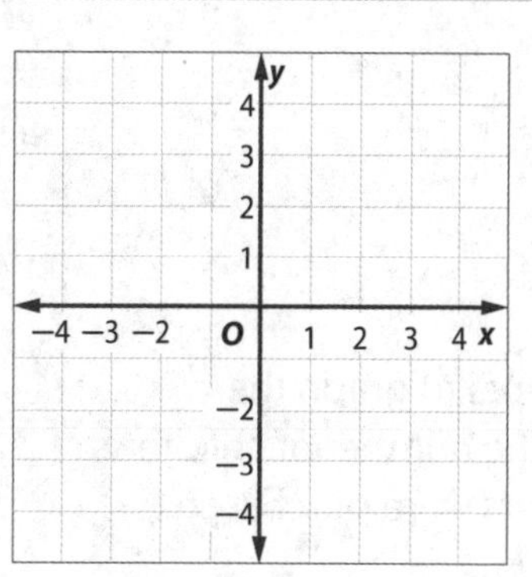

3. $12x + 9y = 15$

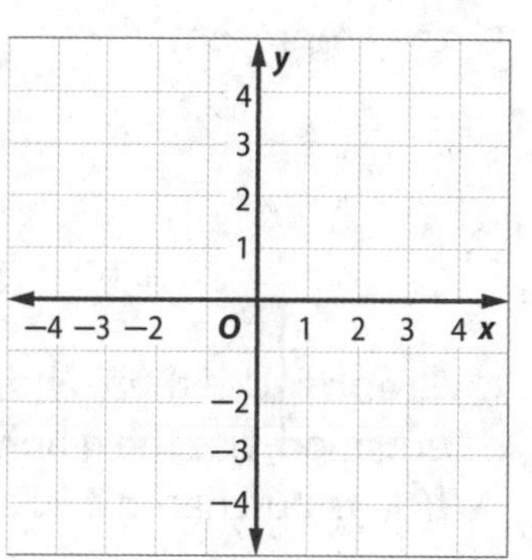

4. The table shows the cost for a clothing store to buy jeans and khakis. The total cost for Saturday's shipment, $1,800, is represented by the equation $15x + 20y = 1{,}800$. Use the *x*- and *y*-intercepts to graph the equation. Then interpret the *x*- and *y*-intercepts. (Examples 2 and 3)

	Jeans	Khakis
Cost per Pair ($)	15	20
Amount Shipped	x	y

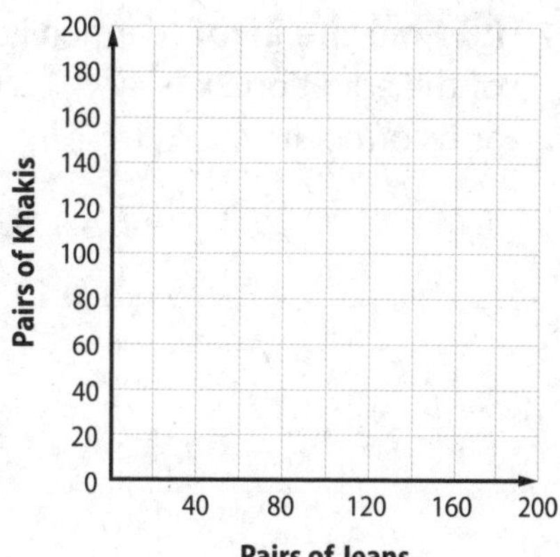

5. The total number of legs, 1,500, on four-legged and two-legged animals in a zoo can be represented by the equation $4x + 2y = 1{,}500$. Use the *x*- and *y*-intercepts to graph the equation. Then interpret the *x*- and *y*-intercepts. (Examples 2 and 3)

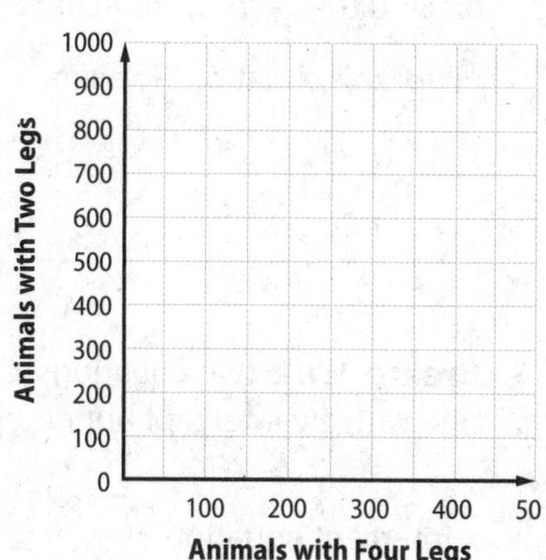

6. **MP Use Multiple Representations** The total cost of a group's tickets to an amusement park is \$1,350. Each adult ticket cost \$45, and each student ticket cost \$30.

   a. **Symbols** Write an equation to represent the number of adult tickets x and children tickets y.

   ____

   b. **Words** What are the x- and y-intercepts and what do they represent? ______________________________

   ____

   ____

   ____

   c. **Graphs** Use the x- and y-intercepts to graph the equation. Use the graph to find the number of children's tickets purchased if 20 adult tickets were purchased.

   ____

Number of Children's Tickets: 0, 5, 10, 15, 20, 25, 30, 35, 40, 45, 50, 55, 60

Number of Adult Tickets: 5, 10, 15, 20, 25, 30, 35, 40, 45, 50, 55, 60

7. **MP Find the Error** Carmen is finding the x-intercept of the equation $3x - 4y = 12$. Find her mistake and correct it.

   ____

   ____

H.O.T. Problems Higher Order Thinking

8. **Analyze** The perimeter of a rectangle x units wide and y units long is 24 feet.

   a. Write an equation in standard form for the perimeter. ______________

   b. Find the x- and y-intercepts. Does either intercept make sense as a solution for this situation? Explain. ______________________________

   ____

   ____

   ____

9. **Create** Write two equations, one with an x-intercept but no y-intercept, and one with a y-intercept but no x-intercept.

   x-intercept equation: ______________

   y-intercept equation: ______________

Name ______________________________

Multi-Step Problem Solving

10. Concession sales for x number of hot dogs and y number of pizza slices at a football game are represented by the equation $2x + 3y = 1{,}728$. Which statement is true? P EE MP

Ⓐ Each hot dog cost \$3.

Ⓑ Each pizza slice cost \$2.

Ⓒ If 0 hot dogs were sold, then 576 pizza sliced were sold.

Ⓓ If 0 hot dogs were sold, then 864 pizza slices were sold.

Use a problem-solving model to solve this problem.

1 Analyze

Read the problem. Circle the information you know.
Underline what the problem is asking you to find.

2 Plan

What will you need to do to solve the problem? Write your plan in steps.

Step 1 Write the equation in ____________ form.

Step 2 Interpret the meaning of the ____________.

3 Solve

Use your plan to solve the problem. Show your steps.

The equation can be written as $y =$ ____________, which means that ______ pizza slices are sold when ______ hot dogs are sold. Since each hot dog costs ______ and each pizza slice costs ______, the correct answer is ______. Fill in that answer choice.

Read to Succeed!
Remember the y-intercept occurs when the x-value is 0.

4 Justify and Evaluate

How do you know your solution is accurate?

____

____

P = Proportionality EE = Expressions, Equations, and Relationships MP = Mathematical Processes

More Multi-Step Problem Solving

Use a problem-solving model to solve each problem.

11. Play ticket sales for x number of Friday evening tickets and y number of Saturday evening tickets are represented by the equation $14x + 21y = 12{,}579$. Which statement is *not* true? P EE MP

Ⓐ Friday night tickets cost $14 each.

Ⓑ Saturday night tickets cost $21 each.

Ⓒ If nobody attended Saturday night, 599 people attended Friday night.

Ⓓ If nobody attended Friday night, 599 people attended Saturday night.

12. Line ℓ shown in the graph below. What is the x-intercept of the line that has the same y-intercept as, but one-half the slope of, ℓ? 

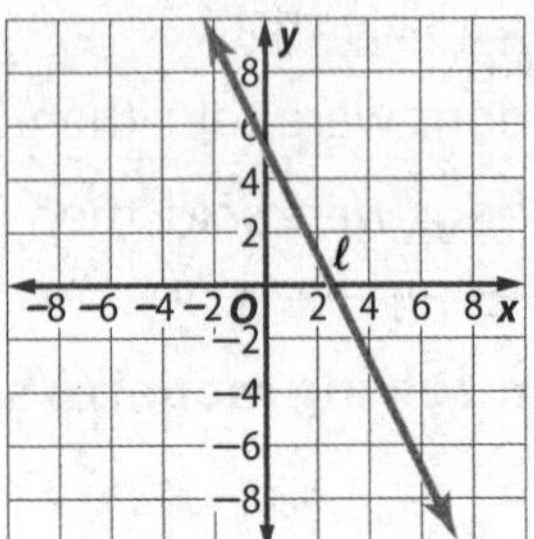

13. The table shows the cost of paint and paint brushes at a local art store. The art store spent $2,400 on the most recent shipment. What is the sum of the slope and y-intercept of the line that represents this shipment? P N MP

	Paint (gal)	Paint Brushes
Cost ($)	14	8
Amount Ordered	x	y

14. Two rectangles are shown below. The perimeter of the smaller rectangle is 130 units. The perimeter of the larger rectangle is 190 units. Write an equation in standard form for each rectangle. What do you know about the y-intercepts of the graphs of the equations? Support your answer. P N MP

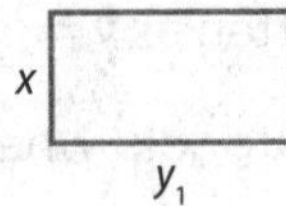

x

y_2

Lesson 8

Write Linear Equations

Launch the Lesson: Real World

The cost for 1, 2, 3, and 4 people to go the zoo is $13, $22, $31, and $40, respectively. If the pattern continues, how much will it cost for any number of people to go to the zoo?

1. Is the relationship linear? Explain.

2. Graph the data.

   How can you find the cost for 10 people? 50 people? 75 people?

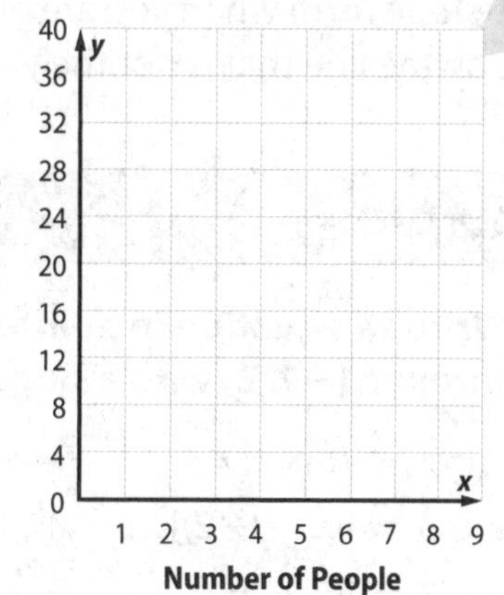

3. What is the slope of the graph? ☐

4. Choose an ordered pair. (☐, ☐) Then substitute the values in the equation below.

   $y = m \cdot x + b$

   $\square = \square \cdot \square + b$

5. Solve for b. Then write an equation of the line in slope-intercept form.

Texas Essential Knowledge and Skills

Targeted TEKS

8.5(I) Write an equation in the form $y = mx + b$ to model a linear relationship between two quantities using verbal, numerical, tabular, and graphical representations. *Also addresses 8.5(B).*

Mathematical Processes

8.1(A), 8.1(B), 8.1(F)

Vocabulary

point-slope form

Essential Question

WHY are graphs helpful?

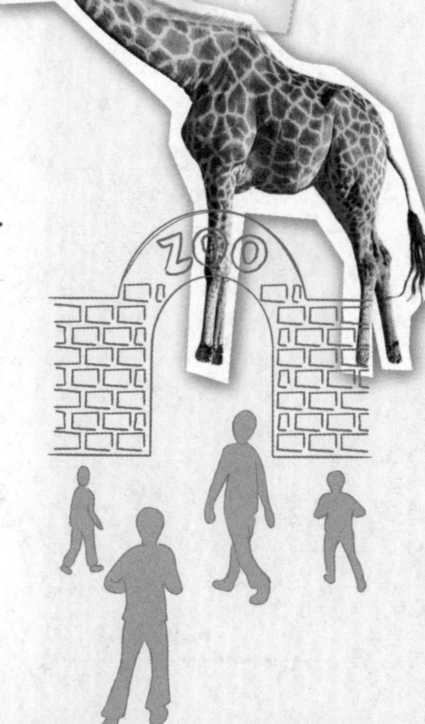

Which MP Mathematical Processes did you use? Shade the circle(s) that applies.

Ⓐ Apply Math to the Real World.
Ⓑ Use a Problem-Solving Model.
Ⓒ Select Tools and Techniques.
Ⓓ Use Multiple Representations.
Ⓔ Organize Ideas.
Ⓕ Analyze Relationships.
Ⓖ Justify Arguments.

Key Concept

Point-Slope Form of a Linear Equation

Words The linear equation $y - y_1 = m(x - x_1)$ is written in point-slope form, where (x_1, y_1) is a given point on a nonvertical line and m is the slope of the line.

Symbols $y - y_1 = m(x - x_1)$

Graph

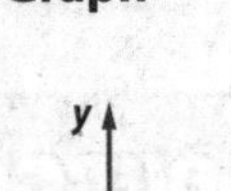
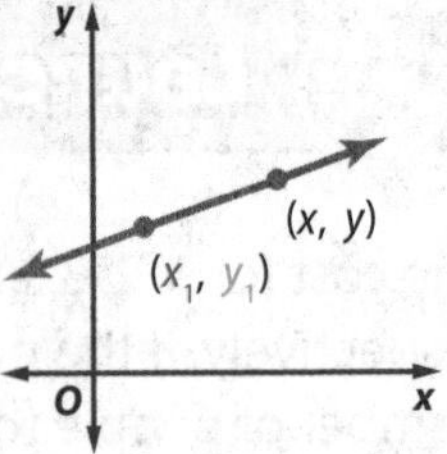

Work Zone

Slope

The point-slope form of a linear equation is tied directly to the definition of slope.

$$\frac{y - y_1}{x - x_1} = m$$

$$(y - y_1) = m(x - x_1)$$

You can write an equation of a line in slope-intercept form when you know the slope and the y-intercept. You can write an equation of a line in **point-slope form** when you are given the slope and the coordinates of a point on the line that is not the y-intercept.

Examples

Tutor

1. Write an equation in point-slope form for the line that passes through (−2, 3) with a slope of 4.

$y - y_1 = m(x - x_1)$ Point-slope form

$y - 3 = 4[x - (-2)]$ $(x_1, y_1) = (-2, 3), m = 4$

$y - 3 = 4(x + 2)$ Simplify.

2. Write the slope-intercept form of the equation from Example 1.

$y - 3 = 4(x + 2)$ Write the equation.

$y - 3 = 4x + 8$ Distributive Property

$\underline{+3 = \quad +3}$ Addition Property of Equality

$y = 4x + 11$ Simplify.

Check: Substitute the coordinates of the given point in the equation.

$y = 4x + 11$

$3 \stackrel{?}{=} 4(-2) + 11$

$3 = 3$ ✓

Got It? Do this problem to find out.

a. Write an equation in point-slope form and slope-intercept form for the line that passes through (−1, 2) and has a slope of $-\frac{1}{2}$.

a. ____________

Write a Linear Equation

Key Concept

From Slope and a Point	• Substitute the slope m and the coordinates of the point in $y - y_1 = m(x - x_1)$.
From Slope and y-intercept	• Substitute the slope m and y-intercept b in $y = mx + b$.
From a Graph	• Find the y-intercept b and the slope m from the graph, then substitute the slope and y-intercept in $y = mx + b$.
From Two Points	• Use the coordinates of the points to find the slope. Substitute the slope and coordinates of one of the points in $y - y_1 = m(x - x_1)$.
From a Table	• Use the coordinates of the two points to find the slope, then substitute the slope and coordinates of one of the points in $y - y_1 = m(x - x_1)$.

The form you use to write a linear equation is based on the information you are given.

Example

Tutor

3. Write an equation in point-slope form and slope-intercept form for the line that passes through (8, 1) and (−2, 9).

Step 1 Find the slope.

$m = \frac{y_2 - y_1}{x_2 - x_1}$ Slope formula

$m = \frac{9 - 1}{-2 - 8}$ $(x_1, y_1) = (8, 1), (x_2, y_2) = (-2, 9)$

$m = \frac{-8}{10}$ or $\frac{-4}{5}$ Simplify.

Step 2 Use the slope and the coordinates of either point to write the equation in point-slope form.

$y - y_1 = m(x - x_1)$ Point-slope form

$y - 1 = -\frac{4}{5}(x - 8)$ $(x_1, y_1) = (8, 1), m = -\frac{4}{5}$.

show your work.

So, the point-slope form of the equation is $y - 1 = -\frac{4}{5}(x - 8)$.

In slope-intercept form, this is $y = -\frac{4}{5}x + \frac{37}{5}$.

Got It? Do these problems to find out.

c. (3, 0) and (6, −3)

d. (−1, 2) and (5, −10)

c. __________

d. __________

Example

Tutor

4. The cost of assistance dog training sessions is shown in the table. Write an equation in point-slope form to represent the cost y of attending x dog training sessions.

Number of Sessions	Cost ($)
5	165
10	290

Find the slope of the line. Then use the slope and one of the points to write the equation of the line.

$m = \frac{290 - 165}{10 - 5}$ $\quad (x_2, y_2) = (10, 290), (x_1, y_1) = (5, 165)$

$m = \frac{125}{5}$ or 25 $\quad$ Simplify.

$y - 165 = 25(x - 5)$ $\quad$ Replace (x_1, y_1) with (5, 165) and m with 25 in the point-slope form equation.

So, the equation of the line is $y - 165 = 25(x - 5)$.

Show your work.

e. ______________

Got It? Do this problem to find out.

e. The cost for making spirit buttons is shown in the table. Write an equation in point-slope form to represent the cost y of making x buttons.

Number of Buttons	Cost ($)
100	25
150	35

Guided Practice

Write an equation in point-slope form and slope-intercept form for each line. (Examples 1–3)

1. passes through (2, 5), slope = 4

____

____

2. passes through (−3, 1) and (−2, −1)

____

____

3. Janelle is planning a party. The cost for 20 people is $290. The cost for 45 people is $590. Write an equation in point-slope form to represent the cost y of having a party for x people. (Example 4)

____

4. **Building on the Essential Question** How does using the point-slope form of a linear equation make it easier to write the equation of a line? ______________

____

____

Rate Yourself!

How confident are you about writing linear equations? Check the box that applies.

Find out online. Use the Self-Check Quiz.

Check

Name ______________________ My Homework ______________________

Independent Practice

8.5(I), 8.5(B), 8.1(D), 8.1(F) TEKS

Write an equation in point-slope form and slope-intercept form for each line. (Examples 1–3)

1. passes through (1, 9), slope = 2

____

2. passes through (4, −1), slope = −3

____

3. passes through (−4, −5), slope = $\frac{3}{4}$

____

4. passes through (3, −6) and (−1, 2)

____

5. passes through (4, −4) and (8, −10)

____

6. passes through (3, 4) and (5, −4)

____

7. **STEM** For a science experiment, Mala measured the height of a plant every week. She recorded the information in the table. Assuming the growth is linear, write an equation in point-slope form to represent the height *y* of the plant after *x* weeks. (Example 4)

Weeks	Height (in)
5	13
10	14

____

8. After 2 seconds on a penalty kick in soccer, the ball travels 160 feet. After 2.75 seconds on the same kick, the ball travels 220 feet. Write an equation in point-slope form to represent the distance y of the ball after *x* seconds. (Example 4) ______________________

MP Use Multiple Representations **Write each equation in standard form.**

9. $y - 4 = -3(x - 3)$

10. $y + 9 = 2(x + 5)$

11. **MP Analyze Relationships** Draw a line connecting the form of the equation to the correct equations.

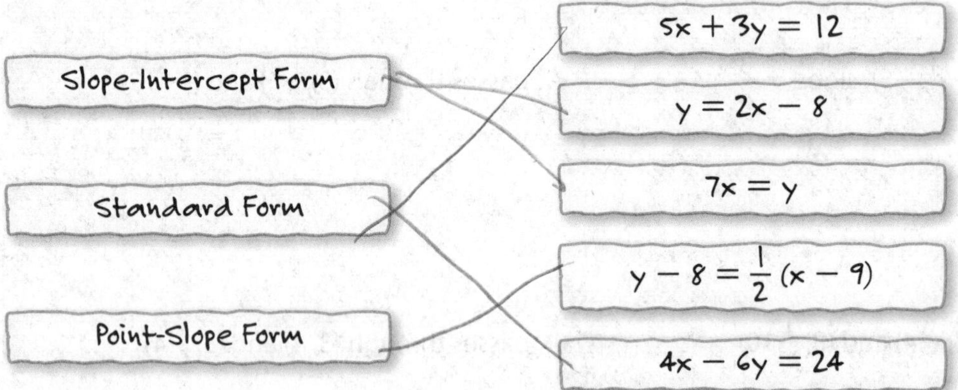

H.O.T. Problems Higher-Order Thinking

12. Create Write a linear equation that is in point-slope form. Identify the slope and name a point on the line.

13. Analyze The equation of a line is $y = -\frac{1}{2}x + 6$. Write an equation in point-slope form for the same line. Justify your answer.

14. Evaluate Order the steps you would take to write a linear equation in slope-intercept form if you know the slope and a point through which the line passes.

_____ Simplify the equation.

_____ Use the Distributive Property to multiply the slope by x and x_1.

_____ Substitute the slope m and the coordinates of the point (x_1, y_1) into the point-slope formula.

_____ Use the Addition Property of Equality.

Name ______________________________

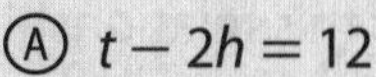

Multi-Step Problem Solving

15. The graph shows the height in inches h of a candle at t number of hours. Which equation represents this relationship? P N MP

Ⓐ $t - 2h = 12$

Ⓑ $t + 2h = 12$

Ⓒ $-t - 2h = 12$

Ⓓ $-t + 2h = 12$

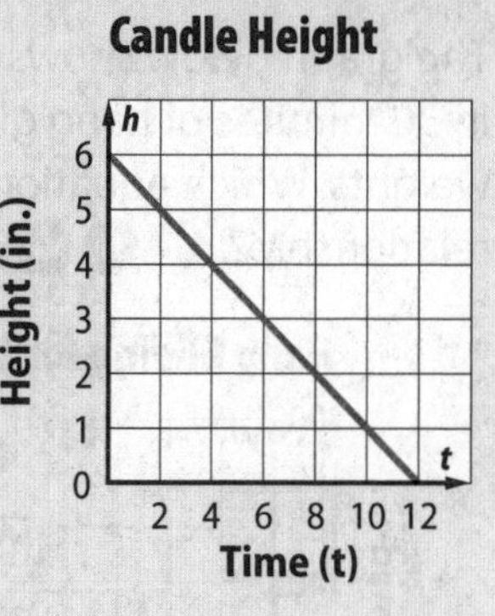

Use a problem-solving model to solve this problem.

1 Analyze

Read the problem. Circle the information you know.
Underline what the problem is asking you to find.

2 Plan

What will you need to do to solve the problem? Write your plan in steps.

Step 1 Use the __________ to write an __________ in slope-intercept form.

Step 2 Write my __________ in standard form.

3 Solve

Use your plan to solve the problem. Show your steps.

The equation __________ represents the relationship. An equivalent equation is __________. So, the correct answer is ______.

Fill in that answer choice.

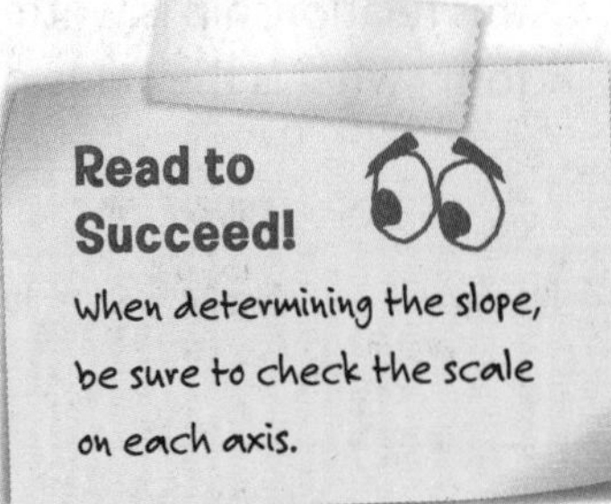

4 Justify and Evaluate

How do you know your solution is accurate?

____

____

____

P = Proportionality N = Number and Operations MP = Mathematical Processes

More Multi-Step Problem Solving

Use a problem-solving model to solve each problem.

16. The graph below shows the Calories burned in 30 minutes of hang gliding at various weights. Which equation represents this relationship? P N MP

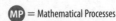

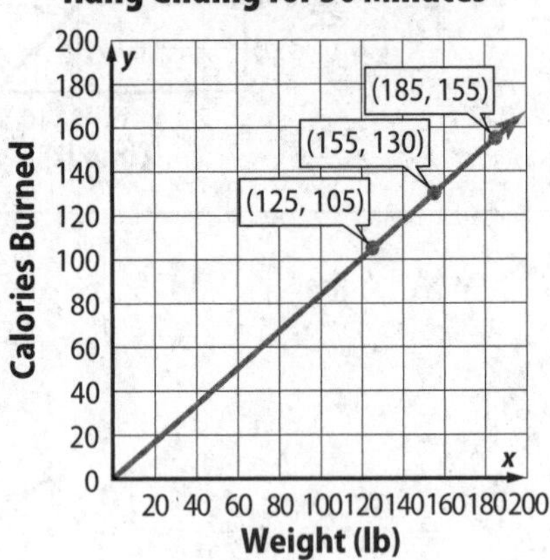

Ⓐ $y = \frac{6}{5}x - \frac{6}{5}$

Ⓑ $y = \frac{6}{5}x + \frac{6}{5}$

Ⓒ $y = \frac{5}{6}x - \frac{5}{6}$

Ⓓ $y = \frac{5}{6}x$

17. A salesperson is paid a daily salary plus commission as shown in the table below. If the equation that represents this relationship is written in slope-intercept form, what is the value of mb? P N MP

Sales x	Earnings y
\$2,000	\$200
\$2,800	\$240
\$3,200	\$260

18. The table below shows the cost C for a taxi ride of m miles. If the equation that represents this relationship is written in slope-intercept form, what is the value of $m + b$? P N MP

Miles	1	2	3
Cost (\$)	6.50	10.00	13.50

19. The rate of water flowing from a hose is shown in the table below. A 30,000-gallon swimming pool starts out with 4,000 gallons. About how many days does it take to fill it to capacity? Support your answer. P N EE MP

Gallons	18	36	45
Minutes	2	4	5

N = Number and Operations P = Proportionality EE = Expressions, Equations, and Relationships MP = Mathematical Processes

Graphing Technology Lab 8-b

Model Linear Behavior

INQUIRY HOW can I select tools and techniques to determine if situations are linear?

Dansela and Jayden walk to school at about 3 miles per hour. Use the Investigation to see if the relationship between time and distance is a linear relationship.

Texas Essential Knowledge and Skills

Targeted TEKS
8.5(C) Contrast bivariate sets of data that suggest a linear relationship with bivariate sets of data that do not suggest a linear relationship from a graphical representation. *Also addresses 8.4(C), 8.5(B), 8.5(F), and 8.5(I).*

Mathematical Processes
8.1 (C), 8.1 (F), 8.1(G)

Hands-On Activity

Step 1 **Set-up the Activity**

- Connect a motion detector to your calculator. Start the data collection program by pressing APPS (CBL/CBR), ENTER, and then select Ranger, Applications, Meters, Set Up/Sample.
- Place the detector on a flat surface, such as a desk or table so that it can read the motion of a walker.
- Mark the floor at a distance of 1 and 5 meters from the detector. Have the walker stand at the 1-meter mark.

Step 2 **Collect the Data**

- Press ENTER and select Start Now to collect data. Have the walker begin to walk away from the detector at a slow but steady pace.
- Stop collecting data when the walker passes the 5-meter mark.

Step 3 **Graph the Data**

- Press ENTER to display a graph of the data. The x-values represent equal intervals of time in seconds. The y-values represent the distances from the detector in meters.

1. Describe the graph of the data. Does the relationship between time and distance appear to be linear? Explain.

Investigate

MP Select Tools and Strategies Refer to the Activity. Work with a partner.

2. Use the TRACE feature on your calculator to find the y-intercept on the graph. Interpret its meaning.

3. Press STAT 1. The time data is in L1 and the distance data is in L2. Calculate the rate of change $\frac{\text{distance}}{\text{time}}$ for three pairs of points.

Point 1 (time, distance)	Point 2 (time, distance)	$\frac{\text{distance}_2 - \text{distance}_1}{\text{time}_2 - \text{time}_1}$	rate of change

4. **MP Justify Arguments** Does your answer to Exercise 3 support your conclusion about the graph in the Activity? Explain .

Analyze and Reflect

5. Predict how the graph and answers to Exercise 3 would change if the walker were to walk at a *quicker* pace? walk *toward* the detector?

Create

6. **MP Analyze Relationships** How could you change the situation to be one that does not display linear behavior?

7. **INQUIRY** HOW can I select tools and techniques to determine if situations linear?

21ST CENTURY CAREER

Mastering Engineer

Do you love listening to music? Are you interested in the technical aspects of music-making? If so, a career creating digital masters might be something to think about! A mastering engineer produces digital masters and is responsible for making songs sound better, having the proper spacing between songs, removing extra noises, and assuring all the songs have consistent levels of tone and balance. Having a great-sounding master helps increase radio airplay and sales for recording artists.

Mathematical Process TEKS
8.1(A) Apply mathematics to problems arising in everyday life, society, and the workplace.
Targeted TEKS 8.4(C)

Is This the Career for You?

Are you interested in a career as a mastering engineer? Take some of the following courses in high school.

- Algebra
- Music Appreciation
- Recording Techniques
- Sound Engineering

Turn the page to find out how math relates to a career in Music.

Explore college and careers at ccr.mcgraw-hill.com

Mastering the Music

Use the information in the tables to solve each problem.

1. At Engineering Hits, is the relationship between the number of songs and the cost linear? Explain your reasoning.

2. Is there a proportional linear relationship between number of songs and cost at Dynamic Mastering? Explain your reasoning.

3. Find the slope of the line represented in the Mastering Mix table. What does the slope represent?

4. Is the linear relationship represented in the Mastering Mix table a direct variation? Explain.

5. Write a direct variation equation to represent number of songs x and cost y at Dynamic Mastering. How much does it cost to master 11 songs?

6. For 4 or more songs at Engineering Hits, the cost varies directly as the number of songs. How much does it cost to master 6 songs?

Engineering Hits	
Number of Songs	Cost ($)
1	100
2	160
3	210
4	250

Dynamic Mastering	
Number of Songs	Cost ($)
2	120
4	240
6	360
8	480

Mastering Mix	
Number of Songs	Cost ($)
1	125
3	275
5	425
7	575

TEKS Career Project

It's time to update your career portfolio! Prepare a brief oral presentation about a mastering engineer and present it to your classmates. As others are presenting, listen carefully to their presentations. At the end, ask any clarifying questions.

Do you think you would enjoy a career as a mastering engineer? Why or why not?

Chapter Review

Vocabulary Check

Work with a partner to complete the crossword puzzle using the vocabulary list at the beginning of the chapter. Take turns saying each sentence aloud while your partner listens carefully.

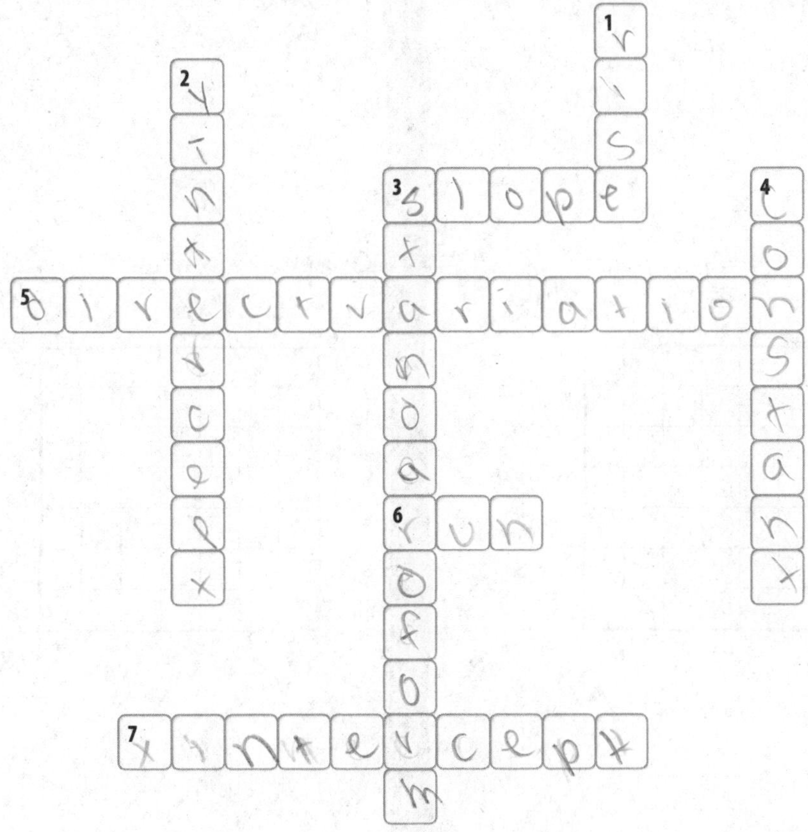

Across

3. to describe the steepness of a straight line
5. a relationship in which the ratio of two variables quantities is constant
6. the horizontal change between the same two points
7. the x-coordinate of the point where the graph crosses the x-axis

Down

1. the vertical change between any two points
2. the y-coordinate of the point where the line crosses the y-axis
3. when an equation is written in the form $Ax + By = C$
4. the word used to describe the rate of change in a linear relationship.

Check

Key Concept Check

Use Your FOLDABLES®

Use your Foldable to help review the chapter. Share your Foldable with a partner and take turns summarizing what you learned in this chapter, while your partner listens carefully. Ask questions for clarification, as needed. TEKS 8.1(E)

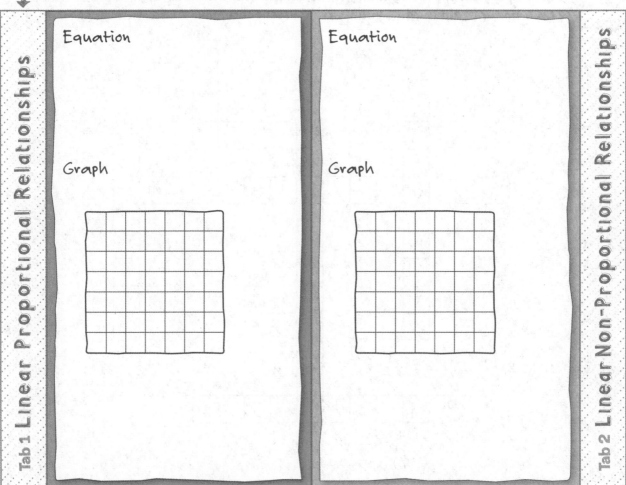

Tab 1 Linear Proportional Relationships

Equation

Graph

Tab 2 Linear Non-Proportional Relationships

Equation

Graph

Got it?

Match each set of information with the correct linear equation.
TEKS 8.5(A), 8.5(B), 8.5(F), 8.5(I)

1. line that passes through (2, 0) and (0, 1)
2. line with a slope of 0.5 and a y-intercept of 1
3. line that passes through (4, 2) and the origin

a. $y = 0.5x$

b. $y = 0.5x + 1$

c. $y = -0.5x + 1$

Multi-Step Problem Solving

4. Teams A and B are participating in a dog-sledding competition. The table shows Team A's times and distances. Team B traveled 3.6 miles in 12 minutes. Assume the distance traveled is directly proportional to the time traveled. For a team to qualify for the championship race, it must travel 110 miles in 6 hours or less. Which team(s) will qualify? Show your work and justify your solution. P N MP

Dog-Sledding Team A	
Time (min)	Distance (mi)
6	2
12	4
18	6

1 Analyze

2 Plan

3 Solve

4 Justify and Evaluate

Got it?

5. Liam and Camila each have a $50 gift card to the same coffee shop. Liam only orders medium iced coffees that cost $2.50 each. Camila only orders grande iced coffees that cost $4 each. The equation $y = 50 - 2.5x$ represents the number of dollars y on Liam's card after x medium iced coffees have been ordered. The equation $y = 50 - 4x$ represents the number of dollars y on Camila's card after x grande iced coffees have been ordered. How many more cups of coffee will Liam have ordered than Camila when there is $30 left on the gift cards? Explain. P N MP

P = Proportionality MP = Mathematical Processes

Reflect

Answering the Essential Question

Use what you learned about graphs to complete the graphic organizer. List three ways in which graphs are helpful. Then give an example for each way.

TEKS 8.1(D), 8.1(F), 8.1(G)

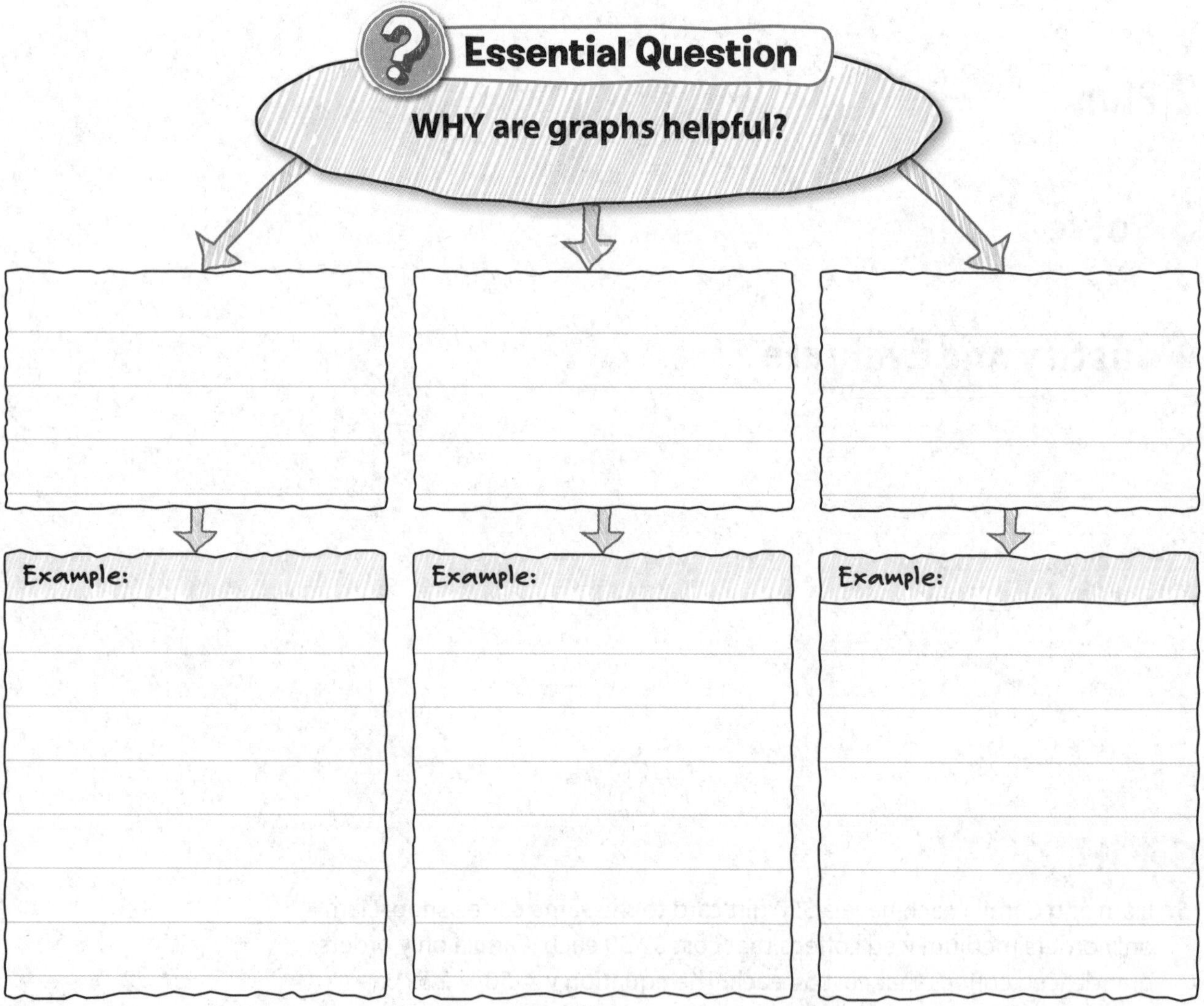

Essential Question

WHY are graphs helpful?

Example:

Example:

Example:

Answer the Essential Question. WHY are graphs helpful? Verbally share yor response with a partner, asking for and providing clarification as needed.

Chapter 4
Functions

Texas Essential Knowledge and Skills

Targeted TEKS

8.5 The student applies mathematical process standards to use proportional and non-proportional relationships to develop foundational concepts of functions. *Also addresses 8.4.*

Mathematical Processes

8.1, 8.1(A), 8.1(B), 8.1(C), 8.1(D), 8.1(E), 8.1(F), 8.1(G)

Essential Question

HOW can we model relationships between quantities?

Math in the Real World

Basketball The American Airlines Center, in Dallas, Texas, is home to the Dallas Mavericks. In basketball, the equation $p = 2x + 3y$ represents the points scored when a team makes x number of 2-point field goals and y number of 3-point field goals. Use the grid below to graph the equation that represents a team score of 96 points.

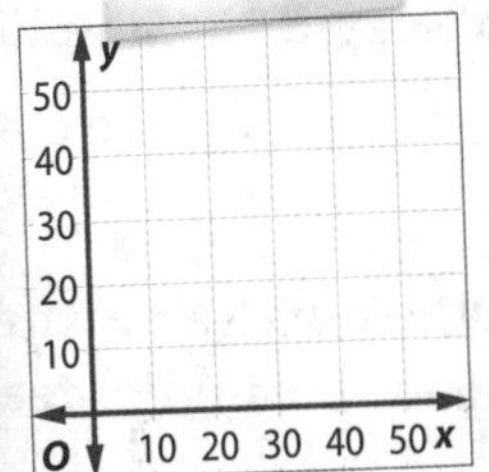

What Tools Do You Need?

Vocabulary

continuous data
dependent variable
discrete data
domain
family of functions
function
independent variable
linear equation
linear function
range
relation

Reading Math

One way to make a word problem easier to understand is to rewrite it using fewer words.

Step 1 **Read the problem and identify the important words and numbers.**

There are a great deal of cell phone plans available for students. With Janelle's plan, she pays $15 per month for 200 minutes, plus $0.10 per minute once she talks for more than 200 minutes. Suppose Janelle can spend $20 each month for her cell phone. How many more minutes can she talk?

Step 2 **Simplify the problem. Keep all of the important words and numbers, but use fewer of them.**

The total monthly cost is $15 for 200 minutes, plus $0.10 times the number of minutes over 200. How many minutes can she talk for $20?

Step 3 **Simplify it again. Use a variable for the unknown.**

The cost of *m* minutes at $0.10 per minute plus $15 is $20.

Work with a partner to rewrite each problem using the method above. Ask for help from your partner or teacher, as needed.

1. Akira is saving money to buy a scooter that costs $125. He has already saved $80 and plans to save an additional $5 each week. In how many weeks will he have enough money for the scooter?

2. Joaquin wants to buy some DVDs that are each on sale for $10 plus a CD that costs $15. How many DVDs can he buy if he has $75 to spend?

When Will You Use This?

Brian and Dion in

Picture This

CLIK!

You should have seen it! It was amazing!

Nice! Did you take any photos?

Yeah, but I haven't gotten them printed yet.

Y'know you can get that done online? Check this out...

Here it is.

Digital Express Photo Company

15¢ per photo plus $2.99 shipping

Perfect!

Now, if I can just figure out how to get the pictures out of the camera...

Your Turn! **You will solve this problem in the chapter.**

Are You Ready?

Quick Review

Review 6.7(A), 6.11(A) TEKS

Example 1

Name the ordered pair for point Q.

Start at the origin. Move right along the x-axis until you reach 1.5. Then move up until you reach the y-coordinate, 2. Point Q is located at (1.5, 2).

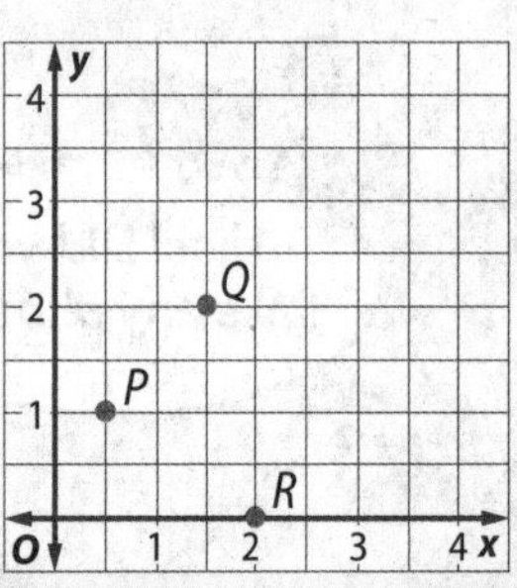

Example 2

Evaluate $6x + 1$ if $x = -4$.

$6x + 1 = 6(-4) + 1$ Replace x with -4.

$= -24 + 1$ Multiply 6 by -4.

$= -23$ Add.

Quick Check

Check 

Coordinate Graphing **Name the ordered pair for each point.**

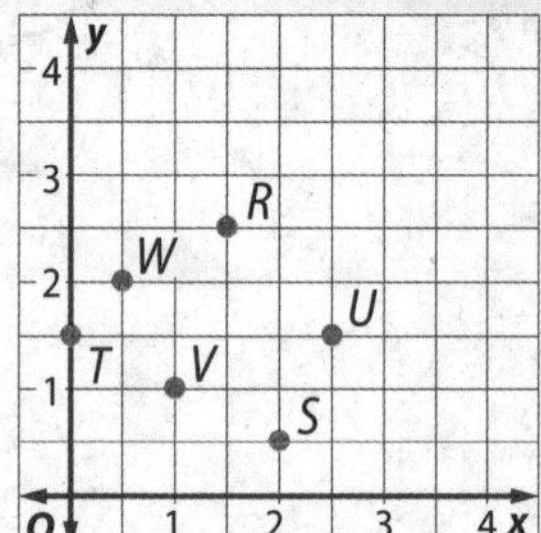

1. R ________
2. S ________
3. T ________
4. U ________
5. V ________
6. W ________

Evaluate Expressions **Evaluate each expression if $x = -6$.**

7. $3x$ ________
8. $4x + 9$ ________
9. $\frac{x}{2}$ ________
10. $\frac{3x}{9}$ ________

11. The weekly profit of a certain company is $48x - 875$, where x represents the number of units sold. Find the weekly profit if the company sells 37 units. ________

How Did You Do?

Which problems did you answer correctly in the Quick Check? Shade those exercise numbers below.

1 2 3 4 5 6 7 8 9 10 11

FOLDABLES®

Use the Foldable throughout the chapter to help you learn about relations and functions.

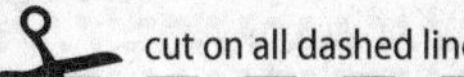
cut on all dashed lines

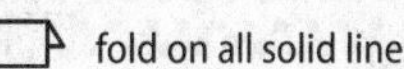
fold on all solid lines

tape to page 324

Relations and Functions

relations

functions

proportional

non-proportional

Use the Foldable throughout the chapter to help you learn about relations and functions.

 cut on all dashed lines   fold on all solid lines    tape to page 324

page 324 Tab 3

Examples

Words

page 324 Tab 2

Examples

Words

page 324 Tab 1

Examples	Examples
Words	Words

Lesson 1

Represent Relationships

Launch the Lesson: Real World

Watch

The orbital velocity of a satellite is about 17,000 miles per hour. Represent the relationship shown in the table using symbols, words, and a graph.

Time (hours)	Distance (miles)
1	17,000
2	34,000
3	51,000
4	68,000
5	85,000

1. Write an algebraic expression for the distance in miles for any number of hours t.

2. Describe the relationship in words.

3. Graph the ordered pairs. What does this tell you about the relationship?

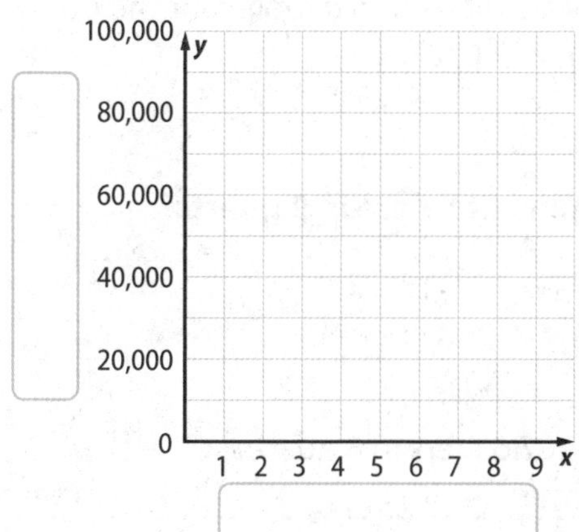

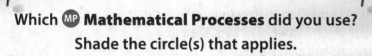

Texas Essential Knowledge and Skills

TEKS

Targeted TEKS

8.5(A) Represent linear proportional situations with tables, graphs, and equations in the form of $y = kx$. *Also addresses 8.4(B), 8.4(C), 8.5(B), and 8.5(I).*

Mathematical Processes

8.1(A), 8.1(B), 8.1(F), 8.1(G)

Vocab

Vocabulary

linear equation

Essential Question

HOW can we model relationships between quantities?

Which MP Mathematical Processes did you use? Shade the circle(s) that applies.

Ⓐ Apply Math to the Real World.
Ⓑ Use a Problem-Solving Model.
Ⓒ Select Tools and Techniques.
Ⓓ Use Multiple Representations.
Ⓔ Organize Ideas.
Ⓕ Analyze Relationships.
Ⓖ Justify Arguments.

Work Zone

Tables, Graphs, and Equations in the form $y = mx$

Recall that an equation is a mathematical sentence stating that two quantities are equal. A **linear equation** is an equation with a graph that is a straight line. Some linear equations contain more than one variable.

Examples

Linear Proportional Relationships

Recall that a linear proportional relationship can be written in the form $y = mx$ or $y = kx$. The relationship in Example 1 is a linear proportional relationship.

The table shows the number of liters in quarts of liquid.

1. Write an equation to determine the number of liters in any number of quarts. Describe the relationship in words.

Quarts, q	Liters, ℓ
1	0.95
2	1.9
3	2.85
4	3.8
5	4.75

+0.95 +0.95 +0.95 +0.95

The rate of change is the rate that describes how one quantity changes in relation to another quantity. The rate of change of quarts to liters is $\frac{1.9 - 0.95}{2 - 1} = \frac{0.95}{1}$ or 0.95 liter in every quart.

Let ℓ represent the liters and q represent the quarts. The equation is $\ell = 0.95q$.

2. About how many liters are in 8 quarts?

$\ell = 0.95q$ Write the equation.

$\ell = 0.95(8)$ Replace q with 8.

$\ell = 7.6$ Multiply.

There are about 7.6 liters in 8 quarts.

Got It? Do these problems to find out.

The total cost of tickets to the school play is shown in the table.

Number of Tickets, t	Total Cost ($), c
1	4.50
2	9.00
3	13.50
4	18.00

a. Write an equation to determine the total cost of any number of tickets. Describe the relationship in words.

b. Use the equation to determine the cost of 15 tickets.

a. ________

b. ________

Tutor

Multi-Step Example

3. The total distance Marlon ran in 5 days is shown in the graph. Write an equation to determine the number of miles ran *y* after any number of days *x*. Then determine how many miles Marlon ran after 2 weeks.

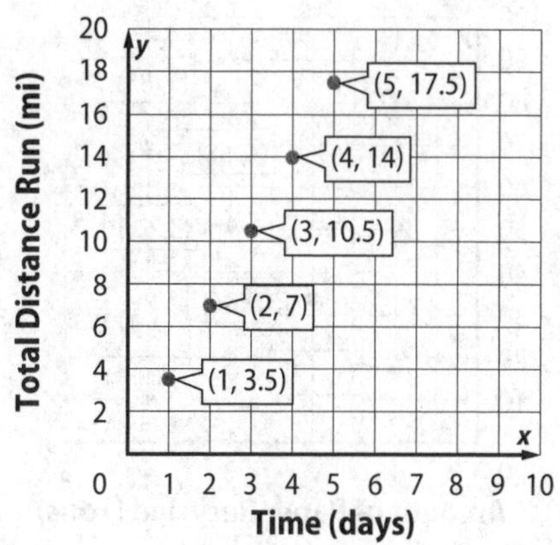

Step 1 Determine the rate of change or the slope of the line.

$m = \frac{y_2 - y_1}{x_2 - x_1}$ Definition of slope

$m = \frac{14 - 7}{4 - 2}$ $(x_1, y_1) = (2, 7); (x_2, y_2) = (4, 14)$

$m = \frac{7}{2}$ or 3.5 Simplify.

Step 2 To determine the *y*-intercept, use the slope and the coordinates of a point to write the equation of the line in slope-intercept form.

$y = mx + b$ Slope-intercept form

$y = 3.5x + b$ Replace *m* with the slope, 3.5.

$7 = 3.5(2) + b$ Use the point (2, 7). $x = 2, y = 7$

$0 = b$ Solve for *b*.

The slope is 3.5 and the *y*-intercept is 0. So, the equation of the line is $y = 3.5x + 0$ or $y = 3.5x$.

Step 3 $y = 3.5x$ Write the equation.

$y = 3.5(14)$ There are 14 days in 2 weeks. Replace *x* with 14.

$y = 49$ Multiply.

Marlon will run 49 miles in 2 weeks.

Linear Non-Proportional Relationships

Recall that a linear proportional relationship can be written in the form $y = mx + b$, where $b \neq 0$. The relationship in Example 3 is a linear proportional relationship.

Got It? Do this problem to find out.

c. The number of trees saved by recycling paper is shown. Write an equation to find the total number of trees y that can be saved for any number of tons of paper x. Then use the equation to determine how many trees could be saved if 500 tons of paper are recycled.

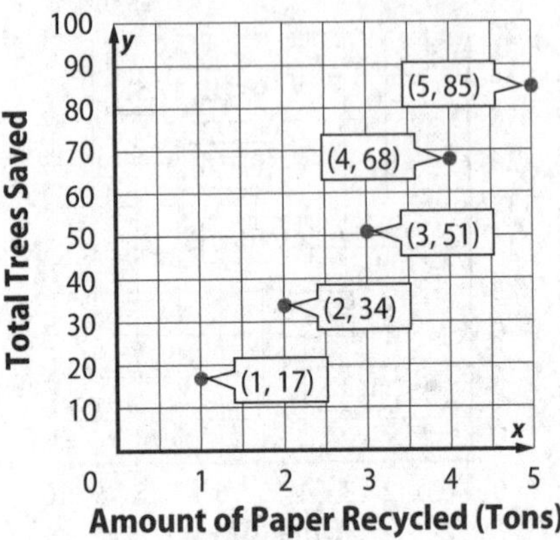

c. ________

Key Concept

Multiple Representations of Linear Proportional and Non-Proportional Relationships

Words

Distance traveled is equal to 12 miles per second times the number of seconds.

Equation

$d = 12s$

Table

Time (seconds)	Distance (miles)
1	12
2	24
3	36
4	48
5	60

Graph

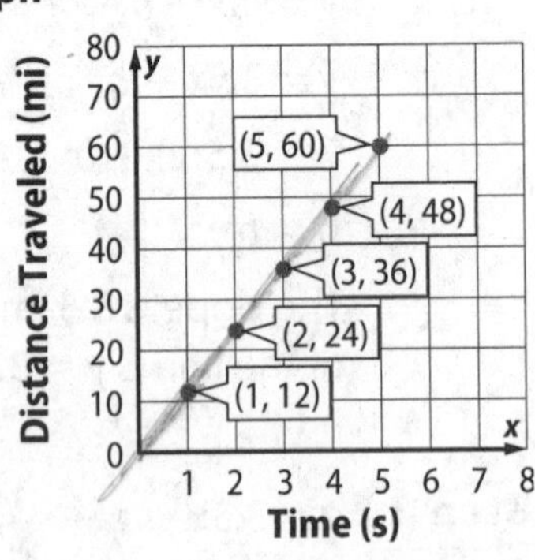

Words, equations, tables, and graphs can be used to represent linear relationships. Not all linear relationships are proportional. Recall that a linear non-proportional relationship can be written in the form $y = mx + b$, where $b \neq 0$. The representations in the Key Concept box above are all linear proportional.

Examples

Tutor

Chloe competes in jump rope competitions. Her average rate is 225 jumps per minute.

4. Write an equation to determine the number of jumps in any number of minutes.

Let j represent the number of jumps and m represent the minutes. The equation is $j = 225m$.

5. Make a table to determine the number of jumps in 1, 2, 3, 4, or 5 minutes. Then graph the ordered pairs.

m	$225m$	j
1	225(1)	225
2	225(2)	450
3	225(3)	675
4	225(4)	900
5	225(5)	1,125

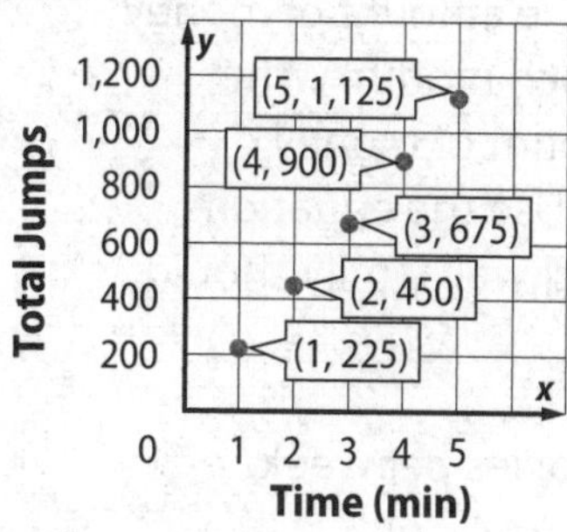

A gym charges an annual membership fee of $10 but you must pay $9.50 for each visit. What equation could be used to represent this real-world situation? Is this relationship linear proportional or linear non-proportional?

Got It? Do these problems to find out.

Financial Literacy **Paul earns $25 for grooming a dog plus $18.50 a day for boarding.**

d. Write an equation to determine the amount of money Paul earned m for grooming a dog once and boarding any number of days d.

e. Make a table to determine his earnings for 5, 6, 7, or 8 days. Then graph the ordered pairs.

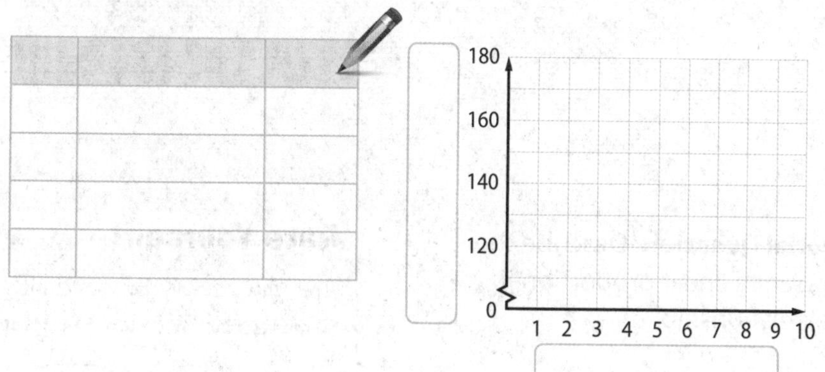

d. ______

$y = 18.5x + 25$

Guided Practice

1. The table shows the total number of text messages that Brad sent over 4 days. (Examples 1 and 2)

Number of Days, d	1	2	3	4
Total Messages, m	50	100	150	200

   a. Write an equation to determine the total number of messages sent in any number of days. Describe the relationship in words.

   ______

   ______

   b. Use the equation to determine how many text messages Brad would send in 30 days. ______

2. **Financial Literacy** The graph shows the amount of money the Rockwell family budgets for food each month. Write an equation to determine the total amount of money c budgeted in any number of months m. Use the equation to determine how much money the Rockwell family should budget for 12 months. (Example 3) ______

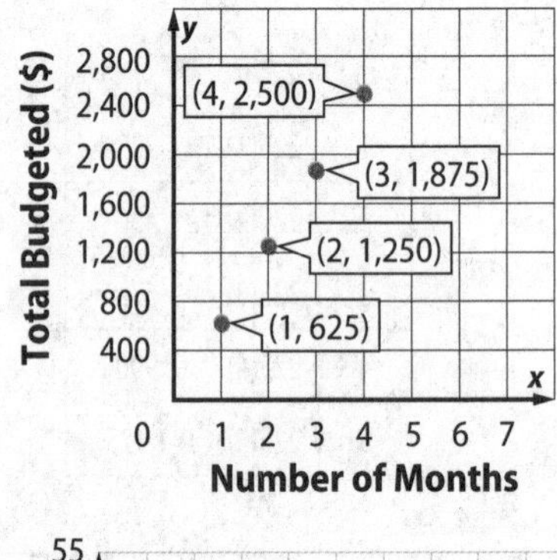

3. A store receives an average of 7 new movies per week. (Examples 4 and 5)

   a. Write an equation to determine the number of new movies m in any number of weeks w. ______

   b. Make a table to determine the number of new movies received in 4, 5, 6, or 7 weeks. Then graph the ordered pairs.

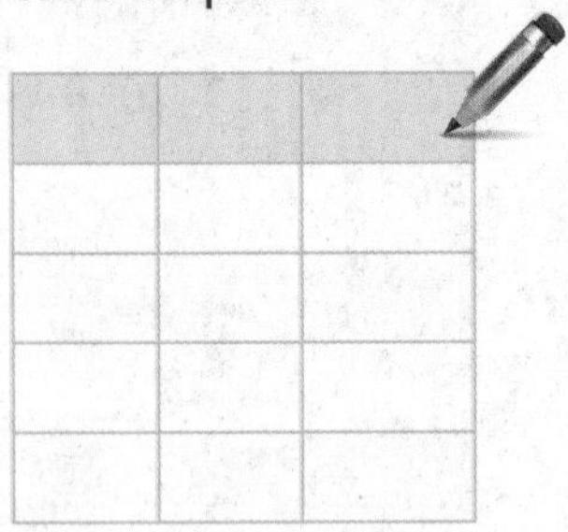

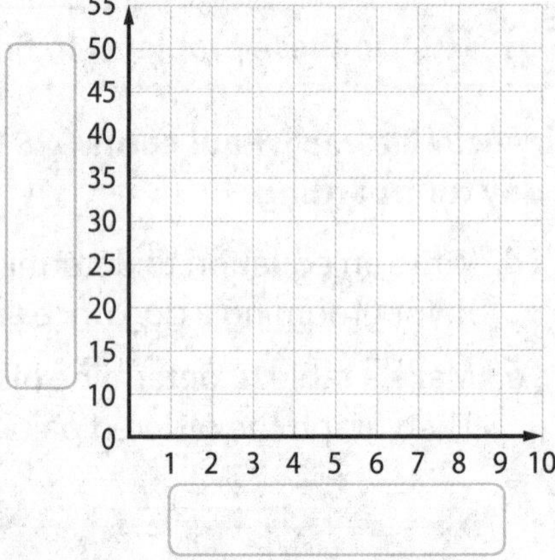

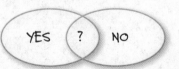

4. **Building on the Essential Question** Describe the different ways you can represent a linear proportional or a linear non-proportional relationship.

______

______

______

______

Rate Yourself!

Are you ready to move on? Shade the section that applies.

YES ? NO

Find out online. Use the Self-Check Quiz.

Name ______________________ My Homework ______________________

Independent Practice

8.5(A), 8.5(B), 8.5(F), 8.5(G) TEKS

1. The number of baskets a company produces each day is shown in the table. (Examples 1 and 2)

Number of Days, d	Total Baskets, b
1	45
2	90
3	135
4	180

a. Write an equation to determine the total number of baskets crafted in any number of days. Describe the relationship in words.

Show your work.

____

b. Use the equation to determine how many baskets the company makes in one non-leap year. ______________________

c. Determine whether this is a linear proportional or linear non-proportional relationship. Explain.

____

2. A type of dragonfly is the fastest insect. The graph shows how far the dragonfly can travel. (Example 3)

Distance Traveled (ft)
120
100
80
60
40
20
0
1 2 3 4 5 6
Time (s)
(1, 23)
(2, 46)
(3, 69)
(4, 92)
(5, 115)

a. Write an equation to determine how far the dragonfly can travel d in any number of seconds s. ______________________

b. How far can the dragonfly travel in one minute? ______________________

3. A library charges a late return fee of \$3.50 plus \$0.15 per day that a book is returned late. (Examples 4 and 5)

a. Write an equation to find the total late fee f for any number of days late d. ______________________

b. Make a table to determine the total fee if a book is 10, 15, 20, or 25 days late. Then graph the ordered pairs.

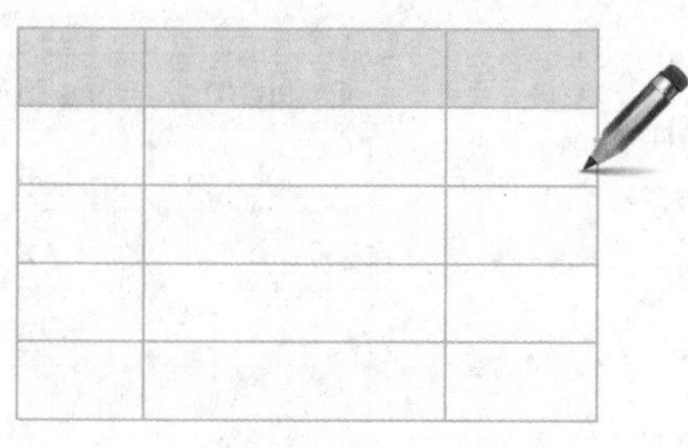

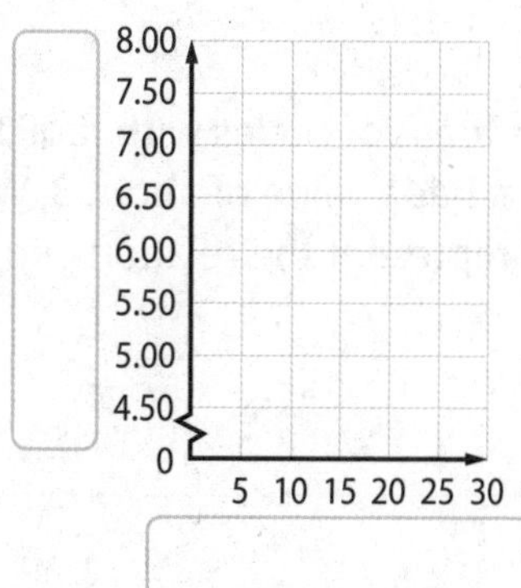

c. Determine whether this is a linear proportional or linear non-proportional relationship. Explain.

____

____

4. **MP Use Multiple Representations** The two fastest times for swimming the English Channel belong to Petar Stoychev and Yvetta Hlaváčová. Petar's average speed was 265 feet per minute. Yvetta's average speed was 249 feet per minute.

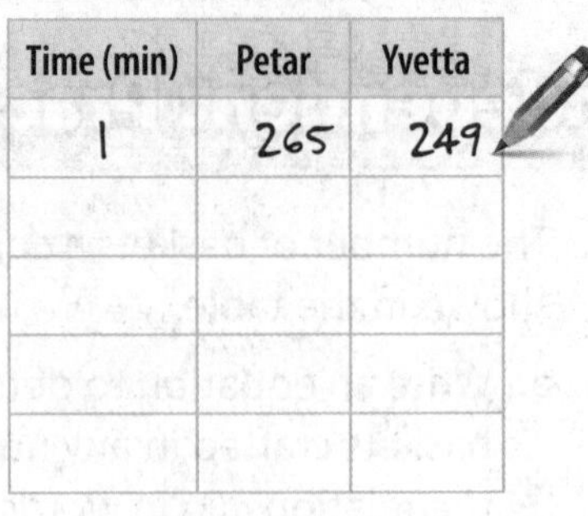

Time (min)	Petar	Yvetta
1	265	249

a. **Tables** Complete the table of ordered pairs in which the *x*-coordinate represents the time and the *y*-coordinate represents the total distance swam in 1–5 minutes.

b. **Graphs** Graph each set of ordered pairs on the coordinate plane.

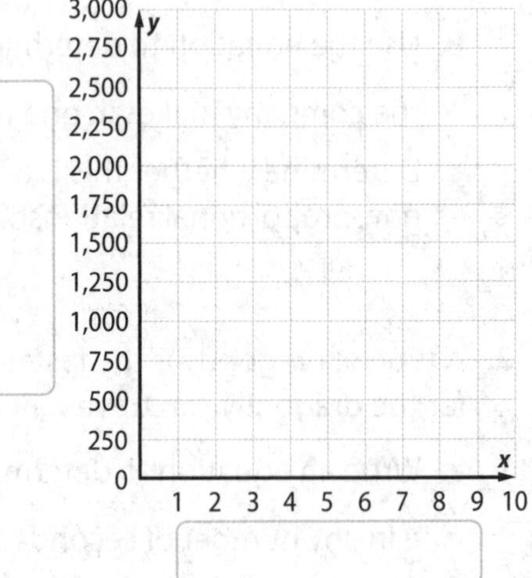

c. **Algebra** Write an equation for each swimmer to determine the number of feet swam *d* in any number of minutes *t*. ______________________

d. **Numbers** If Petar Stoychev swam the Channel in 6 hours, 57 minutes, and 50 seconds, approximately how wide in miles is the English Channel?

(*Hint*: 1 mi = 5,280 ft) ______________________

H.O.T. Problems Higher-Order Thinking

5. **Create** Write an equation with two variables that represents a real-world situation. ______________________

____

6. **Create** The table shows the areas of circles with radii from 1 through 3 feet. Recall that π has a value of about 3. Write an equation in two variables to represent the relationship shown in the table. ______________________

Radius (ft), r	Area (ft^2), A
1	π
2	4π
3	9π

7. **Evaluate** Determine if the table at the right represents a linear proportional relationship. Explain your reasoning. If so, write an equation to represent the relationship.

____

____

x	y
3	5.25
5	8.75
7	12.25
9	15.75

Name ___

Multi-Step Problem Solving

8. Bruno and Mía joined yoga classes. The amount Bruno pays is represented by the equation $y = 5x$, where x represents the number of classes and y represents the total cost. The table shows the amount Mía pays for her yoga classes. What is the difference between the costs of each plan for 10 classes? P N MP

Classes	Cost ($)
1	22
2	24
3	26
4	28

Use a problem-solving model to solve this problem.

1 Analyze

Read the problem. Circle the information you know.
Underline what the problem is asking you to find.

2 Plan

What will you need to do to solve the problem? Write your plan in steps.

Step 1 Determine the ___ of each plan for 10 classes.

Step 2 Determine the ___ in the cost for 10 classes.

Read to Succeed!
Notice that the table does not give the y-intercept.

3 Solve

Use your plan to solve the problem. Show your steps.

Bruno pays ___ (___) or ___ for 10 classes.

Mía's cost increases by ___ per class. So, she pays ___ for 10 classes.

Since ___ − ___ is ___, the difference in cost between the two plans is ___. Complete the grid.

					.		
⊕	0	0	0	0		0	0
⊖	1	1	1	1		1	1
	2	2	2	2		2	2
	3	3	3	3		3	3
	4	4	4	4		4	4
	5	5	5	5		5	5
	6	6	6	6		6	6
	7	7	7	7		7	7
	8	8	8	8		8	8
	9	9	9	9		9	9

4 Justify and Evaluate

How do you know your solution is accurate?

___

___

___

___

P = Proportionality N = Number and Operations MP = Mathematical Processes

More Multi-Step Problem Solving

Use a problem-solving model to solve each problem.

9. The cost of renting a bike using Plan A is given by $y = 5x + 25$, where x represents the number of days and y represents the total cost in dollars. The graph shows the cost for Plan B. What is the difference between the cost of Plan A and Plan B for renting a bike for 8 days? P N MP

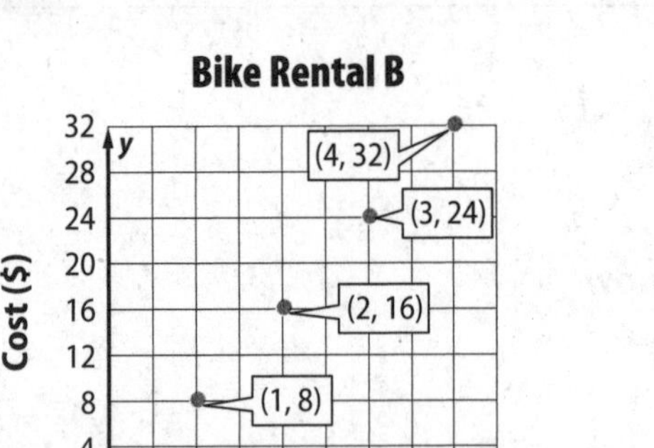

10. Jun recorded the times and distances she rode her bike this weekend. At the rate shown in the table, how long will it take her to ride $71\frac{1}{4}$ miles? P N MP

Minutes	Miles
90	22.5
150	37.5
210	52.5
330	82.5

11. The graph shows the amount, in dollars, in Thiago's savings account each week for several weeks. If the pattern continues, in how many weeks will Thiago have $125 in his savings account? P N MP

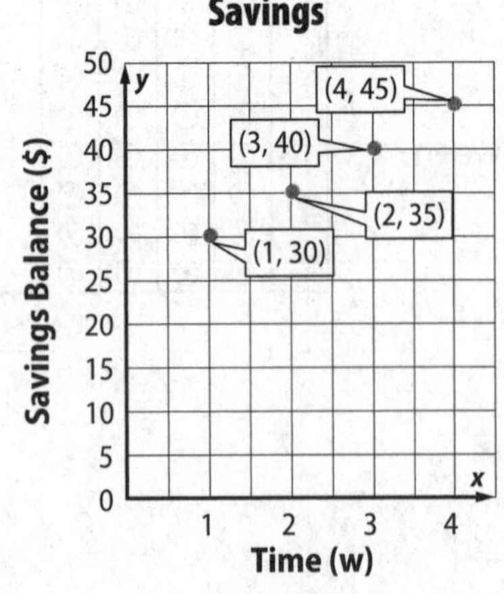

12. Games R Us offers two plans for renting video games. Plan A charges a one-time membership fee of $24 plus $1 for each game rental. Plan B charges $3 per game rental. For what number of games is the cost of both plans the same? Justify your answer. P N MP

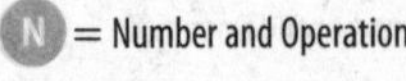

Lesson 2

Relations

Launch the Lesson: Vocabulary

Complete the graphic organizer of the coordinate plane below.

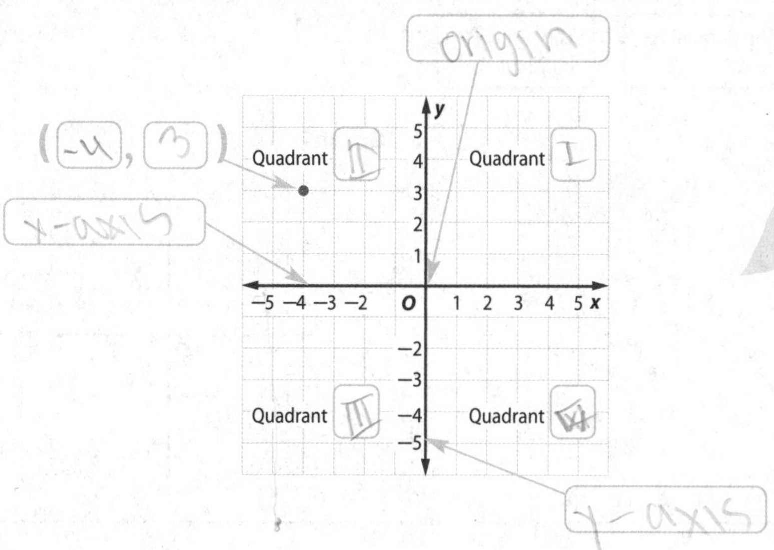

Identify the *x*-coordinate in the point (−5, −7).

Real-World Link

How do maps use the coordinate plane for locating towns?

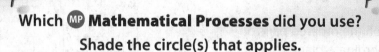

Which MP Mathematical Processes did you use? Shade the circle(s) that applies.

Ⓐ Apply Math to the Real World.
Ⓑ Use a Problem-Solving Model.
Ⓒ Select Tools and Techniques.
Ⓓ Use Multiple Representations.
Ⓔ Organize Ideas.
Ⓕ Analyze Relationships.
Ⓖ Justify Arguments.

Texas Essential Knowledge and Skills

Targeted TEKS
Preparation for 8.5(G) Identify functions using sets of ordered pairs, tables, mappings, and graphs.

Mathematical Processes
8.1(A), 8.1(B), 8.1(F)

Vocabulary
relation
domain
range

Essential Question
HOW can we model relationships between quantities?

Key Concept Relations

Ordered Pairs

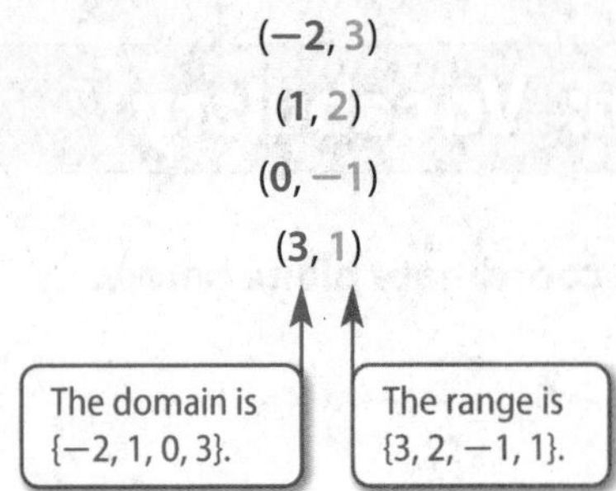

Mapping

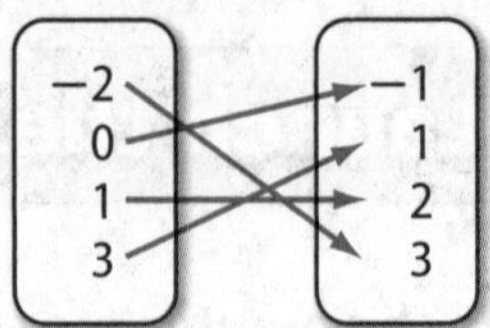

Table

x	y
−2	3
1	2
0	−1
3	1

Graph

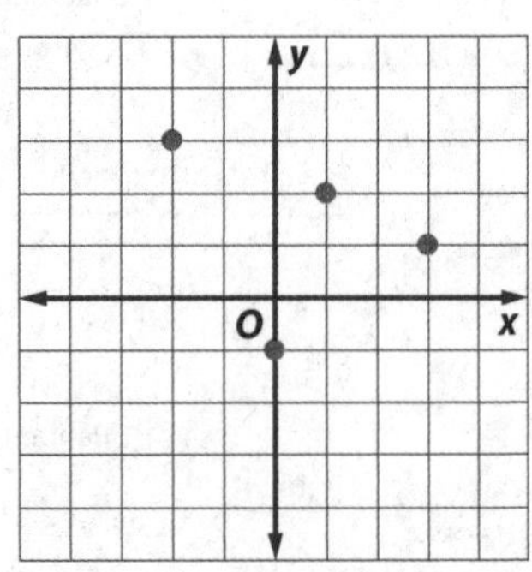

A **relation** is any set of ordered pairs. Relations can be represented as sets of ordered pairs, tables, mappings, or graphs. The **domain** of the relation is the set of x-coordinates. The **range** is the set of y-coordinates.

Watch Tutor

Example

1. Represent the relation {(2, 6), (−4, −8), (−3, 6), (0, −4)} as a table and a graph. Then determine the domain and range.

Place the ordered pairs in a table with x-coordinates in the first column and the y-coordinates in the second column.

x	y
2	6
−4	−8
−3	6
0	−4

Graph the ordered pairs on a coordinate plane.

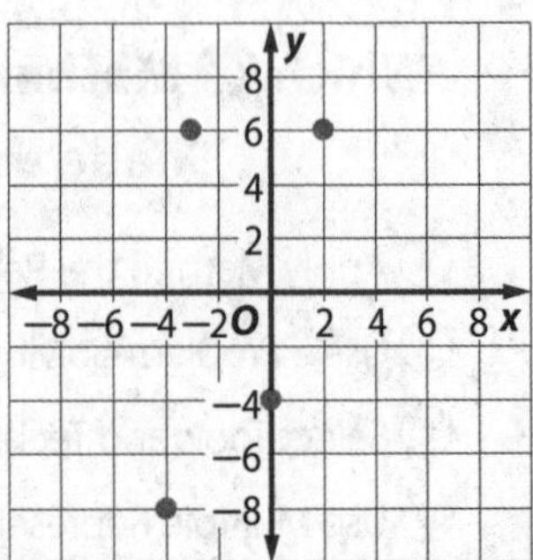

The domain is {−4, −3, 0, 2}.
The range is {−8, −4, 6}.

Domain and Range
If a term in the domain or range appears more than once, only write it one time. In Example 1, the value 6 appears twice in the range.

Got It? Do this problem to find out.

a. Represent the relation {(−5, 2), (3, −1), (6, 2), (1, 7)} as a table and a graph. Then determine the domain and range.

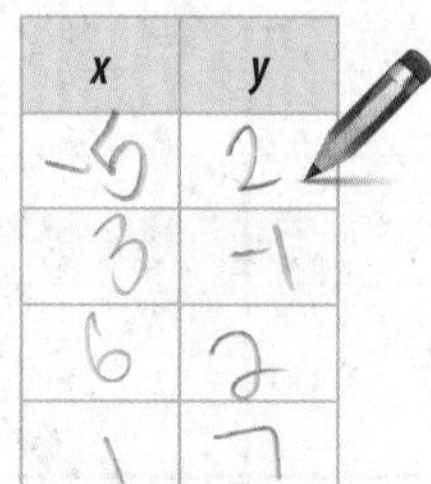

x	y
-5	2
3	-1
6	2
1	7

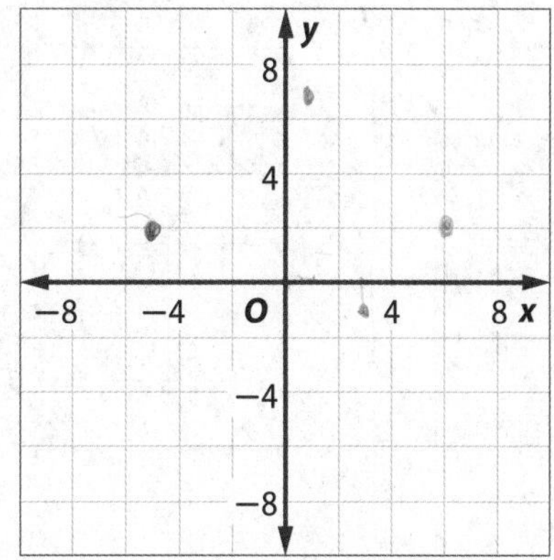

a. D {−5, 3, 6, 1}
R {2, −1, 2, 7}

Example

Show your work.

2. It costs $3 per hour to park at the Wild Wood Amusement Park.

a. Make a table of ordered pairs in which the *x*-coordinate represents the hours and the *y*-coordinate represents the total cost for 3, 4, 5, and 6 hours.

x	y
3	9
4	12
5	15
6	18

b. Graph the ordered pairs.

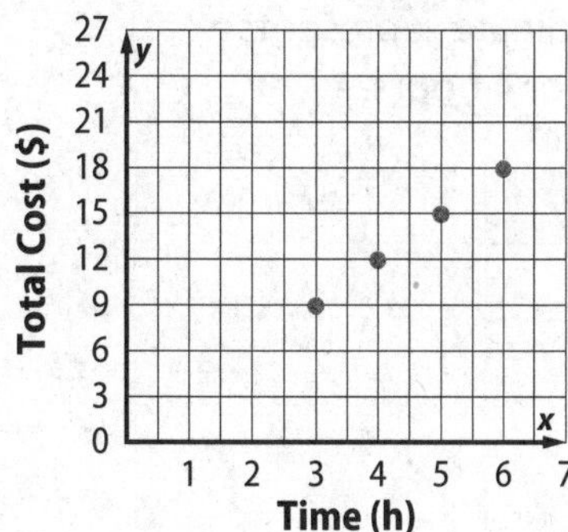

Got It? Do these problems to find out.

A movie rental store charges $3.95 per movie rental.

b. Make a table of ordered pairs in which the *x*-coordinate represents the number of movies rented and the *y*-coordinate represents the total cost for 1, 2, 3, or 4 movies.

c. Graph the ordered pairs.

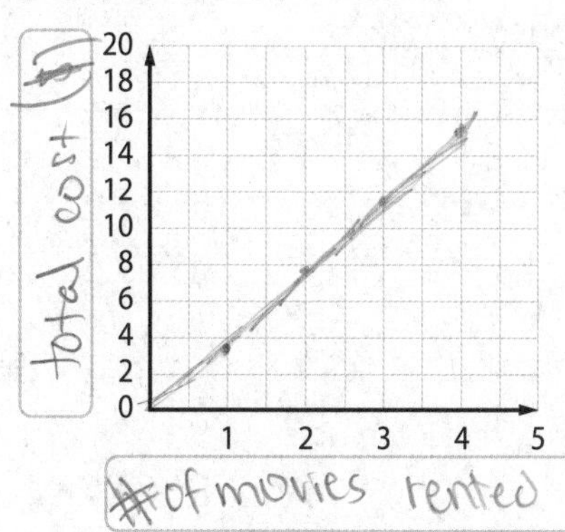

x	y
1	3.95
2	7.9
3	11.85
4	15.8

b. __________

Guided Practice

Represent each relation as a table and a graph. Then determine the domain and range. (Example 1)

1. {(−4, 3), (2, 1), (0, 3), (−3, −2)}

x	y

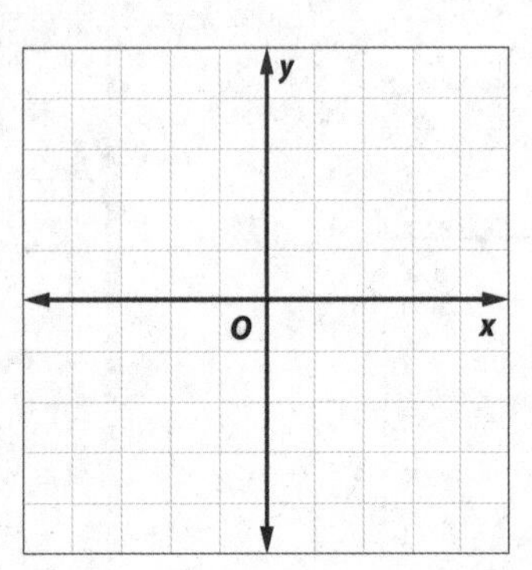

2. {(5, 3), (−4, 1), (2, −5), (3, −4)}

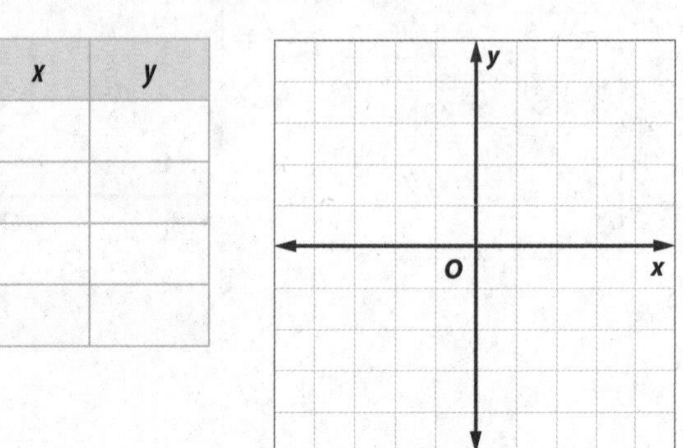

3. At a vacation resort, you can rent a personal watercraft for \$20 per hour. (Example 2)

a. Make a table of ordered pairs in which the x-coordinate represents the number of hours and the y-coordinate represents the total cost for 1, 2, 3, or 4 hours.

x	y

b. Graph the ordered pairs.

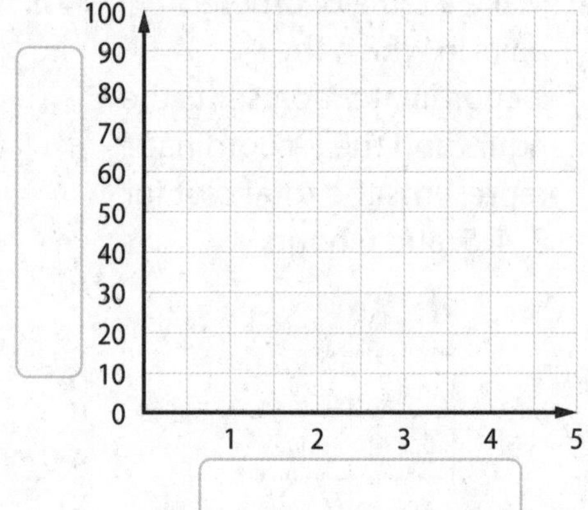

4. **Building on the Essential Question** How can tables and graphs represent relations?

Rate Yourself!

How confident are you about relations? Check the box that applies.

Find out online. Use the Self-Check Quiz.

Check

FOLDABLES Time to update your Foldable!

Independent Practice

Preparation for 8.5(G), 8.1(A), 8.1(F)

Represent each relation as a table and a graph. Then determine the domain and range. (Example 1)

1. {(8, 5), (−6, −9), (2, 5), (0, −8)}

R{8, -6, 2, 0} D{5, -9, 5, -8}

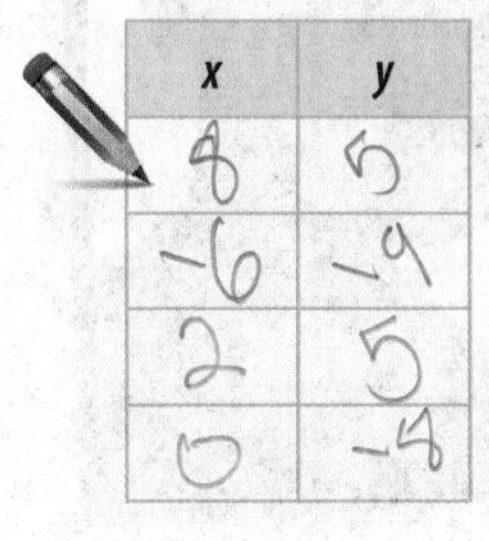

x	y
8	5
-6	-9
2	5
0	-8

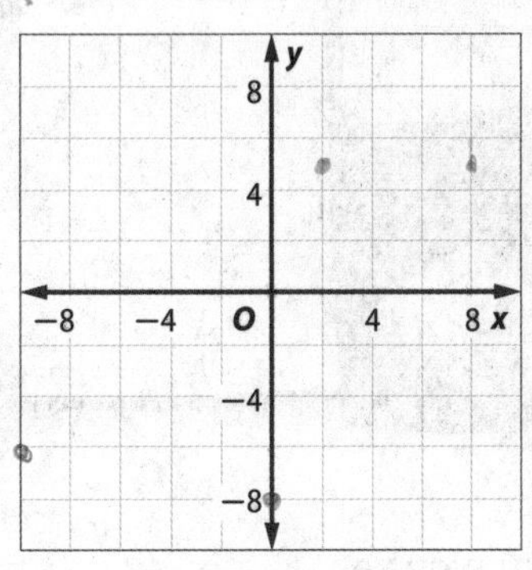

2. $\left\{\left(2\frac{1}{2}, -1\frac{1}{2}\right), \left(2, \frac{1}{2}\right), \left(-1, 2\frac{1}{2}\right), \left(-1, -1\frac{1}{2}\right)\right\}$

x	y

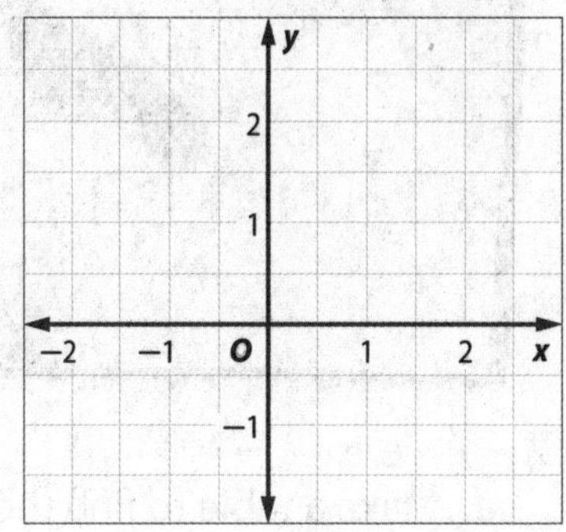

Copy and Solve **Draw the table and graph on a separate sheet of paper. A company can manufacture 825 small cars per day.** (Example 2)

3. Make a table of ordered pairs in which the *x*-coordinate represents the number of days and the *y*-coordinate represents the total number of cars produced in 1, 2, 3, 4, and 5 days.

4. Graph the ordered pairs.

5. MP **Use Multiple Representations** Refer to the table at the right.

x	y
1	1
2	4
3	9
4	16
5	25

a. Words Describe the pattern, if any, in the table. ______________________

b. Numbers Write the ordered pairs (*x*, *y*). ______________________

c. Graphs Graph the ordered pairs on a coordinate plane.

d. Words Describe the graph. How is it different from the other real-world graphs in this lesson?

____

e. Mapping Draw a mapping diagram to represent the relation.

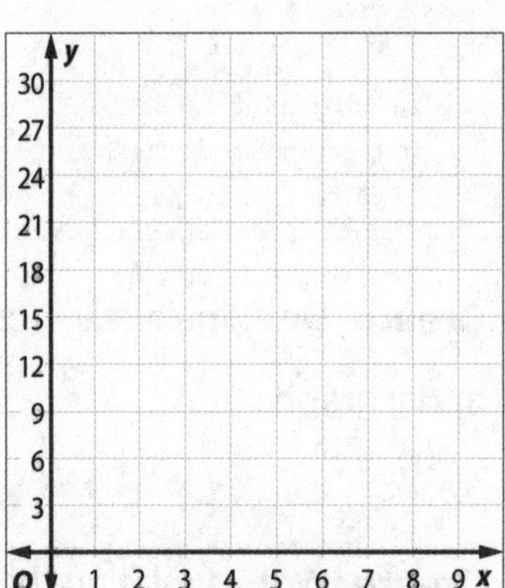

6. **MP Apply Math to the Real World** Refer to the graphic novel frame below for Exercises a–c. Show your work on a separate sheet of paper.

a. Make a table to find the cost to print 10, 20, 30, 40 pictures.

b. Graph the ordered pairs.

c. How much would it cost for Brian to print and ship 75 pictures? 100?

H.O.T. Problems Higher-Order Thinking

7. **Analyze** Refer to the table at the right.

x	y
0	1
1	3
2	5
3	7

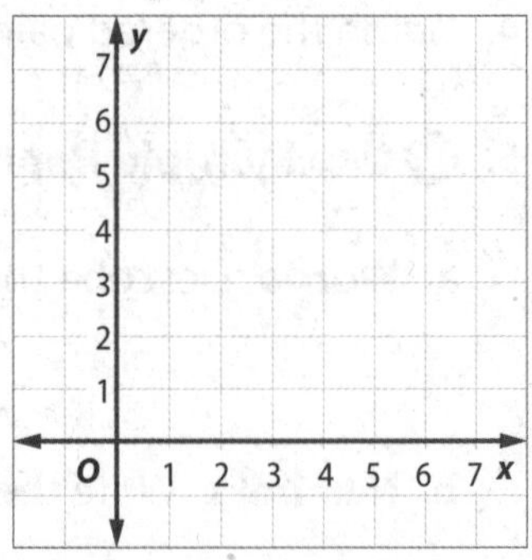

a. Graph the ordered pairs.

b. Reverse the y-coordinates and x-coordinates in each ordered pair.

c. Graph the new ordered pairs on the same coordinate plane in part a.

d. Describe the relationship between the two sets of ordered pairs.

8. **Create** Describe a real-world situation that can be represented using a table and a graph.

9. **Create** Write a relation that consists of 5 ordered pairs, a domain of perfect squares, and a range of perfect cubes.

Name ______________________________

Multi-Step Problem Solving

10. The relations in the graph at the right show the distances driven by Denzel and Mei on the second day of a two-day road trip. Which statement is true when the time equals 5 hours? P EE MP

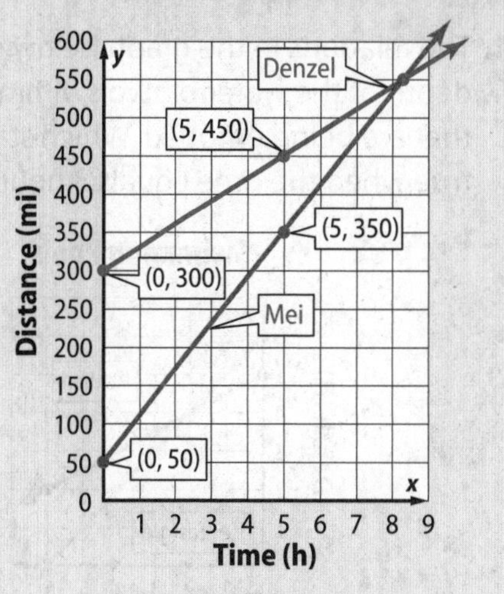

Ⓐ Mei is driving at a faster speed than Denzel.

Ⓑ Denzel is driving at a faster speed than Mei.

Ⓒ Mei and Denzel are driving at the same speed.

Ⓓ The speeds of Mei and Denzel cannot be determined.

Use a problem-solving model to solve this problem.

1 Analyze

Read the problem. Circle the information you know.
Underline what the problem is asking you to find.

2 Plan

What will you need to do to solve the problem? Write your plan in steps.

Step 1 Determine the __________ of each driver.

Step 2 Compare the __________ of the two drivers.

Read to Succeed!
When finding slope, remember to subtract the x-coordinates in the same order that you subtracted the y-coordinates.

3 Solve

Use your plan to solve the problem. Show your steps.

Denzel's speed is ________ or _____ miles per hour.

Mei's speed is ________ or _____ miles per hour.

Since _____ > _____, ________'s speed is faster than ________'s speed.

So, the correct answer is _____. Fill in that answer choice.

4 Justify and Evaluate

How do you know your solution is accurate?

____

____

P = Proportionality EE = Expressions, Equations, and Relationships MP = Mathematical Processes

More Multi-Step Problem Solving

Use a problem-solving model to solve each problem.

11. The relations in the graph below show the depth of the water of two swimming pools that are being emptied. Which statement is true when the time equals 3 hours? P EE MP

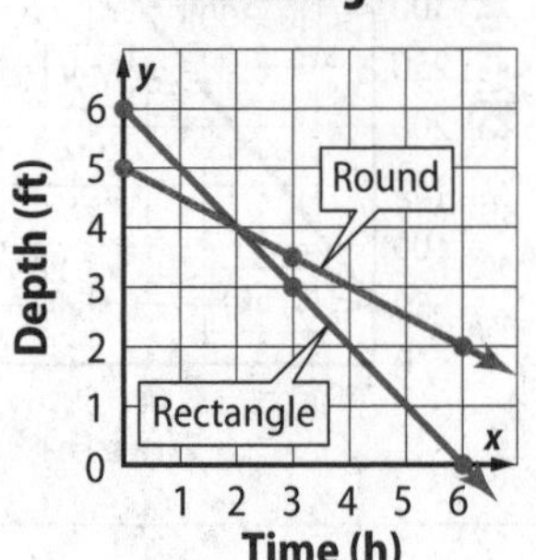

Ⓐ The rectangular pool is being emptied at a slower rate than the round pool.

Ⓑ The round pool is being emptied at a slower rate than the rectangular pool.

Ⓒ The pools are being emptied at the same rate.

Ⓓ The rates at which the pools are being emptied cannot be determined.

12. The table below shows the pressure in pounds per square foot that an object would be under if it were submerged to various depths. What would be the approximate pressure in pounds per square foot of an object submerged to a depth of 20 feet? P EE MP

Depth (ft)	Pressure (lb/ft^2)
0	2,117
4	2,367
8	2,617
10	2,742

13. The relation shown below shows the cost of downloading songs from an online music Web site. Suppose you spent $36.75 on downloads from this site. How many songs did you download? P EE MP

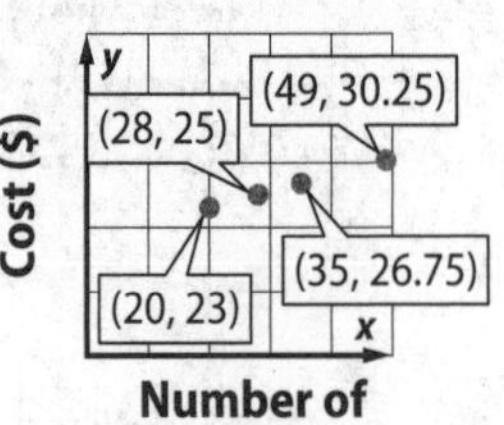

14. A concession stand at a high school football game sells a hot dog meal that includes a drink for $3.50. Write a relation consisting of five ordered pairs where the domain represents the number of meals and the range represents the total cost. Then write an equation that represents your relation. Interpret the slope and y-intercept. P EE MP

P = Proportionality EE = Expressions, Equations, and Relationships MP = Mathematical Processes

Hands-On Lab 3-a

Relations and Functions

INQUIRY HOW can I select tools and techniques to determine if a relation is a function?

Texas Essential Knowledge and Skills

Targeted TEKS

8.5(G) Identify functions using sets of ordered pairs, tables, mappings, and graphs.

Mathematical Processes

8.1(C)

Mrs. Heinl asked three members of her class their favorite type of movie. The mapping diagrams below show some possible results.

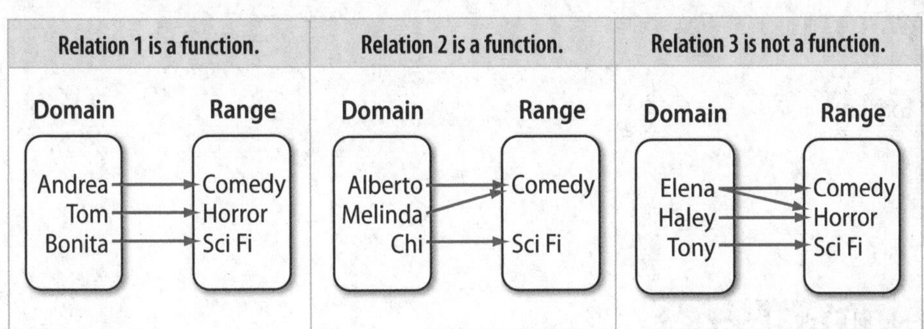

A *function* is a special relation in which each member of the domain is paired with *exactly* one member in the range. In the mapping above, Relation 3 is *not* a function because Elena chose two favorite types of movies, comedy and horror.

Hands-On Activity

Mr. Morgan asked his students how many pets they have. Some of the student responses are shown in the table.

Student Number	1	3	6
Number of Pets	2	5	7

1. Complete the mapping diagram shown.

Domain Range

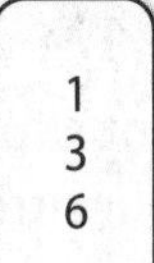

2. Is the relation a function? Explain.

3. Suppose Student 8 has 2 pets. Make a mapping diagram of this situation. Is this relation a function? Explain.

Domain Range

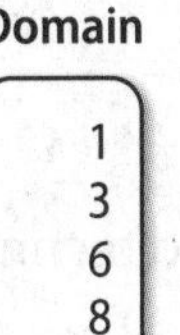

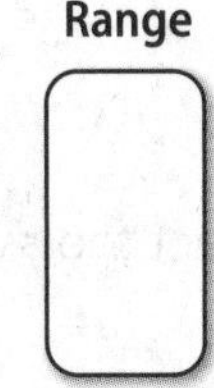

Investigate

Collaborate

MP Select Tools and Techniques Work with a partner. Make a mapping diagram for each relation. Then determine whether each relation is a function.

4. Students were asked about the number of cell phone minutes they use. Some of the responses are shown in the table.

Domain   Range

Student	Sarah	Max	Jacob	Rebekah
Number of Minutes	275	220	350	275

Is this relation a function? Explain. ______________________________

____

Analyze and Reflect

Collaborate

5. **MP Select Tools and Techniques** Make a table and a mapping diagram for the relation {(0, −2), (1, −2), (1, 3), (1, 8)}.

Domain   Range

Domain				
Range				

Is this relation a function? Explain. ______________________________

____

Create

On Your Own

6. Think of a real-world situation that is not a function Complete the mapping diagram for your situation.

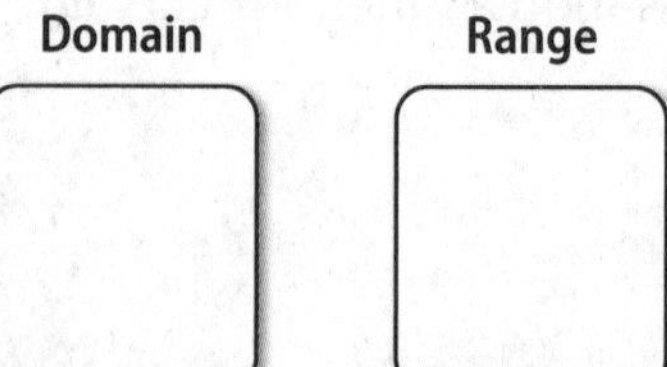

Explain why your situation is not a function.

____

____

7. **INQUIRY** HOW can I select tools and techniques to determine if a relation is a function?

____

____

Lesson 3
Functions

Launch the Lesson: Vocabulary

A **function** is a relation in which every member of the domain (input value) is paired with, or mapped to, exactly one member of the range (output value). An example of a function is $m = 20n$, where m represents the amount of money earned and n represents the number of lawns mowed. In this example, n is the **independent variable** and m is the **dependent variable**.

Independent Variable What I think it means	Dependent Variable What I think it means

For each situation, determine which unknown is the dependent variable and which one is the independent variable.

Independent Variable	Equation	Dependent Variable
number of downloads	The equation $c = 0.99n$ represents the total cost c for n music downloads.	cost
	The equation $d = 4.5h$ represents the number of miles d Amber can run in h hours.	
	The equation $s = g + 3$ represents the final score of the game s after g goals in the final period.	

Which MP Mathematical Processes did you use? Shade the circle(s) that applies.

Ⓐ Apply Math to the Real World.
Ⓑ Use a Problem-Solving Model.
Ⓒ Select Tools and Techniques.
Ⓓ Use Multiple Representations.
Ⓔ Organize Ideas.
Ⓕ Analyze Relationships.
Ⓖ Justify Arguments.

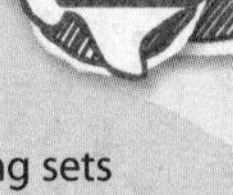

Texas Essential Knowledge and Skills

Targeted TEKS
8.5(G) Identify functions using sets of ordered pairs, tables, mappings, and graphs.

Mathematical Processes
8.1(A), 8.1(B)

Vocabulary
function
independent variable
dependent variable

Essential Question
HOW can we model relationships between quantities?

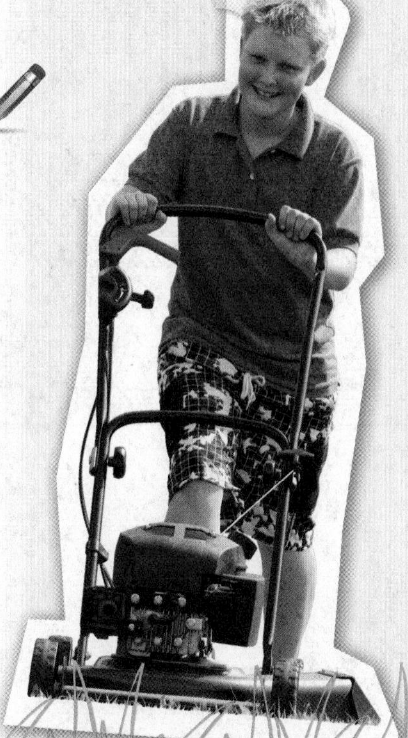

Key Concept

Identify Functions Using Mapping Diagrams and Ordered Pairs

Work Zone

Mapping Diagram: Function

Domain | Range

1 → 3
2 → 5
3 → 5

Mapping Diagram: Not a Function

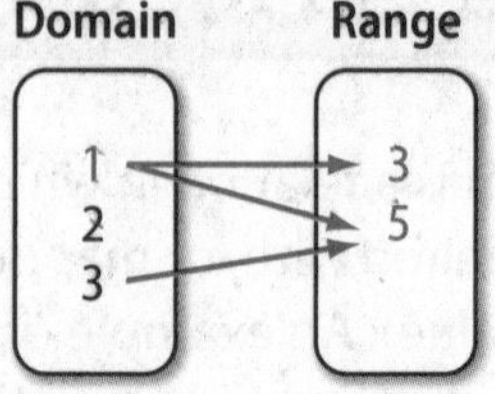

Ordered Pairs: Function

{(1, 3), (2, 5), (3, 5)}

Ordered Pairs: Not a Function

{(1, 3), (1, 5), (3, 5)}

The relation shown by the mapping diagram and ordered pairs on the right side inside the Key Concept Box is a not function because a member of the domain is paired with, or mapped to, more than one member of the range. Specifically, in the ordered pairs (1, 3) and (1, 5), 1 is mapped to both 3 and 5.

Example

1. Determine whether {(1, 1), (1, −1), (4, 2), (9, −3)} is a function. Explain.

Make a mapping diagram. Place the *x*-coordinates in the left oval and the *y*-coordinates in the right oval. Then draw an arrow from each *x*-coordinate to its corresponding *y*-value.

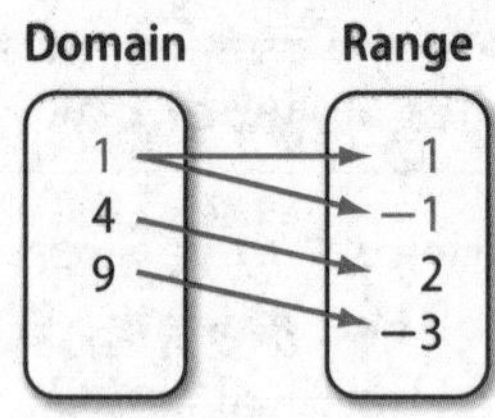

Since 1 is mapped to both 1 and −1, the set of ordered pairs is not a function.

Got It? Do these problems to find out.

Determine whether each relation is a function. Explain your answer.

a. {(3, 4), (3, 5), (5, 5), (5, 6)}

b. {(3, 5), (8, 7), (4, 5), (9, 7)}

a. Not

b. Yes

Identify Functions Using Tables and Graphs

Tables and graphs can be used to represent relations and functions. To determine whether a relation shown in a table or a graph is a function, consider how the members of the domain are mapped to the members of the range.

Tutor 

Examples

2. Determine whether the relation shown in the table is a function. Explain.

x	−2	2	−3	3
y	4	4	9	9

Since −2 is mapped to 4, 2 is mapped to 4, −3 is mapped to 9, and 3 is mapped to 9, each member of the domain is mapped to exactly one member of the range. So, the relation is a function.

Functions

In Example 2, some range members are mapped to more than one domain member. However, the relation is still a function because each member of the domain, or *x*-value, is mapped to exactly one member of the range, or *y*-value.

3. Determine whether the relation shown in the graph is a function. Explain.

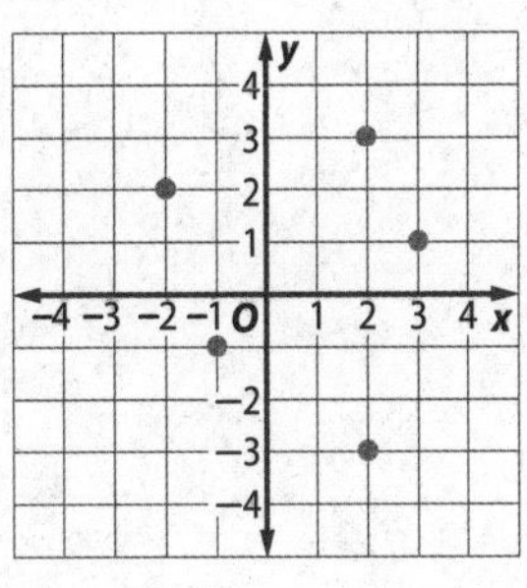

Study each point on the graph.

The points (2, 3) and (2, −3) show that the domain value of 2 is mapped to more than one range value, 3 and −3. So, the relation is not a function.

Got It? Do these problems to find out.

Determine whether each relation is a function. Explain your answer.

c.

x	y
1	3
2	3
3	3
2	4

d.

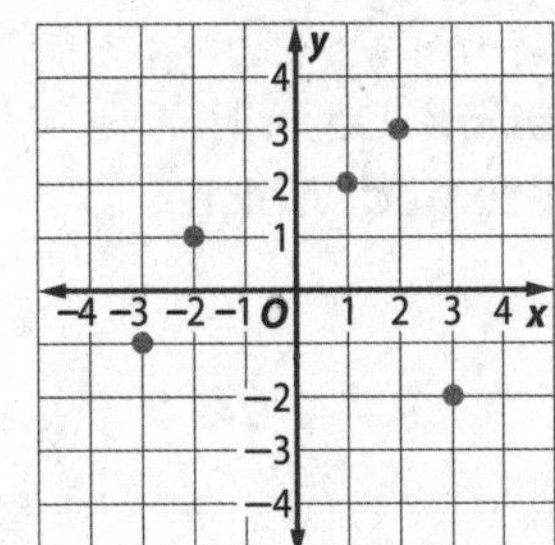

c. ~~Not~~ Yes

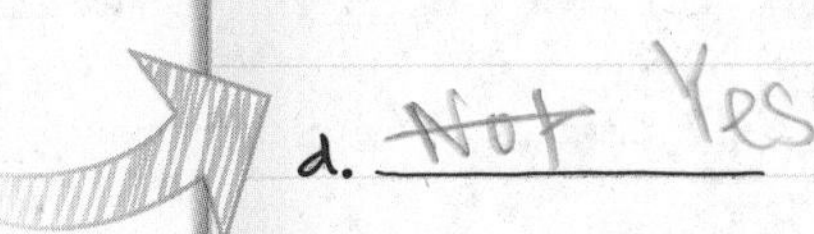

d. ~~Not~~ Yes

Guided Practice

Determine whether each relation is a function. Explain. (Examples 1, 2, and 3)

1. Domain Range

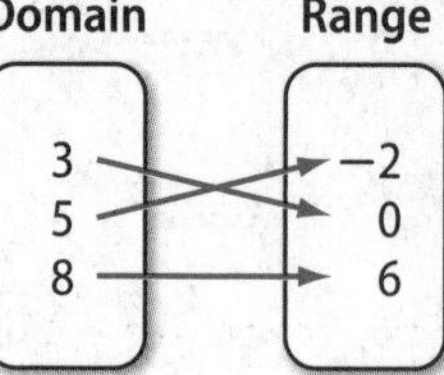

2. {(0, −4), (0, 4), (1, −5), (1, 5)}

3. {(1, 2), (3, 4), (5, 6), (7, 8), (9, 10)}

4.

x	y
1	10
2	20
3	30
4	40

5.

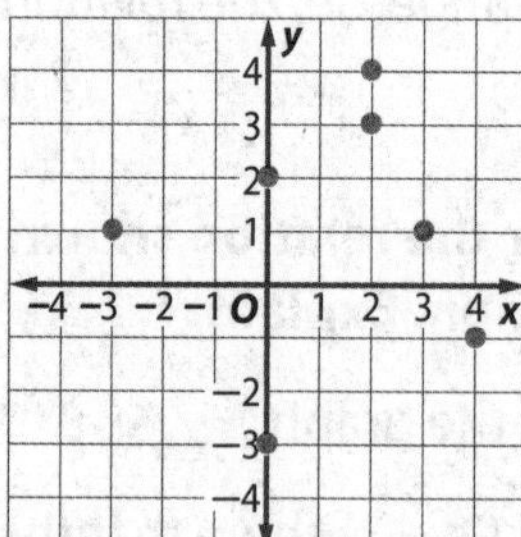

6. **Building on the Essential Question** Describe the ways in which a function can be represented. Which representation(s) do you prefer?

Rate Yourself!

How confident are you about relations? Check the box that applies.

Find out online. Use the Self-Check Quiz.

Check

FOLDABLES Time to update your Foldable!

Name ______________________ My Homework ______________________

Independent Practice

8.5(G), 8.1(F), 8.1(G) TEKS

Determine whether each relation is a function. Explain. (Examples 1, 2, and 3)

1. 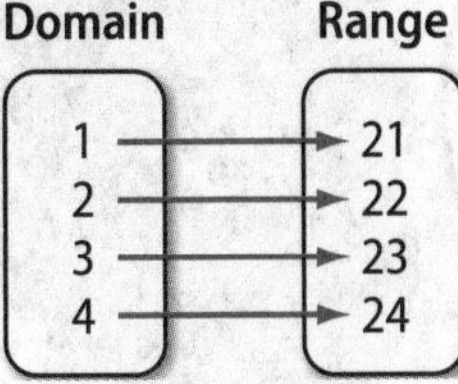

Function

2. 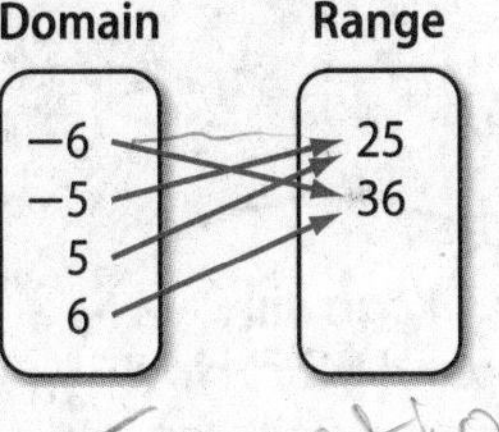

Function

3. {(4, 11), (5, 13), (6, 15), (7, 17)}

Function

4. {(7, −7), (7, 7), (8, −8), (8, 8)}

Not a Function

5.

x	*y*
0	0
1	3.50
2	7
3	10.50

Function

6.

x	*y*
81	−9
81	9
100	−10
100	10

No Function

7. 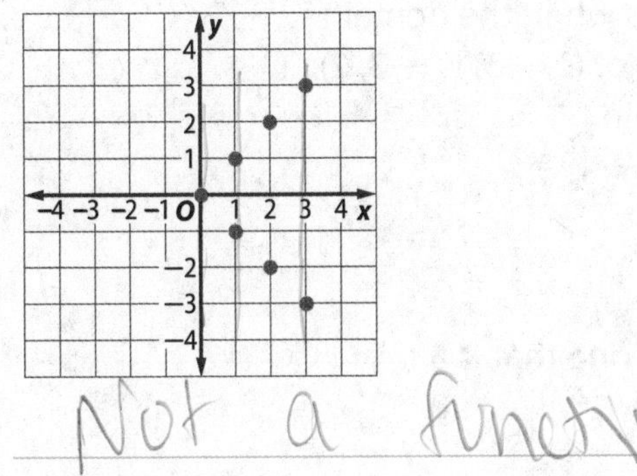

Not a function

8. 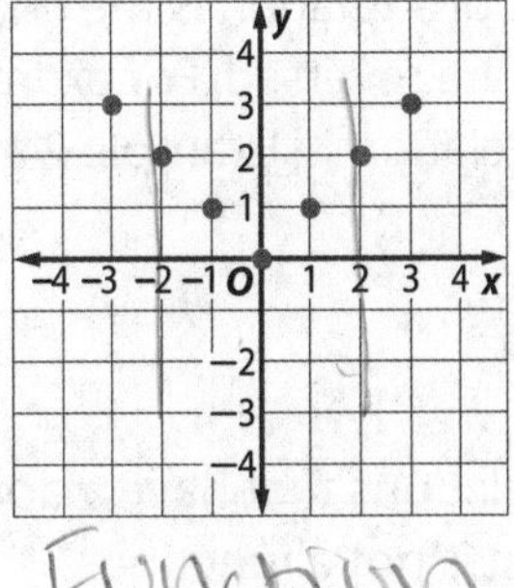

Function

9. Dean earns $9.50 per hour. Are his wages a function of the number of hours he works? Justify your response by creating a set of ordered pairs.

10. **MP Apply Math to the Real World** Refer to the graphic novel frame below for Exercises a–c.

a. Fill in the table to find the total cost of printing and shipping 25, 50, 75, and 100 pictures.

Number of Pictures	25	50	75	100
Cost ($)				

b. Give the domain and range.
domain: { , , , } range: { , , , }

c. Is this relation a function? Explain.

H.O.T. Problems Higher-Order Thinking

11. **Analyze** The *inverse* of a relation is the relation that occurs when the domain and range members are reversed. For example, the inverse of (2, −3) is (−3, 2). Is the inverse of the relation in Example 2 a function? Explain.

12. **Create** Write two relations that have a domain of (1, 2, 3), one that is a function and one that is not a function.

function:

not a function:

13. **Evaluate** Determine whether the following statement is *true* or *false*. Explain.
All relations are functions, and all functions are relations.

Name ______________________________

Multi-Step Problem Solving

14. A store is having a sale on T-shirts. Customers receive one free T-shirt for every three T-shirts purchased. If T-shirts sell for $10 each and a customer selects 6 T-shirts, which of the following statements about the customer's purchase is true? P N MP

Ⓐ The relation is a function and has a range of {1, 2, 3, 4, 5, 6}.

Ⓑ The relation is a function and has a range of {10, 20, 30, 40, 50}.

Ⓒ The relation is not a function and has a range of {1, 2, 3, 4, 5, 6}.

Ⓓ The relation is not a function and has a range of {10, 20, 30, 40, 50}.

Use a problem-solving model to solve this problem.

1 Analyze

Read the problem. Circle the information you know.
Underline what the problem is asking you to find.

2 Plan

What will you need to do to solve the problem? Write your plan in steps.

Step 1 Write a set of ____________ that represents the customer's purchase.

Step 2 Determine if the relation is a __________, and determine its ______.

3 Solve

Use your plan to solve the problem. Show your steps.

The customer's purchase can be represented as the set of ordered pairs (number of T-shirts, total cost).

{(1, 10), (2, 20), (3, ______), (4, ______), (5, ______), (6, ______)}

Since each member of the domain is mapped

to ______________________, the relation is a function. The range is

{______________}. So, the correct answer is ______. Fill in that choice.

Read to Succeed!
When writing your ordered pairs, remember that every 4th T-shirt is free.

4 Justify and Evaluate

How do you know your solution is accurate?

____

____

____

P = Proportionality N = Number and Operations MP = Mathematical Processes

More Multi-Step Problem Solving

Use a problem-solving model to solve each problem.

15. As shown in the table below, Fav Pizza offers half off of each additional topping. Which ordered pair represents the cost of a pizza with 6 toppings? P N MP

Number of Toppings	Fav Pizza Cost ($)
1	11.60
2	12.40
3	12.80
4	13.00

Ⓐ (6, 13.15)
Ⓑ (6, 13.4)
Ⓒ (13.4, 6)
Ⓓ (13.5, 6)

16. In the mapping below, *A* maps onto *B*, and *B* maps onto *C*. Assume the function mapping *A* onto *B* and *B* onto *C* are linear. If the input value for *A* equals 6, what would the output value for *C* equal? P N MP

A	→	*B*	→	*C*
1		4		7
3		6		11
−2		1		1

17. The table shows the cost of purchasing and profit from various numbers of backpacks. What is cost of purchasing 20 backpacks? What is the profit based on purchasing 20 backpacks? P N MP

Number of Backpacks	Cost ($)	Profit ($)
6	120	10
7	135	15
8	150	20
9	165	25

18. The table shows two relations, *A* and *B*. Which relation is not a function? Which single value of *x* or *y* could be changed to make the relation a function? Justify your answers. P N MP

A		*B*	
x	*y*	*x*	*y*
−4	5	−3	−3
0	−4	3	3
−4	−2	0	3

P = Proportionality N = Number and Operations MP = Mathematical Processes

Make a Table

Play Catch Up

Emilio's mom and sister leave for vacation at 7:00 in the morning, driving an average speed of 45 miles per hour. Emilio and his dad leave at 8:15, driving an average speed of 60 miles per hour.

At what time will Emilio and his dad catch up to his mom and sister?

Mathematical Process
8.1(B) Use a problem-solving model that incorporates analyzing given information, formulating a plan or strategy, determining a solution, justifying the solution, and evaluating the problem-solving process and the reasonableness of the solution.

Targeted TEKS 8.5(A), 8.5(B)

Analyze

Read the problem. Circle the information you know.
Underline what the problem is asking you to find.

2 Plan *What is your strategy to solve this problem?*

I will use the ____________________ strategy.

Solve *How can you apply the strategy?*

Time (A.M.)	Distance Traveled (mi)	
7:00	0	0
8:00	45	0
9:00		$\frac{3}{4} \times 60 =$
10:00		
11:00		
12:00		

Read to Succeed!
At 9:00 A.M., Emilio's dad has been traveling for 45 minutes, or $\frac{3}{4}$ hour.

At __________, Emilio and Emilio's dad will catch up to his mom and sister.

Justify and Evaluate *How do you know your solution is reasonable?*

____

____

____

Company	Deposit	Cost Per Day
Mike's Music	$35	$1.25
Karaoke Korner	$32	$1.75

Karaoke Kid

Rina wants to rent a karaoke machine for a family reunion. The prices to rent the machine from two different companies are shown. The deposit is paid once for any number of days.

For how many days must she rent the machine for the cost from each place to be the same?

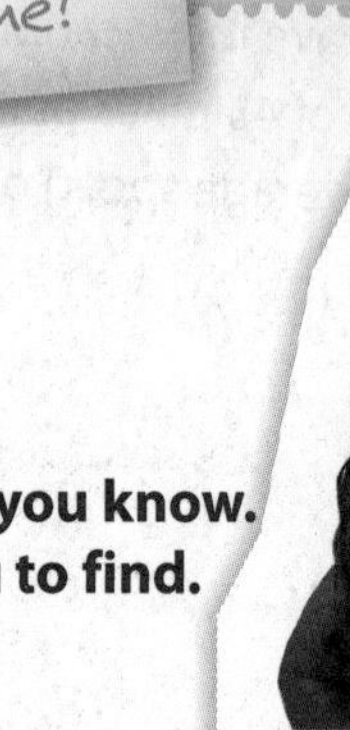

Analyze

Read the problem. Circle the information you know. Underline what the problem is asking you to find.

Plan

What is your strategy to solve this problem?

I will use the ________________ strategy.

Solve

How can you apply the strategy?

Justify and Evaluate

How do you know your solution is accurate?

Multi-Step Problem Solving

Collaborate

Work with a small group to solve the following problems. Show your work on a separate piece of paper.

1. Plants

The table shows the height of a giant bamboo plant for Days 5–9. The bamboo grew at a steady rate each day, starting on Day 5.

From Day 5 to Day 9, the plant grew about what percent of its Day 9 height?

Bamboo Growth

Number of Days	Total Growth (ft)
5	?
6	?
7	10
8	13.5
9	17

2. Financial Literacy

Lucia and Scott opened bank accounts with initial deposits of $50 each. Scott saved 30% of his earnings from his after-school job, which paid $8 per hour. He worked 25 hours each week. Lucia initially saved $45 each week. In the fourth week, she decided to save $30 more per week.

During which week did they have the same amount of money in their bank accounts?

3. Fitness

Marcie created her own fitness plan to increase the amount of time she spends exercising each week.

Week	1	2	3	4	5
Exercise (min)	35	50	80	125	185

If the pattern in the table continues, for about how many hours will she exercise in the 8th week?

4. Animals

The graph shows the maximum length of several animals. The maximum length of a walrus is twice the maximum length of a lion, which is 0.4 meter longer than the maximum length of a giant panda.

Find the maximum length of a walrus.

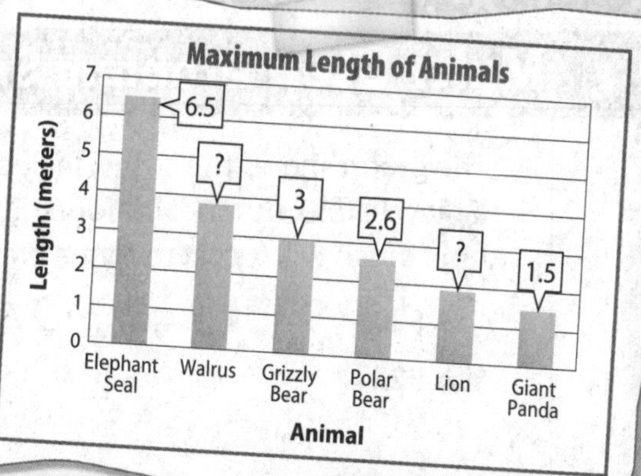

Vocabulary Check

1. Define *function* in your own words. Then write two sets of four ordered pairs, one set that is a function and one that is not a function. TEKS 8.5(G), 8.1(D)

Key Concept Check

2. Complete the graphic organizer by providing a real-world scenario for each type of relationship. Then write an equation for each real-world scenario. TEKS 8.5(A), 8.1(E)

Linear Proportional	Non-Linear Proportional

3. The equation $y = 4.99x$ represents the cost to order a movie from a cable company, where x represents the number of movies and y represents the cost in dollars. Write a relation that shows the cost for renting 1, 2, 3, 4, and 5 movies. TEKS Preparation for 8.5(G), 8.1(C)

Multi-Step Problem Solving

4. The graph shows the cost y, including a deposit fee, to rent a bicycle for x number of hours. If this pattern continues, how much will it cost to rent a bicycle for 24 hours? P MP

Ⓐ \$20 Ⓒ \$30

Ⓑ \$22 Ⓓ \$32

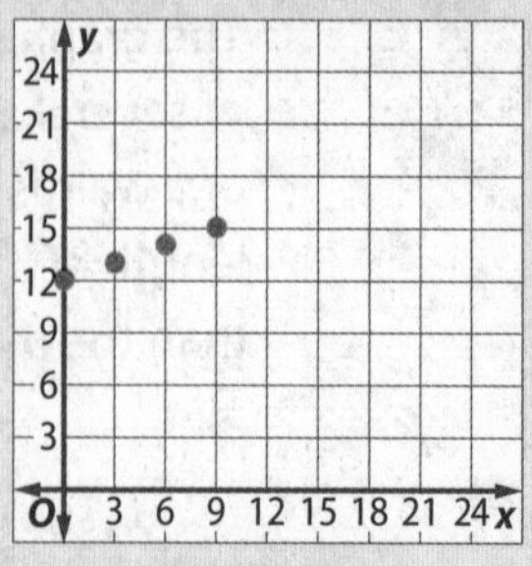

P = Proportionality MP = Mathematical Processes

Lesson 4

Linear Functions

Launch the Lesson: Real World

The Lockheed SR-71 Blackbird has a top speed of 36.6 miles per minute. The function rule for the distance traveled y is $y = 36.6x$ where x represents the minutes traveled at this speed. Let's investigate this relationship.

1. Complete the function table.

Input	x	1	2	3	4
Rule	36.6x	36.6(1)	36.6(2)		
Output	y	36.6			
(Input, Output)	(x, y)	(1, 36.6)			

2. Graph the ordered pairs (x, y) on the coordinate plane provided. What do you notice about the graph?

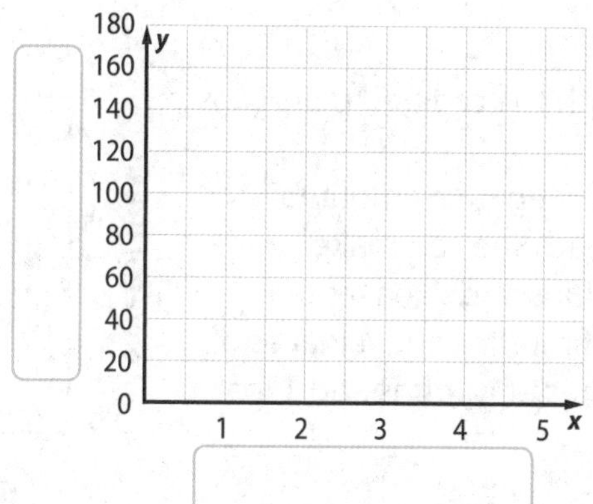

Which MP Mathematical Processes did you use? Shade the circle(s) that applies.

Ⓐ Apply Math to the Real World.
Ⓑ Use a Problem-Solving Model.
Ⓒ Select Tools and Techniques.
Ⓓ Use Multiple Representations.
Ⓔ Organize Ideas.
Ⓕ Analyze Relationships.
Ⓖ Justify Arguments.

Texas Essential Knowledge and Skills

Targeted TEKS

8.5(G) Identify functions using sets of ordered pairs, tables, mappings, and graphs. *Also addresses 8.5(A), 8.5(B), 8.5(I).*

Mathematical Processes

8.1(C), 8.1(D), 8.1(F), 8.1(G)

Vocab

Vocabulary

linear function
continuous data
discrete data

Essential Question

HOW can we model relationships between quantities?

Work Zone

Graph a Function

Sometimes functions are written using two variables. One variable, usually x, represents the domain and the other, usually y, represents the range. When a function is written in this form it is an equation.

Like equations, functions can be represented in words, in a table, with a graph, as a mapping, and as ordered pairs. The graph of a function is the set of ordered pairs consisting of an input and the corresponding output.

Example

Function Notation

The equation $y = 5 - 3x$ can also be written in function notation as $f(x) = 5 - 3x$.

1. Annabelle wants to make muffins and bread. She needs 3 cups of raisins to make one batch of muffins and 1 cup of raisins to make one loaf of bread. She has 7 cups of raisins. The function $y = 7 - 3x$ represents the number of batches of muffins x and the number of loaves of bread y she can make. Graph the function. Interpret the points graphed.

Step 1 Choose values for x and substitute them in the function to find y.

x	$7 - 3x$	y
0	$7 - 3(0)$	7
1	$7 - 3(1)$	4
2	$7 - 3(2)$	1
3	$7 - 3(3)$	−2

Step 2 Graph the ordered pairs (x, y).

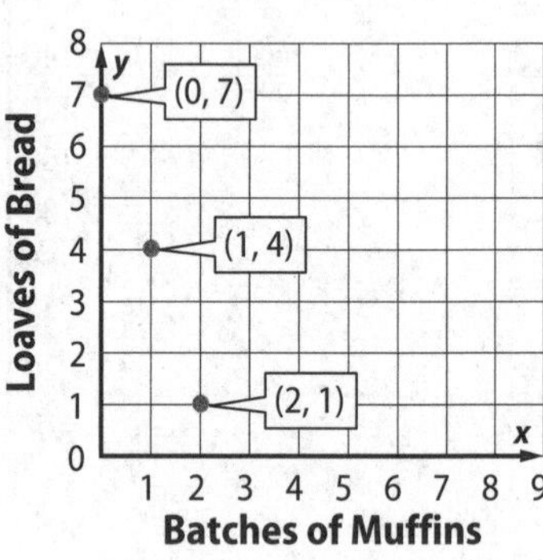

She cannot make negative amounts of muffins or bread. She can make 0 batches of muffins and 7 loaves of bread, 1 batch of muffins and 4 loaves of bread, or 2 batches of muffins and 1 loaf of bread.

Show your work.

Got It? Do this problem to find out.

a. ________

a. The farmer's market sells apples for \$2 per pound and oranges for \$1 per pound. Marjorie has \$10 to spend. The function $y = 10 - 2x$ represents the number of apples x and oranges y Marjorie can purchase. Graph the function and interpret the points graphed.

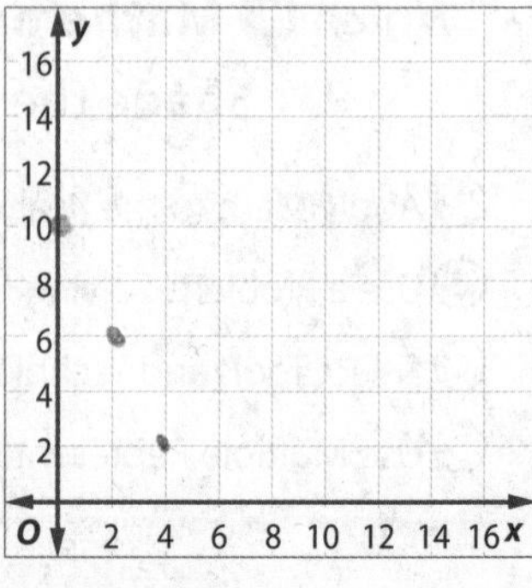

Tutor

Example

2. Graph $y = x + 4$.

Step 1 Make a function table. Select any four values for the domain x. Substitute these values for x to find the values for y. Then write the corresponding ordered pairs.

x	$x + 4$	y	(x, y)
0	$0 + 4$	4	(0, 4)
1	$1 + 4$	5	(1, 5)
2	$2 + 4$	6	(2, 6)
3	$3 + 4$	7	(3, 7)

Step 2 Graph each ordered pair. Draw a line that passes through the points.

The line is the complete graph of the function. Each ordered pair that corresponds to a point on the line is a solution of the equation $y = x + 4$.

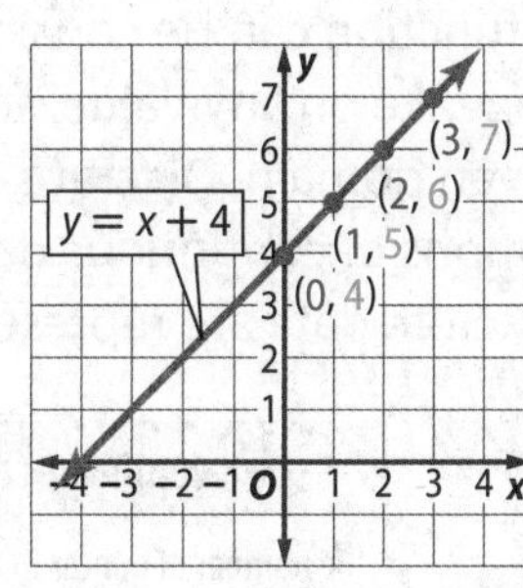

Check

It appears that (−4, 0) lies on the line and is a solution. Check this by substitution.

$y = x + 4$ Write the function.

$0 \stackrel{?}{=} -4 + 4$ Replace x with −4 and y with 0.

$0 = 0$ ✓ Simplify.

Solutions

The solutions of an equation are ordered pairs that make an equation representing the function true.

Got It? Do these problems to find out.

b. $y = x - 5$

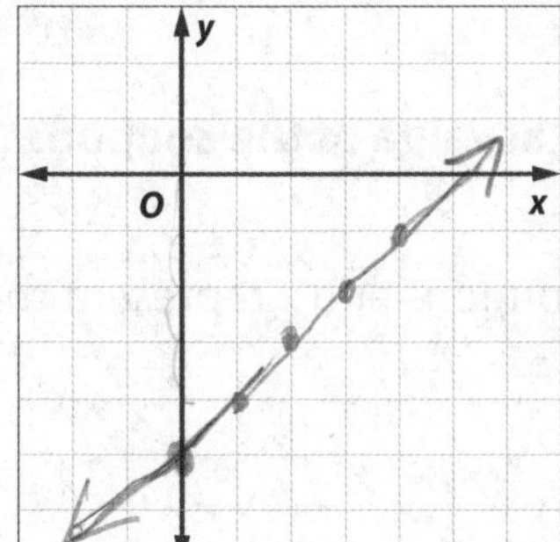

c. $y = -2x$ +0

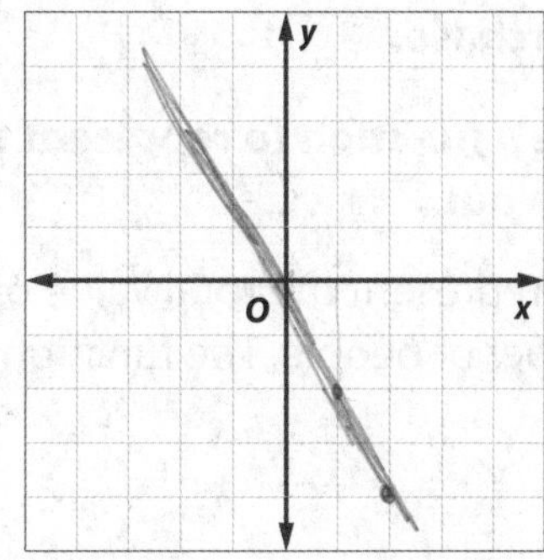

Key Concept

Representing Functions

Words The value of y is one less than the corresponding value of x.

Equation $y = x - 1$

Ordered Pairs (0, −1), (1, 0), (2, 1), (3, 2)

Table

x	y
0	−1
1	0
2	1
3	2

Graph

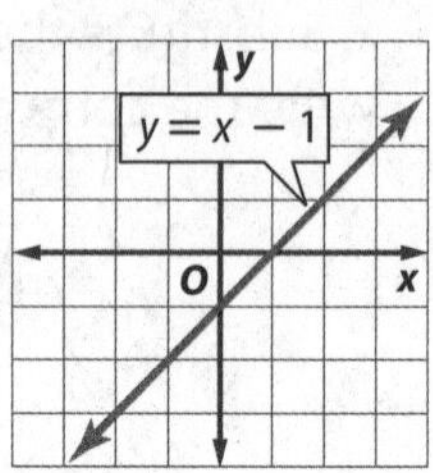

Work Zone

Continuous and Discrete

If the domain of a function is integers, this is an example of a discrete function. If the domain is all real numbers, this is an example of a continuous function.

A **linear function** is a function in which the graph of the ordered pairs forms a straight line. Therefore, an equation of the form $y = mx$ or $y = mx + b$ is a *linear function*.

A function can be considered continuous or discrete. **Continuous data** can take on any value, so there is no space between data values for a given domain. **Discrete data** have space between possible data values. Graphs of continuous data are represented by solid lines and graphs of discrete data are represented by dots.

Continuous Data	Discrete Data
the number of ounces in a glass	the number of glasses in a cupboard
the weight of each chocolate chip	the number of chocolate chips in a bag

You can determine if data that model real-world situations are discrete or continuous by considering whether all numbers are reasonable as part of the domain.

Examples

Tutor

Each person that enters a store receives a coupon for $5 off his or her entire purchase.

3. Write a function to represent the total value of the coupons given out.

Let y represent the total value of the coupons and x represent the number of people. The function is $y = 5x$.

4. **Make a function table to find the total value of the coupons given out to 5, 10, 15, and 20 customers.**

x	$5x$	y
5	5(5)	25
10	5(10)	50
15	5(15)	75
20	5(20)	100

5. **Graph the function. Is the function continuous or discrete? Explain.**

Use the ordered pairs from the function table to graph the function.

There can only be a whole number amount of customers. The function is discrete. So, the points are not connected.

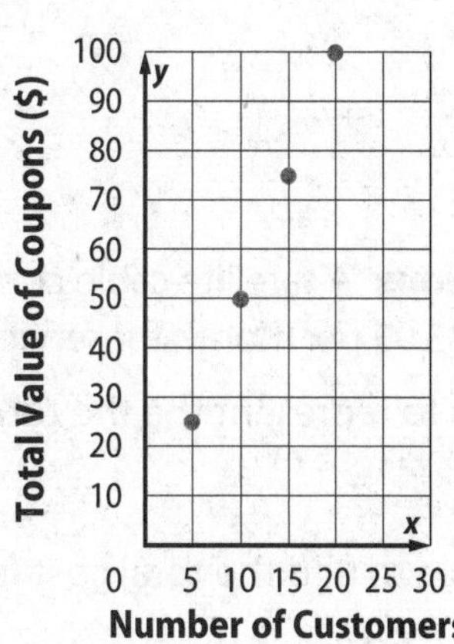

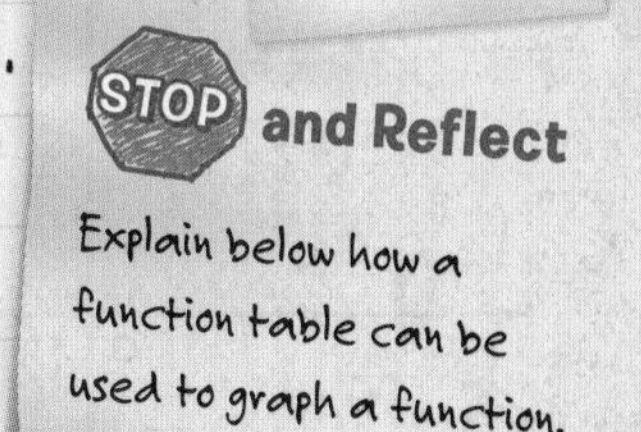

STOP and Reflect
Explain below how a function table can be used to graph a function.

Got It? **Do these problems to find out.**

A store sells assorted nuts for $5.95 per pound.

d. Write a function equation to represent the total cost of any number of pounds of nuts.

e. Complete the function table below to find the total cost of 1, 2, 3, 4, or 5 pounds of nuts.

f. Graph the function. Is the function continuous or discrete? Explain.

X	5.95x	Y
1	5.95(1)	5.95
2	5.95(2)	11.9
3	5.95(3)	17.85
4	5.95(4)	23.8
5	5.95(5)	29.75

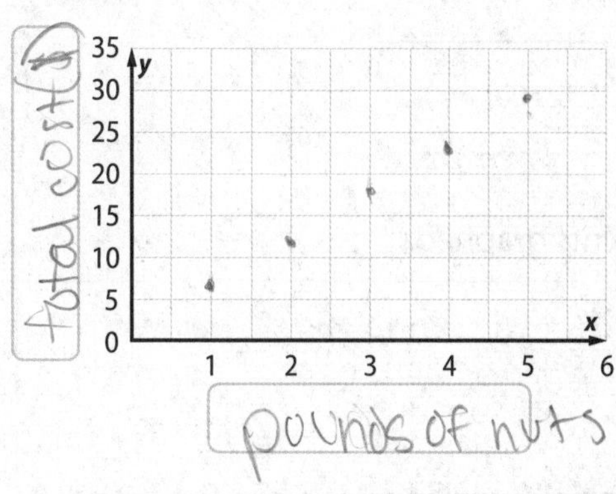

d. y = 5.95x

f. continuas

Guided Practice

Graph each function. (Example 2)

1. $y = x + 5$

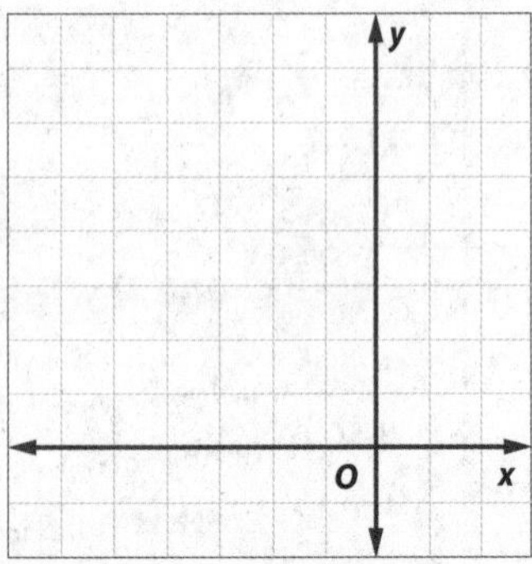

2. $y = 3x - 2$

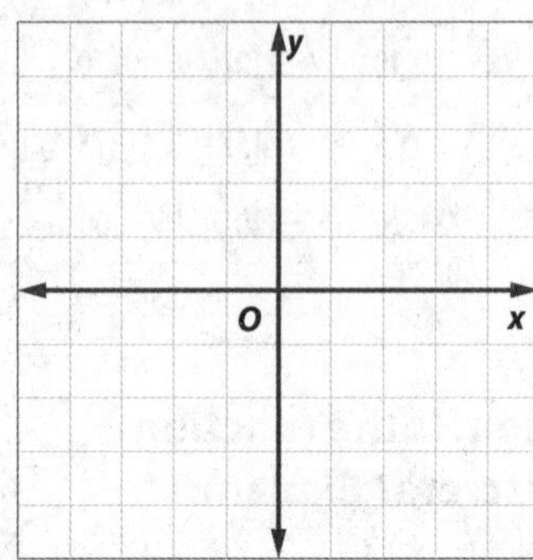

3. **Use Multiple Representations** A satellite cable company charges an installation fee of $50 plus an additional $35.95 per month for service. (Examples 1, 3–5)

a. Equation Write a function to represent the the total cost of any number of months of service. ______

b. Table Make a function table to find the total cost for 1, 2, 3, 4, or 5 months.

c. Graph Graph the function. Is the function continuous or discrete? Explain.

______

______

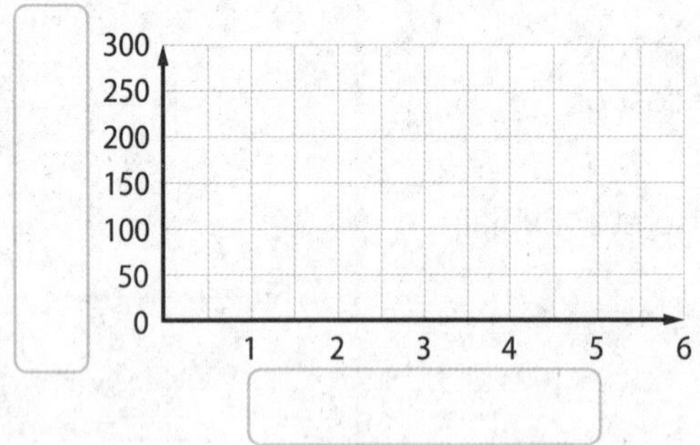

d. Words Interpret the points graphed. ______

______

______

4. **Building on the Essential Question** How can functions be represented in different ways?

______

______

Rate Yourself!

How well do you understand linear functions? Circle the image that applies.

Clear

Somewhat Clear

Not So Clear

Find out online. Use the Self-Check Quiz.

FOLDABLES Time to update your Foldable!

Name ________________ My Homework ________________

Independent Practice

8.5(G), 8.5(I), 8.1(C), 8.1(D), 8.1(F), 8.1(G) TEKS

Graph each function. (Example 2)

1. $y = 4x$ +0

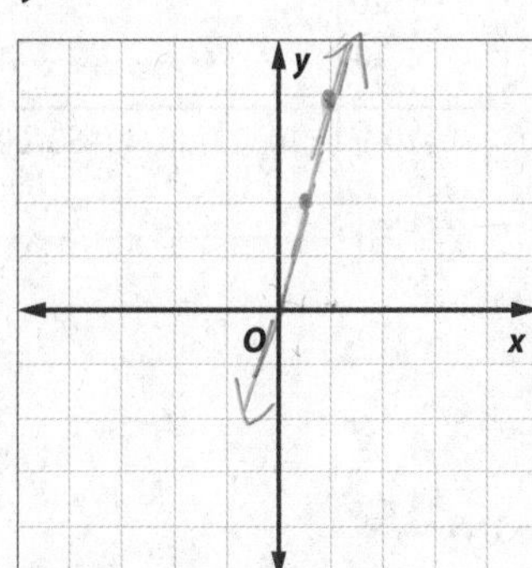

2. $y = -3x$ +0

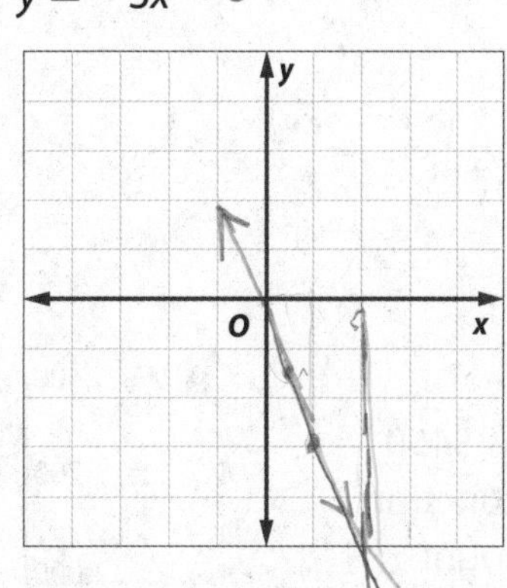

3. $y = x - 3$

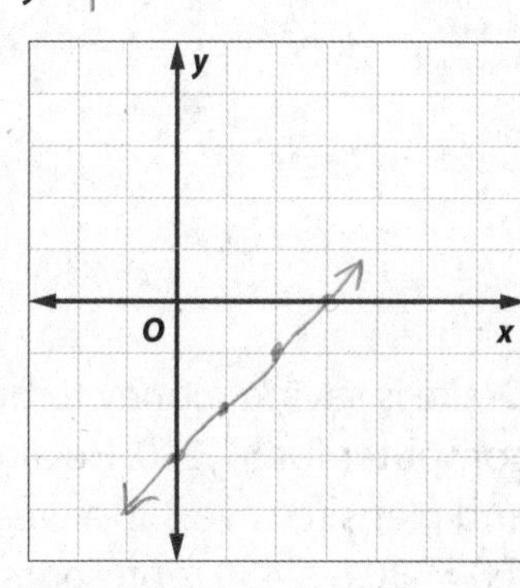

4. **MP Use Multiple Representations** Manuel is saving money for college. He already has $250. He plans to save another $50 per month. (Examples 1, 3–5)

a. Equation Write a function to represent his savings for any number of months. ________________

b. Table Make a function table to find his total savings for 2, 4, 6, 8 and 10 months.

c. Graph Graph the function. Is the function continuous or discrete? Explain. ________________

____

d. Words Interpret the points graphed. ________________

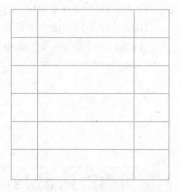

____

____

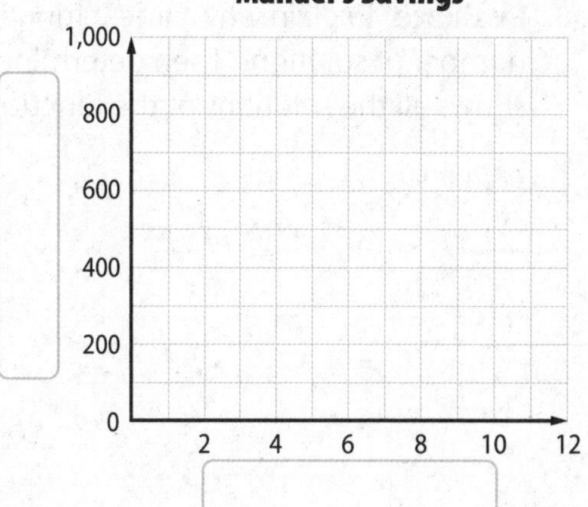

5. Copy and Solve The table shows the cost to rent different items.

Item	Deposit ($)	Cost per Hour ($)
Mountain bike	15	4.25
Scooter	25	2.50

a. Write a function to represent each situation.

____

b. On a separate piece of paper, make a function table to find the total cost to rent each item for 2, 3, 4, or 5 hours.

c. On a separate piece of grid paper, graph the functions on the same coordinate plane. Are the functions continuous or discrete? Explain.

____

____

d. Will the mountain bike or the scooter cost more to rent for 8 hours?

____

e. How much is the cost to rent the mountain bike for 8 hours? ________________

6. MP **Select Tools and Techniques** The formula $F = 1.8C + 32$ compares temperatures in degrees Celsius C to temperatures in degrees Fahrenheit F. Find four ordered pairs (C, F) that are solutions of the equation. Then graph the function.

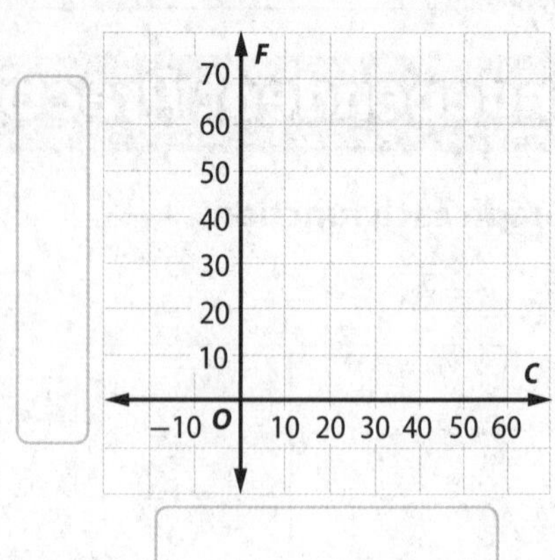

7. Drake is saving money to buy a new computer for $1,200. He already has $450 and plans to save $30 a week. The function $f(x) = 30x + 450$ represents the amount Drake has saved after x weeks. Graph the function to determine the number of weeks it will take Drake to save enough money to buy the computer.

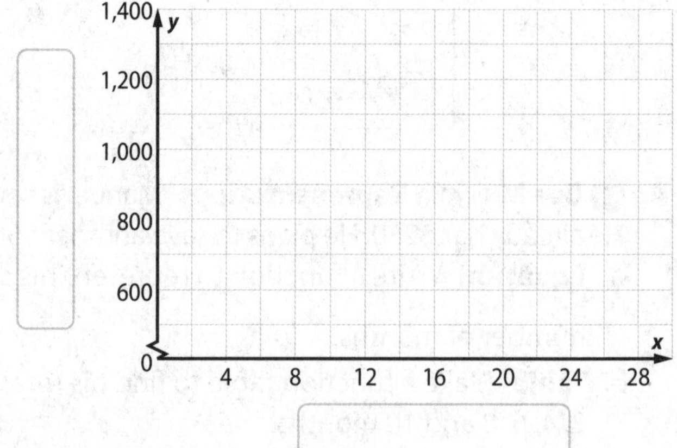

H.O.T. Problems Higher-Order Thinking

8. **Evaluate** Explain why a linear function that is continuous has an infinite number of solutions. Then determine which of the following representations shows all the solutions of the function: a table, a graph, or an equation.

Explain.

9. **Analyze** Name the coordinates of four points that satisfy the linear function shown. Then give the function rule.

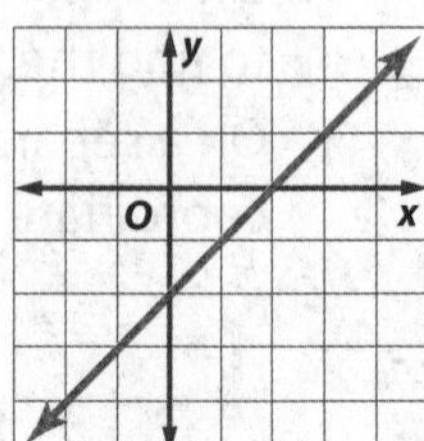

10. **Create** Give a set of four ordered pairs that represents a linear function. Then give the function rule.

Name ______________________________

Multi-Step Problem Solving

11. Which statement is true about the relationships involving a circle shown at the right? P EE MP

	Relationship
1.	(radius, diameter)
2.	(radius, circumference)
3.	(radius, area)

Ⓐ Only Relationships 1 and 2 are linear functions.

Ⓑ Only Relationship 3 is a linear function.

Ⓒ All three of the relationships are linear functions.

Ⓓ None of the relationships are linear functions.

Use a problem-solving model to solve this problem.

1 Analyze

Read the problem. Circle the information you know.
Underline what the problem is asking you to find.

2 Plan

What will you need to do to solve the problem? Write your plan in steps.

Step 1 Determine the ________, ________, and ______ for various radii.

Step 2 Determine which relations, if any, represent ________.

3 Solve

Use your plan to solve the problem. Show your steps.

Write ordered pairs using radii of 1, 2, 3, 4, and 5.

(radius, diameter): {(1, ____), (2, ____), (3, ____), (4, ____), (5, ____)}

(radius, circumference): {(1, ____), (2, ____), (3, ____), (4, ____), (5, ____)}

(radius, area): {(1, ____), (2, ____), (3, ____), (4, ____), (5, ____)}

All three relations are ________, but the third relation does not have a constant ________. So, the correct answer is ____.

Read to Succeed!
Since the circumference and area formulas involve pi, round your calculations to the nearest tenth.

4 Justify and Evaluate

How do you know your solution is accurate?

____

____

P = Proportionality EE = Expressions, Equations, and Relationships MP = Mathematical Processes

More Multi-Step Problem Solving

Use a problem-solving model to solve each problem.

12. Which statement is true about the relations shown in the tables below? P EE N MP

Table 1	
x	y
−4	−4
1	2
5	5

Table 2	
x	y
−1	1
3	5
5	7

Ⓐ Neither table represents a linear function.
Ⓑ Only Table 1 represents a linear function.
Ⓒ Only Table 2 represents a linear function.
Ⓓ Both tables represent linear functions.

13. The table below shows the number of net Calories Silvia burns swimming for various numbers of minutes. Based on Silvia's metabolism, she must burn 3,500 net Calories to lose 16 ounces of fat. If Silvia swims 30 minutes a day, about how many days will it take her to lose at least 5 pounds? P N EE MP

Minutes	Net Calories Burned
2	28
4	56
6	84
8	112

14. Pablo bought tickets at the state fair to play arcade games. Expressions for the number of tickets he used to play three arcade games are shown in the table below. After playing the third game, he had 6 tickets left. How many total tickets did Pablo buy? P EE N MP

Game	Expressions
1	$\frac{1}{2}$(tickets bought − 2)
2	$\frac{1}{4}$ tickets remaining
3	$\frac{1}{3}$ tickets remaining

15. A faucet is dripping at a constant rate of 400 cubic millimeters per minute. A 6 fluid ounce cup is set under the faucet to collect water. How long will it take for the dripping water to fill the cup? Justify your response. (*Hint*: 6 fl oz ≈ 177.67 cm^3) P N EE MP

P = Proportionality 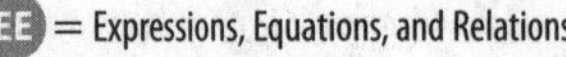 EE = Expressions, Equations, and Relationships 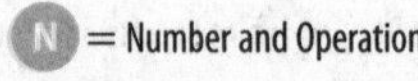 N = Number and Operations 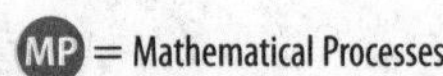 MP = Mathematical Processes

Lesson 5

Proportional and Non-Proportional Functions

Launch the Lesson: Real World

Stephanie belongs to a science museum. Every month, Stephanie pays a $5 membership fee.

1. Complete the table to represent the total cost of Stephanie's membership during a four-month period of time.

Month, x	Total Cost ($), y
1	
2	
3	
4	

2. Write an equation that represents this function.

3. Is this function proportional? Explain.

4. How could you change the real-world situation so that the function is non-proportional?

Texas Essential Knowledge and Skills

Targeted TEKS

8.5(H) Identify examples of proportional and non-proportional functions that arise from mathematical and real-world problems.

Mathematical Processes

8.1(A), 8.1(B), 8.1(E), 8.1(F), 8.1(G)

Essential Question

HOW can we model relationships between quantities?

Which MP Mathematical Processes did you use? Shade the circle(s) that applies.

Ⓐ Apply Math to the Real World.
Ⓑ Use a Problem-Solving Model.
Ⓒ Select Tools and Techniques.
Ⓓ Use Multiple Representations.
Ⓔ Organize Ideas.
Ⓕ Analyze Relationships.
Ⓖ Justify Arguments.

Work Zone

Identify Examples of Proportional Functions

You may recall that a proportional relationship is one in which two quantities have a constant ratio or unit rate. In these Examples, you will learn how to identify examples of proportional functions from tables, equations, and graphs.

Examples

1. The speed of a high speed train operating in China is shown in the table at the right. Is the function proportional? Explain.

Train Rate in China	
Hours	Miles
1	217
2	434
3	651
4	868

To determine if the speed of the train is a proportional function, write the ratios of distance in miles to time in hours for each ordered pair.

$\frac{\text{miles}}{\text{hours}} \rightarrow \frac{217}{1}$ or 217 $\quad \frac{434}{2}$ or 217 $\quad \frac{651}{3}$ or 217 $\quad \frac{868}{4}$ or 217

All of the ratios between the two quantities can be simplified to 217. Since the speed of the train is 217 miles per hour, the function is proportional.

2. The function $y = 140x$, where y is the miles traveled in x hours, represents the speed of the first Japanese high speed train. Is the function proportional? Explain.

Proportional relationships can be written in the form $y = mx$. In $y = 140x$, $m = 140$. So, the function is proportional.

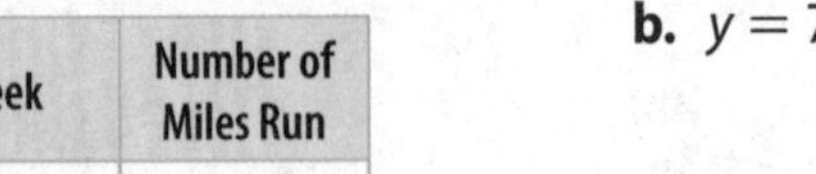

a.

Week	Number of Miles Run
1	3
2	6
3	9
4	12

b. $y = 7x$

a. P

b. P

Example

3. The graph below shows the speed of a zebra. Is the function proportional? Explain.

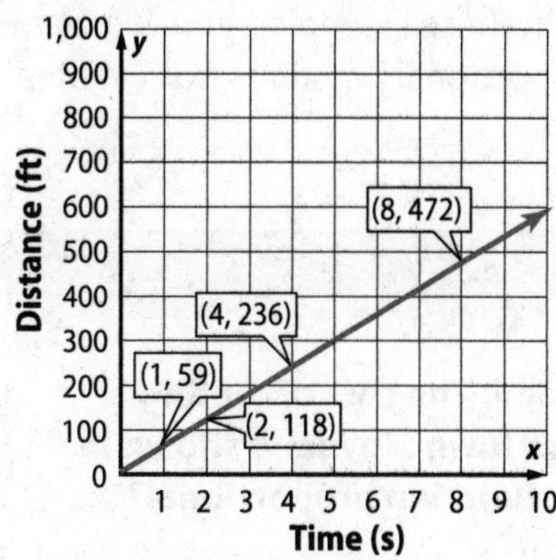

To determine if the speed of the zebra is a proportional function, identify several points on the graph. Then write the ratios of distance in feet to time in seconds for each ordered pair.

The points (1, 59), (2, 118), (4, 236), and (8, 472) lie on the graph.

$\frac{\text{distance (ft)}}{\text{time (s)}} \rightarrow \frac{59}{1}$ or 59 $\quad \frac{118}{2}$ or 59 $\quad \frac{236}{4}$ or 59 $\quad \frac{472}{8}$ or 59

All of the ratios between the two quantities can be simplified to 59. The speed of the zebra is 59 feet per second.

So, the function is proportional.

Check The graph of a proportional function is a straight line that passes through the origin. Since the graph is a straight line that passes through the origin, this function is proportional. ✓

Got It? Do this problem to find out.

c. The gas mileage of a certain sport utility vehicle is represented by the function shown in the graph. Determine whether the function is a proportional function. Justify your response.

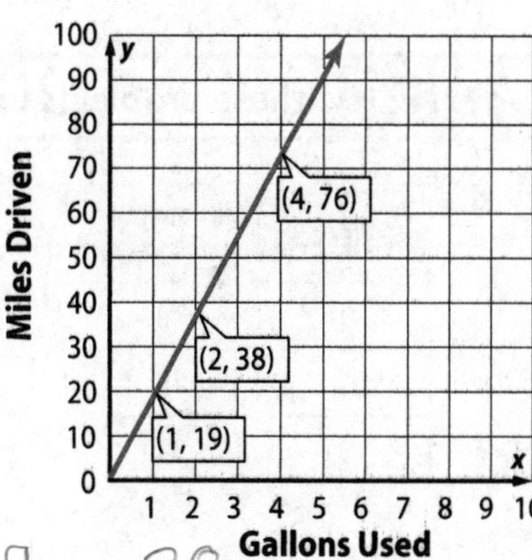

Work Zone

Identify Examples of Non-Proportional Functions

Non-proportional functions also can be represented by graphs, tables, equations, or words. In these Examples, you will learn how to identify examples of non-proportional functions from tables, equations, or graphs.

Examples

Tutor 

4. Financial Literacy **The cost of renting a truck from Cross Town Movers is shown in the table. Is the function proportional? Explain.**

Cross Town Movers	
Miles	Cost ($)
5	20
10	30
30	45

To determine if the function is proportional, write the ratios of cost per mile for each ordered pair.

$\frac{\text{cost}}{\text{time}} \rightarrow \frac{20}{5}$ or 4 $\quad \frac{30}{10}$ or 3 $\quad \frac{45}{30}$ or 1.5

Since $4 \neq 3 \neq 1.5$, the ratios are not equal. So, the function is non-proportional.

5. Financial Literacy **The function $y = 0.5x + 30$, where y represents the total cost in dollars and x represents the miles driven, can be used to find the cost of renting a truck from Ron's Rentals. Is the function proportional? Explain.**

Proportional relationships can be written in the form $y = mx$. The function $y = 0.5x + 30$ is not written in the form $y = mx$. So, the function is non-proportional.

Show your work.

d. NP

e. NP

Got It? Do these problems to find out.

d.

Week	Number of New Games
1	8
2	15
3	31

e. The number of new movies a store receives can be represented by the function $m = 7w + 2$, where m represents the number of movies and w represents the number of weeks.

Example

Tutor

6. Financial Literacy **Benjamin's monthly cell phone bill is shown in the graph. Is the function proportional? Explain.**

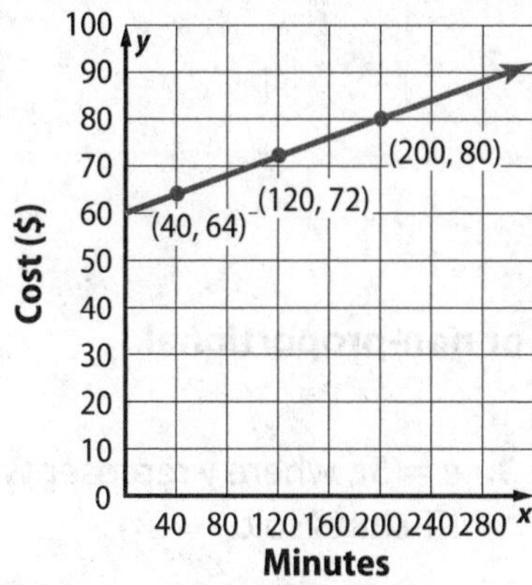

To determine if Benjamin's cell phone bill is a proportional function, identify several points on the graph. Then write the ratios of cost to minutes for each ordered pair.

The points (0, 60), (120, 72), and (200, 80) lie on the graph.

$\frac{\text{cost (\$)}}{\text{time}} \rightarrow \frac{64}{40}$ or 1.6 $\quad \frac{72}{120}$ or 0.6 $\quad \frac{80}{200}$ or 0.4

Since the ratios are not equal, the function is non-proportional.

Check The graph of a proportional function is a straight line that passes through the origin. Since the line does not pass through the origin, it is a non-proportional function. ✓

Got It? Do this problem to find out.

f. The cost of Sarah's gym membership is shown in the graph at the right. Determine if the function is a proportional function. Justify your response.

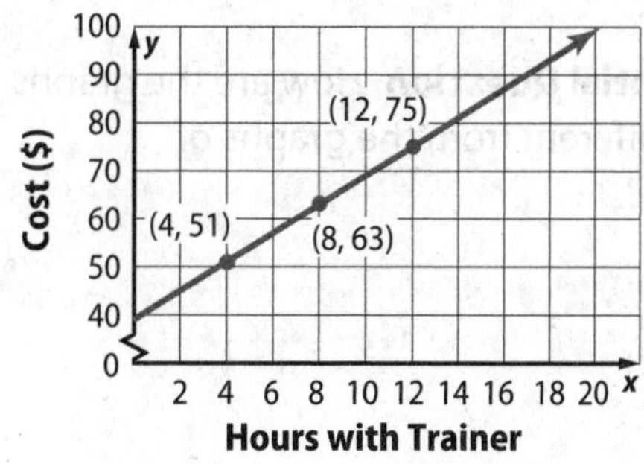

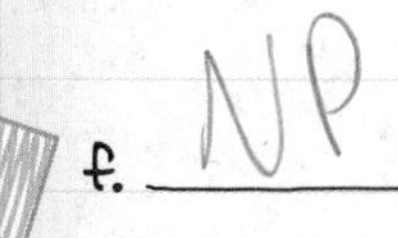

f. NP

Guided Practice

1. Carol's profit at a craft fair is shown in the table. Is the function proportional? Explain. (Examples 1 and 4)

Bracelets Sold	Profit ($)
10	35
20	85
30	135
40	185

Determine whether each function is proportional or non-proportional. Explain. (Examples 2 and 5)

2. $y = 7x + 3$, where y represents the cost of having x pizzas delivered

3. $e = 5t$, where y represents the earnings from t T-shirts sold

4. The graph shows the pounds of food an elephant in captivity eats per day. Determine whether the function is proportional or non-proportional. Justify your response.

(Examples 3 and 6)

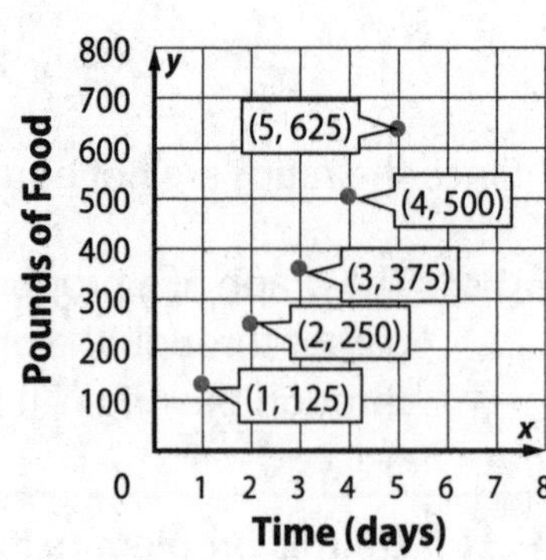

5. Building on the Essential Question How are the graphs of proportional functions different from the graphs of non-proportional functions?

Rate Yourself!

Are you ready to move on? Shade the section that applies.

YES ? NO

Find out online. Use the Self-Check Quiz. Check

FOLDABLES Time to update your Foldable!

Name ______________________________ My Homework ______________________

Independent Practice

8.5(H), 8.1(E), 8.1(F), 8.1(G) TEKS

1. The late fees for a school library are shown in the table. Is the function proportional? Explain. (Examples 1 and 4)

Days Late	1	2	3
Cost ($)	1.25	1.50	1.75

____

____

Determine whether each function is proportional or non-proportional. Explain. (Examples 2 and 5)

2. $y = 9x$, where y represents money earned for x hours worked

____

____

3. $c = 50h + 100$, where c represents the total cost of hiring a deejay for h hours of work

____

____

____

4. Matt purchases baseball cards each week. The graph shows the number of cards Matt has in his collection for various number of weeks. Determine whether the function is proportional or non-proportional. Justify your response. (Examples 3 and 6)

____

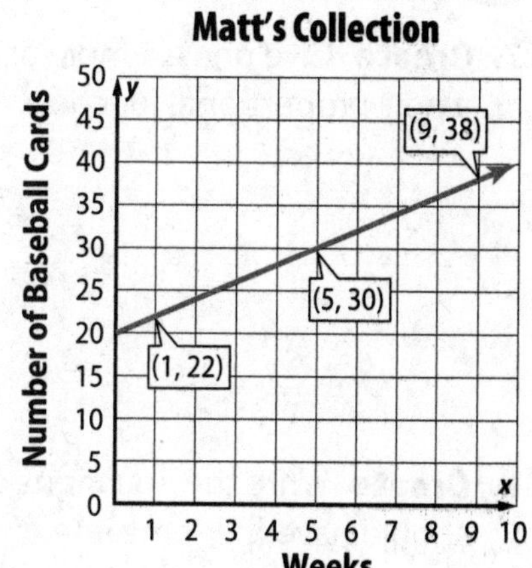

5. For each situation, determine if the function is proportional or non-proportional. Write *proportional* or *non-proportional*.

Situation	Proportional or Non-Proportional?
All sandwiches cost $2.50 in the school cafeteria.	
A caterer charges $8 per dinner, plus a $30 booking fee.	
A beach chair rental costs $20 for the first day and $10 days for each additional day.	
A babysitter charges $10 per hour.	

6. **MP Organize Ideas** Write the letter of each statement below in the section of the Venn diagram to which the statement applies.

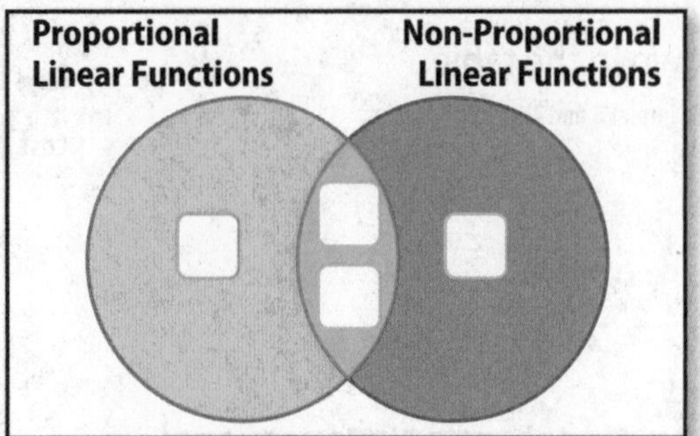

A. Each element of the domain maps to exactly one element of the range.

B. Graphs will not pass through the origin.

C. Graphs have a constant rate of change.

D. There is a constant of proportionality.

H.O.T. Problems Higher-Order Thinking

7. **Create** Give one example of a proportional function and one example of a non-proportional function.

8. **Create** Write the equations of two functions. Both of your equations should have the same rate of change, but one equation should represent a proportional function and the other equation should represent a non-proportional function.

proportional: ______ non-proportional: ______

9. **Evaluate** This year, Andrea celebrated her 10th birthday, and her brother Carlos celebrated his 5th birthday. Andrea noted that she was now twice as old as her brother was. Is the relationship between their ages proportional? Defend your answer.

Name

Multi-Step Problem Solving

10. A librarian is considering two options for calculating overdue late fees. The first option uses $L = 0.30d + 0.50$, where L is the late fee in dollars and d is the number of days late. The second option is shown in the table. Which statement describes how the late fees compare for a book that is 8 days late? P N MP

Option 2				
Days Late	1	2	3	4
Late Fee ($)	0.40	0.80	1.20	1.60

Ⓐ The late fee in the proportional option is $0.30 more.

Ⓑ The late fee in the non-proportional plan is $0.30 more.

Ⓒ The late fee in the proportional plan is $0.90 more.

Ⓓ The late fee in the non-proportional plan is $0.90 more.

Use a problem-solving model to solve this problem.

1 Analyze

Read the problem. Circle the information you know. Underline what the problem is asking you to find.

2 Plan

What will you need to do to solve the problem? Write your plan in steps.

Step 1 Determine which option is ______________. For each option, determine the late fee for a book that is ______________.

Step 2 Determine which statement is correct.

Read to Succeed!
Recall that the quantities in proportional relationships have equal ratios. Equations of proportional relationships can be written in $y = mx$ form.

3 Solve

Use your plan to solve the problem. Show your steps.

Option 1: L = $______(_____) + $______ = $______

Option 2: $______(_____) = $______

The fee for a book that is 8 days late is __________ under Option _____, which is the ______________ option. So, the correct answer is _____.

4 Justify and Evaluate

How do you know your solution is accurate?

P = Proportionality N = Number and Operations MP = Mathematical Processes

More Multi-Step Problem Solving

Use a problem-solving model to solve each problem.

11. Sonia's profits from mowing lawns is given by $y = 5.50x$, where y is the profit in dollars and x is the number of hours worked. Victor's profits are shown in the table.

Victor's Profits				
Hours Worked	1	2	3	4
Profit ($)	1.50	8.00	14.50	21.00

Which option describes how the profits compare for 7 hours of work? P N MP

Ⓐ The profit of the proportional function is $2.00 more.

Ⓑ The profit of the non-proportional function is $2.00 more.

Ⓒ The profit of the proportional function is $7.00 more.

Ⓓ The profit of the non-proportional function is $7.00 more.

12. Leto is considering buying books on display at four different tables. Each table has one of the following signs.

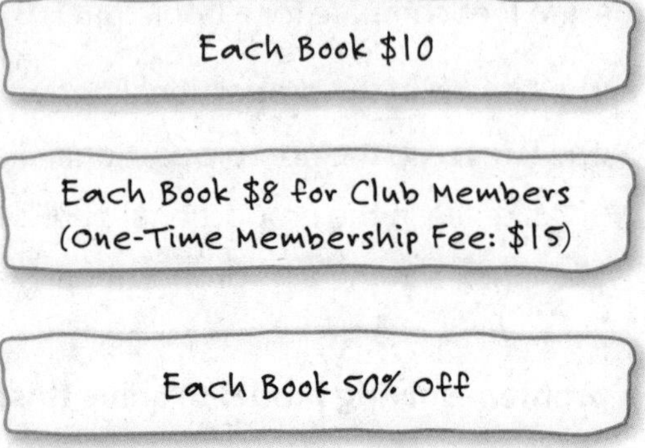

Each Book $10
Each Book $8 for Club Members
(One-Time Membership Fee: $15)
Each Book 50% off

What will be the total cost if Leto buys 6 books from the table whose sign indicates a non-proportional relationship? P MP

13. Hugo's elevation as he drives his car is represented by $y = 175x$, where y is elevation in feet and x is the number of minutes he has driven. Irene's elevation is shown in the graph.

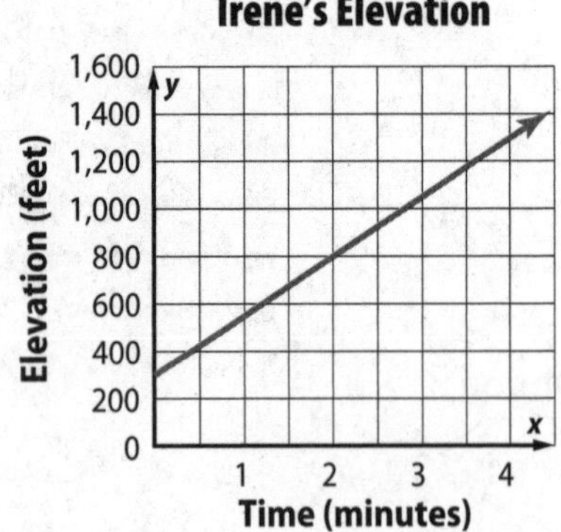

What is the rate of change of the elevation in the non-proportional function? P MP

14. Ed and Rayna are cycling in the same direction on the same straight road. Ed's distance from a roadside rest area is given by $d = 6t$. Rayna's distance from the same rest area is given by $d = 4.5t + 12$. In each function, d is distance in miles and t is time in hours. Determine which function(s) is proportional or non-proportional. When are Ed and Rayna the same distance from the rest area? Defend your answers. P MP

P = Proportionality N = Number and Operations MP = Mathematical Processes

Lesson 6

Write Equations of Functions

Launch the Lesson: Real World

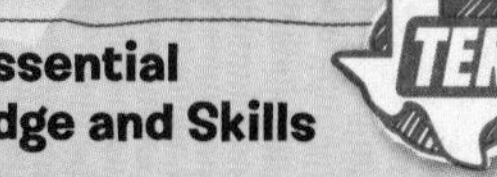

Texas Essential Knowledge and Skills

Targeted TEKS

8.4(C) Use data from a table or graph to determine the rate of change or slope and *y*-intercept in mathematical and real-world problems. *Also addresses 8.5(I).*

Mathematical Processes

8.1(A), 8.1(B)

Essential Question

HOW can we model relationships between quantities?

The table shows how much a skating rink charges for a birthday party. What does the rink charge for a party fee?

Number of Guests, x	Total Cost (\$), y
1	53
2	56
3	59
4	62
5	65
6	68

1. Choose two points from the table and find the rate of change.

2. Use the rate of change you found in Exercise 1 to determine the value of y when $x = 0$. What does this value represent?

3. Graph the ordered pairs. Then extend the line of the graph until it crosses the y-axis.

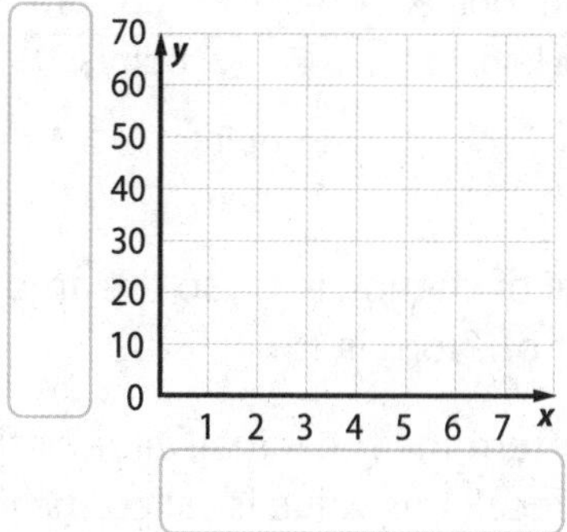

4. Write an equation in the form $y = mx + b$ that represents this situation.

whoah!

Which MP Mathematical Processes did you use? Shade the circle(s) that applies.

Ⓐ Apply Math to the Real World.
Ⓑ Use a Problem-Solving Model.
Ⓒ Select Tools and Techniques.
Ⓓ Use Multiple Representations.
Ⓔ Organize Ideas.
Ⓕ Analyze Relationships.
Ⓖ Justify Arguments.

Work Zone

Find the Initial Value of a Function

The *initial value of a function* is the corresponding *y*-value when *x* equals 0. The initial value is also called the *y*-intercept. You can determine the initial value of a linear function from graphs, words, and tables. To determine the initial value, you may need to first find the rate of change. Determining the initial value and the rate of change is useful for writing the equation of the line.

$y = mx + b$
$y = 3x + b$
$y = 3x + b$
$15 = 3(1) + b$
$15 = 3 + b$
$-3 \quad -3$
$12 = b$

Real World

Example

Tutor 

1. A shoe store offers free points when you sign up for their rewards card. Then, for each pair of shoes purchased, you earn an additional number of points. The graph shows the total points earned for several pairs of shoes. Determine and interpret the rate of change and initial value.

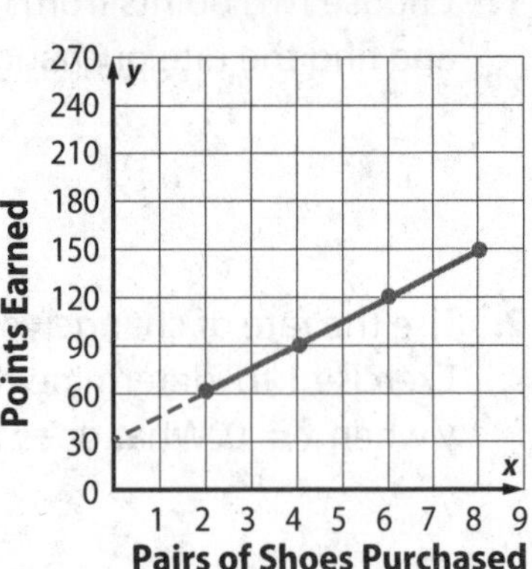

Step 1 To determine the rate of change, choose two points from the graph.

$$\frac{\text{change in points}}{\text{change in pairs}} = \frac{(90 - 60) \text{ points}}{(4 - 2) \text{ points}}$$

$$= \frac{15 \text{ points}}{1 \text{ pair}}$$

The rate of change is 15, so the amount of points earned per pair of shoes is 15.

Step 2 Next determine the initial value or the *y*-value when $x = 0$. Recall this value is called the *y*-intercept. Extend the line so it intersects the *y*-axis. The value for *y* when $x = 0$ is 30. So, the initial number of points earned is 30.

Got It? Do this problem to find out.

Show your work.

ROC = 3
IV = 12

a. __________

a. Music Inc. charges a yearly subscription fee plus a monthly fee. The total cost for different numbers of months, including the yearly fee, is shown in the graph. Determine and interpret the rate of change and initial value.

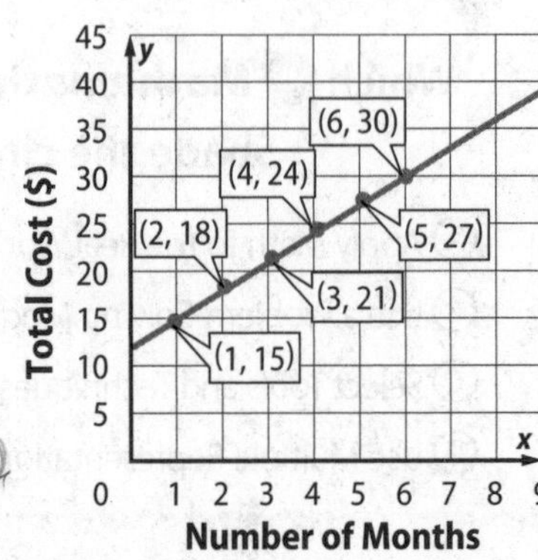

$\frac{(18-15)}{(2-1)} = \frac{3}{1}$

Write Equations of Linear Functions

Once you have determined the rate of change and initial value of a linear function, you can write the equation of the function in $y = mx + b$ form. The rate of change is m, the slope. The initial value is b, the y-intercept.

Examples

2. Joan plans to add 12 photos in her photo album each week. After 8 weeks, there are 120 photos in the album. Assume the relationship is linear. Determine and interpret the rate of change and initial value. Write the equation in $y = mx + b$ form.

Since each week Joan adds 12 photos to her photo album the rate of change is 12. To determine the initial value, use slope-intercept form to find the y-intercept.

$y = mx + b$	Slope-intercept form
$y = 12x + b$	Replace m with the rate of change, 12.
$120 = 12(8) + b$	Replace y with 120 and x with 8
$24 = b$	Solve for b.

The y-intercept is 24. So, the initial number of photos is 24.

The equation of the line in $y = mx + b$ form is $y = 12x + 24$.

3. The table shows how much money Ava has saved. Assume the relationship between the two quantities is linear. Determine and interpret the rate of change and initial value. Then write the equation in $y = mx + b$ form.

Number of Months, x	Money Saved (\$), y
3	110
4	130
5	150
6	170

Choose any two points to determine the the rate of change. The rate of change is $\frac{150 - 110}{5 - 3}$ or 20, so Ava saves \$20 each month. To determine the initial value, use the slope-intercept form to find the y-intercept.

$y = mx + b$	Slope-intercept form
$y = 20x + b$	Replace m with the rate of change, 20.
$110 = 20(3) + b$	Use the point (3, 110). $x = 3, y = 110$
$50 = b$	Solve for b.

The y-intercept is 50, so Ava had initially saved \$50.

The equation in $y = mx + b$ form is $y = 20x + 50$.

b. ____________

Got It? Do this problem to find out.

b. The table shows the monthly cost of sending text messages. Assume the relationship between the two quantities is linear. Determine and interpret the rate of change and intial value. Then write the equation in $y = mx + b$ form.

Number of Messages, x	Cost ($), y
5	10.50
6	10.60
7	10.70

Guided Practice

1. As part of a grand opening, an arcade gave out free tokens to the first 100 customers. The graph shows the number of tokens customers received for each dollar spent at the Play More Arcade. Detemine and interpret rate of change and the initial value. (Example 1)

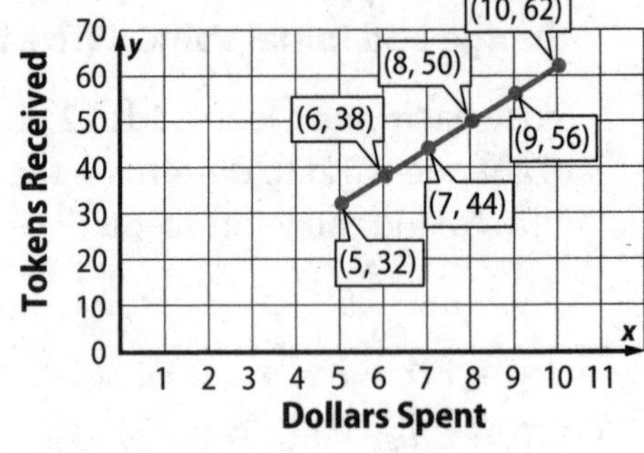

For Exercises 2 and 3, determine and interpret the rate of change and initial value. Then write the equation in $y = mx + b$ form.

2. A historic museum charges a rental fee plus $2 per hour for an audio tour guide. The total cost for 4 hours is $12. (Example 2)

3. A science center charges an initial membership fee. The total cost of the membership depends on the number of people on the membership as shown in the table. Assume the relationship between the two quantities is linear. (Example 3)

Number of People, x	2	3	4	5
Additional Cost ($), y	65	80	95	110

4. **Building on the Essential Question** How can finding the initial value help you to write the equation of a function in $y = mx + b$ form?

Rate Yourself!

☐ I understand how to construct functions.

Great! You're ready to move on!

☐ I still have questions about constructing functions.

No problem! Go online to access a Personal Tutor.

Name ______________________ My Homework ______________________

Independent Practice

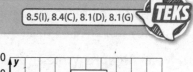

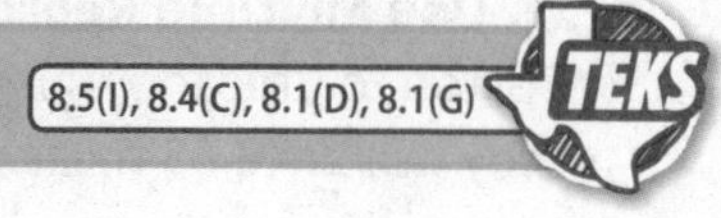

1. A teacher read part of a book to a class. The graph shows the number of pages read by the teacher over the next several days. Determine and interpret the rate of change and the initial value. (Example 1)

____

____

Number of Pages Read (y): 0, 100, 200, 300, 400, 500, 600, 700, 800, 900, 1,000

Time (days) (x): 1, 2, 3, 4, 5, 6, 7, 8, 9, 10

(3, 450), (4, 550), (5, 650), (6, 750), (7, 850)

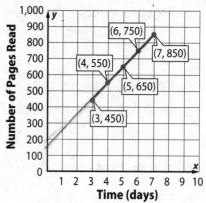

For Exercises 2–5, determine and interpret the rate of change and the initial value. Then write the equation in $y = mx + b$ form.

2. A water park charges a rental fee plus $1.50 per hour to rent inflatable rafts. The total cost to rent a raft for 6 hours is $15. Assume the relationship is linear.

(Example 2) ______________________

____

3. A teacher already had a certain number of canned goods for the food drive. Each day of the food drive, the class plans to bring in 10 cans. The total number of canned goods for day 10 is 205. Assume the relationship is linear.
(Example 2)

____

____

4. Melissa frosted some cupcakes in the morning for a party. The table shows the total number of cupcakes frosted after she starts up after lunch. Assume the relationship between the two quantities is linear. (Example 3)

Time (min), x	5	10	15	20
Number of Cupcakes, y	28	32	36	40

____

____

5. Jonas has a certain number of DVDs in his collection. The table shows the total number of DVDs in his collection over several months. Assume the relationship between the two quantities is linear. (Example 3)

Month, x	3	6	9	12
Number of DVDs, y	18	27	36	45

____

____

6. **Use Multiple Representations** The Coughlin family is driving from Boston to Chicago. The total distance of the trip is 986 miles and each hour they will drive 65 miles.

a. **Algebra** Write an equation to represent the number of remaining miles y after driving any number of hours x.

b. **Graphs** Graph the equation from part **a** on a coordinate plane.

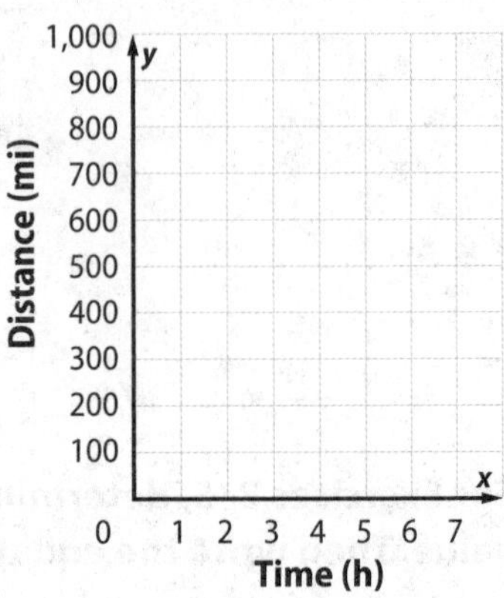

c. **Numbers** What is the rate of change and y-intercept of the line?

d. **Words** Explain why the line *slopes down* by 65 for each hour.

e. **Words** Why does the line cross the y-axis at 986?

H.O.T. Problems Higher-Order Thinking

7. **Analyze** Explain why a horizontal line has a rate of change of zero.

8. **Create** Write and solve a real-world problem in which you need to find the initial value of a function. Then explain to a classmate how you solved your problem.

9. **Evaluate** You are asked to write a linear equation for a function in which the rate of change is −7 and the initial value is −2. You wrote the equation $y = -7x + (-2)$. Your classmate wrote the equation $y = -7x - 2$. Another classmate wrote the equation $y = (-2) + (-7)x$. Your teacher wrote the equation $y = -2 - 7x$ Who is correct? Justify your response.

Name ____________________

Multi-Step Problem Solving

10. Felicia wants to fence in a rectangular region whose length will be twice its width. She also wants to fence in a rectangular dog pen that will share a length of fence, as shown in the diagram at the right. Which equation represents the amount of fencing Felicia needs? P EE MP

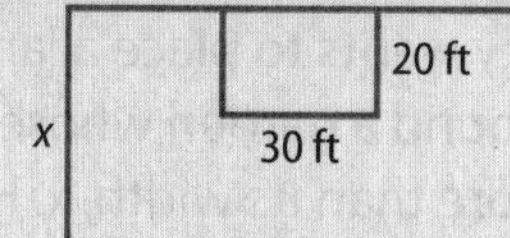

Ⓐ $y = 3x + 70$

Ⓑ $y = 6x + 70$

Ⓒ $y = 3x + 100$

Ⓓ $y = 6x + 100$

Use a problem-solving model to solve this problem.

1 Analyze

Read the problem. Circle the information you know.
Underline what the problem is asking you to find.

2 Plan

What will you need to do to solve the problem? Write your plan in steps.

Step 1 Determine the sum of the perimeters of the ____________ and the ________.

Step 2 Subtract the ________ length of fencing.

3 Solve

Use your plan to solve the problem. Show your steps.

The perimeter of the rectangular region is 2(________) + 2(________) or ________ square feet.

The perimeter of the dog pen is 2(________) + 2(________) or ________ square feet.

So, the total amount of fencing, less the shared length, is _____ + _____ − _____ or _____ + _____ square feet. The correct answer is _____. Fill in that answer.

Read to Succeed!
Remember even though coefficients are added or subtracted when combining like terms, the variables remain the same.

4 Justify and Evaluate

How do you know your solution is accurate?

____

____

____

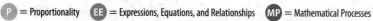

P = Proportionality EE = Expressions, Equations, and Relationships MP = Mathematical Processes

More Multi-Step Problem Solving

Use a problem-solving model to solve each problem.

11. Izzy wants to place a landscape border around a garden whose length will be 50% more than its width, x. He also wants to place the border on two edges of the patio, as shown in the diagram below.

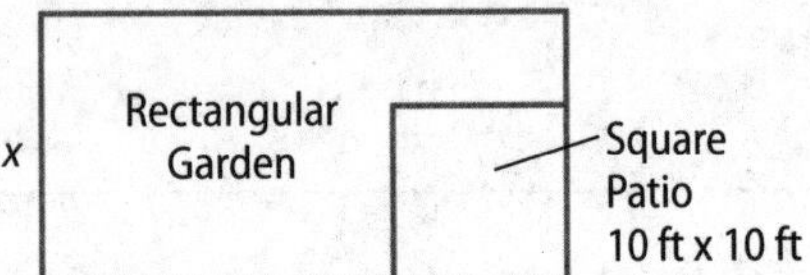

Which equation represents the amount of border Izzy will need? P EE MP

Ⓐ $y = 2.5x + 20$

Ⓑ $y = 3x + 20$

Ⓒ $y = 5x + 20$

Ⓓ $y = 5x + 40$

12. Rosa wants to buy a motor scooter. The graph shows information about two different scooters.

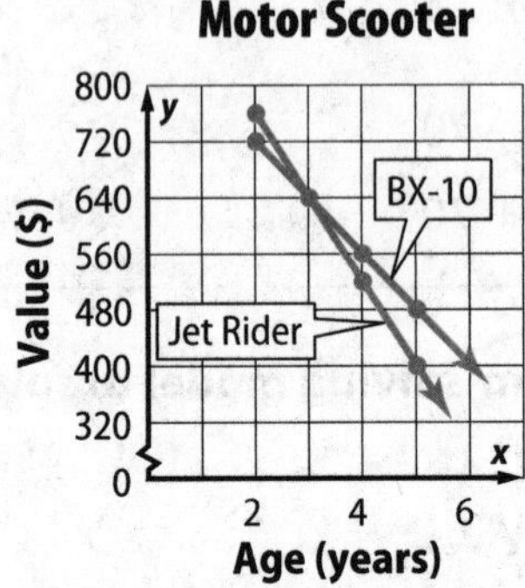

Assuming that the patterns continue, what will be the difference in values of the two scooters when they are 8 years old? P EE MP

13. The population of a city has grown according to the pattern shown in the table, where x represents the number of years since the year 2000. P EE N MP

Years, x	City Population, y
3	$3.5 \times 10^5 + 3(5 \times 10^5)$
4	$3.5 \times 10^5 + 4(5 \times 10^5)$
5	$3.5 \times 10^5 + 5(5 \times 10^5)$

Using the pattern in the table, what is the value of $\frac{\text{population in 2000}}{\text{rate of increase in population}}$?

14. Jack and Ryan save at the rates shown in the graph below. In about how many weeks will the boys have a combined savings of $500?

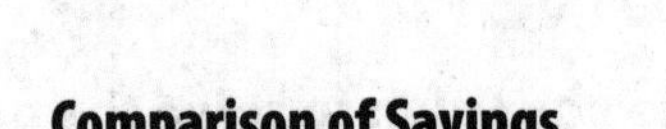

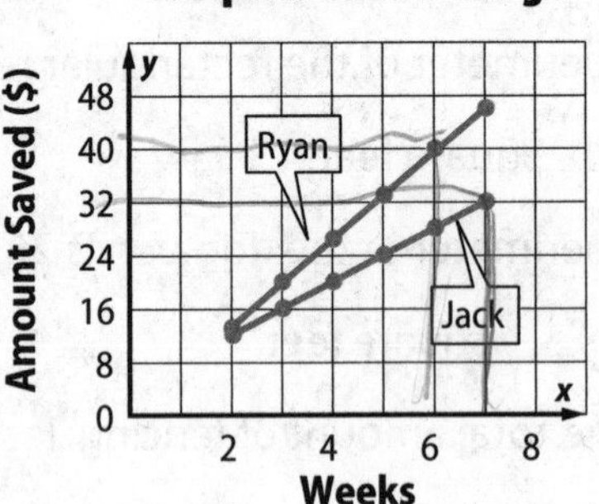

P = Proportionality EE = Expressions, Equations, and Relationships N = Number and Operations MP = Mathematical Processes

Graphing Technology Lab 6-b

Family of Linear Functions

INQUIRY HOW can I select tools and techniques to study the effect of changing the slope and/or *y*-intercept of a linear function on its equation and graph?

The cost of a student ticket to the school play is \$1. The total cost *y* of any number of student tickets *x* can be represented by the equation $y = x$. The cost of an adult ticket to the school play is \$4. The total cost *y* of any number of adult tickets *x* can be represented by the equation $y = 4x$. How do the graphs of these equations compare?

Texas Essential Knowledge and Skills TEKS

Targeted TEKS

8.5(F) Distinguish between proportional and non-proportional situations using tables, graphs, and equations in the form $y = kx$ or $y = mx + b$, where $b \neq 0$.

Also addresses 8.4(B), 8.5(A), 8.5(B), 8.5(H), 8.5(I).

Mathematical Processes

8.1(C), 8.1(D), 8.1(E), 8.1(F)

Vocab

Vocabulary

family of functions

Hands-On Activity 1

A graphing calculator allows you to graph multiple functions. This is useful for investigating families of linear functions. A **family of functions** is a set of functions that is related in some way.

Step 1 Clear any existing equations from the list by pressing [Y=] [CLEAR].

Step 2 Enter $y = x$, $y = 4x$, and $y = \frac{1}{4}x$. Press [X,T,θ,*n*] [ENTER] 4 [X,T,θ,*n*] [ENTER] [(] 1 [÷] 4 [)] [X,T,θ,*n*] [ENTER].

Step 3 Press [ZOOM] 6 to set the viewing window.

Draw your calculator screen on the blank screen at the right.

1. What is the same about each of these graphs?

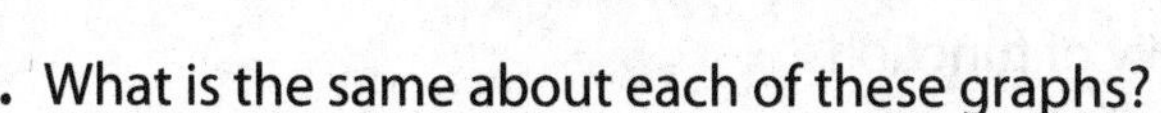

2. What is different about each of these graphs?

3. How does the slope affect the graph?

4. How do the graphs of $y = x$ and $y = 4x$ compare?

Hands-On Activity 2

Step 1 Clear any existing equations from the list by pressing Y= CLEAR.

Step 2 Enter $y = 2x$, $y = 2x + 5$, $y = 2x - 4$. Press 2 X,T,θ,n ENTER 2 X,T,θ,n ENTER + 1 ENTER 2 X,T,θ,n − 1.

Step 3 Press ZOOM 6.

Draw your calculator screen on the blank screen.

5. What is the same about each of these graphs?

6. What is different about each of these graphs?

7. How does the y-intercept affect the graph?

8. Write two more equations that are part of this family of functions.

CHECK Check that your equations are members of this family of functions by graphing them on a graphing calculator. ✓

Investigate

Collaborate

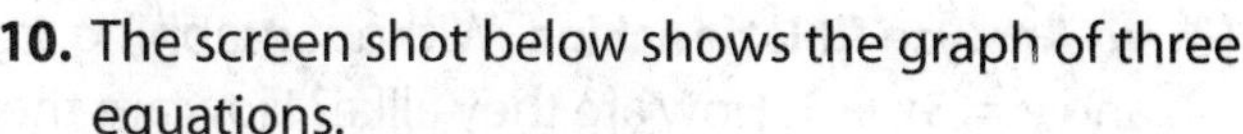

Work with a partner.

9. The screen shot below shows the graph of three equations.

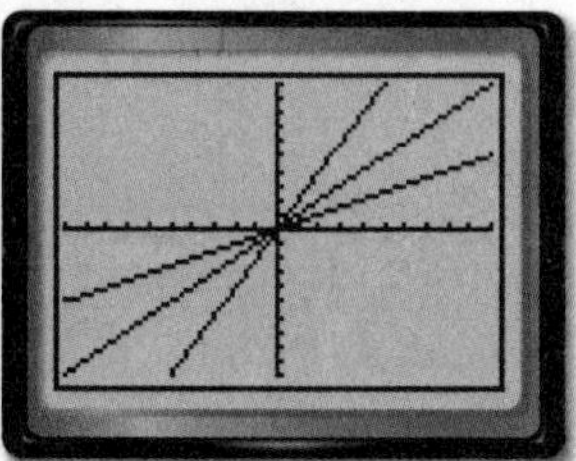

What are the equations graphed?

10. The screen shot below shows the graph of three equations.

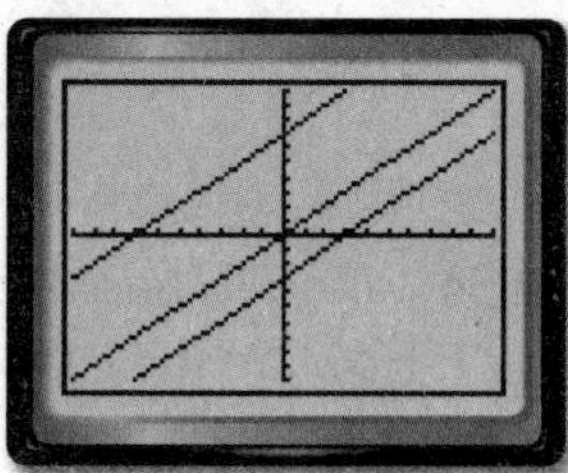

What are the equations graphed?

11. Use a graphing calculator to graph $y = 3x$, $y = 3x + 4$, and $y = 3x - 4$. Copy your calculator screen on the blank screen shown.

How does changing the value of b in the equation $y = 3x + b$ affect the graph?

12. Use a graphing calculator to graph $y = 3x$, $y = \frac{1}{3}x$, and $y = 6x$. Copy your calculator screen on the blank screen shown.

How does changing the value of k in the equation $y = kx$ affect the graph?

Analyze and Reflect

Work with a partner.

13. **MP Analyze Relationships** Without graphing, compare the graphs of $y = 3x$ and $y = 3x + 1$. How are they alike? How are they different?

14. **MP Analyze Relationships** Without graphing, compare the graphs of $y = 2x + 1$ and $y = 3x + 1$. How are they alike? How are they different?

15. A landscape company charges $30 per cubic yard for mulch plus a $40 delivery fee.

    a. Write an equation that represents the total cost.

    b. Describe the change in the graph if the delivery fee was $35. What would be the new equation?

    c. Describe the change in the graph if the price of the mulch changed to $25 per cubic yard. What would be the new equation?

Create

16. All of the equations in the lab are members of the linear family of functions. Each family of functions has a parent function. What equation is the parent function for the linear family of functions?

17. **INQUIRY** HOW can I select tools and techniques to study the effect of changing the slope and/or y-intercept of a linear function on its equation and graph?

21ST CENTURY CAREER

Physical Therapist

Are you a compassionate person? Do you have a strong desire to help others? If so, a career as a physical therapist might be a good choice for you. Physical therapists help restore function, improve mobility, and relieve pain of patients suffering from injuries or disease. One of their jobs is to teach exercises or recommend activities to help patients regain balance, flexibility, endurance, and strength.

Mathematical Process TEKS
8.1(A) Apply mathematics to problems arising in everyday life, society, and the workplace.
Targeted TEKS 8.5(A)

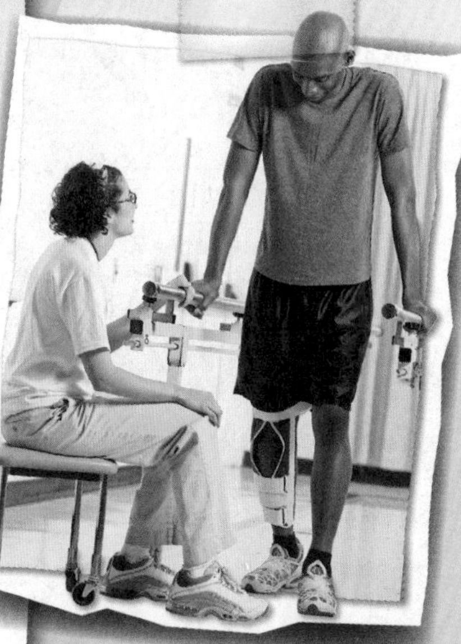

Is This the Career for You?

Are you interested in a career as a physical therapist? Take some of the following courses in high school.

- Algebra
- Biology
- Chemistry
- Introduction To Physical Therapy

Turn the page to find out how math relates to a career in Physical Therapy.

Explore college and careers at ccr.mcgraw-hill.com

Focusing on Recovery

Use the information in the table below to solve each problem.

1. The function $t(r) = 12r$, where r is the number of repetitions, represents the total time $t(r)$ in seconds to complete a flexibility exercise. Find $t(8)$. Then interpret the solution. ______________________

2. Refer to the information in Exercise 1. Make a function table to find the time it will take to complete 1, 2, 5, and 10 repetitions.

r	$12r$	$t(r)$

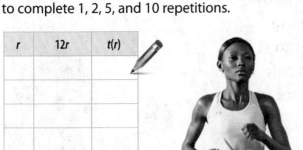

3. Write a function to represent the distance d in miles a runner will travel in t minutes.

____

4. Refer to the function that you wrote in Exercise 3. How far will a runner travel after 80 minutes? ______________________

5. Graph the function from Exercise 3. Then use the graph to estimate the distance a runner will travel after 90 minutes.

____

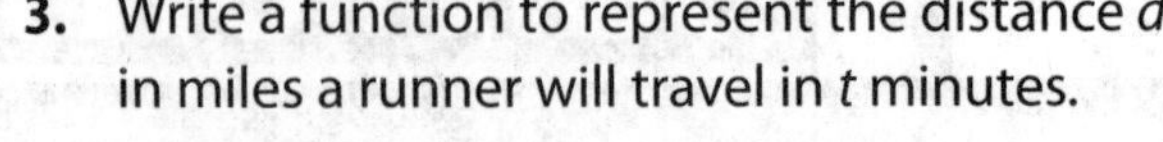

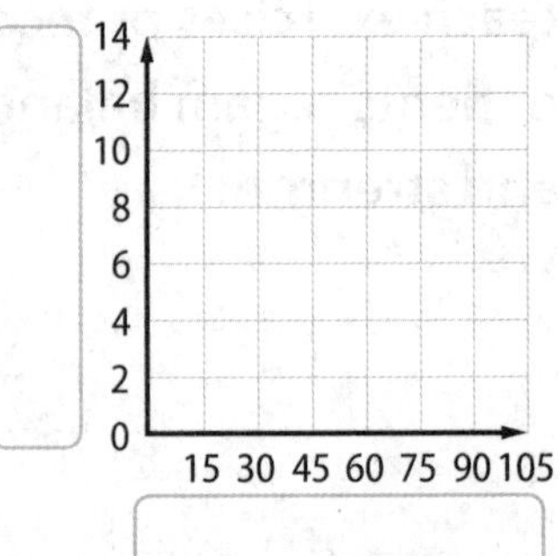

Endurance Exercise: Cross-Country Running	
Time (min)	**Distance (mi)**
15	2.25
30	4.5
45	6.75
60	9.0

TEKS Career Project

Investigate the education and training requirements for a career as a physical therapist. Prepare a brief oral presentation and present it to your classmates. As others are presenting, listen carefully to their presentations. Ask questions for clarification as needed.

List other careers that someone with an interest in physical therapy could pursue.

-
-
-
-
-

Chapter Review

Vocabulary Check

Vocab

Work with a partner to complete the puzzles by unscrambling the letters below each column to complete the definition of a word from the vocabulary list at the beginning of the chapter. Seek clarification of each vocabulary term as needed.

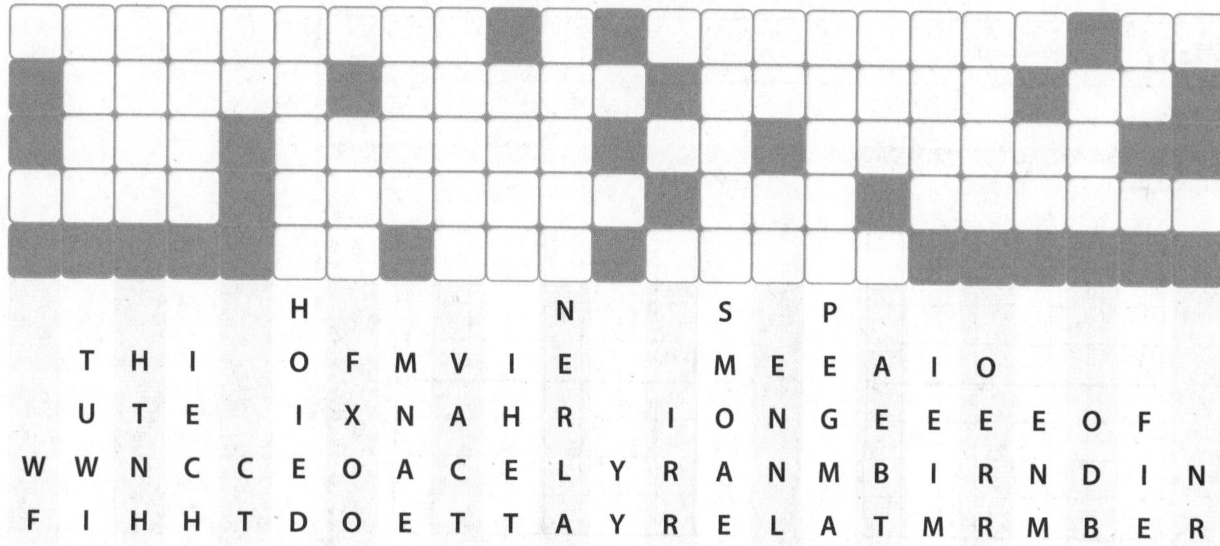

Complete each sentence using the vocabulary list at the beginning of the chapter.

1. A ______________ is any set of ordered pairs.
2. The variable for the range is called the ______________ because it depends on the domain.
3. A ______________ function is a function in which the graph of the ordered pairs forms a straight line.
4. The variable for the domain is called the ______________ because it can be any number.
5. ______________ can take on any value, so there is no space between data values for a given domain.
6. A ______________ is a set of functions related in some way.
7. A ______________ is a relation in which every member of the domain is paired with exactly one member of the range.

Key Concept Check

Use Your FOLDABLES®

Use your Foldable to help review the chapter. Share your Foldable with your partner and take turns summarizing what you learned in this chapter, listening carefully when your partner speaks. Ask for clarification of any concepts, as needed.

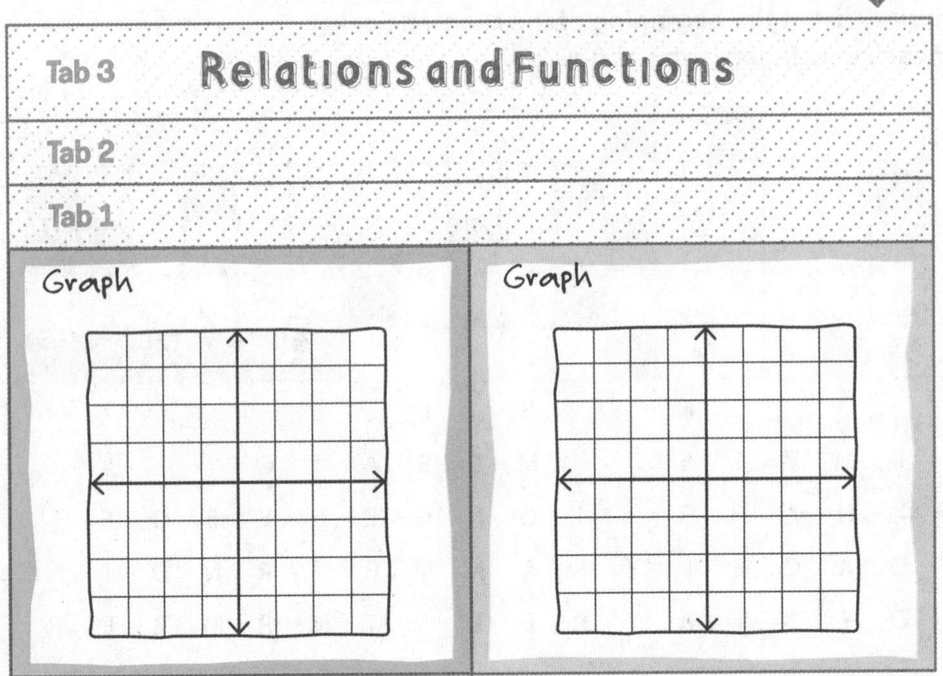

Got it?

Match each function with the correct graph.

1. $-x + y = -3$ **2.** $2x + y = 6$ **3.** $-2x + 3y = -9$ **4.** $x + 2y = 4$

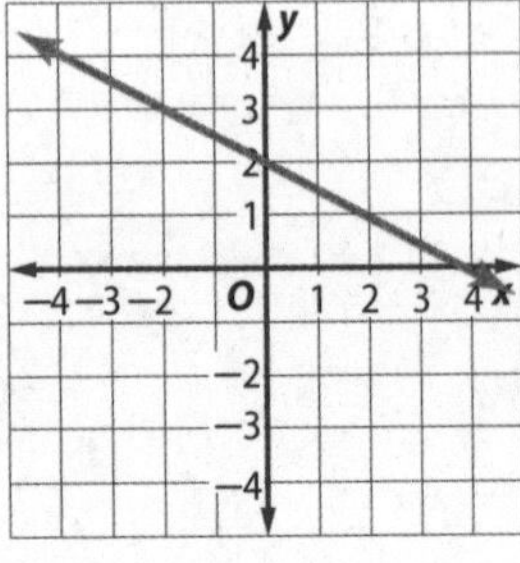

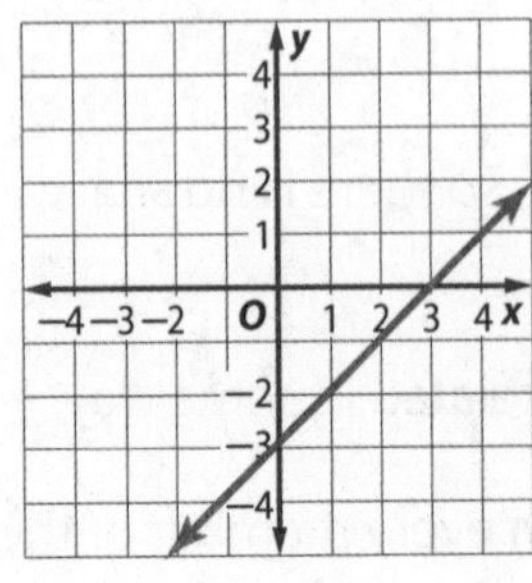

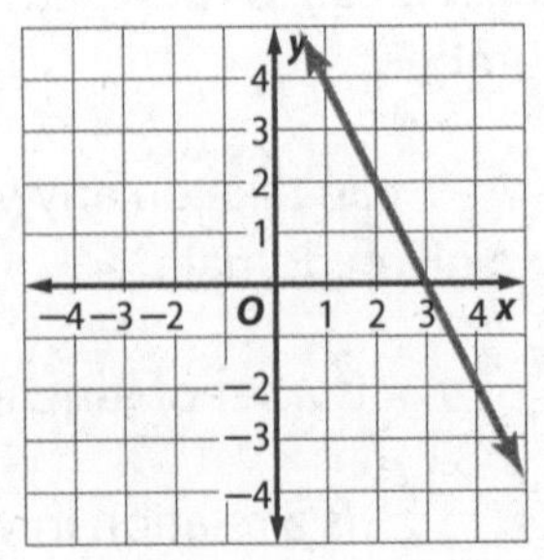

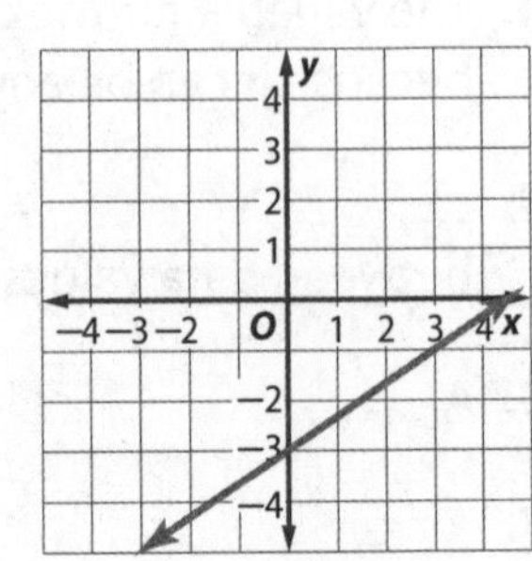

Multi-Step Problem Solving

5. Each week, Robert earns a salary plus a commission of 7.5% of his total sales. Jasper also earns a salary plus a commission of 9% of his total sales. Last week, Robert sold $800 worth of merchandise and earned a total of $520. Jasper sold $750 worth of merchandise and earned a total of $525. Who earns a greater salary, not including commission? Defend your answer. P N MP

1 Analyze

2 Plan

3 Solve

4 Justify and Evaluate

Got it?

6. A fish tank contains a certain number of gallons of water. The table shows how much water is in the tank over time. In how many minutes will there be 20 gallons of water left in the tank? Assume the relationship between the two quantities is linear. Defend your answer. 8.1(A), 8.1(B), 8.4(C), 8.5(I)

Fish Tank	
Time (min)	Water in Tank (gal)
5	77.5
10	65
15	52.5

P = Proportionality N = Number and Operations MP = Mathematical Processes

Reflect

Answering the Essential Question

Use what you learned about functions to complete the graphic organizer. Show four ways functions can be represented. TEKS 8.1(D), 8.1(F), 8.1(G)

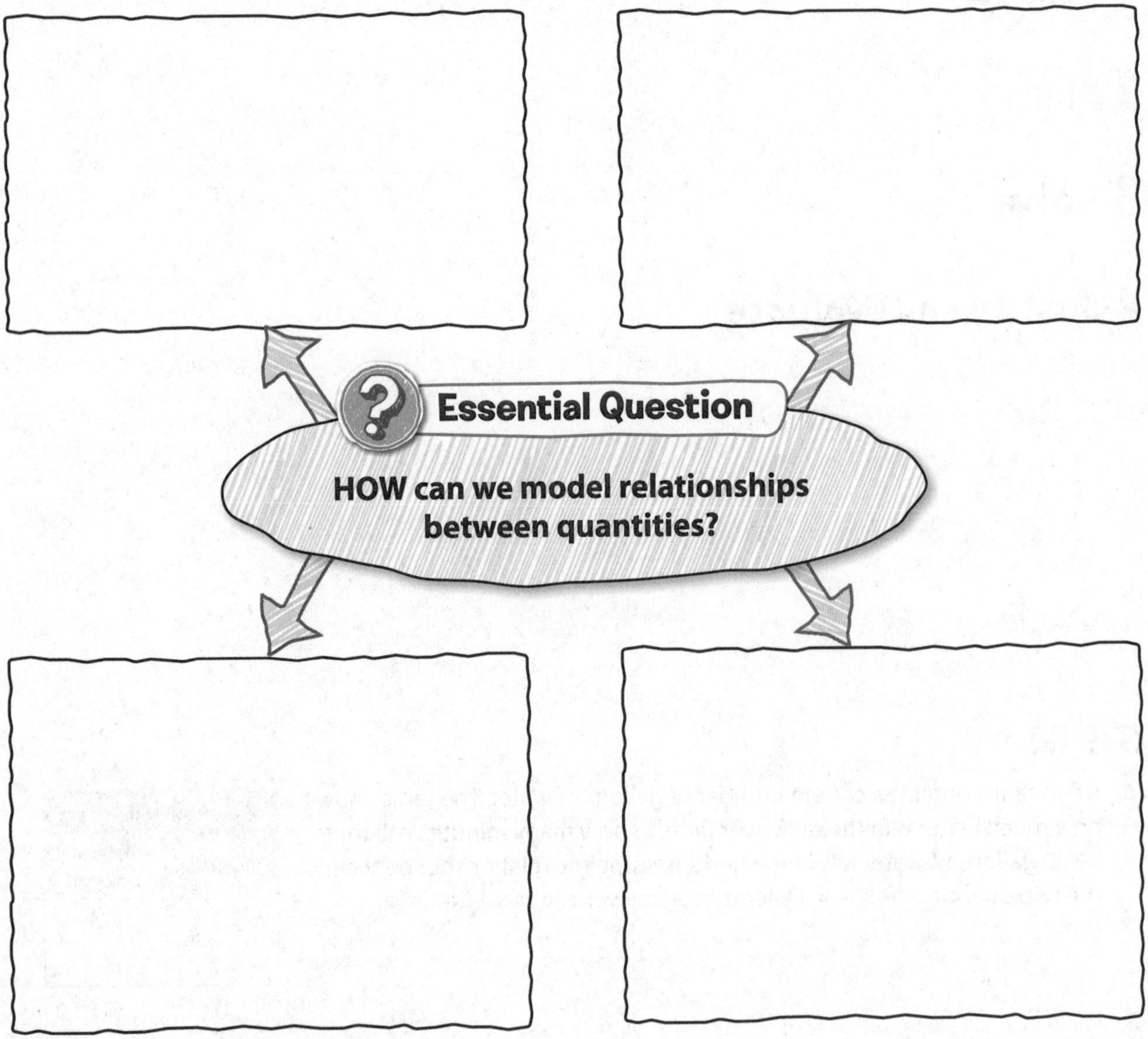

Essential Question

HOW can we model relationships between quantities?

Answer the Essential Question. HOW can we model relationships between quantities? Verbally share your response with a partner, asking for and providing clarification as needed.

Glossary/Glosario

Vocab

Go online for the eGlossary.

The eGlossary contains words and definitions in the following 13 languages:

Arabic
Bengali
Brazilian Portuguese
Cantonese
English
Haitian Creole
Hmong
Korean
Russian
Spanish
Tagalog
Urdu
Vietnamese

English

Español

Aa

accuracy The degree of closeness of a measurement to the true value.

exactitud Cercanía de una medida a su valor verdadero.

acute angle An angle whose measure is less than 90°.

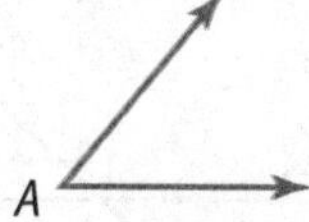

ángulo agudo Ángulo que mide menos de 90º.

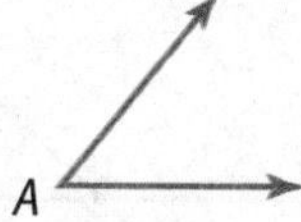

acute triangle A triangle with all acute angles.

triángulo acutángulo Triángulo con todos los ángulos agudos.

Addition Property of Equality If you add the same number to each side of an equation, the two sides remain equal.

propiedad de adición de la igualdad Si sumas el mismo número a ambos lados de una ecuación, los dos lados permanecen iguales.

adjacent angles Angles that share a common vertex, a common side, and do not overlap. In the figure, the adjacent angles are $\angle 5$ and $\angle 6$.

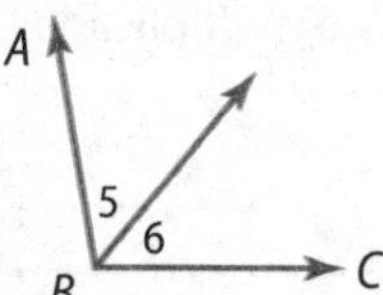

ángulos adyacentes Ángulos que comparten un vértice, un lado común y no se traslapan. En la figura, los ángulos adyacentes son $\angle 5$ y $\angle 6$.

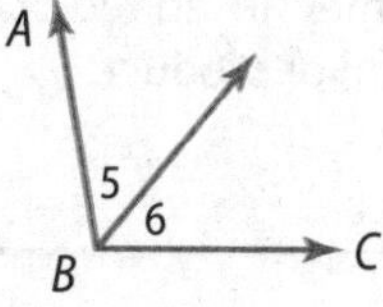

algebra A branch of mathematics that involves expressions with variables.

álgebra Rama de las matemáticas que trabaja con expresiones con variables.

algebraic expression A combination of variables, numbers, and at least one operation.

expresión algebraica Una combinación de variables, números y por lo menos una operación.

alternate exterior angles Exterior angles that lie on opposite sides of the transversal. In the figure, transversal *t* intersects lines ℓ and *m*. $\angle 1$ and $\angle 7$, and $\angle 2$ and $\angle 8$ are alternate exterior angles. If line ℓ and *m* are parallel, then these pairs of angles are congruent.

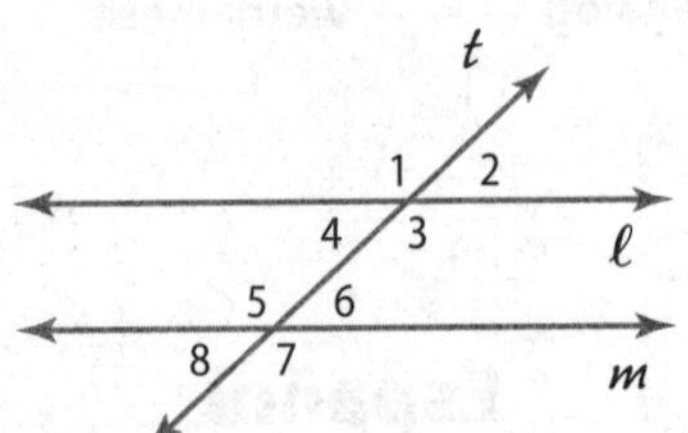

ángulos alternos externos Ángulos externos que se encuentran en lados opuestos de la transversal. En la figura, la transversal *t* interseca las rectas ℓ y *m*. $\angle 1$ y $\angle 7$, y $\angle 2$ y $\angle 8$ son ángulos alternos externos. Si las rectas ℓ y *m* son paralelas, entonces estos ángulos son pares de ángulos congruentes.

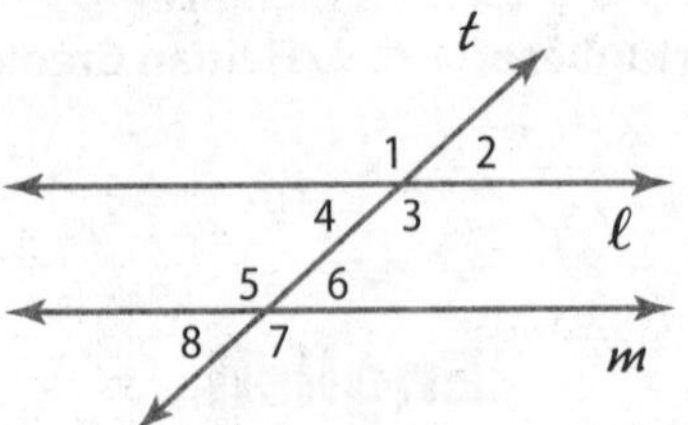

alternate interior angles Interior angles that lie on opposite sides of the transversal. In the figure below, transversal *t* intersects lines ℓ and *m*. $\angle 3$ and $\angle 5$, and $\angle 4$ and $\angle 6$ are alternate interior angles. If lines ℓ and *m* are parallel, then these pairs of angles are congruent.

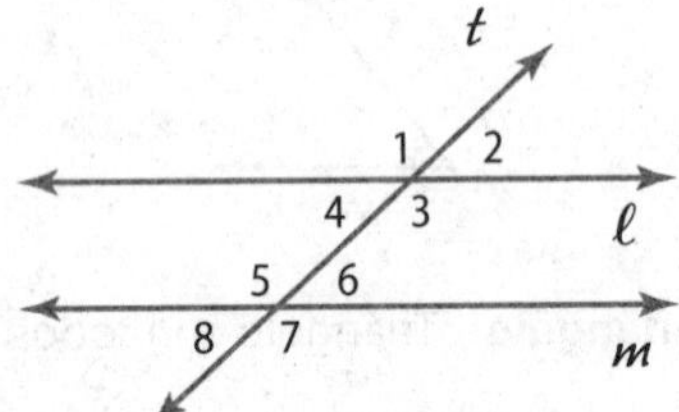

ángulos alternos internos Ángulos internos que se encuentran en lados opuestos de la transversal. En la figura, la transversal *t* interseca las rectas ℓ y *m*. $\angle 3$ y $\angle 5$, y $\angle 4$ y $\angle 6$ son ángulos alternos internos. Si las rectas ℓ y *m* son paralelas, entonces estos ángulos son pares de ángulos congruentes.

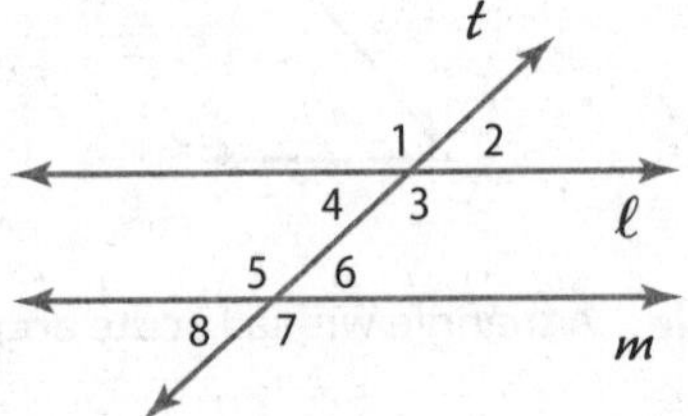

angle of rotation The degree measure of the angle through which a figure is rotated.

ángulo de rotación Medida en grados del ángulo sobre el cual se rota una figura.

arc One of two parts of a circle separated by a central angle.

arco Una de dos partes de un círculo separadas por un ángulo central.

Associative Property The way in which three numbers are grouped when they are added or multiplied does not change their sum or product.

propiedad asociativa La forma en que se agrupan tres números al sumarlos o multiplicarlos no altera su suma o producto.

base In a power, the number that is the common factor. In 10^3, the base is 10. That is, $10^3 = 10 \times 10 \times 10$.

base En una potencia, número que es el factor común. En 10^3, la base es 10. Es decir, $10^3 = 10 \times 10 \times 10$.

base One of the two parallel congruent faces of a prism.

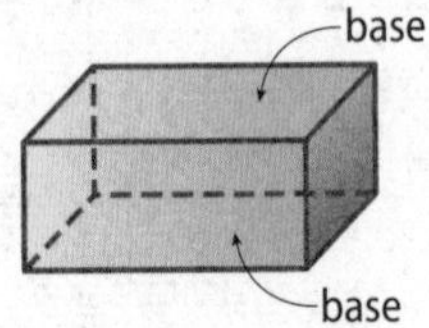

base Una de las dos caras paralelas congruentes de un prisma.

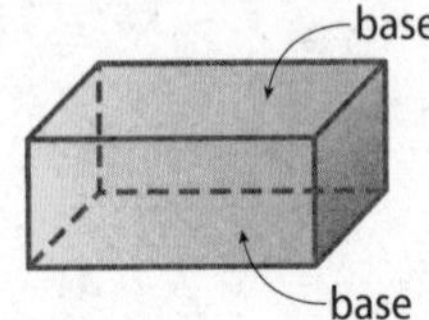

biased sample A sample drawn in such a way that one or more parts of the population are favored over others.

bivariate data Data with two variables, or pairs of numerical observations.

box plot A method of visually displaying a distribution of data values by using the median, quartiles, and extremes of the data set. A box shows the middle 50% of the data.

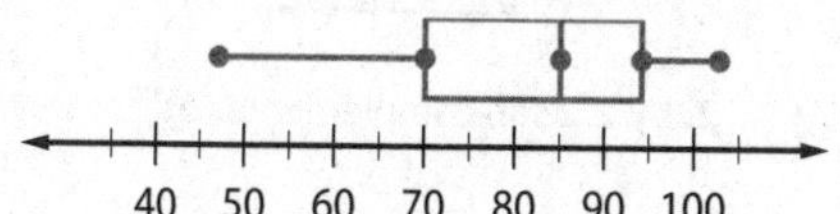

center The given point from which all points on a circle are the same distance.

center of dilation The center point from which dilations are performed.

center of rotation A fixed point around which shapes move in a circular motion to a new position.

central angle An angle that intersects a circle in two points and has its vertex at the center of the circle.

circle The set of all points in a plane that are the same distance from a given point called the center.

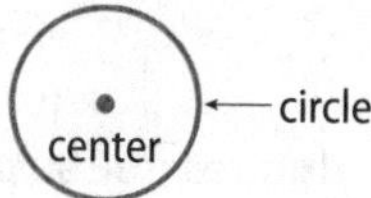

circumference The distance around a circle.

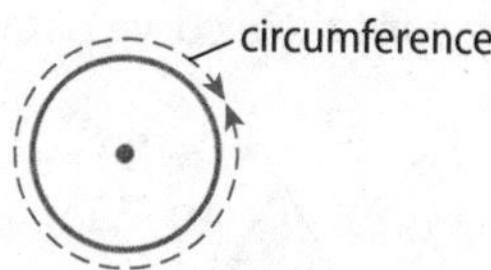

chord A segment with endpoints that are on a circle.

coefficient The numerical factor of a term that contains a variable.

common difference The difference between any two consecutive terms in an arithmetic sequence.

muestra sesgada Muestra en que se favorece una o más partes de una población.

datos bivariantes Datos con dos variables, o pares de observaciones numéricas.

diagrama de caja Un método de mostrar visualmente una distribución de valores usando la mediana, cuartiles y extremos del conjunto de datos. Una caja muestra el 50% del medio de los datos.

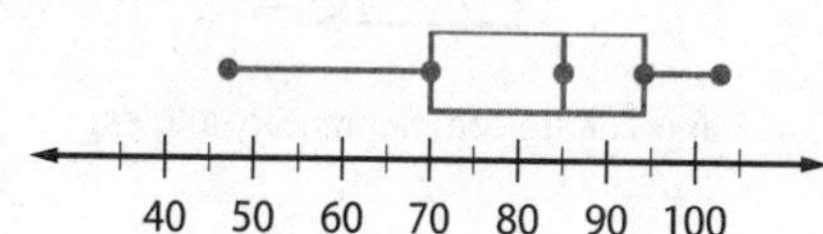

centro Un punto dado del cual equidistan todos los puntos de un círculo.

centro de la homotecia Punto fijo en torno al cual se realizan las homotecias.

centro de rotación Punto fijo alrededor del cual se giran las figuras en movimiento circular alrededor de un punto fijo.

ángulo central Ángulo que interseca un círculo en dos puntos y cuyo vértice es el centro del círculo.

círculo Conjunto de todos los puntos en un plano que equidistan de un punto dado llamado centro.

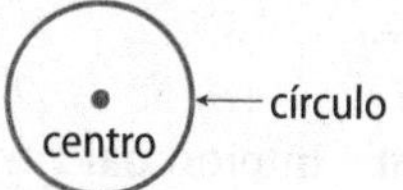

circunferencia La distancia alrededor de un círculo.

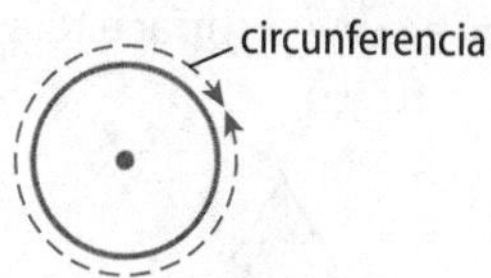

cuerda Segmento cuyos extremos están sobre un círculo.

coeficiente Factor numérico de un término que contiene una variable.

diferencia común La diferencia entre cualquier par de términos consecutivos en una sucesión aritmética.

Commutative Property The order in which two numbers are added or multiplied does not change their sum or product.

propiedad conmutativa La forma en que se suman o multiplican dos números no altera su suma o producto.

complementary angles Two angles are complementary if the sum of their measures is 90°.

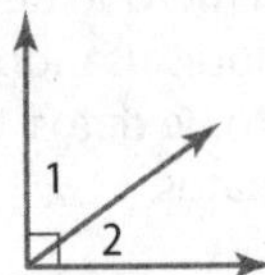

∠1 and ∠2 are complementary angles.

ángulos complementarios Dos ángulos son complementarios si la suma de sus medidas es 90°.

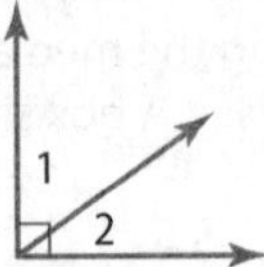

∠1 y ∠2 son complementarios.

composite figure A figure that is made up of two or more shapes.

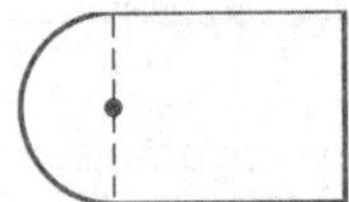

figura compleja Figura compuesta de dos o más formas.

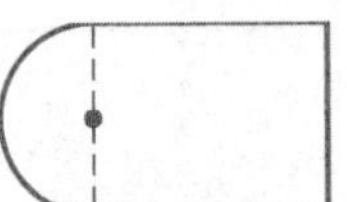

composite solid An object made up of more than one type of solid.

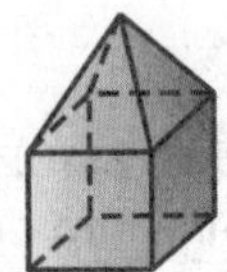

sólido complejo Cuerpo compuesto de más de un tipo de sólido.

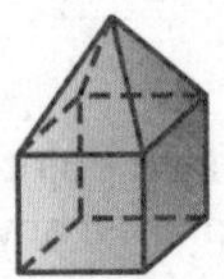

composition of transformations The resulting transformation when a transformation is applied to a figure and then another transformation is applied to its image.

composición de transformaciones Transformación que resulta cuando se aplica una transformación a una figura y luego se le aplica otra transformación a su imagen.

compound event An event that consists of two or more simple events.

evento compuesto Evento que consta de dos o más eventos simples.

compound interest Interest paid on the initial principal and on interest earned in the past.

interés compuesto Interés que se paga por el capital inicial y sobre el interés ganado en el pasado.

cone A three-dimensional figure with one circular base connected by a curved surface to a single vertex.

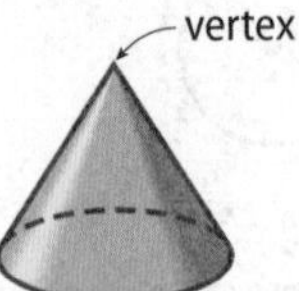

cono Una figura tridimensional con una circular base conectada por una superficie curva para un solo vértice.

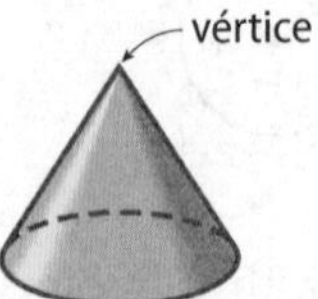

congruent Having the same measure; if one image can be obtained by another by a sequence of rotations, reflections, or translations.

congruente Que tienen la misma medida; si una imagen puede obtenerse de otra por una secuencia de rotaciones, reflexiones o traslaciones.

constant A term without a variable.

constante Término sin variables.

constant of proportionality The constant ratio in a proportional linear relationship.

constante de proporcionalidad La razón constante en una relación lineal proporcional.

constant of variation A constant ratio in a direct variation.

constant rate of change The rate of change between any two points in a linear relationship is the same or *constant.*

continuous data Data that can take on any value. There is no space between data values for a given domain. Graphs are represented by solid lines.

convenience sample A sample which includes members of the population that are easily accessed.

converse The converse of a theorem is formed when the parts of the theorem are reversed. The converse of the Pythagorean Theorem can be used to test whether a triangle is a right triangle. If the sides of the triangle have lengths *a, b,* and *c,* such that $c^2 = a^2 + b^2$, then the triangle is a right triangle.

coordinate plane A coordinate system in which a horizontal number line and a vertical number line intersect at their zero points.

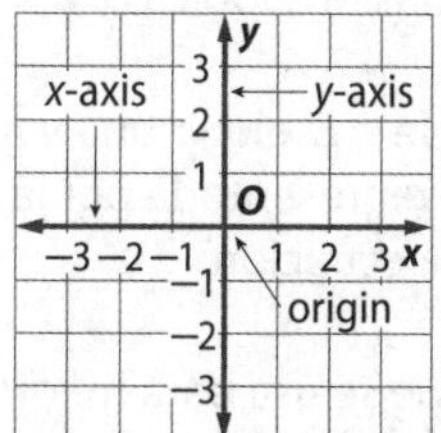

coplanar Lines that lie in the same plane.

corresponding angles Angles that are in the same position on two parallel lines in relation to a transversal.

corresponding parts Parts of congruent or similar figures that match.

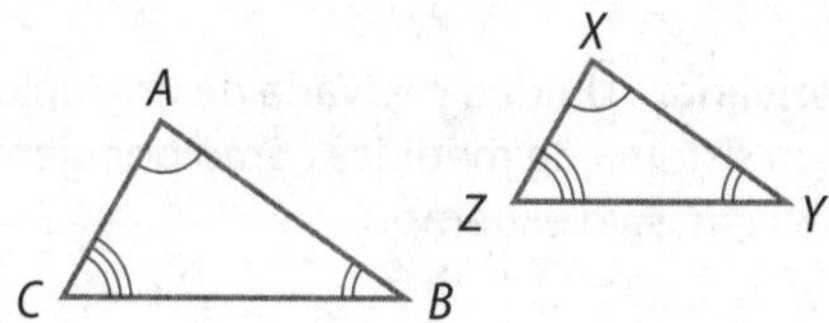

counterexample A statement or example that shows a conjecture is false.

credit card A card that allows a buyer to put off paying for a purchase until a time in the future.

constante de variación Razón constante en una relación de variación directa.

tasa constante de cambio La tasa de cambio entre dos puntos cualesquiera en una relación lineal permanece igual o *constante.*

datos continuos Datos que pueden tomar cualquier valor. No hay espacio entre los valores de los datos para un dominio dado. Las gráficas se representan con rectas sólidas.

muestra de conveniencia Muestra que incluye miembros de una población fácilmente accesibles.

recíproco El recíproco de un teorema se forma cuando se invierten las partes del teorema. El recíproco del teorema de Pitágoras puede usarse para averiguar si un triángulo es un triángulo rectángulo. Si las longitudes de los lados de un triángulo son *a, b* y *c,* tales que $c^2 = a^2 + b^2$, entonces el triángulo es un triángulo rectángulo.

plano de coordenadas Sistema de coordenadas en que una recta numérica horizontal y una recta numérica vertical se intersecan en sus puntos cero.

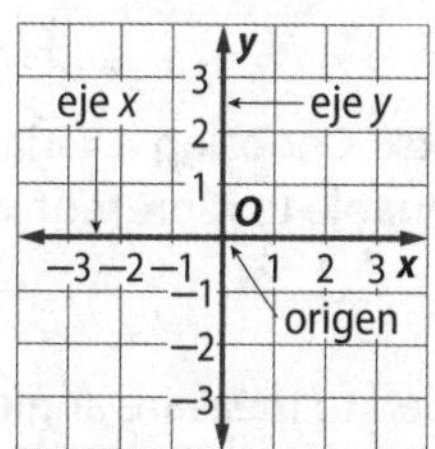

coplanario Rectas que yacen en el mismo plano.

ángulos correspondientes Ángulos que están en la misma posición sobre dos rectas paralelas en relación con la transversal.

partes correspondientes Partes de figuras congruentes o semejantes que coinciden.

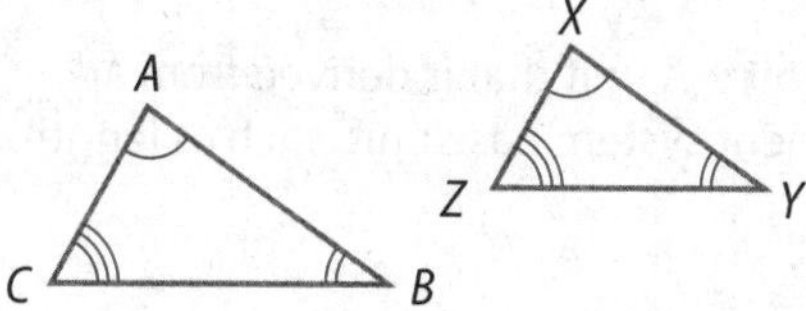

contraejemplo Ejemplo o enunciado que demuestra que una conjetura es falsa.

tarjeta de crédito Tarjeta que permite a un comprador postergar el pago de una compra hasta algún momento en el futuro.

cross section The intersection of a solid and a plane.

sección transversal Intersección de un sólido y un plano.

cube root One of three equal factors of a number. If $a^3 = b$, then a is the cube root of b. The cube root of 64 is 4 since $4^3 = 64$.

raíz cúbica Uno de tres factores iguales de un número. Si $a^3 = b$, entonces a es la raíz cúbica de b. La raíz cúbica de 64 es 4, dado que $4^3 = 64$.

cylinder A three-dimensional figure with two parallel congruent circular bases connected by a curved surface.

cilindro Una figura tridimensional con dos paralelas congruentes circulares bases conectados por una superficie curva.

Dd

debit card A card that allows a buyer to make purchases while immediately removing money from a linked account.

tarjeta de débito Tarjeta que permite a un comprador hacer compras extrayendo de inmediato dinero de una cuenta asociada.

deductive reasoning A system of reasoning that uses facts, rules, definitions, or properties to reach logical conclusions.

razonamiento deductivo Sistema de razonamiento que emplea hechos, reglas, definiciones o propiedades para obtener conclusions lógicas.

defining a variable Choosing a variable and a quantity for the variable to represent in an expression or equation.

definir una variable El elegir una variable y una cantidad que esté representada por la variable en una expresión o en una ecuación.

degree A unit used to measure angles.

grado Unidad que se usa para medir ángulos.

degree A unit used to measure temperature.

grado Unidad que se usa para medir la temperatura.

dependent events Two or more events in which the outcome of one event does affect the outcome of the other event or events.

eventos dependientes Dos o más eventos en que el resultado de uno de ellos afecta el resultado de los otros eventos.

dependent variable The variable in a relation with a value that depends on the value of the independent variable.

variable dependiente La variable en una relación cuyo valor depende del valor de la variable independiente.

derived unit A unit that is derived from a measurement system base unit, such as length, mass, or time.

unidad derivada Unidad derivada de una unidad básica de un sistema de medidas como por ejemplo, la longitud, la masa o el tiempo.

diagonal A line segment whose endpoints are vertices that are neither adjacent nor on the same face.

diagonal Segmento de recta cuyos extremos son vértices que no son ni adyacentes ni yacen en la misma cara.

diameter The distance across a circle through its center.

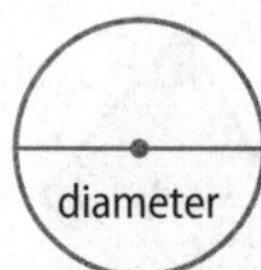

diámetro La distancia a través de un círculo pasando por el centro.

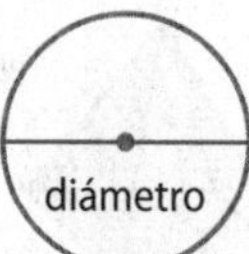

dilation A transformation that enlarges or reduces a figure by a scale factor.

homotecia Transformación que produce la ampliación o reducción de una imagen por un factor de escala.

dimensional analysis The process of including units of measurement when you compute.

análisis dimensional Proceso que incorpora las unidades de medida al hacer cálculos.

direct variation A relationship between two variable quantities with a constant ratio.

variación directa Relación entre dos cantidades variables con una razón constante.

discount The amount by which a regular price is reduced.

descuento La cantidad de reducción del precio normal.

discrete data Data with space between possible data values. Graphs are represented by dots.

datos discretos Datos con espacios entre posibles valores de datos. Las gráficas están representadas por puntos.

disjoint events Events that cannot happen at the same time.

eventos disjuntos Eventos que no pueden ocurrir al mismo tiempo.

Distance Formula The distance d between two points with coordinates (x_1, y_1) and (x_2, y_2) is given by the formula

$$d = \sqrt{(x_1 - x_2)^2 + (y_1 - y_2)^2}.$$

fórmula de la distancia La distancia d entre dos puntos con coordenadas (x_1, y_1) and (x_2, y_2) viene dada por la fórmula

$$d = \sqrt{(x_1 - x_2)^2 + (y_1 - y_2)^2}.$$

distribution A way to show the arrangement of data values.

distribución Una manera de mostrar la agrupación de valores.

Distributive Property To multiply a sum by a number, multiply each addend by the number outside the parentheses.

$$5(x + 3) = 5x + 15$$

propiedad distributiva Para multiplicar una suma por un número, multiplica cada sumando por el número fuera de los paréntesis.

$$5(x + 3) = 5x + 15$$

Division Property of Equality If you divide each side of an equation by the same nonzero number, the two sides remain equal.

propiedad de división de la igualdad Si cada lado de una ecuación se divide entre el mismo número no nulo, los dos lados permanecen iguales.

domain The set of x-coordinates in a relation.

dominio Conjunto de coordenadas x en una relación.

double box plot Two box plots graphed on the same number line.

doble diagrama de puntos Dos diagramas de caja sobre la misma recta numérica.

Ee

easy-access loan A short-term loan that usually has a high interest rate.

préstamo accesible Préstamo a corto plazo que usualmente tiene una tasa de interés alta.

edge The line segment where two faces of a polyhedron intersect.

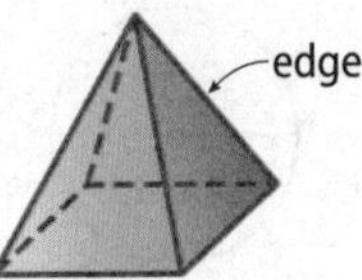

arista El segmento de línea donde se cruzan dos caras de un poliedro.

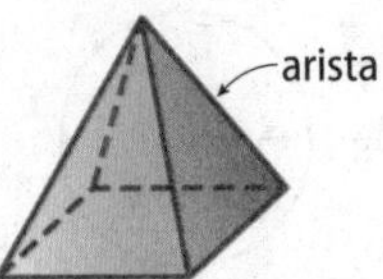

equation A mathematical sentence stating that two quantities are equal.

ecuación Enunciado matemático que establece que dos cantidades son iguales.

equiangular A polygon in which all angles are congruent.

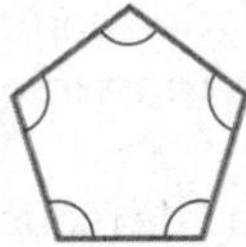

equiangular Polígono en el cual todos los ángulos son congruentes.

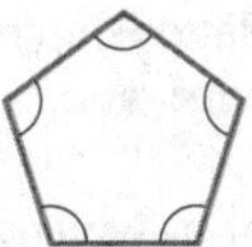

equilateral triangle A triangle with three congruent sides.

triángulo equilátero Triángulo con tres lados congruentes.

equivalent expressions Expressions that have the same value regardless of the value(s) of the variable(s).

expresiones equivalentes Expresiones que poseen el mismo valor, sin importar los valores de la(s) variable(s).

event An outcome is a possible result.

evento Un resultado posible.

experimental probability An estimated probability based on the relative frequency of positive outcomes occurring during an experiment.

probabilidad experimental Probabilidad estimada que se basa en la frecuencia relativa de los resultados positivos que ocurren durante un experimento.

exponent In a power, the number of times the base is used as a factor. In 10^3, the exponent is 3.

exponente En una potencia, el número de veces que la base se usa como factor. En 10^3, el exponente es 3.

exponential function A nonlinear function in which the base is a constant and the exponent is an independent variable.

función exponencial Función no lineal en la cual la base es una constante y el exponente es una variable independiente.

exterior angles The four outer angles formed by two lines cut by a transversal.

ángulo externo Los cuatro ángulos exteriores que se forman cuando una transversal corta dos rectas.

face A flat surface of a polyhedron.

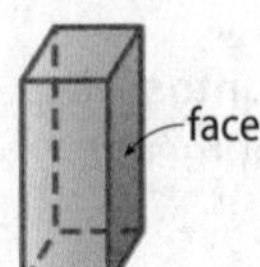

cara Una superficie plana de un poliedro.

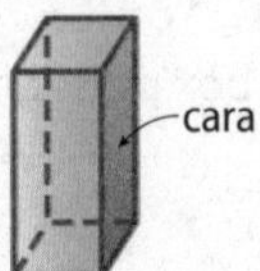

fair game A game where each player has an equally likely chance of winning.

juego justo Juego donde cada jugador tiene igual posibilidad de ganar.

family of functions A set of functions related in some way.

familia de funciones Un juego de funciones que están relacionado de alguna manera

financial responsibility Managing your money and other assets in a manner that is productive and in your and your family's best interests.

responsabilidad financiera Administración del dinero y otros activos de manera lucrativa y en beneficio de uno y de su familia.

financial irresponsibility Managing your money and other assets in a manner that is not productive and not in your and your family's best interests.

irresponsabilidad financiera Administración del dinero y otros activos de manera no lucrativa y no en beneficio de uno y de su familia.

five-number summary A way of characterizing a set of data that includes the minimum, first quartile, median, third quartile, and the maximum.

resumen de los cinco números Una manera de caracterizar un conjunto de datos que incluye el mínimo, el primer cuartil, la mediana, el tercer cuartil y el máximo.

formal proof A two-column proof containing statements and reasons.

demostración formal Demostración endos columnas contiene enunciados y razonamientos.

function A relation in which each member of the domain (input value) is paired with exactly one member of the range (output value).

función Relación en la cual a cada elemento del dominio (valor de entrada) le corresponde exactamente un único elemento del rango (valor de salida).

Fundamental Counting Principle Uses multiplication of the number of ways each event in an experiment can occur to find the number of possible outcomes in a sample space.

principio fundamental de contar Método que usa la multiplicación del número de maneras en que cada evento puede ocurrir en un experimento, para calcular el número de resultados posibles en un espacio muestral.

geometric sequence A sequence in which each term after the first is found by multiplying the previous term by a constant.

sucesión geométrica Sucesión en la cual cada término después del primero se determina multiplicando el término anterior por una constante.

half-plane The part of the coordinate plane on one side of the boundary.

semiplano Parte del plano de coordenadas en un lado de la frontera.

hemisphere One of two congruent halves of a sphere.

hemisferio Una de dos mitades congruentes de una esfera.

hypotenuse The side opposite the right angle in a right triangle.

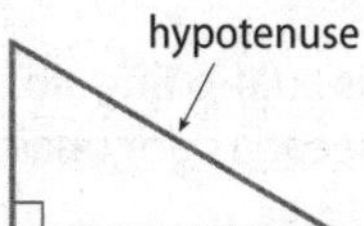

hipotenusa El lado opuesto al ángulo recto de un triángulo rectángulo.

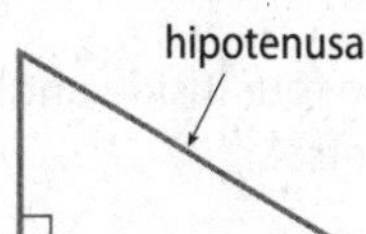

identity An equation that is true for every value for the variable.

identidad Ecuación que es verdad para cada valor de la variable.

image The resulting figure after a transformation.

imagen Figura que resulta después de una transformación.

independent events Two or more events in which the outcome of one event does not affect the outcome of the other event(s).

eventos independientes Dos o más eventos en los cuales el resultado de un evento no afecta el resultado de los otros eventos.

independent variable The variable in a function with a value that is subject to choice.

variable independiente Variable en una función cuyo valor está sujeto a elección.

indirect measurement A technique using properties of similar polygons to find distances or lengths that are difficult to measure directly.

medición indirecta Técnica que usa las propiedades de polígonos semejantes para calcular distancias o longitudes difíciles de medir directamente.

inductive reasoning Reasoning that uses a number of specific examples to arrive at a plausible generalization or prediction. Conclusions arrived at by inductive reasoning lack the logical certainty of those arrived at by deductive reasoning.

razonamiento inductivo Razonamiento que usa varios ejemplos especificos para lograr una generalización o una predicción plausible. Las conclusions obtenidas por razonamiento inductivo carecen de la certeza lógica de aquellas obtenidas por razonamiento deductivo.

inequality A mathematical sentence that contains $<, >, \neq, \leq,$ or $\geq$.

desigualdad Enunciado matemático que contiene $<, >, \neq, \leq,$ o $\geq$.

inscribed angle An angle that has its vertex on the circle. Its sides contain chords of the circle.

ángulo inscrito Ángulo cuyo vértice está en el círculo y cuyos lados contienen cuerdas del círculo.

informal proof A paragraph proof.

demonstración informal Demonstración en forma de párrafo.

interest The amount of money paid or earned for the use of money.

interés Cantidad que se cobra o se paga por el uso del dinero.

interest rate A percentage of an amount of money that is charged for the money's use.

tasa de interés Porcentaje de una cantidad de dinero que se cobra por el uso del dinero.

interior angle An angle inside a polygon.

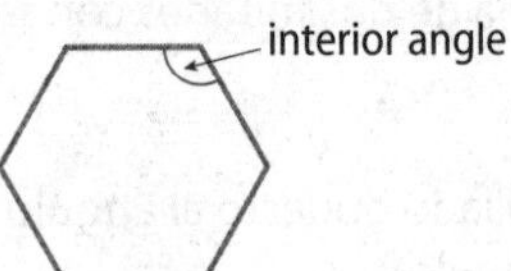

ángulo interno Ángulo dentro de un polígono.

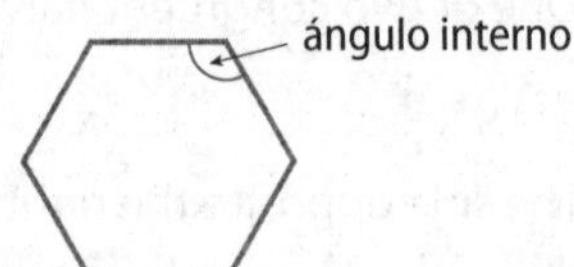

interior angles The four inside angles formed by two lines cut by a transversal.

ángulo interno Los cuatro ángulos internos formados por dos rectas intersecadas por una transversal.

interquartile range A measure of variation in a set of numerical data. It is the difference between the first quartile and the third quartile.

rango intercuartílico Una medida de la variación en un conjunto de datos numéricos. Es la diferencia entre el primer y el tercer cuartil.

inverse operations Pairs of operations that undo each other. Addition and subtraction are inverse operations. Multiplication and division are inverse operations.

peraciones inversas Pares de operaciones que se anulan mutuamente. La adición y la sustracción son operaciones inversas. La multiplicación y la división son operaciones inversas.

irrational number A number that cannot be expressed as the quotient $\frac{a}{b}$, where a and b are integers and $b \neq 0$.

números irracionales Número que no se puede expresar como el cociente $\frac{a}{b}$, donde a y b son enteros y $b \neq 0$.

isosceles triangle A triangle with at least two congruent sides.

triángulo isóceles Triángulo con por lo menos dos lados congruentes.

lateral area The sum of the areas of the lateral faces of a solid.

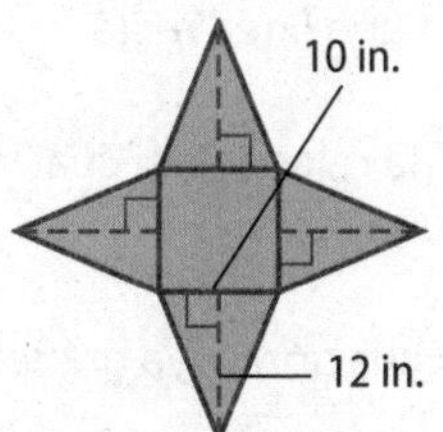

lateral area $= 4\left(\frac{1}{2} \times 10 \times 12\right) = 240$ square inches

área lateral La suma de las áreas de las caras laterales de un sólido.

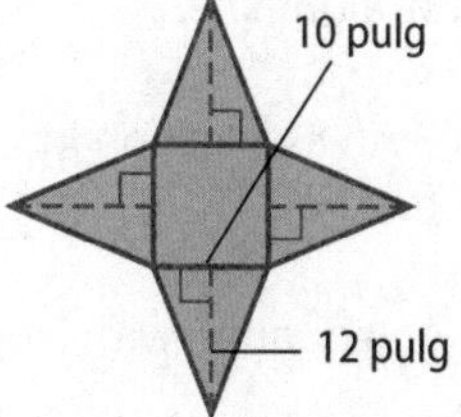

área lateral $= 4\left(\frac{1}{2} \times 10 \times 12\right) = 240$ pulgadas cuadradas

lateral face Any flat surface that is not a base.

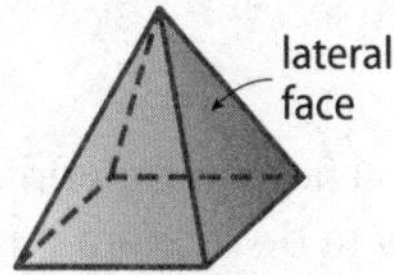

cara lateral Cualquier superficie plana que no es la base.

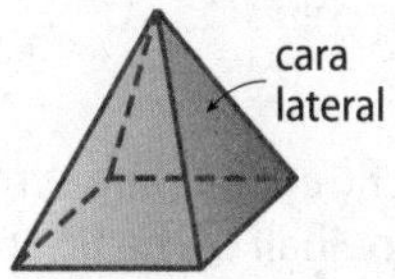

legs The two sides of a right triangle that form the right angle.

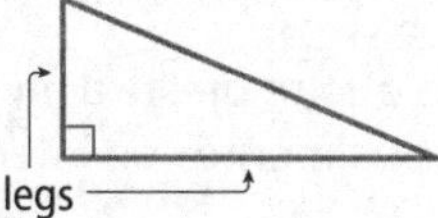

catetos Los dos lados de un triángulo rectángulo que forman el ángulo recto.

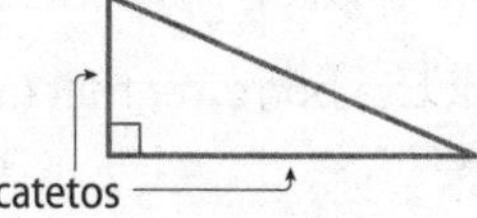

like fractions Fractions that have the same denominators.

fracciones semejantes Fracciones que tienen el mismo denominador.

like terms Terms that contain the same variable(s) to the same powers.

términos semejantes Términos que contienen la misma variable o variables elevadas a la misma potencia.

line of best fit A line that is very close to most of the data points in a scatter plot.

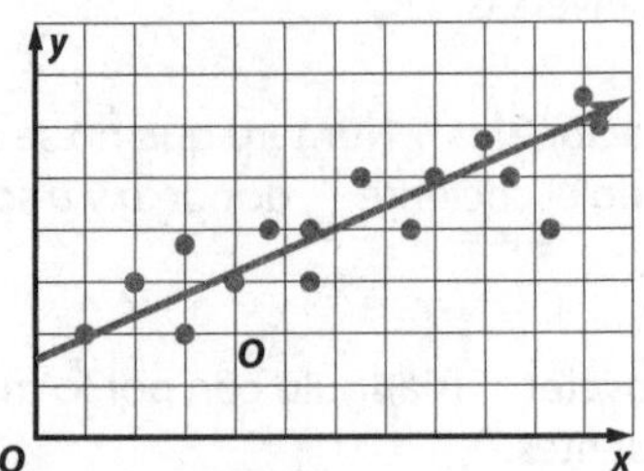

line of reflection The line over which a figure is reflected.

line of symmetry Each half of a figure is a mirror image of the other half when a line of symmetry is drawn.

linear To fall in a straight line.

linear association An association in which the data appear to lie close to a line.

linear equation An equation with a graph that is a straight line.

linear function A function in which the graph of the solutions forms a line.

linear relationship A relationship that has a straight-line graph.

line symmetry A figure has line symmetry if a line can be drawn so that one half of the figure is a mirror image of the other half.

literal equation An equation or formula that has more than one variable.

loan Money lent to a borrower that must be repaid, usually with interest.

recta de mejor ajuste Recta que más se acerca a la mayoría de puntos de los datos en un diagrama de dispersión.

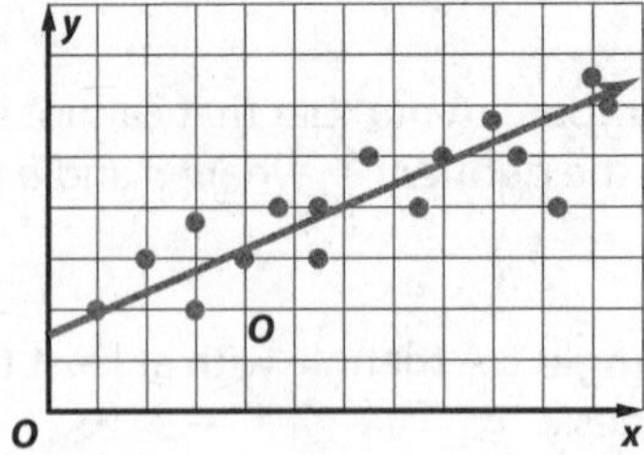

línea de reflexión Línea a través de la cual se refleja una figura.

eje de simetría Recta que divide una figura en dos mitades especulares.

lineal Que cae en una línea recta.

relación lineal Una relación en cual los datos parecen situados cerco de una recta.

ecuación lineal Ecuación cuya gráfica es una recta.

función lineal Función en la cual la gráfica de las soluciones forma un recta.

relación lineal Relación cuya gráfica es una recta.

simetría lineal Una figura tiene simetría lineal si se puede trazar una recta de manera que una mitad de la figura sea una imagen especular de la otra mitad.

ecuación literal Ecuación o fórmula con más de una variable.

préstamo Dinero que se presta a un prestatario y que debe devolverse, usualmente con interés.

markup The amount the price of an item is increased above the price the store paid for the item.

mean The sum of the data divided by the number of items in the set.

mean absolute deviation The average of the absolute values of differences between the mean and each value in a data set.

margen de utilidad Cantidad de aumento en el precio de un artículo por encima del precio que paga la tienda por dicho artículo.

media La suma de datos dividida entre el número total de artículos.

desviación media absoluta El promedio de los valores absolutos de diferencias entre el medio y cada valor de un conjunto de datos.

measures of center Numbers that are used to describe the center of a set of data. These measures include the mean, median, and mode.

medidas del centro Números que describen el centro de un conjunto de datos. Estas medidas incluyen la media, la mediana y la moda.

measures of variation Numbers used to describe the distribution or spread of a set of data.

medidas de variación Números que se usan para describir la distribución o separación de un conjunto de datos.

median A measure of center in a set of numerical data. The median of a list of values is the value appearing at the center of a sorted version of the list—or the mean of the two central values, if the list contains an even number of values.

mediana Una medida del centro en un conjunto de datos numéricos. La mediana de una lista de valores es el valor que aparece en el centro de una versión ordenada de la lista, o la media de los dos valores centrales si la lista contiene un número par de valores.

mode The number(s) or item(s) that appear most often in a set of data.

moda El número(s) o artículo(s) que aparece con más frecuencia en un conjunto de datos.

monomial A number, a variable, or a product of a number and one or more variables.

monomio Un número, una variable o el producto de un número por una o más variables.

Multiplication Property of Equality If you multiply each side of an equation by the same number, the two sides remain equal.

propiedad de multiplicación de la igualdad Si cada lado de una ecuación se multiplica por el mismo número, los lados permanecen iguales.

multiplicative inverses Two numbers with a product of 1. The multiplicative inverse of $\frac{2}{3}$ is $\frac{3}{2}$.

inversos multiplicativo Dos números cuyo producto es 1. El inverso multiplicativo de $\frac{2}{3}$ es $\frac{3}{2}$.

negative association An association in which the y-value decreases as the x-value increases.

relación negativa Una relación en cual el valor y disminuye mientras el valor x aumenta.

net A two-dimensional pattern of a three-dimensional figure.

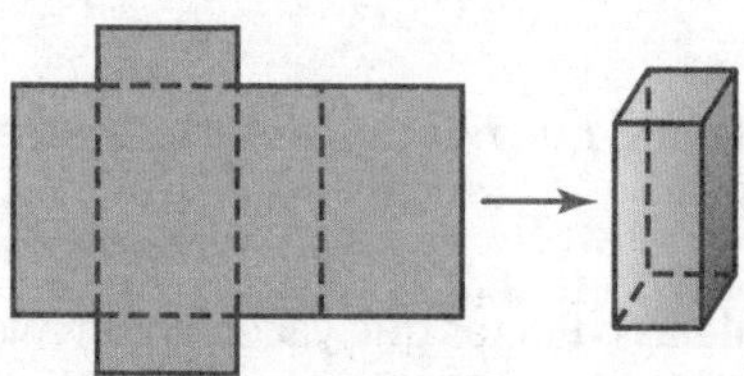

red Patrón bidimensional de una figura tridimensional.

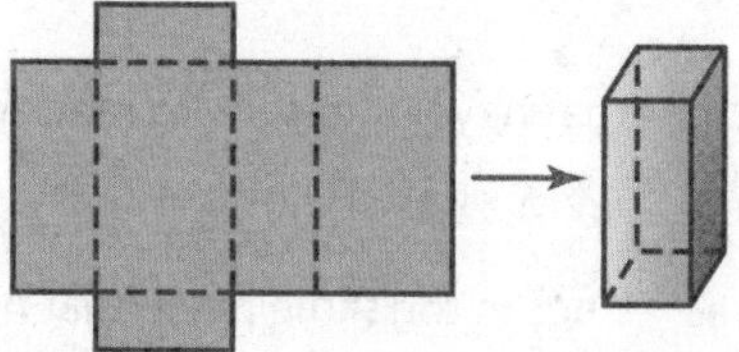

no association When there is no pattern in the observed data.

ninguna relación Cuando no existe un patrón en los datos observados.

non-linear association When data points do not lie close to a line.

relación no lineal Cuando los puntos de datos no están situados cerca de una recta

null set The empty set.

conjunto nulo El conjunto vacío.

obtuse angle An angle whose measure is between 90° and 180°.

ángulo obtuso Ángulo cuya medida está entre 90º y 180º.

obtuse triangle A triangle with one obtuse angle.

triángulo obtusángulo Triángulo con un ángulo obtuso.

ordered pair A pair of numbers used to locate a point in the coordinate plane. The ordered pair is written in this form: (*x*-coordinate, *y*-coordinate).

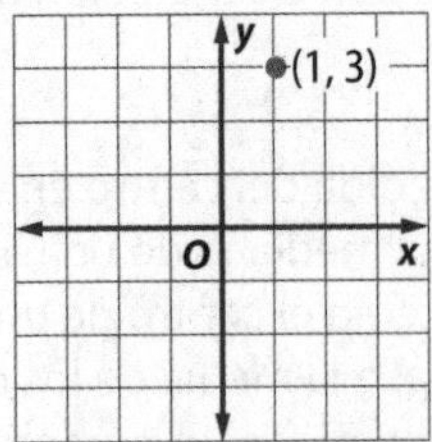

par ordenado Par de números que se utiliza para ubicar un punto en un plano de coordenadas. Se escribe de la siguiente forma: (coordenada *x*, coordenada *y*).

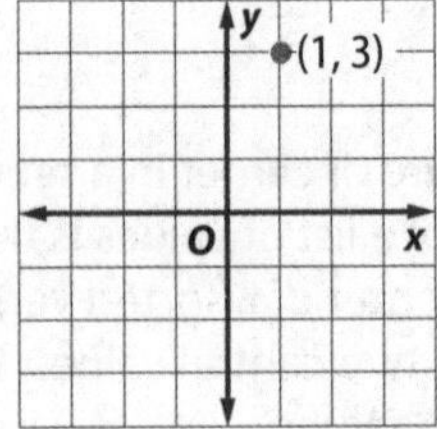

orientation A figure's relative direction.

orientación El sentido relativo de una figura.

origin The point of intersection of the *x*-axis and *y*-axis in a coordinate plane.

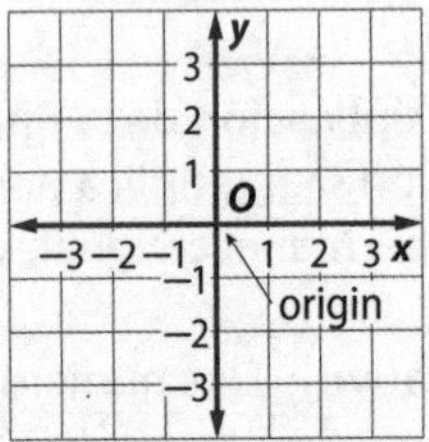

origen Punto en que el eje *x* y el eje *y* se intersecan en un plano de coordenadas.

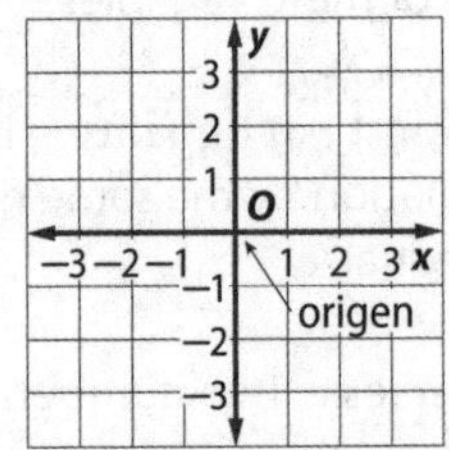

outcome One possible result of a probability event. For example, 4 is an outcome when a number cube is rolled.

resultado Una consecuencia posible de un evento de probabilidad. Por ejemplo, 4 es un resultado posible al lanzar un cubo numérico.

outlier Data that are more than 1.5 times the interquartile range from the first or third quartiles.

valor atípico Datos que distan de los cuartiles respectivos más de 1.5 veces la amplitud intercuartílica.

parallel Lines that never intersect no matter how far they extend.

paralelo Rectas que nunca se intersecan sea cual sea su extensión.

parallel lines Lines in the same plane that never intersect or cross. The symbol || means parallel.

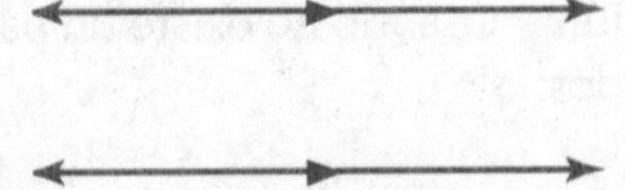

rectas paralelas Rectas que yacen en un mismo plano y que no se intersecan. El símbolo || significa paralela a.

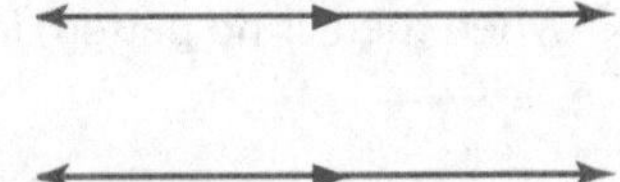

parallelogram A quadrilateral with both pairs of opposite sides parallel and congruent.

paralelogramo Cuadrilátero con ambos pares de lados opuestos, paralelos y congruentes.

percent equation An equivalent form of a percent proportion in which the percent is written as a decimal.

part = percent • whole

ecuación porcentual Forma equivalente de proporción porcentual en la cual el por ciento se escribe como un decimal.

parte = por ciento • entero

percent of change A ratio that compares the change in quantity to the original amount.

$$\text{percent of change} = \frac{\text{amount of change}}{\text{original amount}}$$

percent of decrease When the percent of change is negative.

percent of increase When the percent of change is positive.

percent proportion Compares part of a quantity to the whole quantity using a percent.

$$\frac{\text{part}}{\text{whole}} = \frac{\text{percent}}{100}$$

perfect cube A rational number whose cube root is a whole number. 27 is a perfect cube because its cube root is 3.

perfect square A rational number whose square root is a whole number. 25 is a perfect square because its square root is 5.

periodic savings plan A plan for how much a person might need to save for a designated period of time to achieve a certain financial goal.

permutation An arrangement or listing in which order is important.

perpendicular lines Two lines that intersect to form right angles.

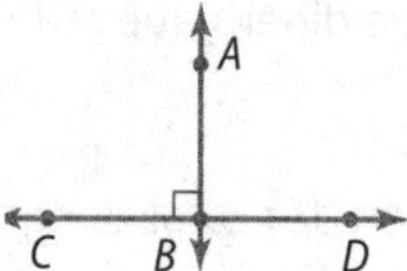

pi The ratio of the circumference of a circle to its diameter. The Greek letter π represents this number. The value of pi is always 3.1415926… .

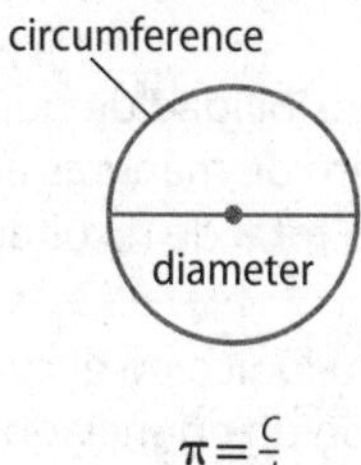

$$\pi = \frac{C}{d}$$

point-slope form An equation of the form $y - y_1 = m(x - x_1)$, where m is the slope and (x_1, y_1) is a given point on a nonvertical line.

porcentaje de cambio Razón que compara el cambio en una cantidad a la cantidad original.

$$\text{procentaje de cambio} = \frac{\text{cantidad de cambio}}{\text{cantidad original}}$$

porcentaje de disminución Cuando el porcentaje de cambio es negativo.

porcentaje de aumento Cuando el porcentaje de cambio es positivo.

proporción porcentual Compara parte de una cantidad con la cantidad total mediante un por ciento.

$$\frac{\text{parte}}{\text{entero}} = \frac{\text{por ciento}}{100}$$

cubo perfecto Número racional cuya raíz cúbica es un número entero. 27 es un cubo perfecto porque su raíz cúbica es 3.

cuadrados perfectos Número racional cuya raíz cuadrada es un número entero. 25 es un cuadrado perfecto porque su raíz cuadrada es 5.

periodic savings plan Plan de lo que una persona debería ahorrar durante un período determinado para lograr algún objetivo financiero.

permutación Arreglo o lista donde el orden es importante.

rectas perpendiculares Dos rectas que se intersecan formando ángulos rectos.

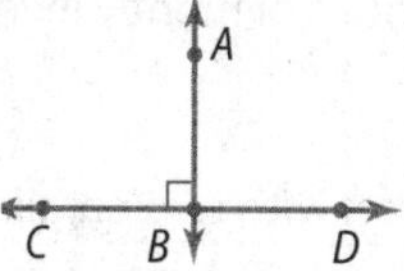

pi Razón de la circunferencia de un círculo al diámetro del mismo. La letra griega π representa este número. El valor de pi es siempre 3.1415926… .

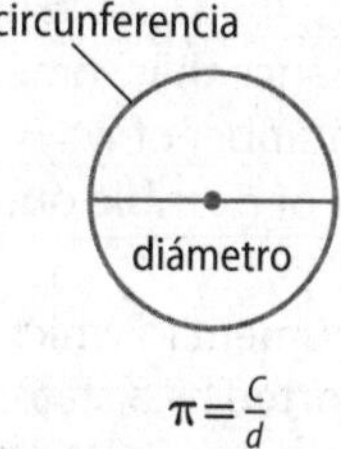

$$\pi = \frac{C}{d}$$

forma punto-pendiente Ecuación de la forma $y - y_1 = m(x - x_1)$ donde m es la pendiente y (x_1, y_1) es un punto dado de una recta no vertical.

polygon A simple, closed figure formed by three or more line segments.

polígono Figura simple y cerrada formada por tres o más segmentos de recta.

polyhedron A three-dimensional figure with faces that are polygons.

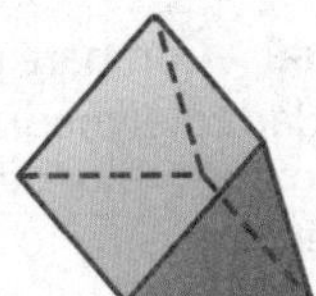

poliedro Una figura tridimensional con caras que son polígonos.

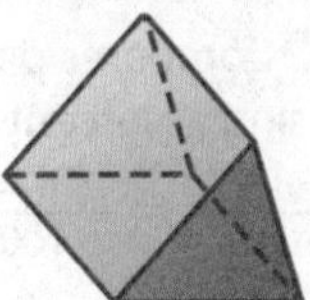

population The entire group of items or individuals from which the samples under consideration are taken.

población El grupo total de individuos o de artículos del cual se toman las muestras bajo studio.

positive association An association in which the *y*-value increases as the *x*-value increases.

relación positiva Una relación en cual el valor *y* aumenta mientras el valor *x* disminuye.

power A product of repeated factors using an exponent and a base. The power 7^3 is read *seven to the third power,* or *seven cubed.*

potencia Producto de factores repetidos con un exponente y una base. La potencia 7^3 se lee *siete a la tercera potencia* o *siete al cubo.*

precision The ability of a measurement to be consistently reproduced.

precisión Capacidad de una medida a ser reproducida consistentemente.

preimage The original figure before a transformation.

preimagen Figura original antes de una transformación.

principal The amount of money invested or borrowed.

capital Cantidad de dinero que se invierte o que se toma prestada.

prism A polyhedron with two parallel congruent faces called bases.

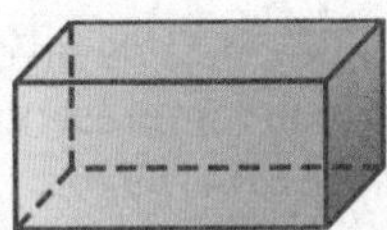

prisma Poliedro con dos caras congruentes y paralelas llamadas bases.

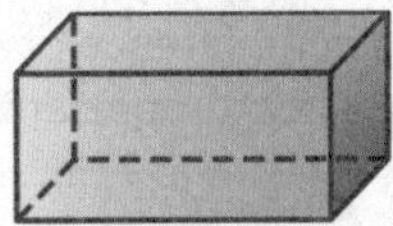

probability The chance that some event will happen. It is the ratio of the number of ways a certain event can occur to the number of possible outcomes.

probabilidad La posibilidad de que suceda un evento. Es la razón del número de maneras en que puede ocurrir un evento al número total de resultados posibles.

proof A logical argument in which each statement that is made is supported by a statement that is accepted as true.

prueba Argumento lógico en el cual cada enunciado hecho se respalda con un enunciado que se acepta como verdadero.

property A statement that is true for any numbers.

propiedad Enunciado que se cumple para cualquier número.

pyramid A polyhedron with one base that is a polygon and three or more triangular faces that meet at a common vertex.

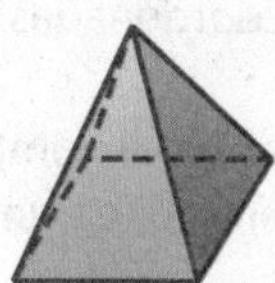

pirámide Un poliedro con una base que es un polígono y tres o más caras triangulares que se encuentran en un vértice común.

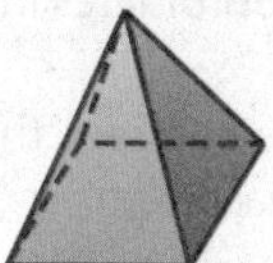

Pythagorean Theorem In a right triangle, the square of the length of the hypotenuse *c* is equal to the sum of the squares of the lengths of the legs *a* and *b*. $a^2 + b^2 = c^2$

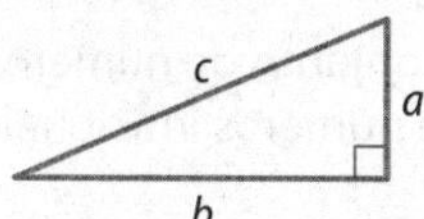

Teorema de Pitágoras En un triángulo rectángulo, el cuadrado de la longitud de la hipotenusa es igual a la suma de los cuadrados de las longitudes de los catetos. $a^2 + b^2 = c^2$

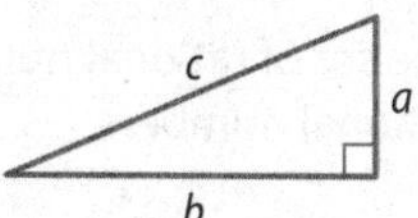

Qq

quadrants The four sections of the coordinate plane.

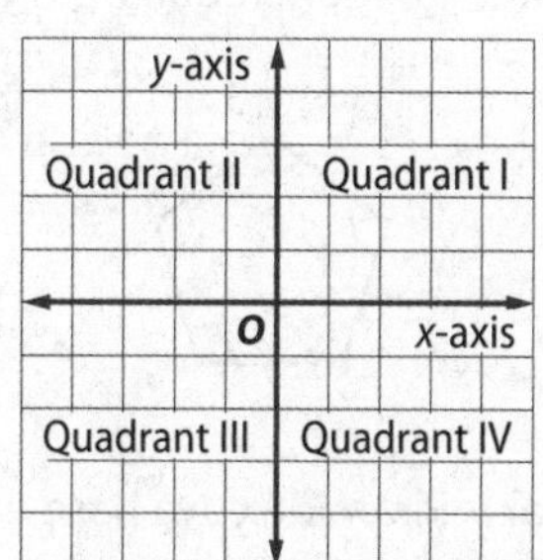

cuadrantes Las cuatro secciones del plano de coordenadas.

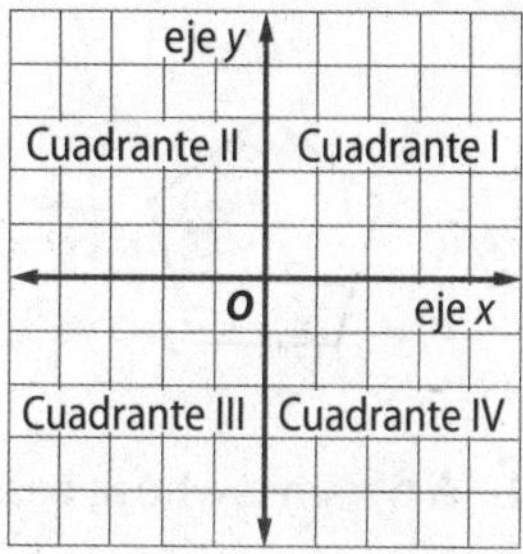

quadrilateral A closed figure with four sides and four angles.

cuadrilátero Figura cerrada con cuatro lados y cuatro ángulos.

quantitative data Data that can not be given a numerical value.

datos cualitativos Datos que no se pueden dar un valor numérico.

quartiles Values that divide a set of data into four equal parts.

cuartiles Valores que dividen un conjunto de datos en cuatro partes iguales.

Rr

radical sign The symbol used to indicate a positive square root, $\sqrt{}$.

signo radical Símbolo que se usa para indicar una raíz cuadrada no positiva, $\sqrt{}$.

radius The distance from the center of a circle to any point on the circle.

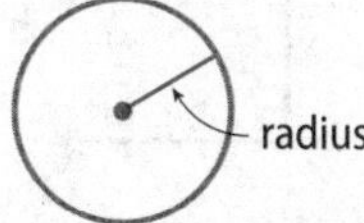

radio Distancia desde el centro de un círculo hasta cualquier punto del mismo.

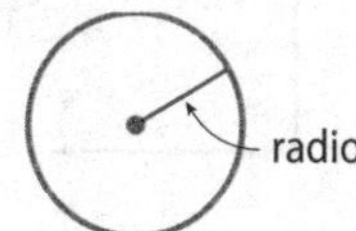

random Outcomes occur at random if each outcome is equally likely to occur.

azar Los resultados ocurren al azar si todos los resultados son equiprobables.

range The set of *y*-coordinates in a relation.

rango Conjunto de coordenadas *y* en una relación.

range The difference between the greatest number (maximum) and the least number (minimum) in a set of data.

rango La diferencia entre el número mayor (máximo) y el número menor (mínimo) en un conjunto de datos.

rational number Numbers that can be written as the ratio of two integers in which the denominator is not zero. All integers, fractions, mixed numbers, and percents are rational numbers.

número racional Números que pueden escribirse como la razón de dos enteros en los que el denominador no es cero. Todos los enteros, fracciones, números mixtos y porcentajes son números racionales.

real numbers The set of rational numbers together with the set of irrational numbers.

número real El conjunto de números racionales junto con el conjunto de números irracionales.

reciprocals The multiplicative inverse of a number. The product of reciprocals is 1.

recíproco El inverso multiplicativo de un número. El producto de recíprocos es 1.

reflection A transformation where a figure is flipped over a line. Also called a flip.

reflexión Transformación en la cual una figura se voltea sobre una recta. También se conoce como simetría de espejo.

regular polygon A polygon that is equilateral and equiangular.

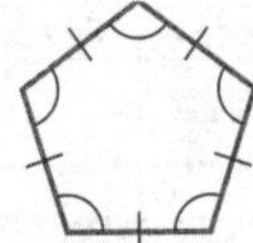

polígono regular Polígono equilátero y equiangular.

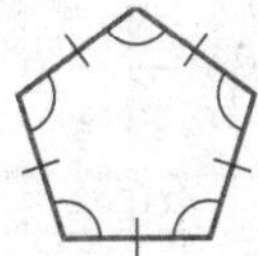

regular pyramid A pyramid whose base is a regular polygon.

pirámide regular Pirámide cuya base es un polígono regular.

relation Any set of ordered pairs.

relación Cualquier conjunto de pares ordenados.

relative frequency The ratio of the number of experimental successes to the total number of experimental attempts.

frecuencia relativa Razón del número de éxitos experimentales al número total de intentos experimentales.

remote interior angles The angles of a triangle that are not adjacent to a given exterior angle.

ángulos internos no adyacentes Ángulos de un triángulo que no son adya centes a un ángulo exterior dado.

repeating decimal Decimal form of a rational number.

decimal periódico Forma decimal de un número racional.

rhombus A parallelogram with four congruent sides.

rombo Paralelogramo con cuatro lados congruentes.

right angle An angle whose measure is exactly 90°.

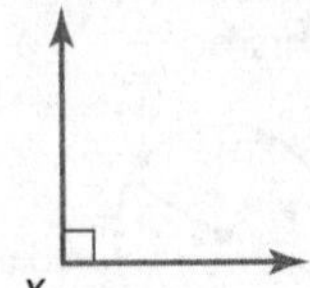

ángulo recto Ángulo que mide exactamente 90º.

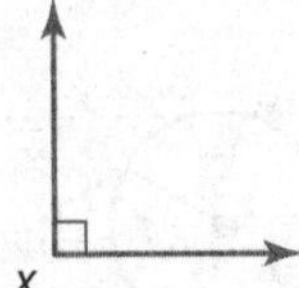

right triangle A triangle with one right angle.

rise The vertical change between any two points on a line.

rotation A transformation in which a figure is turned about a fixed point.

rotational symmetry A type of symmetry a figure has if it can be rotated less than 360° about its center and still look like the original.

run The horizontal change between any two points on a line.

sales tax An additional amount of money charged on certain goods and services.

sample A randomly-selected group chosen for the purpose of collecting data.

sample space The set of all possible outcomes of a probability experiment.

scale factor The ratio of the lengths of two corresponding sides of two similar polygons.

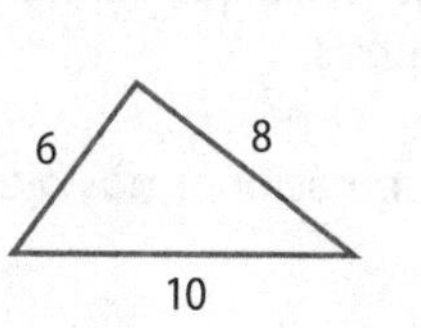

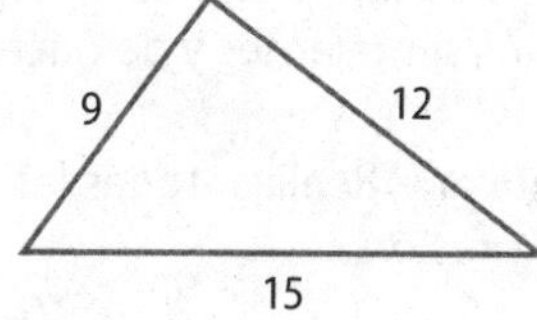

scale factor $= \frac{3}{2}$

scalene triangle A triangle with no congruent sides.

scatterplot A graph that shows the relationship between a data set with two variables graphed as ordered pairs on a coordinate plane.

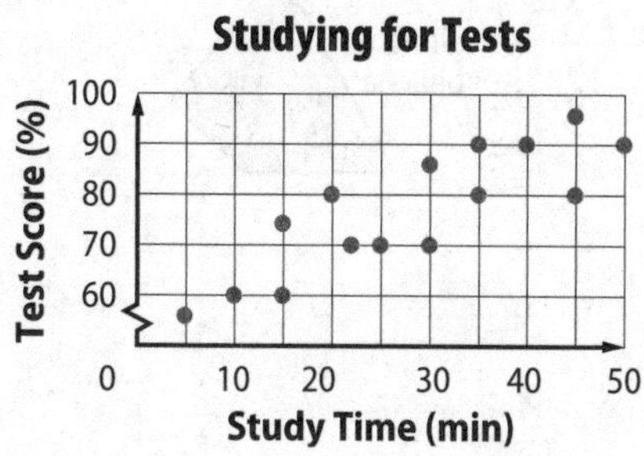

triángulo rectángulo Triángulo con un ángulo recto.

elevación El cambio vertical entre cualquier par de puntos en una recta.

rotación Transformación en la cual una figura se gira alrededor de un punto fijo.

simetría rotacional Tipo de simetría que tiene una figura si se puede girar menos que 360° en torno al centro y aún sigue viéndose como la figura original.

carrera El cambio horizontal entre cualquier par de puntos en una recta.

impuesto sobre las ventas Cantidad de dinero adicional que se cobra por ciertos artículos y servicios.

muestra Subconjunto de una población que se usa con el propósito de recoger datos.

espacio muestral Conjunto de todos los resultados posibles de un experimento de probabilidad.

factor de escala La razón de las longitudes de dos lados correspondientes de dos polígonos semejantes.

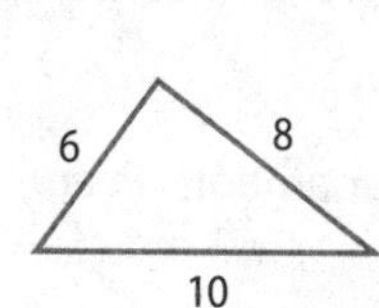

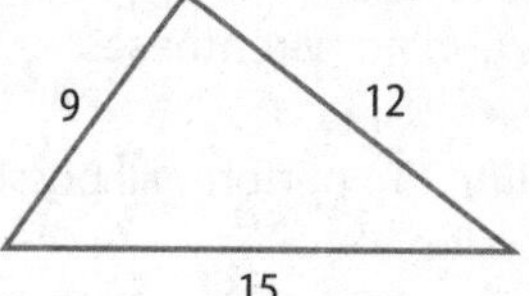

factor de escala $= \frac{3}{2}$

triángulo escaleno Triángulo sin lados congruentes.

diagrama de dispersión Gráfica que muestra la relación entre un conjunto de datos con dos variables graficadas como pares ordenados en un plano de coordenadas.

Glossary/Glosario

scientific notation A compact way of writing numbers with absolute values that are very large or very small. In scientific notation, 5,500 is 5.5×10^3.

notación científica Manera abreviada de escribir números con valores absolutos que son muy grandes o muy pequeños. En notación científica, 5,500 es 5.5×10^3.

selling price The amount the customer pays for an item.

precio de venta Cantidad de dinero que paga un consumidor por un artículo.

semicircle An arc measuring 180°.

semicírculo Arco que mide 180°.

sequence An ordered list of numbers, such as 0, 1, 2, 3 or 2, 4, 6, 8.

sucesión Lista ordenada de números, tales como 0, 1, 2, 3 o 2, 4, 6, 8.

similar If one image can be obtained from another by a sequence of transformations and dilations.

similar Si una imagen puede obtenerse de otra mediante una secuencia de transformaciones y dilataciones.

similar polygons Polygons that have the same shape.

polígonos semejantes Polígonos con la misma forma.

similar solids Solids that have exactly the same shape, but not necessarily the same size.

sólidos semejantes Sólidos que tienen exactamente la misma forma, pero no necesariamente el mismo tamaño.

simple interest Interest paid only on the initial principal of a savings account or loan.

interés simple Interés que se paga sólo sobre el capital inicial de una cuenta de ahorros o préstamo.

simple random sample A sample where each item or person in the population is as likely to be chosen as any other.

muestra aleatoria simple Muestra de una población que tiene la misma probabilidad de escogerse que cualquier otra.

simplest form An algebraic expression that has no like terms and no parentheses.

forma reducida Expresión algebraica que carece de términos semejantes y de paréntesis.

simplify To perform all possible operations in an expression.

simplificar Realizar todas las operaciones posibles en una expresión.

simulation An experiment that is designed to model the action in a given situation.

simulacro Un experimento diseñado para modelar la acción en una situación dada.

simultaneous linear equations A set of two or more linear equations with the same variables.

ecuaciones lineales simultáneas Un juego de dos o más ecuaciones lineales con las mismas variables.

slant height The altitude or height of each lateral face of a pyramid.

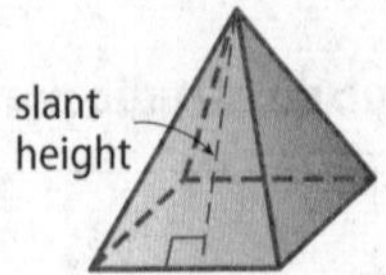

altura oblicua La longitud de la altura de cada cara lateral de una pirámide.

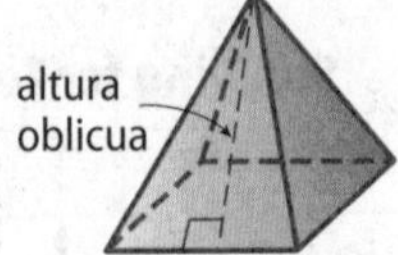

slope The rate of change between any two points on a line. The ratio of the rise, or vertical change, to the run, or horizontal change.

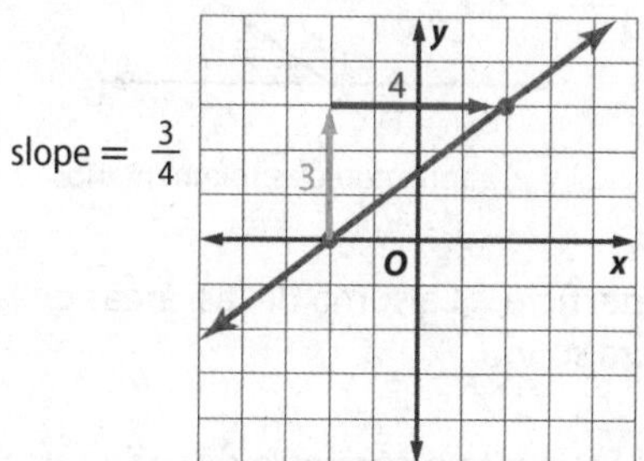

pendiente Razón de cambio entre cualquier par de puntos en una recta. La razón de la altura, o cambio vertical, a la carrera, o cambio horizontal.

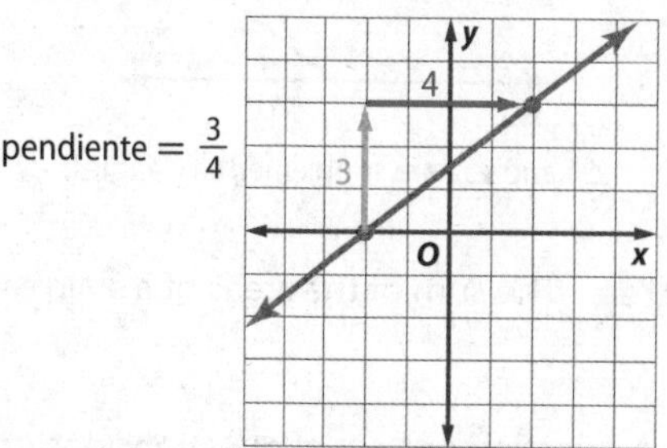

slope-intercept form An equation written in the form $y = mx + b$, where m is the slope and b is the y-intercept.

forma pendiente intersección Ecuación de la forma $y = mx + b$, donde m es la pendiente y b es la intersección y.

solid A three-dimensional figure formed by intersecting planes.

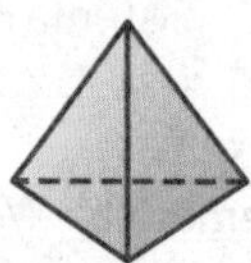

sólido Figura tridimensional formada por planos que se intersecan.

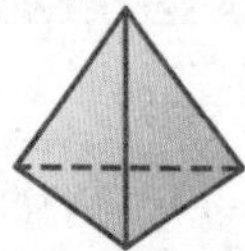

sphere The set of all points in space that are a given distance from a given point called the center.

esfera Conjunto de todos los puntos en el espacio que están a una distancia dada de un punto dado llamado centro.

square root One of the two equal factors of a number. If $a^2 = b$, then a is the square root of b. A square root of 144 is 12 since $12^2 = 144$.

raíz cuadrada Uno de dos factores iguales de un número. Si $a^2 = b$, la a es la raíz cuadrada de b. Una raíz cuadrada de 144 es 12 porque $12^2 = 144$.

standard decimal notation A number written without exponents.

notación decimal estándar Un número que no contiene exponents.

standard form An equation written in the form $Ax + By = C$.

forma estándar Ecuación escrita en la forma $Ax + By = C$.

stored-value card A card with a prepaid value that allows a buyer to buy goods or services.

tarjeta de valor almacenado Tarjeta que tiene un valor prepagado que permite que un comprador compre bienes o servicios.

straight angle An angle whose measure is exactly 180°.

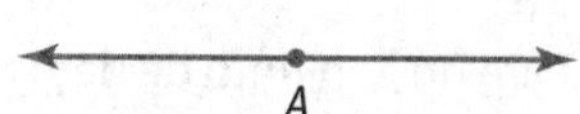

ángulo llano Ángulo que mide exactamente 180º.

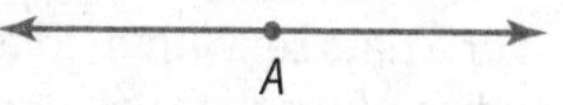

substitution An algebraic model that can be used to find the exact solution of a system of equations.

sustitución Modelo algebraico que se puede usar para calcular la solución exacta de un sistema de ecuaciones.

Subtraction Property of Equality If you subtract the same number from each side of an equation, the two sides remain equal.

propiedad de sustracción de la igualdad Si sustraes el mismo número de ambos lados de una ecuación, los dos lados permanecen iguales.

supplementary angles Two angles are supplementary if the sum of their measures is 180°.

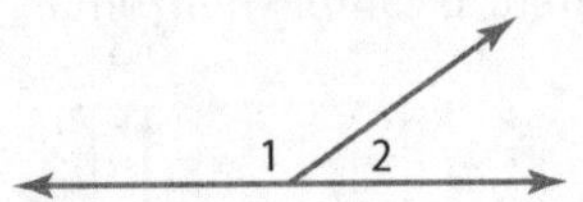

∠1 and ∠2 are supplementary angles.

ángulos suplementarios Dos ángulos son suplementarios si la suma de sus medidas es 180°.

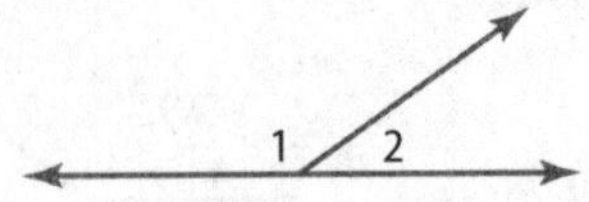

∠1 y ∠2 son ángulos suplementarios.

surface area The sum of the areas of a solid's faces.

área de superficie La suma de las áreas de las caras de una figura sólida.

survey A question or a set of questions designed to collect data about a specific group of people, or population.

encuesta Pregunta o conjunto de preguntas diseñadas para recoger datos sobre un grupo específico de personas o población.

symmetric A description of the shape of a distribution in which the left side of the distribution looks like the right side.

simétrico Una descripción de la forma de una distribución en la que el lado izquierdo de la distribución se parece el lado derecho.

system of equations A set of two or more equations with the same variables.

sistema de ecuaciones Sistema de ecuaciones con las mismas variables.

systematic random sample A sample where the items or people are selected according to a specific time or time interval.

muestra aleatoria sistemática Muestra en que los elementos o personas se eligen según un intervalo de tiempo o elemento específico.

Tt

term A number, a variable, or a product of numbers and variables.

término Un número, una variable o un producto de números y variables.

term Each part of an algebraic expression separated by an addition or subtraction sign.

término Cada parte de un expresión algebraica separada por un signo adición o un signo sustracción.

terminating decimal A repeating decimal where the repeating digit is zero.

decimal finito Un decimal periódico donde el dígito que se repite es cero.

theorem A statement or conjecture that can be proven.

teorema Un enunciado o conjetura que puede probarse.

theoretical probability Probability based on known characteristics or facts.

probabilidad teórica Probabilidad que se basa en características o hechos conocidos.

third quartile For a data set with median M, the third quartile is the median of the data values greater than M.

tercer cuartil Para un conjunto de datos con la mediana M, el tercer cuartil es la mediana de los valores mayores que M.

three-dimensional figure A figure with length, width, and height.

figura tridimensional Figura que tiene largo, ancho y alto.

total surface area The sum of the areas of the surfaces of a solid.

área de superficie total La suma del área de las superficies de un sólido.

transformation An operation that maps a geometric figure, preimage, onto a new figure, image.

transformación Operación que convierte una figura geométrica, la pre-imagen, en una figura nueva, la imagen.

translation A transformation that slides a figure from one position to another without turning.

traslación Transformación en la cual una figura se desliza de una posición a otra sin hacerla girar.

transversal A line that intersects two or more other lines.

transversal Recta que interseca dos o más rectas.

trapezoid A quadrilateral with exactly one pair of parallel sides.

trapecio Cuadrilátero con exactamente un par de lados paralelos.

tree diagram A diagram used to show the total number of possible outcomes in a probability experiment.

diagrama de árbol Diagrama que se usa para mostrar el número total de resultados posibles en un experimento de probabilidad.

trend line A line close to most of the data points.

recta de tendencia Recta que se acerca a la mayoría de puntos en un diagrama de dispersión.

triangle A figure formed by three line segments that intersect only at their endpoints.

triángulo Figura formada por tres segmentos de recta que se intersecan sólo en sus extremos.

two-column proof A formal proof that contains statements and reasons organized in two columns. Each step is called a statement, and the properties that justify each step are called reasons.

demostración de dos columnas Demonstración formal que contiene enunciados y razones organizadas en dos columnas. Cada paso se llama enunciado y las propiedades que lo justifican son las razones.

two-step equation An equation that contains two operations.

ecuación de dos pasos Ecuación que contiene dos operaciones.

two-step inequality An inequality that contains two operations.

desigualdad de dos pasos Desigualdad que contiene dos operaciones.

Uu

unbiased sample A sample that is selected so that it is representative of the entire population.

muestra no sesgada Muestra que se selecciona de modo que sea representativa de la población entera.

unit rate/ratio A rate or ratio with a denominator of 1.

tasa/razón unitaria Una tasa o razón con un denominador de 1.

univariate data Data with one variable.

datos univariate Datos con una variable.

unlike fractions Fractions whose denominators are different.

fracciones con distinto denominador Fracciones cuyos denominadores son diferentes.

variable A symbol, usually a letter, used to represent a number in mathematical expressions or sentences.

variable Un símbolo, por lo general, una letra, que se usa para representar números en expresiones o enunciados matemáticos.

vertex The point where the sides of an angle meet.

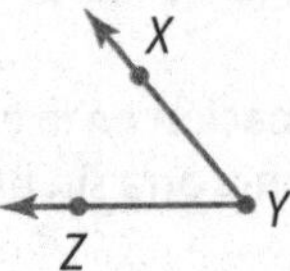

vértice Punto donde se encuentran los lados.

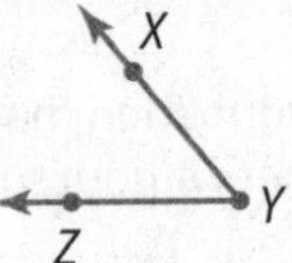

vertex The point where three or more faces of a polyhedron intersect.

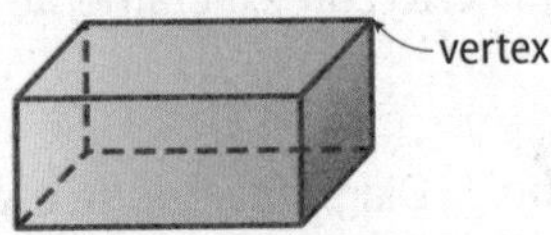

vértice El punto donde tres o más caras de un poliedro se cruzan.

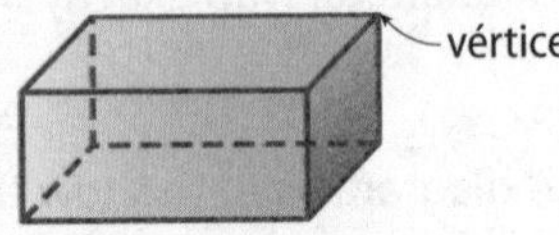

vertex The point at the tip of a cone.

vértice El punto en la punta de un cono.

vertical angles Opposite angles formed by the intersection of two lines. Vertical angles are congruent. In the figure, the vertical angles are $\angle 1$ and $\angle 3$, and $\angle 2$ and $\angle 4$.

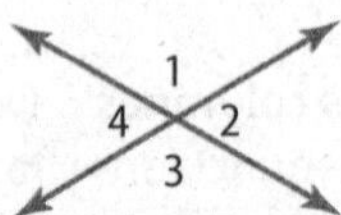

ángulos opuestos por el vértice Ángulos congruentes que se forman de la intersección de dos rectas. En la figura, los ángulos opuestos por el vértice son $\angle 1$ y $\angle 3$, y $\angle 2$ y $\angle 4$.

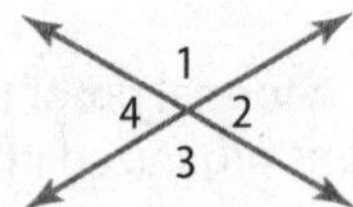

volume The measure of the space occupied by a solid. Standard measures are cubic units such as in^3 or ft^3.

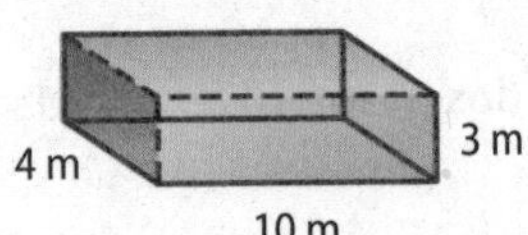

$V = 10 \times 4 \times 3 = 120$ cubic meters

volumen Medida del espacio que ocupa un sólido. Las medidas estándares son las unidades cúbicas, como $pulg^3$ o $pies^3$.

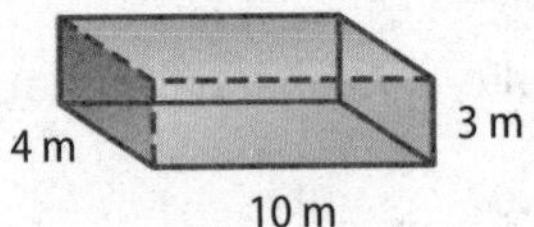

$V = 10 \times 4 \times 3 = 120$ metros cúbicos

voluntary response sample A sample which involves only those who want to participate in the sampling.

muestra de respuesta voluntaria Muestra que involucra sólo aquellos que quieren participar en el muestreo.

Xx

x-axis The horizontal number line that helps to form the coordinate plane.

eje x La recta numérica horizontal que ayuda a formar el plano de coordenadas.

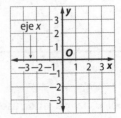

x-coordinate The first number of an ordered pair.

coordenada x El primer número de un par ordenado.

***x*-intercept** The *x*-coordinate of the point where the line crosses the *x*-axis.

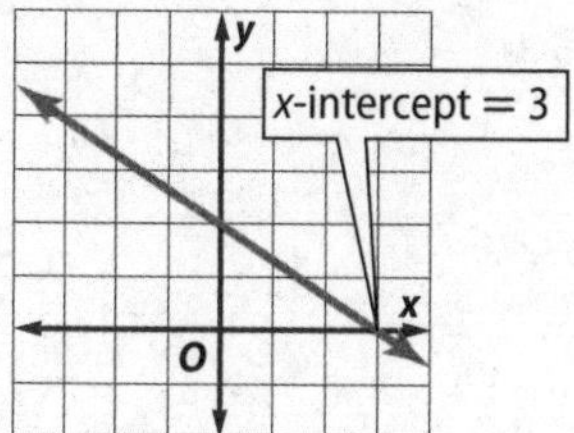

intersección *x* La coordenada *x* del punto donde cruza la gráfica el eje *x*.

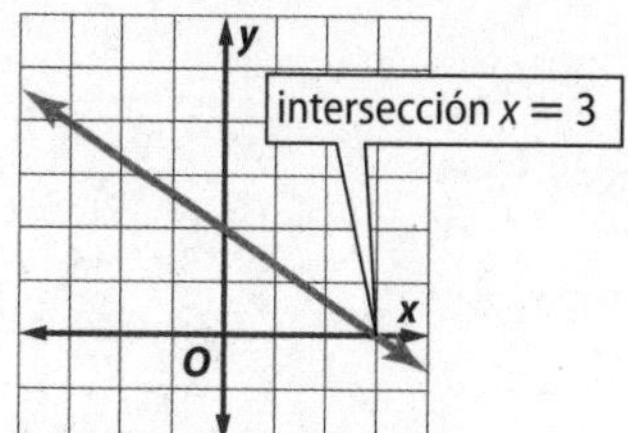

Glossary/Glosario

Yy

***y*-axis** The vertical number line that helps to form the coordinate plane.

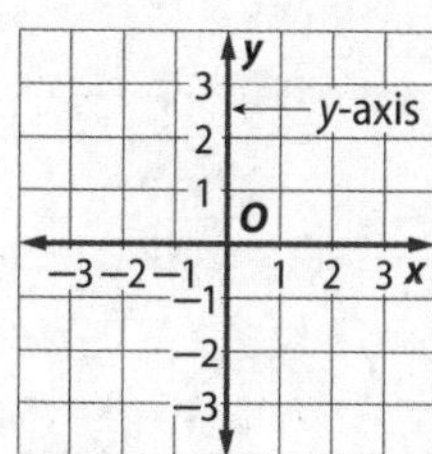

eje *y* La recta numérica vertical que ayuda a formar el plano de coordenadas.

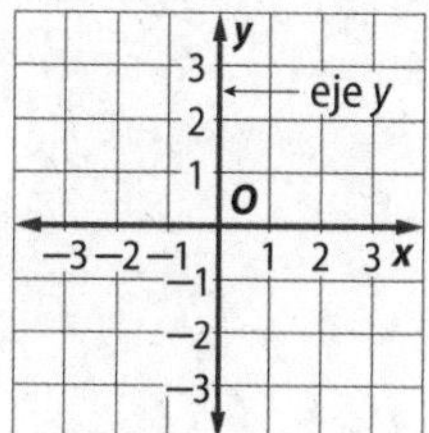

***y*-coordinate** The second number of an ordered pair.

coordenada *y* El segundo número de un par ordenado.

***y*-intercept** The *y*-coordinate of the point where the line crosses the *y*-axis.

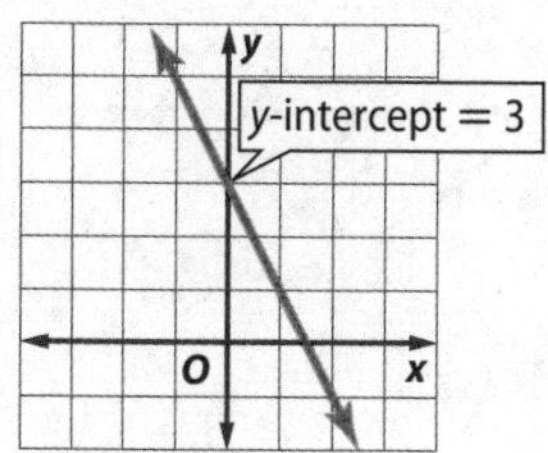

intersección *y* La coordenada *y* del punto donde cruza la gráfica el eje *y*.

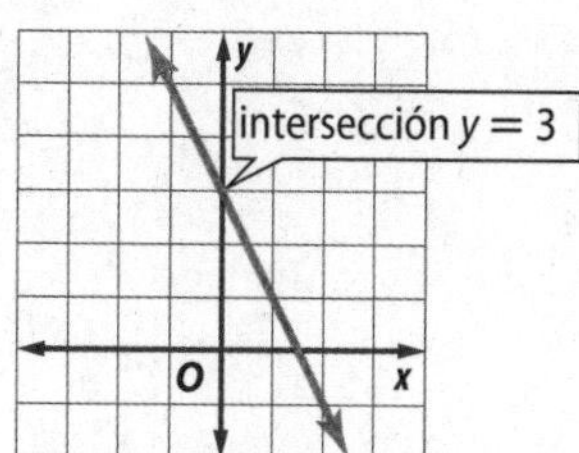

Chapter 1 Real Numbers

Page 22 Chapter 1 Are You Ready?

1. 256 **3.** $2,048 **5.** $2 \times 2 \times 2 \times 3$ **7.** $2 \times 2 \times 5 \times 5$ **9.** $-1 \times 2 \times 3 \times 7$

Pages 29–30 Lesson 1-1 Independent Practice

1. 0.4 **3.** 0.825 **5** $-0.\overline{54}$ **7a.** $0.0\overline{6}$ **7b.** $0.1\overline{6}$ **7c.** 0.333 **7d.** 0.417 **9** $-7\frac{8}{25}$ **11.** $5\frac{13}{20}$ **13.** $10\frac{39}{125}$ **15.** $2\frac{7}{9}$ **17.** $\frac{7}{8}$ in.; 0.875 in. **19.** Sample answer: $0.\overline{12}$; Since $0.\overline{12} = \frac{4}{33}$, it is a rational number. **21.** Sample answer: When the digits repeat, the repeating digits are the numerator and 1 less than the decimal place value is the denominator.

Pages 31–32 Lesson 1-1 Multi-Step Problem-Solving

23. B **25.** $\frac{6}{13}$ **27.** $0.058\overline{3}$ in²; Sample answer: area of shaded rectangle $= \frac{1}{2} \cdot \frac{1}{4}$ or $\frac{1}{8}$ in²; area of unshaded rectangle $= \frac{1}{3} \cdot \frac{1}{5}$ or $\frac{1}{15}$ in²; difference in areas: $\frac{1}{8} - \frac{1}{15} = \frac{15}{120} - \frac{8}{120} = \frac{7}{120}$ or $0.058\overline{3}$

Pages 37–38 Lesson 1-2 Independent Practice

1. $(-5)^4$ **3.** m^5 **5.** $\frac{1}{81}$ **7** 8,000,000,000 or 8 billion **9** −311 **11.** 16 **13a.** 10^2 **13b.** 10^6 **13c.** 10^9 **13d.** 10^{15} **15.** Sample answer: As the exponent decreases by 1, the simplified answer is divided by 3; $\frac{1}{2}$

Pages 39–40 Lesson 1-2 Multi-Step Problem-Solving

17. A **19.** 729 **21.** $91 + 93 + 95 + 97 + 99 + 101 + 103 + 105 + 107 + 109 = 1{,}000 = 10^3$; Sample answer: In each equation, the number of values added is equal to the base. The first numbers are 1, 3, 7, 13, and 21. So, the first numbers are increasing by 2, 4, 6, and 8. Continuing the pattern gives first numbers of 1, 3, 7, 13, 21, 31, 43, 57, 73, and 91. So, the tenth equation starts with 91.

Pages 45–46 Lesson 1-3 Independent Practice

1. $\frac{1}{7^{10}}$ **3.** $\frac{1}{g^7}$ **5.** 12^{-4} **7.** 5^{-3} **9.** $10^{-1}, 10^{-2}, 10^{-3}, 10^{-6}$ **11.** $\frac{1}{w^3}$ **13** $\frac{4}{y^9}$ **15.** 1 **17.** 1 **19** 10^5 or 100,000 times **21.** $11^{-3}, 11^0, 11^2$; Sample answer: The exponents in order from least to greatest are −3, 0, 2. **23.** Sample answer: $\left(\frac{1}{2}\right)^{-1} = 2, \left(\frac{34}{43}\right)^{-1} = \frac{43}{34}, \left(\frac{56}{65}\right)^{-1} = \frac{65}{56}$; When you raise a fraction to the −1 power, it is the same as finding the reciprocal of the fraction.

Pages 39–40 Lesson 1-3 Multi-Step Problem-Solving

25. D **27.** 63 ft² **29.** 24; Sample answer: I rewrote $\frac{1}{512}$ as 2^{-9}. So, I am looking for three negative exponents that add to −9. The sum of the negative integers −2, −3, and −4 is −9 So, *a* can equal −2, *b* can equal −3, and *c* can equal −4. Since the product of −2, −3, and −4 is −24, $|abc| = |-24| = 24$.

Pages 53–54 Lesson 1-4 Independent Practice

1. 3,160 **3.** 0.0000252 **5.** 7.2×10^{-3} **7** Arctic, Southern, Indian, Atlantic, Pacific **9.** 17.32 millimeters; the number is small so choosing a smaller unit of measure is more meaningful. **11** < **13.** 1.2×10^6; 1.2×10^5 is only 120,000, but 1.2×10^6 is just over one million. **15.** Sample answer: 3.01×10^2, 5.01×10^2; $3.01 \times 10^2 < 5.01 \times 10^2$

Page 56 Lesson 1-4 Multi-Step Problem-Solving

17. D **19.** 7

Page 63 Focus on Mathematical Processes

1. 18 tour guides **3.** $2n + 1$; 201 toothpicks

Pages 69–70 Lesson 1-5 Independent Practice

1. 4 **3.** no real solution **5** −1.6 **7.** ±9 **9.** ±0.13 **11.** −0.5 **13** 6.25 m² **15.** 44 in. **17.** 24 m **19.** 36 **21.** $\frac{25}{81}$ **23.** Sample answer: The square root of a number squared is the original number. **25.** Sample answer: $(\sqrt[3]{8})^2 = 4$

Page 72 Lesson 1-5 Multi-Step Problem-Solving

27. 1 foot **29.** 1,728 cm²; The surface area of the whole prism is 360 + 360 + 360 + 360 + 144 + 144 or 1,728 cm².

Pages 79–80 Lesson 1-6 Independent Practice

1. 5 **3.** 4 **5.** 3 **7** 10 **9.** Sample answer: 54 ft and 57 ft; 55.5 ft and 55.8 feet; 55.71 ft and 55.74 feet; 56 feet **11** about 2.8 seconds **13.** $\sqrt[3]{105}, 5, \sqrt{38}, 7$ **15.** 10; Since 94 is less than 100, $\sqrt{94}$ is less than 10. **17.** Sample answers: 50; 60. Since 49 < 50 < 64 and 50 is closer to 49 than to 64, $\sqrt{50}$ is closer to 7 than to 8. Since 49 < 60 < 64 and 60 is closer to 64 than to 49, $\sqrt{60}$ is closer to 8 than to 7. **19.** sometimes; Sample answer: $\sqrt{9}$ is greater than $\sqrt[3]{11}$, but $\sqrt{2}$ is less than $\sqrt[3]{18}$.

Page 82 Lesson 1-6 Multi-Step Problem-Solving

21. C **23.** 11

Pages 87–88 Lesson 1-7 Independent Practice

1. rational **3** rational **5.** False; Sample answer: 0.5 is a real number that is not natural. **7.** False; Sample answer: $\sqrt{3}$ is an irrational number that is real. 9 Yes; $\sqrt{30 \times 0.8 \times 90} \approx 46$, so the car was speeding. **11.** $\sqrt{3}$; All of the other numbers are rational numbers. **13.** $\sqrt{1}$; All of the other numbers are irrational numbers. **15.** always **17.** −5

Pages 89–90 Lesson 1-7 Multi-Step Problem-Solving

19. D **21.** 17 cm^2
23. Sample answer: The rational and irrational numbers combine to form the set of real numbers.

Pages 95–96 Lesson 1-8 Independent Practice

1. < 3 <

5.

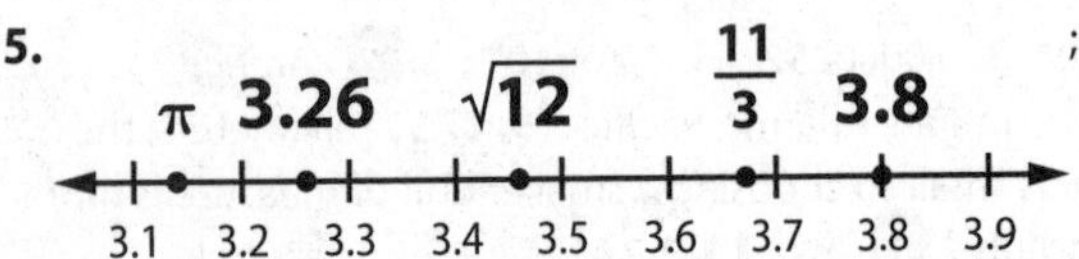

;

$\pi, 3.26, \sqrt{12}, \frac{11}{3}, 3.8$
7 quiz 2, quiz 4, quiz 3, quiz 1 **9.** > **11.** < **13.** Sample answer: −1.2 **15.** Sample answer: 0.125 **17.** Sample answer: 1.5; $\sqrt{2} \approx 1.41$ **19.** $8.\overline{14}$; Sample answer: $8\frac{1}{7} - 8 \approx 0.143$, $8.\overline{14} - 8 = 0.1414...$, $8 - \frac{15}{2} = 0.5$, Since the least difference is 0.1414..., $8.\overline{14}$ is the closest to 8.

Pages 97–98 Lesson 1-8 Multi-Step Problem-Solving

21. D **23.** 2 cm^2 **25.** 14 m

Page 101 Chapter Review Vocabulary Check

1. RADICAL SIGN **3.** EXPONENT **5.** PERFECT CUBE
7. RATIONAL NUMBER

Page 102 Chapter Review Key Concept Check

1. 2 × 2 × 2 **3.** < **5.** less than

Page 103 Chapter Review Multi-Step Problem-Solving

7. 24.51 ft^2; Sample answer: Convert each side length to decimal notation: $7\frac{3}{8} = 7.375$, $\frac{37}{5} = 7.4$, and $\sqrt{54} \approx 7.35$. The greatest side length is $\frac{37}{5}$. The area of the new garden is 7.4^2 or 54.76 ft^2. The area of the old garden is 5.5^2 or 30.25 ft^2. So, 54.76 − 30.25 is 24.51.

Chapter 2 Similarity and Dilations

Page 108 Chapter 2 Are You Ready?

1. 3.5 **3.** 14.8 **5.** 2 **7.** $y = 3x$

Pages 117–118 Lesson 2-1 Independent Practice

1 $\angle P \cong J$, $\angle Q \cong K$, $\angle R \cong L$, $\angle S \cong M$; $\frac{PQ}{JK} = \frac{QR}{KL} = \frac{RS}{LM} = \frac{SP}{MJ}$

3 $3.\overline{3}$; **5a.** Figure 1: 96 cm^2; Figure 2: 294 cm^2;

5b. Sample answer: The scale factor of the side lengths is $\frac{14}{8}$ or $\frac{7}{4}$. The ratio of the areas is $\frac{49}{16}$. The ratio of the areas is the scale factor of the side lengths squared. **7.** 400 ft **9.** false; Sample answer: In rectangles, all corresponding angles are congruent but not all sides are proportional.
Rectangle *A* is not similar to Rectangle *B*, since $\frac{4}{4} \neq \frac{1}{2}$.

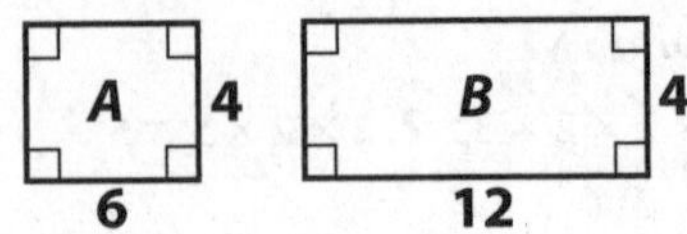

Page 120 Lesson 2-1 Multi-Step Problem-Solving

13. C **15.** 6.25

Pages 125–126 Lesson 2-2 Independent Practice

1. The triangles are not similar. **3.** 200 ft 5 37.5 m
7 $\frac{136}{34} = \frac{h}{1.5}$; 6 feet tall **11.** Sample answer: The length of the tall object's shadow, the length of the shadow of a nearby object with a height that is directly measurable, and the height of the nearby object.

Pages 127–128 Lesson 2-2 Multi-Step Problem-Solving

13. C **15.** 51 **17.** 15 feet; Sample answer: Since $\angle H \cong \angle H$ and $\angle HPJ \cong \angle HJK$, $\triangle HPJ \sim \triangle HJK$. Since $\angle K \cong \angle K$ and $\angle JPK \cong \angle HJK$, $\triangle JPK \sim \triangle HJK$. So, $\frac{10}{x} = \frac{a}{b}$ and $\frac{x}{22} = \frac{a}{b}$. Therefore, $\frac{10}{x} = \frac{x}{22}$. I solved this proportion to find that $x = \sqrt{220}$, which is between 14 and 15, closer to 15.

Page 131 Focus on Mathematical Processes

1. 20 people **3.** 3

Pages 141–142 Lesson 2-3 Independent Practice

1 $C'(2, 8)$, $A'(4, 4)$, $T'(10, 10)$;

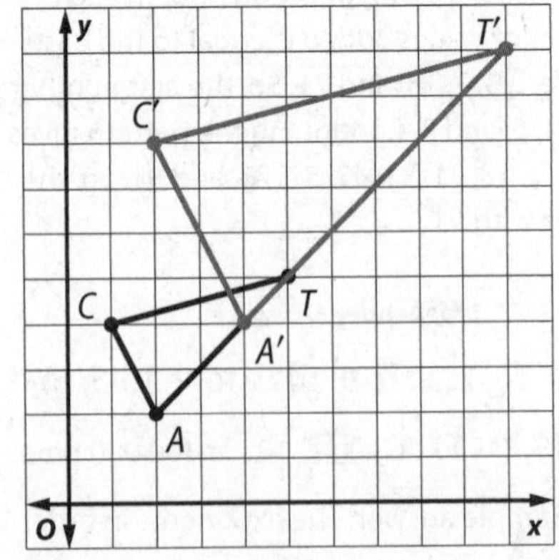

3. $(x, y) \rightarrow (2x, 2y)$; $(x, y) \rightarrow \left(\frac{3}{4}x, \frac{3}{4}y\right)$ 5 $\frac{1}{5}$

7.

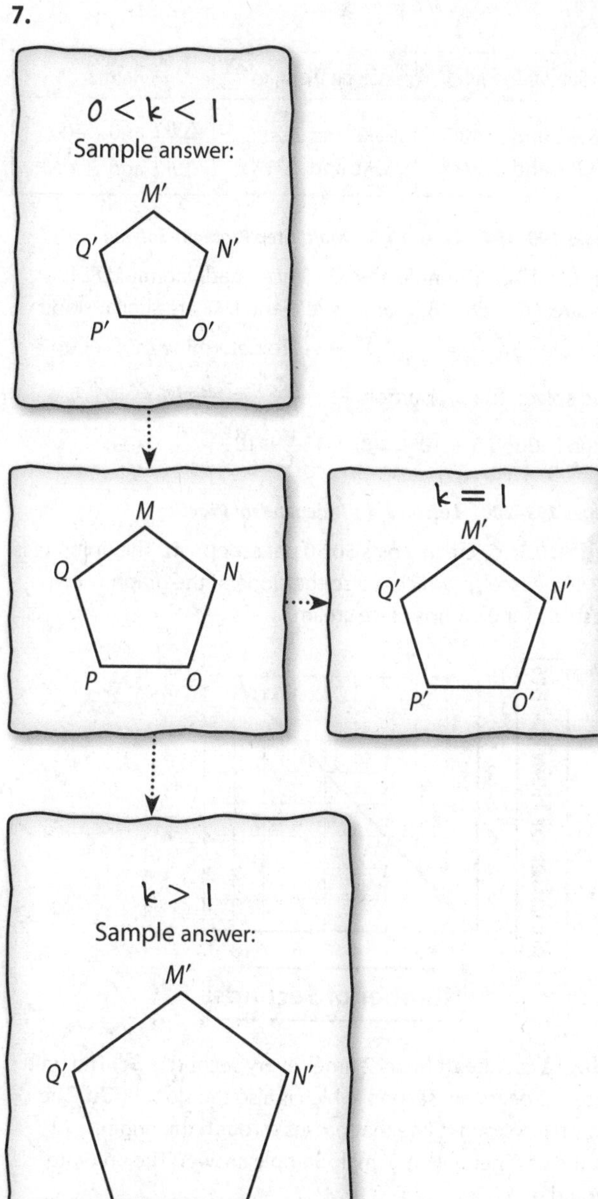

9. No; Sample answer: both coordinates of all the points must be multiplied by the same scale factor.

Pages 143–144 Lesson 2-3 Multi-Step Problem-Solving

11. C **13.** 4.84 **15.** 75; Sample answer: I drew *PQRS* and found it has a perimeter of 30 units. I wrote $P(-4, -2) \rightarrow P'(-10, -5) = (-4k, -2k)$ to represent the dilation with a scale factor k and solved $-2k = -5$ to find that $k = 2.5$. Since every side of polygon *P′Q′R′S′* is 2.5 times the corresponding side of polygon *PQRS*, its perimeter is 2.5 times the perimeter of polygon *PQRS*. So, the perimeter of polygon *P′Q′R′S′* is 2.5×30, or 75 units.

Page 153–154 Lesson 2-4 Independent Practice

1 57 mm **3.** 160 ft **5** 126 ft^2

7.

If the scale factor is...	Multiply the ... Length by	Width by	Perimeter by	Area by
2	2	2	2	4
4	4	4	4	16
0.5	0.5	0.5	0.5	0.25
$\frac{2}{3}$	$\frac{2}{3}$	$\frac{2}{3}$	$\frac{2}{3}$	$\frac{4}{9}$
k	k	k	k	k^2

9. Robert is thinking of size in terms of area and Denise is thinking of size in terms of perimeter.

Pages 155–156 Lesson 2-4 Multi-Step Problem-Solving

11. \$150 **13.** 200 cm^2 **15.** trapezoid; Sample answer: The scale factors are $\sqrt{2}$ for the circle, 1.5 for the rectangle, 2 for the trapezoid.

Page 159 Chapter Review Vocabulary Check

1. similar **3.** dilation

Page 160 Chapter Review Key Concept Check

1. enlargement **3.** similar

Page 161 Chapter Review Multi-Step Problem-Solving

5. 60 ft; 200 ft^2

Chapter 3 Proportional Relationships and Slope

Page 166 Chapter 3 Are You Ready?

1. 9 **3.** −7 **5.** 6 **7.** $\frac{2}{5}$ **9.** $\frac{1}{5}$ **11.** $-\frac{2}{5}$

Pages 173–174 Lesson 3-1 Independent Practice

1 Yes; the rate of change between cost and time for each hour is a constant 3¢ per hour. **3.** Yes; the rate of change between vinegar and oil for each cup of oil is a constant $\frac{3}{8}$ cup vinegar per cup of oil. **5** Yes; the rate of change between the actual distance and the map distance for each inch on the map is a constant 7.5 mi/in. **7.** Yes; the ratio of the cost to time is a constant 3¢ per hour, so the relationship is proportional. **9.** Yes; the ratio of actual distance to map distance is a constant $\frac{15}{2}$ miles per inch, so the relationship is proportional.

11. Sample answer:

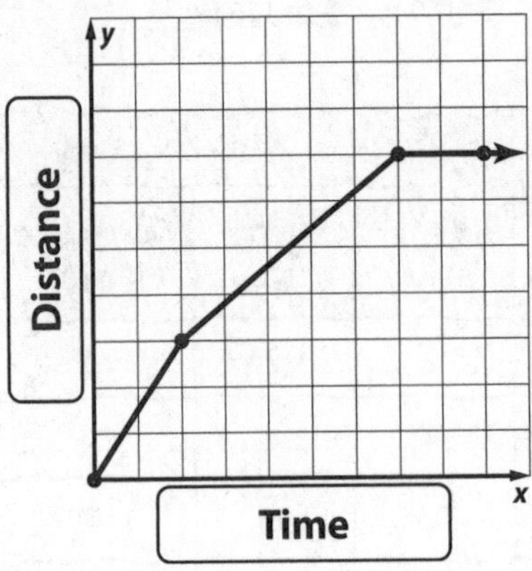

13. no; Sample answer: $\frac{6}{2} \neq \frac{24}{6}$

Pages 175–176 Lesson 3-1 Multi-Step Problem-Solving

15. B **17.** 960 **19.** 17; The rate of change is $\frac{21-9}{9-3} = \frac{12}{6} = 2$. Because the relationship is linear, the rate of change is constant; $2 = \frac{21-k}{9-7}$; $2 = \frac{21-k}{2}$; $4 = 21 - k$; $k = 17$.

Pages 183–184 Lesson 3-2 Independent Practice

1 $\frac{2}{3}$ **3.** $-\frac{3}{4}$ **5.** 2 **7** -4 **9.** yes; $\frac{1}{15} < \frac{1}{12}$

11. Jacob did not use the x-coordinates in the same order as the y-coordinates. $m = \frac{3-2}{4-0}$ $m = \frac{1}{4}$ **13.** Sample answers are given. **13a.** (1, 1), (2, 6), (3, 11) **13b.** (1, 1), (6, 2), (11, 3) **13c.** (1, 1), (0, 6), (−1, 11)

Page 186 Lesson 3-2 Multi-Step Problem-Solving

15. B **17.** 408

Page 191–192 Lesson 3-3 Independent Practice

1 $\frac{AC}{AB} = \frac{NM}{NL}$, or $\frac{1}{1}$

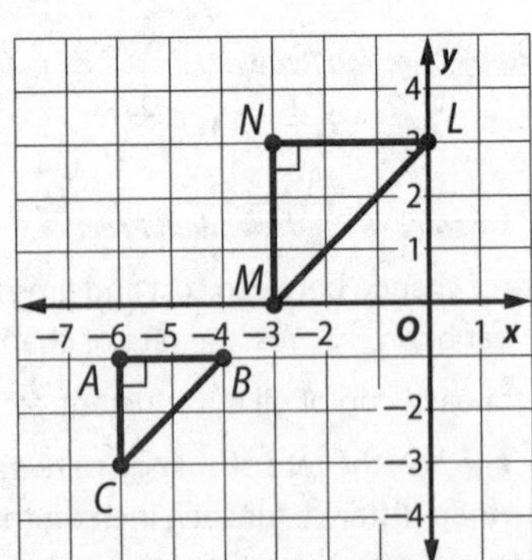

3 $m = -\frac{2}{5}$; The other slope should equal $-\frac{2}{5}$. **5.** $P(5,3)$

9.

Similar Triangles	Slope Triangles	Neither
△*JKL* and △*ABC* △*JKL* and △*WXY*	△*JKL* and △*ABC* △*JKL* and △*WXY*	△*JKL* and △*RST* △*JKL* and △*MNP*

Pages 193–194 Lesson 3-3 Multi-Step Problem-Solving

11. C **13.** 72; Sample answer: Since quadrilateral *ACFE* is a square, $FC = EF = 8$. Triangles *ABC* and *DAE* are similar slope triangles. So, $\frac{6}{10} = \frac{8}{AD}$; $AD = 13\frac{1}{3}$. To determine *DE*, I set up and solved the proportion $\frac{BC}{AE} = \frac{AC}{DE}$; $\frac{6}{8} = \frac{8}{DE}$; $DE = 10\frac{2}{3}$. Then I added $6 + 10 + 4(8) + 13\frac{1}{3} + 10\frac{2}{3}$.

Pages 199–200 Lesson 3-4 Independent Practice

1 **a.** 0.5; ice cream costs \$0.50 per scoop **b.** The unit rate is \$0.50 per scoop, which is also the slope of the graph. **c.** It costs \$0 for 0 scoops of ice cream.

3a.

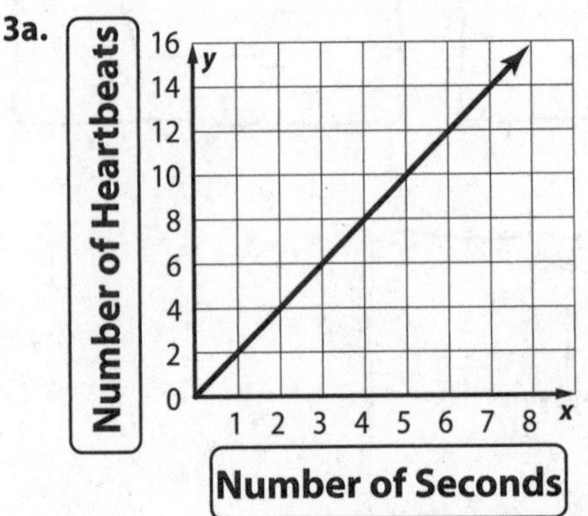

3b. 2; a cat's heart beats 2 times every second. **3c.** The unit rate is 2 beats per second, which is also the slope. **3d.** The graph is a straight line that passes through the origin.
5. the cost per gallon of milk; Sample answer: The unit rate would be \$2.50.

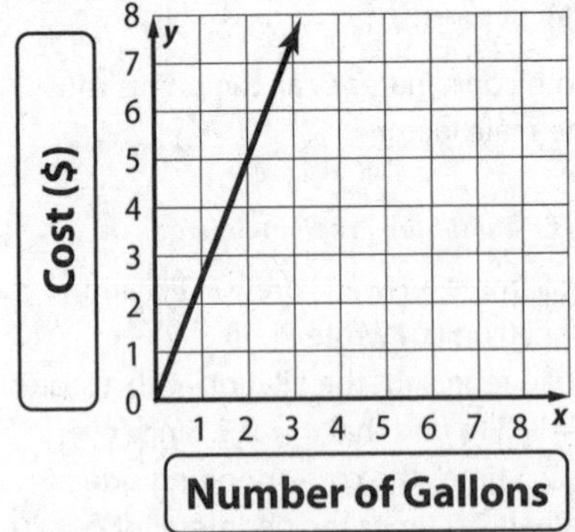

7. Sample answer: The total cost y of buying x boxes of popcorn is a proportional linear relationship. If you buy x boxes of popcorn and a drink for \$1, the relationship between the total cost and the boxes of popcorn becomes nonproportional.

Pages 201–202 Lesson 3-4 Multi-Step Problem-Solving

9. Deepak; 30 more words **11.** 1

Pages 207–208 Lesson 3-5 Independent Practice

1. $y = 5x$; $\frac{5}{1}$ or 5; For every mile you are from the lightning, you will hear the thunder 5 seconds after you see the lightning. **3** Computers R Us; Sample answer: The unit cost for Computer Access is \$25 per hour. The unit cost for Computers R Us is \$23.50; $23.5 < 25$. **5.** yes; 4 **7** 12.7 cm **9.** $y = -\frac{4}{3}x$; $5\frac{1}{3}$ **11.** $y = \frac{3}{7}x$; $-9\frac{1}{3}$ **13.** The constant of variation affects the steepness of the line of the graph. **15.** true; A direct variation relationship is a special type of linear relationship whose graph is a straight line that passes through the origin.

Page 210 Lesson 3-5 Multi-Step Problem-Solving

17. C **19.** 10

Page 213 Focus on Mathematical Processes

1. Sample answer: 3 packages of 8 cards and 4 packages of 12 cards **3.** 53 rolls

Pages 223–224 Lesson 3-6 Independent Practice

1 $y = -\frac{3}{4}x - 2$ **3.** $y = \frac{4}{3}x + 10$ **5.** $y = -\frac{1}{3}x + 5$

7 **a.**

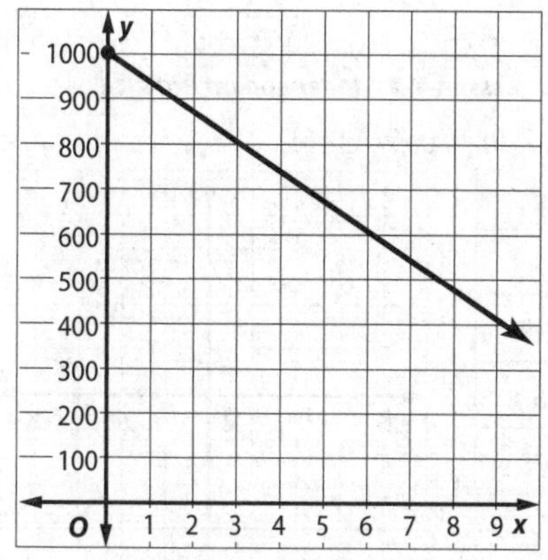

b. The driving rate, 65 mph; the distance from which they began their trip, 1,000 miles.

9.

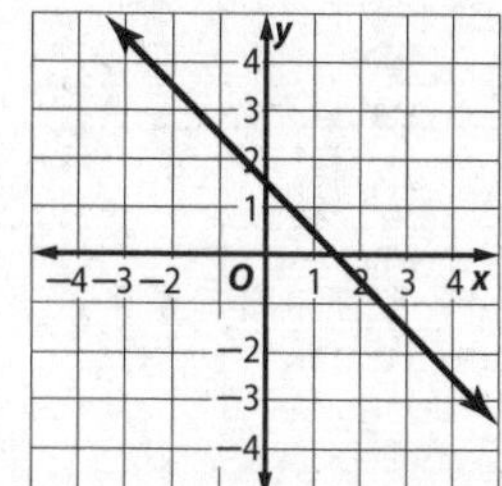

11a. $y = \$0.83x + 3$ **11b.** $y = \$0.67x + 3$ **13.** Sample answer: $y = 4x$, $y = 4x + 2$

Pages 225–226 Lesson 3-6 Multi-Step Problem-Solving

15. D **17.** \$22.80 **19.** $y = x + 1$

Pages 231–232 Lesson 3-7 Independent Practice

1. x-intercept: 3.5; y-intercept: 7

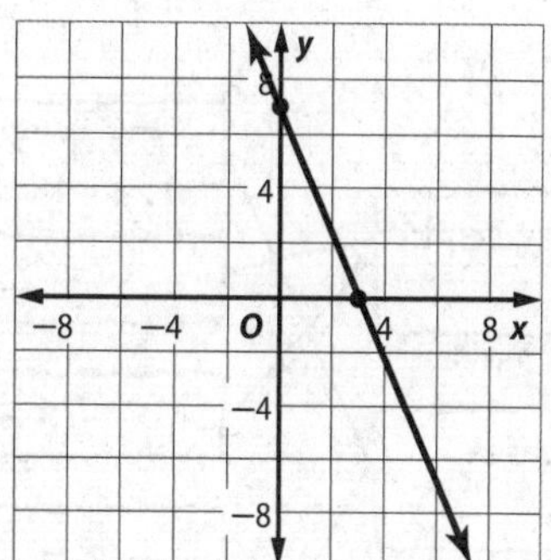

3 x-intercept: $1\frac{1}{4}$; y-intercept: $1\frac{2}{3}$

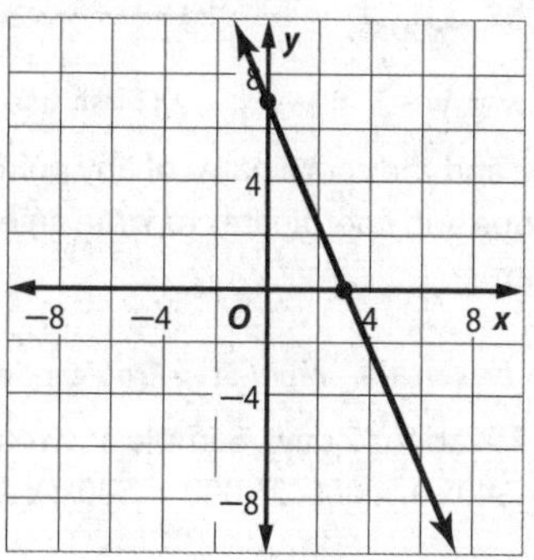

5 The x-intercept of 375 means that if the zoo had only four-legged animals, there would be 375 of them. The y-intercept of 750 means that if the zoo had only two-legged animals, there would be 750 of them.

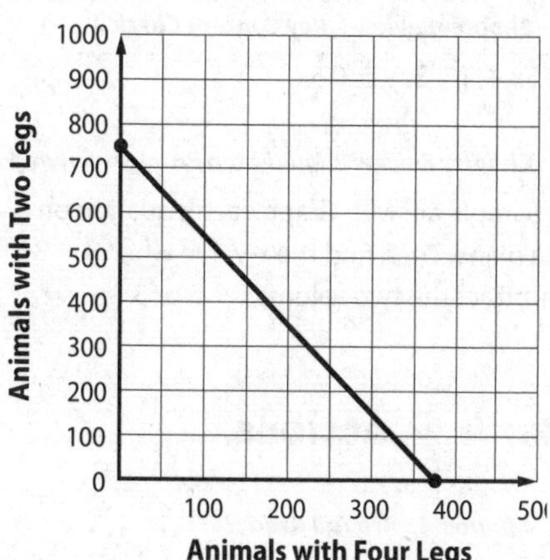

7. After $3x = 12$, Carmen didn't divide both sides by 3 to get the x-intercept of 4. **9.** Sample answers: $x = 2$; $y = 2$

Page 234 Lesson 3-7 Multi-Step Problem-Solving

11. C **13.** 298.25

Pages 239–240 Lesson 3-8 Independent Practice

1. $y - 9 = 2(x - 1); y = 2x + 7$ **3.** $y + 5 = \frac{3}{4}(x + 4);$ $y = \frac{3}{4}x - 2$ **5** Sample answer: $y + 4 = -\frac{3}{2}(x - 4);$ $y = -\frac{3}{2}x + 2$ **7.** Sample answer: $y - 14 = \frac{1}{5}(x - 10)$ **9** $3x + y = 13$

11.

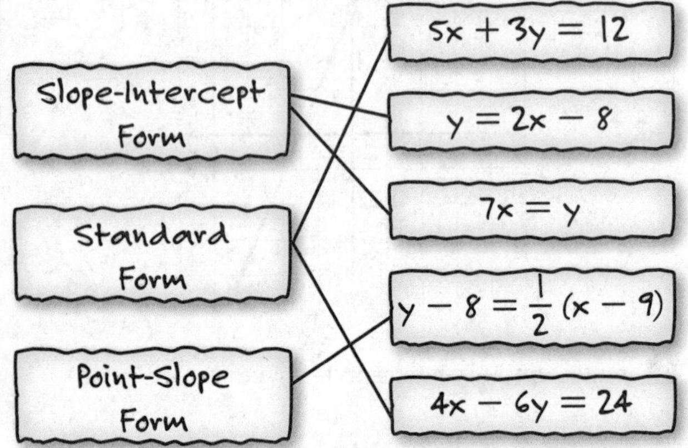

13. Sample answer: $y - 5 = -\frac{1}{2}(x - 2)$; First, use the equation to find the slope and the coordinates of any point on the line. Then use the slope and coordinates to write an equation in point-slope form.

Pages 241–242 Lesson 3-8 Multi-Step Problem-Solving

15. B **17.** 5 **19.** about 2 days; Sample answer: $y = 540x + 4{,}000$; $30{,}000 = 540x + 4{,}000$; $26{,}000 = 540x$; $x \approx 48.15$ hours or $\frac{48.15}{24} \approx 2$ days.

Page 247 Chapter Review Vocabulary Check

1. RISE **3.** SLOPE; STANDARD FORM **5.** DIRECT VARIATION **7.** *X* INTERCEPT

Page 248 Chapter Review Key Concept Check

1. $y = -0.5x + 1$ **3.** $y = 0.5x$

Page 248 Chapter Review Multi-Step Problem-Solving

5. 3 cups; Sample answer: Graph each equation on a coordinate plane. Then find the *x*-value when $y = 30$ for each line and subtract the two values. $8 - 5$ or 3.

Chapter 4 Functions

Page 254 Chapter 4 Are You Ready?

1. (1.5, 2.5) **3.** (0, 1.5) **5.** (1, 1) **7.** −18 **9.** −3 **11.** $901

Pages 263–264 Lesson 4-1 Independent Practice

1 **a.** $b = 45d$; Forty-five baskets are produced every day **b.** 16,425 baskets **c.** Linear proportional; the equation $b = 45d$ is in the form $y = mx$. **3** **a.** $f = 3.5 + 0.15d$

b.

d	$3.5 + 0.15d$	f
10	3.5 + 0.15(10)	5.00
15	3.5 + 0.15(15)	5.75
20	3.5 + 0.15(20)	6.50
25	3.5 + 0.15(25)	7.25

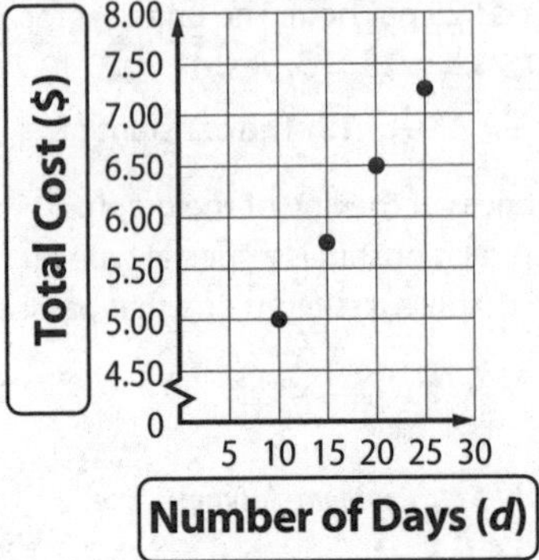

c. Linear non-proportional; the equation is in the form $y = mx + b$. **5.** Sample answer: $d = 60t$; A car is traveling at a rate of 60 miles per hour. **7.** yes; Sample answer: There is a constant ratio, 1.75; $y = 1.75x$.

Page 266 Lesson 4-1 Multi-Step Problem-Solving

9. $1 **11.** 20

Pages 271–272 Lesson 4-2 Independent Practice

1 D: {−6, 0, 2, 8}; R: {−9, −8, 5}

x	y
8	5
−6	−9
2	5
0	−8

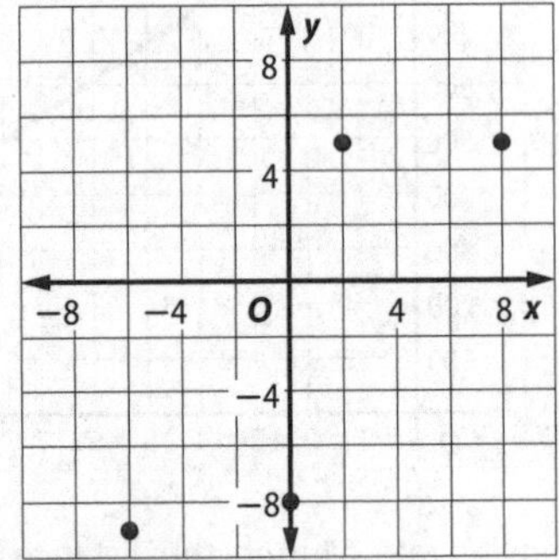

3.

x	$825x$	y
1	825(1)	825
2	825(2)	1,650
3	825(3)	2,475
4	825(4)	3,300
5	825(5)	4,125

5 **a.** To get the *y*-value, the *x*-value was multiplied by itself. **b.** (1, 1), (2, 4), (3, 9), (4, 16), (5, 25)

5c.

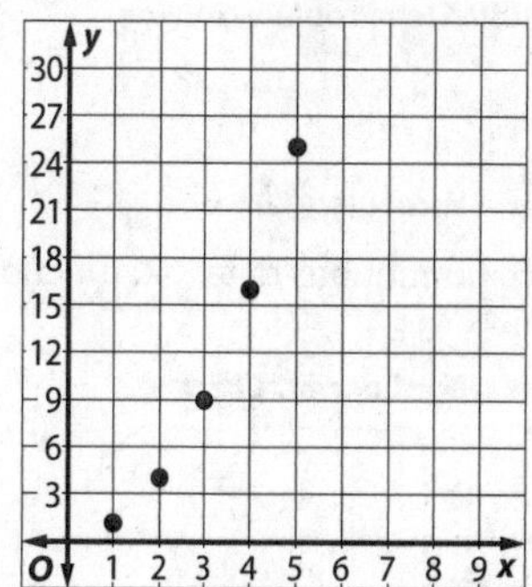

d. Sample answer: This graph curves upward. The points in all of the other graphs in the lesson lie in a straight line.

e.

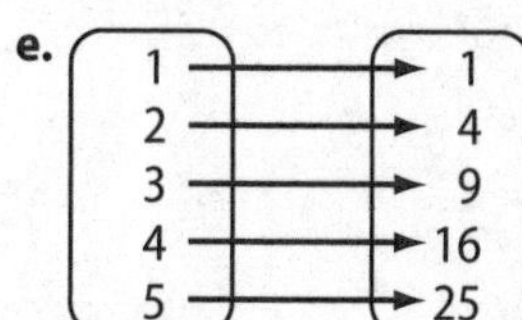

7a.

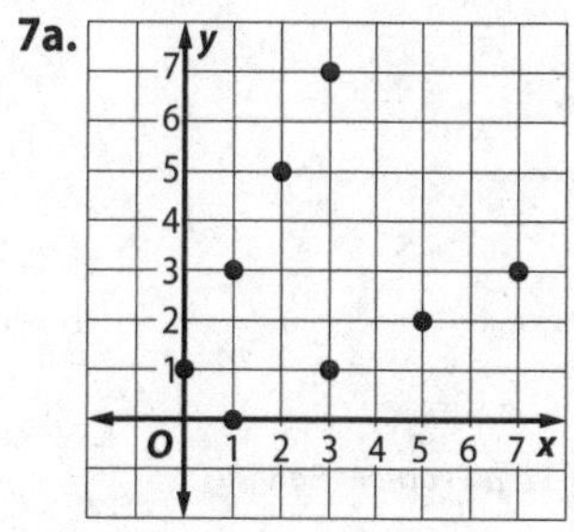

7b. (1, 0), (3, 1), (5, 2), (7, 3)
7d. Sample answer: The distance between each point in the original table and the x-axis is the same as the distance between the points with the reversed ordered pairs and the y-axis.
9. Sample answer: (1, 1), (4, 8), (9, 27), (25, 125), (36, 216)

Page 274 Lesson 4-2 Multi-Step Problem-Solving

11. B **13.** 75 songs

Pages 281–282 Lesson 4-3 Independent Practice

1. Yes; each member of the domain is mapped to exactly one member of the range. **3** Yes; each member of the domain is mapped to exactly one member of the range. **5.** Yes; each member of the domain is mapped to exactly one member of the range. **7.** No; 1 is mapped to −1 and 1, 2 is mapped to −2 and 2, 3 is mapped to −3 and 3. **9** yes; Sample answer: {(0, 0), (1, 9.50), (2, 19), (3, 28.50)} **11.** no; Sample answer: The inverse is (4, −2), (4, 2), (9, −3), (9, 3), and 4 and 9 are paired with more than one member of the range. **13.** false; Sample answer: Not all relations are functions.

Page 284 Lesson 4-3 Multi-Step Problem-Solving

15. A **17.** \$330; \$80

Page 287 Focus on Mathematical Processes

1. Sample answer: about 82% **3.** about 7.6 hours

Pages 295–296 Lesson 4-4 Independent Practice

1

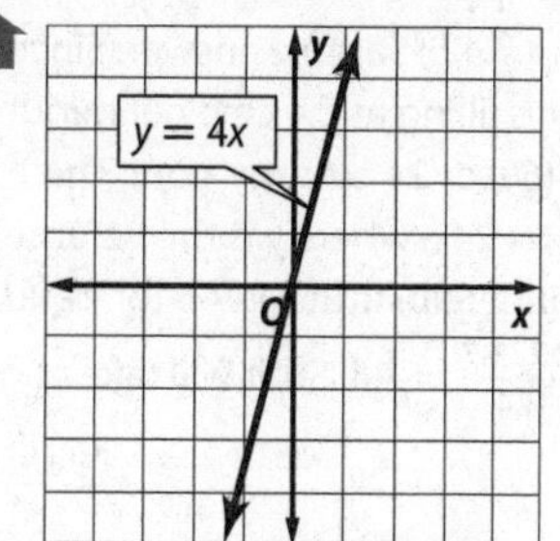

3.

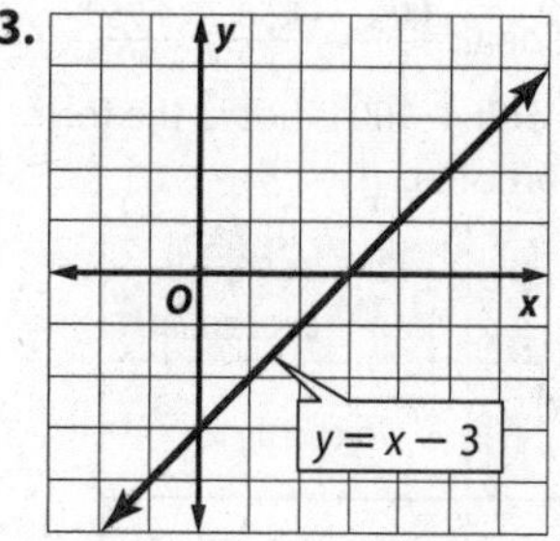

5a. bike: $c = 15 + 4.25h$; scooter: $c = 25 + 2.5h$

5b.

Mountain Bike Rental		
h	$15 + 4.25h$	c
2	15 + 4.25(2)	23.50
3	15 + 4.25(3)	27.75
4	15 + 4.25(4)	32.00
5	15 + 4.25(5)	36.25

Scooter Rental		
h	$25 + 2.5h$	c
2	25 + 2.5(2)	30.00
3	25 + 2.5(3)	32.50
4	25 + 2.5(4)	35.00
5	25 + 2.5(5)	37.50

5c.

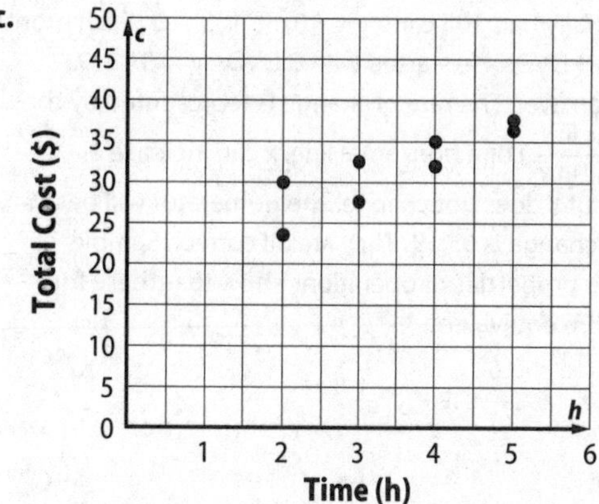

Both situations are discrete because you cannot rent either piece of equipment for a partial hour. **5d.** mountain bike **5e.** \$49 **7** 25 weeks **9.** Sample answer: (−2, −4), (0, −2), (2, 0), (4, 2); $y = x - 2$

Pages 297–298 Lesson 4-4 Multi-Step Problem-Solving

11. A **13.** 42 days **15.** about 7.4 *h*; Sample answer: Since 400 $mm^3 = 0.4$ cm^3, the water is filling at 0.4 cm^3 per minute; 0.4 cm^3 per minute equals 0.4(60) or 24 cm^3 per hour. The equation for the cup filling is $y = 24x$, where y is the volume of the cup and x is the time in hours. Substitute 177.6 for y and solve for x; $177.67 = 24x$, $x = \frac{177.67}{24} \approx 7.4$. So, it will take about 7.4 hours to fill the cup.

Pages 305–306 Lesson 4-5 Independent Practice

1 The function is non-proportional; $\frac{1.25}{1} \neq \frac{1.50}{2} \neq \frac{1.75}{3}$. **3** non-proportional; Since $c = 50h + 100$ is not in the form $y = mx$, the function is non-proportional.

5.

Situation	Proportional or Non-Proportional?
All sandwiches cost $2.50 in the school cafeteria.	proportional
A caterer charges $8 per dinner, plus a $30 booking fee.	non-proportional
A beach chair rental costs $20 for the first day and $10 days for each additional day.	non-proportional
A babysitter charges $10 per hour.	proportional

7. Sample answer: An admission price of *x* dollars per person in a car is proportional. If there is a parking fee in addition to the cost per person, the function is non-proportional. **9.** No; the relationship is not proportional. Sample answer: When Andrea is 11, her brother will be 6; $\frac{10}{5} \neq \frac{11}{6}$.

Page 308 Lesson 4-5 Multi-Step Problem-Solving

11. B **13.** 250 ft/min

Pages 313–314 Lesson 4-6 Independent Practice

1 The teacher read 100 pages per day. The teacher initially read 150 pages. **3** The class brings in 10 cans per day. The teacher initially had 105 cans; $y = 10x + 105$. **5.** Each month Jonas adds 3 DVDs. He started with 9 DVDs; $y = 3x + 9$.
7. Sample answer: The rate of change is represented by the ratio $\frac{\text{change in } y}{\text{change in } x}$. For a horizontal line, x can increase or decrease, but y does not change. The numerator will be 0, so the rate of change is 0. **9.** They are all correct; Sample answer: The properties of operations show that these four equations are equivalent.

Page 316 Lesson 4-6 Multi-Step Problem-Solving

11. C **13.** 0.7

Page 323 Chapter Review Vocabulary Check

1. relation **3.** linear **5.** Continuous data **7.** function

Page 324 Chapter Review Key Concept Check

1.

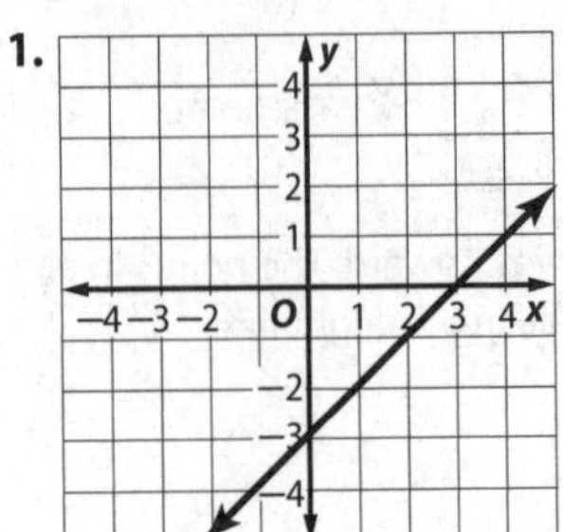

3.

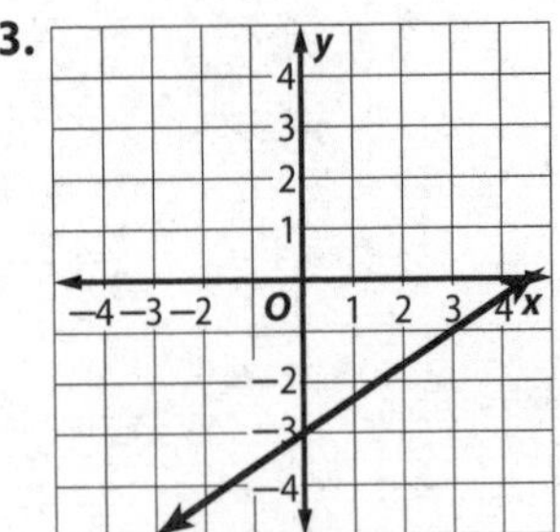

Page 325 Chapter Review Multi-Step Problem Solving

5. Sample answer: Write an equation in the form $y = mx + b$ for each person's salary. Let x represent the total amount of merchandise sold, y represent the total dollars earned, m represent the percent of commission, and b represent the salary. Solve each equation for b. Robert: $520 = 0.075(800) + b$, $b = 460$; Jasper: $525 = 0.09(750) + b$, $b = 457.5$; $460 > 457.5$

Index

21st Century Careers
car designer, 157–158
computer animator, 611–612
mastering engineer, 245–246
physical therapist, 321–322
robotics engineer, 99–100
skateboard designer, 463–464
space architect, 539–540
sports marketer, 687–688
travel agent, 389–390

Alternate exterior angles, 336
Alternate interior angles, 336, 337
Analyze, 30, 41, 46, 54, 65, 70, 118, 121, 126, 142, 149, 154, 174, 192, 200, 208, 224, 232, 240, 272, 282, 296, 314, 340, 366, 378, 386, 406, 414, 426, 438, 500, 516, 526, 536, 560, 582, 594, 606, 632, 666
Analyze and Reflect, 58, 60, 74, 112, 136, 148, 178, 218, 244, 276, 320, 334, 346, 360, 372, 420, 450, 486, 510, 520, 530, 554, 576, 588, 600, 610, 624, 636, 648, 686. *See also* Reflect; Stop and Reflect
Angle-angle similarity (AA)
defined, 122
of triangles, 121–131
indirect measurement and, 123–124
Angles, 336, 337
congruent, 114
corresponding, 336
exterior, 336
alternate, 336
of a triangle, 349–350
finding missing measures, 337
interior, 336, 348
alternate, 336, 337
parallel lines and, 335–342
in the preimage, 556
remote interior, 349
right, 362
of rotation, 576
of triangles, 343–346
Angle sum of a triangle, 348–349
Answer the Essential Question, 18, 104, 162, 250, 326, 394, 468, 544, 616, 692, 720, 724, 726, 728, 730, 732. *See also* Building on the Essential Question; Essential Question
Approximate answers, exact and, 496
Area of similar figures, 149–156
Are You Ready?, 22, 108, 166, 254, 330, 398, 472, 548, 619, 696
Associations
linear, 626, 627, 645–648
non-linear, 626, 645–648
other patterns in, 627
variable, 627

Bar notation, 26
Base of a power, 34
Biased samples, 678
Bivariate data, 626
Building on the Essential Question, 28, 36, 44, 52, 68, 78, 86, 94, 116, 124, 140, 152, 172, 182, 190, 198, 206, 222, 230, 238, 262, 270, 280, 294, 304, 312, 338, 350, 364, 376, 384, 404, 412, 424, 436, 444, 456, 478, 490, 498, 514, 524, 534, 558, 566, 580, 592, 604, 630, 640, 656, 664, 672, 680. *See also* Answer the Essential Question; Essential Question

Career Projects, 100, 158, 246, 390, 464, 540, 612, 688
Career Readiness. *See* 21st Century Careers
Center
of data distribution, 671
of dilation, 134, 138
of rotation, 578
Changes
in dimensions, 145–148, 531–538
in scale, 529–530
Chapter Review, 101–103, 159–162, 247–250, 323–325, 391–393, 465–467, 541–543, 613–616, 689–691, 717
Circles, 476
radius of, 476
Clockwise, 577
Cluster, 669
Collaborate, 723, 725, 727, 729, 731
College, saving for, 713–716
Common error, 403
Composite solids
defined, 477
volume of, 477–478, 489
Composition of transformations, 585–588
Compound interest, 701, 702
Cones
cylinders and, 488
defined, 488
modeling volume of, 483–486
volume of, 487–494
Congruence, 585, 601–608
defined, 602
determining missing measures, 604
identifying, 590–591
transformations and, 589–596, 609–610
Congruent angles, 114
Congruent figures, 556
corresponding parts of, 602
Congruent triangles, investigating, 597–600
Connect Models to Rules, 148, 346, 359, 370, 420, 475, 486, 510, 520
Connect with Economics
Business Literacy, 726
Connect with Health
Health Literacy, 724
Connect with Physical Education
Global Awareness, 732
Connect with Science
Environmental Literacy, 728
Connect with Social Studies, 730
Consistent units, 513
Constant
of proportionality, 204
of variation, 204
Constant rate of change, 169–176
Continuous data, 292

Converse, 363
of the Pythagorean Theorem, 363–364
using, in problem solving, 375–376
Coordinate plane, 267, 546
dilations in the, 138–140
distance on the, 381–388
reflections in the, 564
similar triangles and, 188
translations in the, 556
Corresponding angles, 336
Corresponding parts, 114, 602
of congruent figures, 602
Counterclockwise, 577
Counterexample, 85
Create, 30, 46, 54, 60, 74, 80, 118, 126, 148, 149, 154, 174, 178, 184, 192, 200, 208, 224, 232, 240, 244, 264, 272, 276, 282, 296, 306, 314, 320, 334, 340, 346, 352, 360, 366, 372, 378, 386, 406, 414, 420, 426, 438, 446, 450, 458, 462, 480, 486, 492, 500, 510, 516, 520, 554, 560, 568, 576, 582, 588, 594, 600, 606, 610, 624, 632, 642, 648, 658, 666, 682, 686
Credit card, 705
Cube roots, 67
estimating, 76
Cylinders
cones and, 488
defined, 476
nets of, 519–520
surface area of, 521–528
volume of, 475–482

Data
bivariate, 626
continuous, 292
discrete, 292
quantitative, 654
scatterplots in, 649–651
constructing, 623–624
trend lines in, 635–636, 637–644
univariate, 654
Data distributions
analysis of, 669–676
describing, by shape, 670
describing center and spread of, 671
skewed, 674
Debit card, 705
Decimals
repeating, 26
terminating, 26
Dependent variable, 277
Descriptive statistics, 653–660
Diagrams
drawing, 129–131
mapping, 278
Venn, 84, 86, 90
Dilations, 137–144, 590
center of, 134, 138
in the coordinate plane, 138–140
defined, 134
Dimensions, changes in, 145–148, 531–538
Direct variation, 203–210
Discrete data, 292
Distance, 382
on the coordinate plane, 381–388
formula for, 382–383
Distribution, describing, by shape, 670
Domain, 268
Drawing of diagrams, 129–131

Easy-access loans, 697
Equations. *See also* Linear equations
linear, 258
modeling, with variables on each side, 417–420
multi-step, solving, 433–440
solving, with variables on each side, 421–428
two-step
solving, 401–408
writing, 409–416
writing, for functions, 309–316
writing, to represent real-world problems, 423–424
in $y = mx + b$ form, 219–226
in $y = mx$ form, 195–202
Essential Question, 18, 19, 25, 33, 41, 49, 65, 75, 83, 91, 105, 113, 121, 137, 149, 162, 163, 169, 179, 187, 195, 203, 219, 227, 235, 250, 251, 257, 267, 289, 299, 309, 326, 327, 335, 347, 361, 373, 381, 394, 395, 401, 409, 421, 433, 441, 451, 468, 469, 475, 487, 495, 511, 521, 531, 544, 545, 563, 577, 589, 601, 616, 617, 625, 637, 653, 661, 669, 677, 693, 697, 701, 705, 709, 713, 720. *See also* Answer the Essential Question; Building on the Essential Question
Estimation, 639
of roots, 75–82
Evaluate, 30, 35, 70, 80, 118, 126, 142, 154, 174, 184, 192, 200, 208, 224, 240, 264, 282, 296, 306, 314, 352, 386, 406, 438, 446, 458, 480, 492, 500, 516, 536, 560, 568, 594, 606, 674, 682
Exact answers, approximate and, 496
Exponents
negative, 42
powers and, 33–40
Exterior angles
alternate, 336
of a triangle, 349–350
External angles, 336

Family of functions, 317
Figures
area and perimeter of similar, 149–156
congruent, 556, 602
rotation of, around apoint, 578
Financial irresponsibility, 710
Financial literacy, 207, 302, 303
Financial responsibility, 709–712
defined, 710
Find the Error, 80, 126, 184, 232, 352, 366, 426, 492, 568, 606, 658, 674
Five-number summary, 654–655
Flowchart, using, 328
Focus on Mathematical Processes. *See also* Mathematical Processes; Mathematical Process Handbook
Act It Out, 571
Draw a Diagram, 129–131
The Four-Step Plan, 61–62
Guess, Check, and Revise, 211–212
Look for a Pattern, 355–357
Make a Table, 285–286
Solve a Simpler Problem, 503–505
Use a Scatterplot, 649–651
Work Backward, 429–431
Foldables® Study Organizer, 23–24, 102, 109–110, 160, 167–168, 248, 255–256, 324, 331–332, 392, 399–400, 466, 473–474, 542, 549–550, 614, 621–622, 690, 718

Formulas
for compound interest, 702
for distance, 382–383
for slope, 181–182

Functions, 275–276, 277–284
defined, 275, 277
finding the initial value of, 310
graphing, 290–291
identifying, using mapping diagrams and ordered pairs, 278
linear, 289–298, 292
non-proportional, identifying examples of, 302–303
notation for, 290
proportional, identifying examples of, 300–301
representing, 292–293
writing equations of, 309–316
linear, 311–312

Graphing Technology Labs
Family of Linear Functions, 317–320
Linear and Non-Linear Association, 645–648
Model Linear Behavior, 243–244
Rate of Change, 177–178
Sets of Linear Equations, 449–450

Graphs
finding slope using, 180–181
of functions, 290
identifying functions using, 279
line using intercepts, 227–234

Guided Practice, 28, 36, 44, 68, 78, 86, 94, 116, 124, 140, 152, 172, 182, 190, 198, 206, 222, 230, 238, 262, 270, 280, 294, 304, 312, 338, 350, 364, 376, 384, 404, 412, 424, 436, 444, 456, 478, 490, 498, 514, 524, 534, 558, 566, 580, 592, 604, 630, 640, 656, 664, 672, 680

Hands-on Labs. *See also* Graphing Technology Labs; Virtual Manipulative Labs
Analyze Simultaneous Linear Equations, 461–462
Angles of Triangles, 343–346
changes in dimensions, 145–148
Changes in Scale, 529–530
Composition of Transformations, 585–588
Construct Scatterplots, 623–624
Investigate Congruent Triangles, 597–600
Model Dilations, 133–136
Model Right Triangle Relationships, 359–360
Model Trend Lines, 635–636
Model Volume of Cones, 483–486
Nets of Cylinders, 519–520
Nets of Prisms, 507–510
Parallel Lines, 333–334
Proportional and Non-Proportional Relationships, 215–218
Relations and Functions, 275–276
Roots of Non-Perfect Squares, 73–74
Rotational Symmetry, 575–584
Scientific Notation using Technology, 57–60
Similar Triangles, 111–112
Transformations, 551–554
Transformations and Congruence, 609–610
Verify the Pythagorean Theorem, 369–372

Hemispheres
defined, 497
volume of, 497–498

H.O.T. (Higher-Order Thinking), 30, 38, 46, 54, 70, 80, 88, 96, 118, 126, 142, 154, 174, 184, 200, 208, 224, 232, 240, 264, 272, 282, 296, 306, 314, 340, 352, 366, 378, 386, 406, 414, 426, 438, 446, 458, 480, 492, 500, 516, 526, 536, 560, 568, 582, 594, 606, 632, 642, 658, 666, 674, 682

Hypotenuse, 361

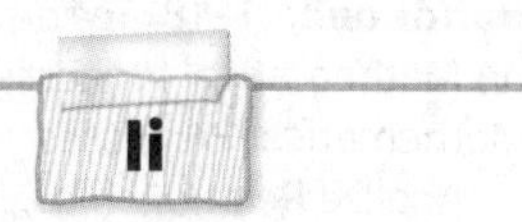

Identity, 434

Image, 555

Independent Practice, 29–30, 37–38, 45–46, 53–54, 69–70, 79, 87–88, 95–96, 117–118, 125–126, 141–142, 153–154, 173–174, 183–184, 191–192, 199–200, 207–208, 223–224, 231–232, 239–240, 263–264, 271–272, 281–282, 295, 305–306, 313–314, 339–340, 351–352, 365–366, 377–378, 385–386, 405–406, 413–414, 425–426, 437–438, 445–446, 457–458, 479–480, 491–492, 499–500, 515–516, 525–526, 535–536, 559–560, 567–568, 581–582, 593–594, 605–606, 631–632, 641–642, 657–658, 665–666, 673–674, 681–682, 699, 703, 707, 711, 715

Independent variables, 277

Indirect measurement, 123–124

Inequalities, 76
with variables on each side, 441–448
writing, to represent real-world problems, 442
writing real-world problems given, 443

Inquiry, 60, 73, 74, 111, 112, 133, 136, 145, 148, 177, 178, 215, 218, 243, 244, 275, 276, 317, 320, 333, 334, 343, 346, 359, 360, 369, 372, 420, 449, 450, 461, 462, 483, 486, 507, 510, 519, 520, 529, 530, 551, 554, 575, 576, 585, 588, 597, 600, 609, 610, 623, 624, 635, 636, 645, 648, 685, 686

Intercepts, 455
graphing a line using, 227–234

Interest, 694
compound, 701, 702
simple, 701, 702

Interest rate, 697

Interior angles, 336, 348
alternate, 336, 337
remote, 349

Interquartile range, 655

Investigate, 58, 60, 74, 112, 113, 135, 147, 149, 178, 187, 217, 244, 276, 319, 334, 344, 360, 370, 372, 419, 450, 462, 485, 509, 520, 530, 553, 563, 576, 587, 589, 599, 610, 624, 636, 647, 686. *See also* Real-World Investigation

Irrational numbers, 84, 85

Isometries, 590

Key Concept(s), 26, 42, 67, 114, 122, 138, 150, 171, 181, 189, 236, 237, 260, 268, 278, 292, 336, 348, 349, 362, 382, 434, 476, 488, 496, 512, 522, 532, 533, 556, 564, 579, 602

Key Concept Check, 64, 102, 132, 160, 214, 248, 288, 358, 392, 432, 466, 506, 542, 574, 614, 652, 690, 718

Lateral area, 512, 522

Launch the Lesson
- Real World, 33, 41, 49, 75, 83, 91, 113, 121, 149, 169, 187, 195, 203, 219, 227, 235, 257, 289, 299, 309, 347, 361, 373, 381, 409, 421, 433, 441, 451, 475, 487, 511, 521, 531, 563, 577, 589, 601, 637, 661, 697, 701, 709, 713
- Vocabulary, 65, 137, 179, 267, 335, 401, 555, 625, 653, 669, 705

Legs, 361

Linear association, 626, 627, 645–648

Linear behavior, modeling, 243–244

Linear equations, 258
- point-slope form of, 236
- sets of, 449–450
- solving simultaneous, 451–460
- writing, 235–242

Linear functions, 289–298
- family of, 317–320
- writing equations of, 311–312

Linear non-proportional relationships, 259
- multiple representations of, 260–261

Linear proportional relationships, 258
- multiple representations of, 260–261

Linear relationships, 170
- proportional, 171–172, 196

Lines
- graphing, using intercepts, 227–234
- parallel, 333–334, 335–342
- perpendicular, 336
- of reflection, 564
- slope-intercept form of a, 220–221

Line segments, 556

Line symmetry, 563

Loans, 697, 705
- calculating the total cost to repay, 698
- easy-access, 697
- interest rates and, 697–70

Mapping diagrams, identifying functions using, 278

Mathematical Processes. *See also* Focus on Mathematical Processes; Mathematical Processes Handbook
- Analyze Relationships, 14, 30, 58, 74, 112, 136, 148, 191, 208, 218, 240, 244, 320, 334, 344, 346, 351, 360, 372, 405, 413, 420, 437, 450, 458, 462, 492, 515, 530, 554, 567, 576, 600, 605, 624, 636, 648, 666, 674, 686
- Apply Math to the Real World, 4, 6, 74, 118, 224, 272, 282, 340, 406, 438, 479, 526, 560, 582, 632, 636, 642, 699
- Justify Arguments, 16, 46, 183, 244, 377, 515, 536, 554, 559
- Organize Ideas, 12, 88, 136, 142, 154, 218, 306, 344, 366, 378, 588, 681
- Select Tools and Techniques, 8, 58, 60, 64, 74, 112, 132, 134, 136, 192, 214, 244, 276, 296, 334, 360, 372, 419, 420, 450, 462, 552, 574, 610, 624, 647, 652, 686
- Use a Problem-Solving Model, 80, 117, 125, 208, 408, 500, 518, 536, 538, 666, 700, 708, 712, 716
- Use Multiple Representations, 200, 218, 223, 240
- algebra, 264, 314, 426
- equations, 294, 295
- geometry, 593
- graphs, 184, 232, 264, 271, 294, 295, 314, 386, 593, 658
- mapping, 271
- numbers, 184, 264, 271, 314, 386, 480, 593, 658
- symbols, 232, 426, 480
- tables, 264, 294, 295
- words, 184, 232, 271, 294, 295, 314, 386, 426, 480, 593

Mathematical Processes Handbook, 1–18. *See also* Focus on Mathematical Processes; Mathematical Processes
- Analize Relationships, 13–14
- Apply Math to the Real World, 3–4
- Justify Arguments, 15–16
- Organize Ideas, 11–12
- Select Tools and Techniques, 7–8
- Use a Problem-Solving Model, 5–6
- Use Multiple Representations, 9–10

Math in the Real World, 19, 105, 163, 251, 327, 395, 469, 545, 617, 693

Mean, 654, 671

Mean absolute deviation, 661–668
- comparing variation, 663–664
- defined, 662
- determining, 662

Measures of center and variability, 654

Median, 654

Mid-Chapter Check, 64, 132, 214, 288, 358, 432, 506, 574, 652

Mirror image, 563

Mode, 654

Models
- connecting to rules, 148, 346, 359, 370, 420, 475, 486, 510, 520
- of dilations, 133–136

Multiple representations of linear proportional and non-proportional relationships, 260–261

Multi-step equations
- number of solutions, 434
- solving, 433–440

Multi-Step Example, 27–28, 151–152, 205–206, 259–260, 338, 436, 477, 497, 513, 603, 604, 698

Multi-Step Problem Solving, 31–32, 39–40, 47–48, 55–56, 63, 64, 71–72, 81–82, 89–90, 97–98, 103, 119–120, 127–128, 132, 143–144, 155–156, 161, 175–176, 185–186, 193–194, 201–202, 209–213, 214, 225–226, 233–234, 241–242, 249, 265–266, 273–274, 283–286, 288, 297–298, 307–308, 315–316, 325, 341–342, 353–356, 357, 367–368, 379–380, 387–388, 393, 407–408, 415–416, 427–428, 429–431, 432, 439–440, 447–448, 459–460, 467, 481–482, 493–494, 501–505, 506, 517–518, 527–528, 537–538, 543, 561–562, 569–573, 574, 583–584, 595–596, 607–608, 633–634, 643–644, 649–650, 651, 652, 659–660, 667–668, 675–676, 683–684, 691, 700, 704, 708, 712, 716
- analyze, 31, 39, 47, 55, 71, 81, 89, 97, 103, 119, 127, 129, 130, 143, 155, 161, 175, 185, 193, 201, 209, 211, 212, 225, 233, 241, 249, 265, 273, 283, 285, 286, 297, 307, 315, 325, 341, 353, 355, 356, 367, 379, 387, 393, 407, 415, 427, 429, 430, 439, 447, 459, 467, 481, 493, 501, 503, 504, 517, 527, 537, 543, 561, 569, 571, 572, 583, 595, 607, 615, 633, 643, 649, 650, 659, 667, 675, 683, 691, 719
- justify and evaluate, 31, 39, 47, 55, 71, 81, 89, 97, 103, 119, 127, 129, 130, 143, 155, 161, 175, 185, 193, 201, 209, 211, 212, 225, 233, 241, 249, 265, 273, 283, 285, 286, 297,

307, 315, 325, 341, 353, 355, 356, 367, 379, 387, 393, 407, 415, 427, 429, 430, 439, 447, 459, 467, 481, 493, 501, 503, 504, 517, 527, 537, 543, 561, 569, 571, 572, 583, 595, 607, 615, 633, 643, 649, 650, 659, 667, 675, 683, 691, 719
plan, 31, 39, 47, 55, 71, 81, 89, 97, 103, 119, 127, 129, 130, 143, 155, 161, 175, 185, 193, 201, 209, 211, 212, 225, 233, 241, 249, 265, 273, 283, 285, 286, 297, 307, 315, 325, 341, 353, 355, 356, 367, 379, 387, 393, 407, 415, 427, 429, 430, 439, 447, 459, 467, 481, 493, 501, 503, 504, 517, 527, 537, 543, 561, 569, 571, 572, 583, 595, 607, 615, 633, 643, 649, 650, 659, 667, 675, 683, 691, 719
solve, 31, 39, 47, 55, 71, 81, 89, 97, 103, 119, 127, 129, 130, 143, 155, 161, 175, 185, 193, 201, 209, 211, 212, 225, 233, 241, 249, 265, 273, 283, 285, 286, 297, 307, 315, 325, 341, 353, 355, 356, 367, 379, 387, 393, 407, 415, 427, 429, 430, 439, 447, 459, 467, 481, 493, 501, 503, 504, 517, 527, 537, 543, 561, 569, 571, 572, 583, 595, 607, 615, 633, 643, 649, 650, 659, 667, 675, 683, 691, 719

Negative exponents, 42
variables with, 43
Nets
of cylinders, 519–520
defined, 507
of prisms, 507–510
Non-linear association, 626, 645–648
Non-perfect squares, roots of, 73–74
Non-proportional functions, identifying examples of, 302–303
Non-proportional relationships, 215–218
Non-symmetric distribution, 670
Notation
bar, 26
function, 290
scientific, 49–60
Null set, 434
Numbers
irrational, 84, 85
rational, 25, 84, 85
real, 84

Ordered pairs, identifying functions using, 278
Orientation, 552, 585
Origin, 267
rotations about the, 579
Outlier, 669

Parallel lines, 333–334
angle relationships and, 335–342
Pattern, looking for a, 355–357
Payment methods, 705–708
disadvantages and advantages of, 706
Peak, 669
Perfect cubes, 67
Perfect squares, 65
Perimeter of similar figures, 149–156
Periodic deposit calculators, 714
Periodic savings plan, 714
Perpendicular lines, 336
Personal Financial Literacy, 693–720
Personal Financial Literacy Projects
College Savings, 716
Compare Payment Methods, 708
Financial Responsibility, 712
Plan for Retirement, 704
Use an Online Loan Calculator, 700
Point, rotation of figure about a, 578
Point-slope form of a linear equation, 236
Polygons, properties of similar, 113–120
Population, 677
Powers
exponents and, 33–40
negative, 42
of ten, 50
Predictions
using sampling for making, 679
using trend lines to make, 637–644
Preimage, 556
angles in the, 556
defined, 555
Prime symbols, 556
Principal, 701
Prisms
surface area of, 511–518
rectangular, 512
triangular, 513–514
Problem solving
using the converse of the Pythagorean Theorem in, 375–376
using the Pythagorean Theorem in, 374–375
Problem-Solving Projects
Design that Ride, 729–730
Green Thumb, 727–728
Music to My Ears, 723–724
Olympic Games, 731–732
Web Design 101, 725–726
Projects. *See* Career Projects; Problem-Solving Projects
Properties, defined, 401
Proportional functions, identifying examples of, 300–301
Proportional linear relationships, 171–172, 196
Proportional relationships, 171, 215–218
Pythagorean Theorem, 361–368
converse of, 363–364
using, in problem solving, 375–376
using, 373–380
in problem solving, 374–375
verifying, 369–372

Quartiles, 654

Radical sign √, 66
Radius of circles, 476
Random samples, 677–684

simulating, 685–686
Range, 268, 654
interquartile, 655
Rate of change, constant, 169–176
Rates, 164
unit, 164, 170
Rate Yourself!, 28, 36, 44, 52, 68, 78, 86, 94, 116, 124, 140, 152, 172, 182, 190, 198, 206, 222, 230, 238, 262, 270, 280, 294, 304, 312, 338, 350, 364, 376, 384, 404, 412, 424, 436, 444, 456, 478, 490, 498, 514, 524, 534, 558, 566, 580, 592, 604, 630, 640, 656, 664, 672, 680
Rational numbers, 25–32, 84, 85
defined, 25
Ratios, 25, 41
Reading Math, 252
topic sentences, 618
Read to Succeed!, 31, 39, 47, 55, 71, 81, 89, 97, 119, 127, 143, 155, 175, 185, 193, 201, 209, 225, 233, 241, 265, 273, 283, 297, 307, 315, 341, 353, 367, 379, 387, 407, 415, 427, 439, 447, 459, 481, 493, 501, 517, 527, 537, 561, 569, 583, 595, 607, 633, 643, 659, 667, 675, 683
Real numbers
comparing, 92
defined, 84
ordering, 93
sets of, 85
Real number system, 83–90
Real-World Investigation, 555, 625, 653, 705. *See also* Investigate
Real-World Link, 25, 65, 137, 179, 267, 335, 361, 401, 495, 669, 677
Real-world problems
writing, given inequalities, 443
writing equation to represent, 423–424
writing inequalities to represent, 442
Rectangular prism, surface area of, 512
Reflect, 18, 104, 162, 250, 326, 394, 468, 544, 616, 692, 720, 724, 726, 728, 730, 732. *See also* Analyze and Reflect; Stop and Reflect
Reflections, 563–570
in the coordinate plane, 564
defined, 564
Relations, 275–276
defined, 268
domain of, 268
range of, 268
Relationships
linear non-proportional, 259, 260–261
linear proportional, 258, 260–261
non-proportional, 215–218
proportional, 171, 215–218
proportional linear, 171–17, 196
representing, 257–266
Remote interior angles, 349
Repeating decimal, 26
Review Vocabulary, 164, 470, 546, 694
Right angles, 362
Right triangles
hypotenuse of, 361
legs of, 361
modeling relationships, 359–360
Roots
cube, 67
estimating, 75–82
of non-perfect squares, 73–74
square, 65, 66
Rotational symmetry, 575–584
defined, 575
Rotations, 577–584
about the origin, 579
center of, 578
defined, 578
description of, 578
of figure about a point, 578
Rules, connecting models to, 148, 346, 359, 370, 420, 475, 486, 510, 520

Samples, 677
biased, 678
in making predictions, 679
random, 677–684
unbiased, 678
Saving for college, 713–716
Scale, changes in, 529–530
Scale factor, 115–116, 133, 137, 139, 145, 151
Scatterplots
association and, 625–634
constructing, 623–624, 626
defined, 626
using, 649–651
Scientific notation, 49–56
defined, 50
using technology, 57–60
Segments, 348
Sets
of linear equations, 449–450
of real numberss, 85
Shadow reckoning, 123
Shape, describing distribution by, 670
Share, 724, 726, 728, 730, 732
Shopping: payment methods, 705–708
Similar figures, area and perimeter of, 149–156
Similar polygons
defined, 114
determining missing measures, 115–116
properties of, 113–120
Similar solids
defined, 532
surface area of, 532
volume of, 533–534
Similar triangles, 111–112
coordinate plane and, 188
slope and, 187–194
Simple interest, 701, 702
Simultaneous linear equations, 452
analyzing, 461–462
number of solutions for, 454–455
solving, 451–460
Skewed distribution, 674
Slope, 179–186, 455
defined, 181
finding, using a graph or table, 180–181
formula for, 181–182
interpreting, 221–222
similar triangles and, 187–194
Slope-intercept form of a line, 220–221, 228
Solve a simpler problem, 503–505
Spheres
defined, 495
volume of, 495–502
Square roots, 65, 66
estimating, 76
Squares, perfect, 65
Standard form, 229
Statements, writing equations to represent, 410
Statistics, descriptive, 653–660
STEM, 43, 46, 51, 52, 78, 79, 117, 140, 239, 404
Stop and Reflect, 43, 77, 84, 122,

139, 189, 229, 261, 293, 337, 349, 364, 384, 410, 435, 476, 489, 534, 565, 579, 591, 603, 638. *See also* Analyze and Reflect; Reflect

Stored-value card, 705

Surface area
- of cylinders, 521–528
- defined, 512
- of prisms, 511–518
  - rectangular, 512
  - triangular, 513–514
- of similar solids, 532
- total, 522

Surveys, 677

Symbols
- radical sign √, 66

Symmetric distribution, 670

Symmetry, rotational, 575–584

System of equations, 452

Tables
- finding slope using, 180–181
- identifying, using tables and graphs, 279
- identifying functions using, 279
- making, in problem solving, 285–286

Tables, graphs, and equations in the form $y = mx$, 258

Technology, scientific notation using, 57–60

Terminating decimal, 26

Texas Essential Knowledge and Skills
- Mathematical Processes, 19, 25, 33, 41, 49, 57, 61, 65, 73, 75, 83, 91, 99, 105, 111, 113, 121, 133, 137, 145, 149, 157, 163, 169, 179, 187, 195, 203, 211, 215, 219, 227, 235, 243, 245, 251, 257, 267, 275, 277, 285, 289, 299, 309, 317, 327, 335, 343, 347, 355, 359, 361, 373, 381, 395, 401, 409, 417, 421, 433, 441, 449, 451, 461, 469, 475, 483, 487, 495, 503, 507, 511, 519, 521, 529, 531, 539, 545, 551, 555, 563, 571, 575, 577, 585, 589, 597, 601, 609, 611, 617, 623, 625, 635, 637, 645, 649, 653, 661, 669, 677, 685, 687, 693, 697, 701, 705, 709, 713
- Math Symbols, 137
- Targeted TEKS, 3, 5, 7, 11, 13, 15, 19, 25, 33, 41, 49, 57, 61, 65, 73, 75, 83, 91, 105, 111, 113, 121, 133, 137, 145, 149, 163, 169, 179, 187, 195, 203, 211, 215, 219, 227, 235, 243, 251, 257, 267, 275, 277, 285, 289, 299, 309, 317, 327, 335, 343, 347, 355, 359, 361, 373, 381, 395, 401, 409, 417, 421, 433, 441, 449, 451, 461, 469, 475, 483, 487, 495, 503, 507, 511, 519, 521, 529, 531, 539, 545, 551, 555, 563, 571, 575, 577, 585, 589, 597, 601, 609, 611, 617, 623, 625, 635, 637, 645, 649, 653, 661, 669, 677, 685, 687, 693, 697, 701, 705, 709, 713, 723, 725, 727, 729, 731

Theorem, 362

Total surface area, 522

Transformations, 551–554
- composition of, 585–588
- congruence and, 589–596, 609–610
- defined, 555
- determining, 591

Translations, 555–562
- in the coordinate plane, 556
- defined, 555

Transversal, 333, 336

Trend lines
- defined, 638
- modeling, 635–636
- using, to make predictions, 637–644

Triangles
- angle-angle similarity of, 121–131
- angles of, 343–346
- angle sum of, 348–349
- exterior angles of, 349–350
- formation of, 348
- similar, 111–112

Triangular prisms, surface area of, 513–514

Two-step equations
- defined, 402
- solving, 401–408
- writing, 409–416
  - to represent statements, 410

Unbiased samples, 678

Unit rates, 164, 170

Units, consistent, 513

Univariate data, 654

Use a Mnemonic Device, 20

Use a Web, 106

Variable associations, 627

Variables
- defining the, 412
- dependent, 277
- independent, 277
- inequalities with, on each side, 441–448
- modeling equations with, on each side, 417–420
- with negative exponents, 43
- solving equations, with on each side, 421–428

Variation, direct, 203–210

Venn diagrams, 84, 86, 90

Virtual Manipulative Labs
- Model Equations with Variables on Each Side, 417–420
- Simulate Random Samples, 685–686

Vocabulary, 20, 25, 33, 49, 65, 83, 106, 113, 121, 133, 164, 169, 179, 203, 219, 227, 235, 252, 257, 267, 289, 317, 328, 335, 347, 361, 381, 396, 401, 433, 441, 451, 470, 475, 487, 495, 507, 511, 521, 531, 546, 551, 563, 575, 577, 585, 601, 618, 625, 637, 653, 661, 669, 677, 694, 697, 701, 705, 709, 713. *See also* Launch the Lesson; Review Vocabulary; Vocabulary Check

Vocabulary Check, 64, 101, 132, 159, 214, 247, 288, 323, 358, 391, 432, 465, 506, 541, 574, 613, 652, 689, 717

Volume
- of composite solids, 477–478, 489
- of cones, 487–494
  - modeling, 483–486
- of cylinders, 475–482
- defined, 476
- of hemispheres, 497–498

of similar solids, 533–534
of spheres, 495–502

Web, using a, 106
What Tools Do You Need?, 20, 106, 164, 252, 328, 396, 470, 546, 618, 694
When Will You Use This?, 21, 107, 165, 253, 329, 397, 471, 547, 619, 695
Which One Doesn't Belong?, 378, 458, 568
Work Backward, 429–431
Work with a partner, 319, 370, 372, 462, 485, 509, 530, 541, 624, 636, 647, 648
Writing Math
Justify Your Answer, 396

***x*-axis,** 267
***x*-coordinates,** 267, 565
***x*-intercept,** 228, 229

***y*-axis,** 267
***y*-coordinates,** 219, 565
***y*-intercept,** 473
interpreting, 221–222

Zero, 42

Name ______________________________

0 1 2 3 4 5 6 7 8 9

–11 –10 –9 –8 –7 –6 –5 –4 –3 –2 –1 0 1 2 3 4 5 6 7 8 9 10 11

Name ____

Name ______________________________

What are VKVs® and How Do I Create Them?

Visual Kinethestic Vocabulary Cards® are flashcards that animate words by focusing on their structure, use, and meaning. The VKVs in this book are used to show cognates, or words that are similar in Spanish and English.

Step 1

Go to the back of your book to find the VKVs for the chapter vocabulary you are currently studying. Follow the cutting and folding instructions at the top of the page. The vocabulary word on the BLUE background is written in English. The Spanish word is on the ORANGE background.

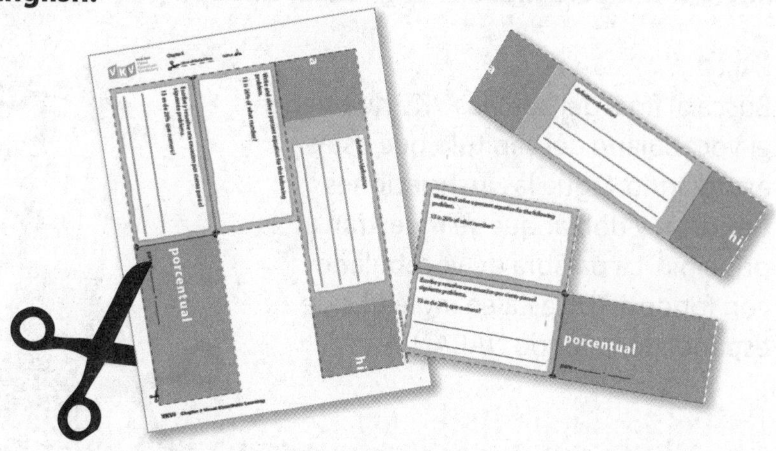

Step 2

There are exercises for you to complete on the VKVs. When you understand the concept, you can complete each exercise. All exercises are written in English and Spanish. You only need to give the answer once.

Step 3

Individualize your VKV by writing notes, sketching diagrams, recording examples, and forming plurals (radius: radii or radiuses).

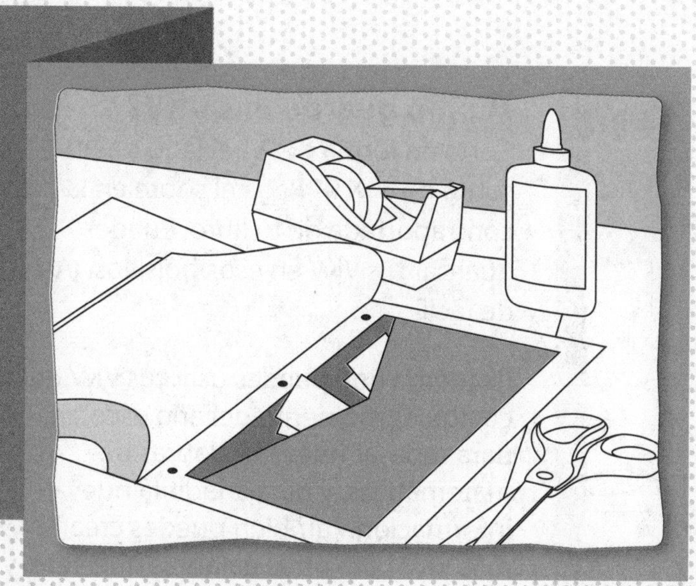

How Do I Store My VKVs?

Take a 6" x 9" envelope and cut away a V on one side only. Glue the envelope into the back cover of your book. Your VKVs can be stored in this pocket!

Remember you can use your VKVs ANY time in the school year to review new words in math, and add new information you learn. Why not create your own VKVs for other words you see and share them with others!

¿Qué son las VKV y cómo se crean?

Las tarjetas de vocabulario visual y cinético (VKV) contienen palabras con animación que está basada en la estructura, uso y significado de las palabras. Las tarjetas de este libro sirven para mostrar cognados, que son palabras similares en español y en inglés.

Paso 1

Busca al final del libro las VKV que tienen el vocabulario del capítulo que estás estudiando. Sigue las instrucciones de cortar y doblar que se muestran al principio. La palabra de vocabulario con fondo AZUL está en inglés. La de español tiene fondo NARANJA.

Paso 2

Hay ejercicios para que completes con las VKV. Cuando entiendas el concepto, puedes completar cada ejercicio. Todos los ejercicios están escritos en inglés y español. Solo tienes que dar la respuesta una vez.

Paso 3

Da tu toque personal a las VKV escribiendo notas, haciendo diagramas, grabando ejemplos y formando plurales (radio: radios).

¿Cómo guardo mis VKV?

Corta en forma de "V" el lado de un sobre de 6" X 9". Pega el sobre en la contraportada de tu libro. Puedes guardar tus VKV en esos bolsillos. ¡Así de fácil!

Recuerda que puedes usar tus VKV en cualquier momento del año escolar para repasar nuevas palabras de matemáticas, y para añadir la nueva información. También puedes crear más VKV para otras palabras que veas, y poder compartirlas con los demás.

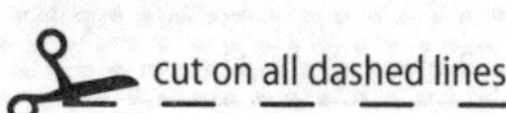

Define exponent. (Define exponente.)

exponente

b^x

base

Define base. (Define base.)

racional

Circle the irrational number.

Spanish Translation

$\frac{5}{8}$ -6.5 12%

$\sqrt{8}$ $0.2222\ldots$

irrational number

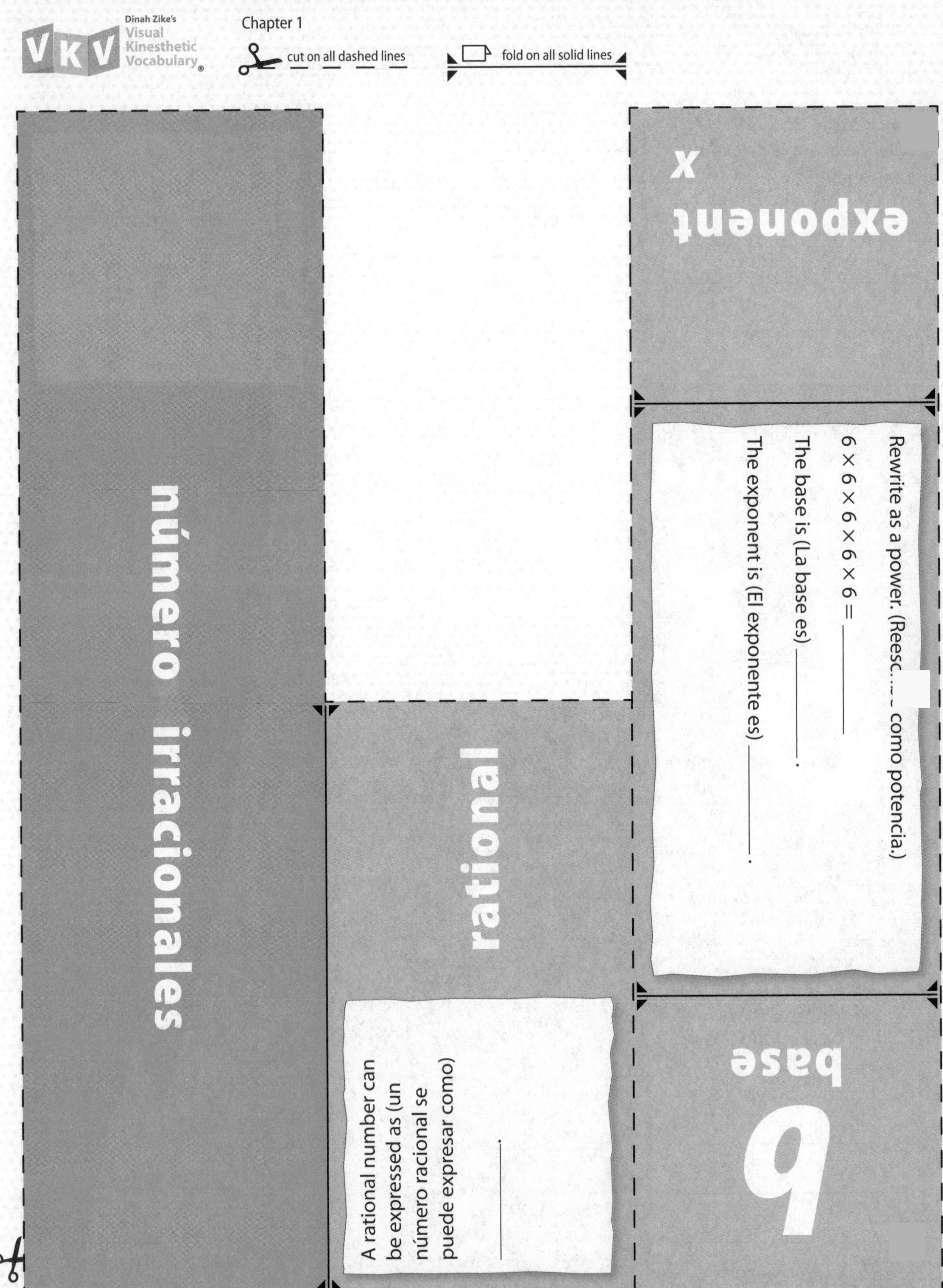

Dinah Zike's
VKV
Visual Kinesthetic Vocabulary®
Chapter 1
cut on all dashed lines
fold on all solid lines
exponent
x
número irracionales
Rewrite as a power. (Reesc como potencia.)
6 × 6 × 6 × 6 × 6 = ____
The base is (La base es) ____.
The exponent is (El exponente es) ____.
rational
A rational number can be expressed as (un número racional se puede expresar como)
____.
base
b

cut on all dashed lines

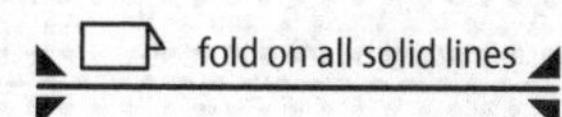

fold on all solid lines

Circle the correct phrase to complete the sentence below.

If the scale factor is less than 1, the image is (an enlargement, a reduction) of the preimage.

scale factor

Encierra en un círculo la frase que completa correctamente la siguiente oración.

Si el factor de escala es menor que 1, la imagen es (más grande, más pequeña) que la preimagen.

Dinah Zike's
VKV
Visual
Kinesthetic
Vocabulary®

Chapter 2

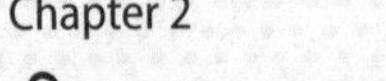

cut on all dashed lines

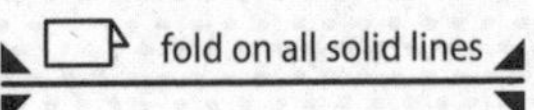
fold on all solid lines

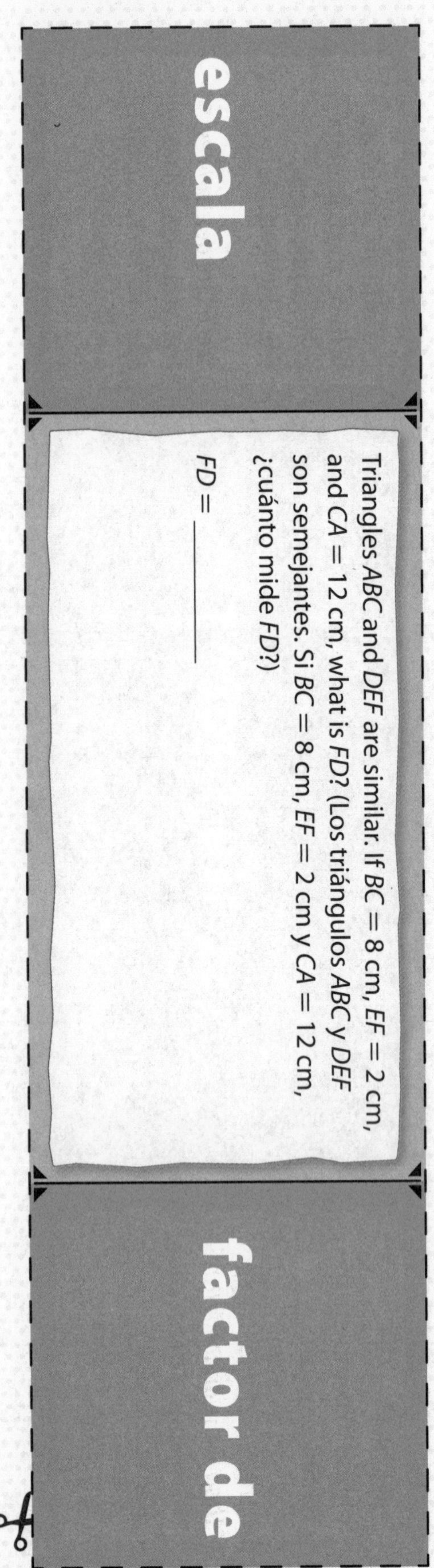
escala
Triangles *ABC* and *DEF* are similar. If *BC* = 8 cm, *EF* = 2 cm,
and *CA* = 12 cm, what is *FD*? (Los triángulos *ABC* y *DEF*
son semejantes. Si *BC* = 8 cm, *EF* = 2 cm y *CA* = 12 cm,
¿cuánto mide *FD*?)
FD = ______
factor de

Dinah Zike's Visual Kinesthetic Vocabulary®

Chapter 3

cut on all dashed lines

fold on all solid lines

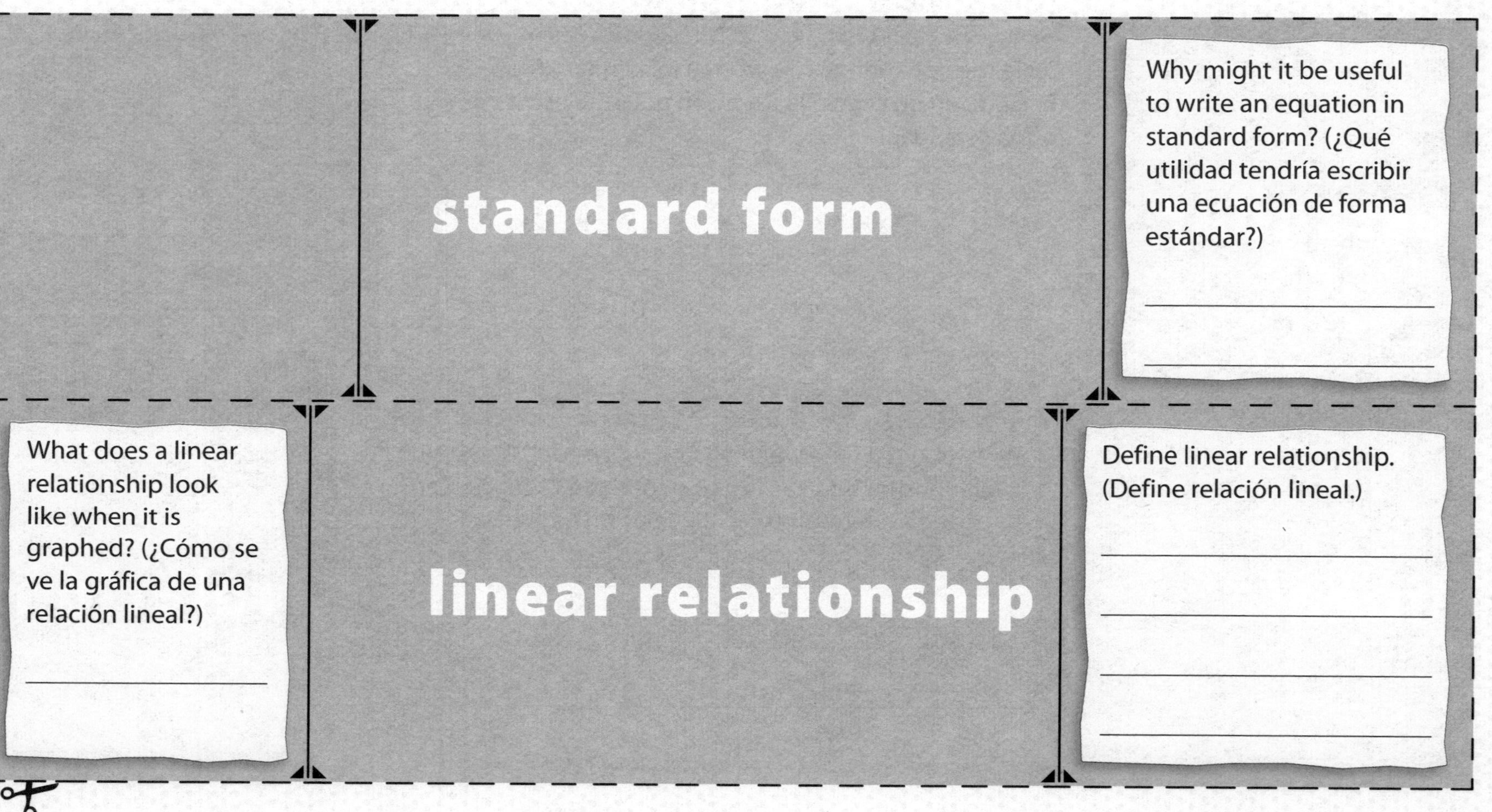

standard form
Why might it be useful to write an equation in standard form? (¿Qué utilidad tendría escribir una ecuación de forma estándar?)
What does a linear relationship look like when it is graphed? (¿Cómo se ve la gráfica de una relación lineal?)
linear relationship
Define linear relationship. (Define relación lineal.)

Dinah Zike's VKV Visual Kinesthetic Vocabulary®

Chapter 3

cut on all dashed lines

fold on all solid lines

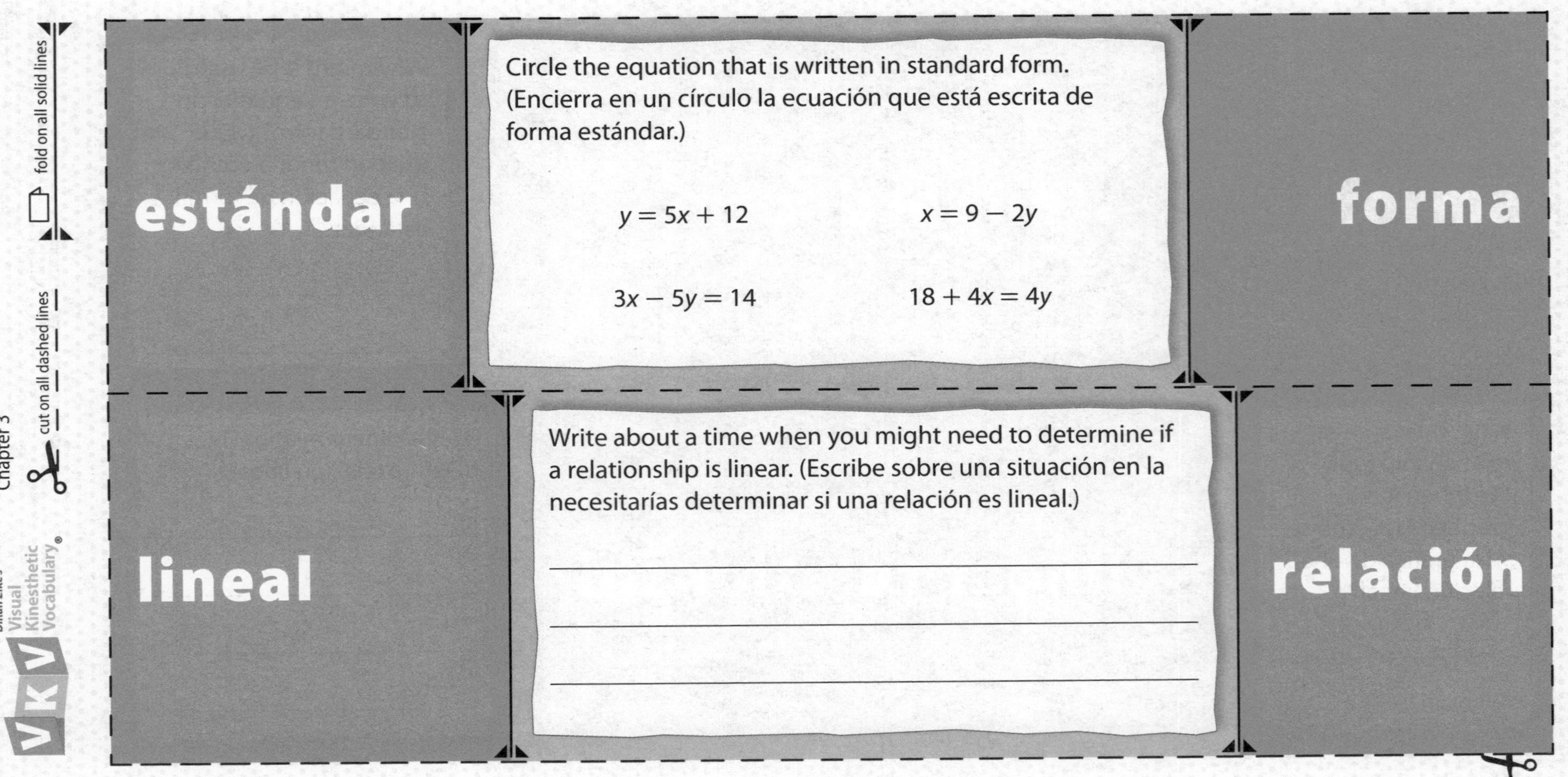

estándar
Circle the equation that is written in standard form. (Encierra en un círculo la ecuación que está escrita de forma estándar.)
y = 5x + 12
x = 9 − 2y
3x − 5y = 14
18 + 4x = 4y
forma
lineal
Write about a time when you might need to determine if a relationship is linear. (Escribe sobre una situación en la necesitarías determinar si una relación es lineal.)
relación

cut on all dashed lines

fold on all solid lines

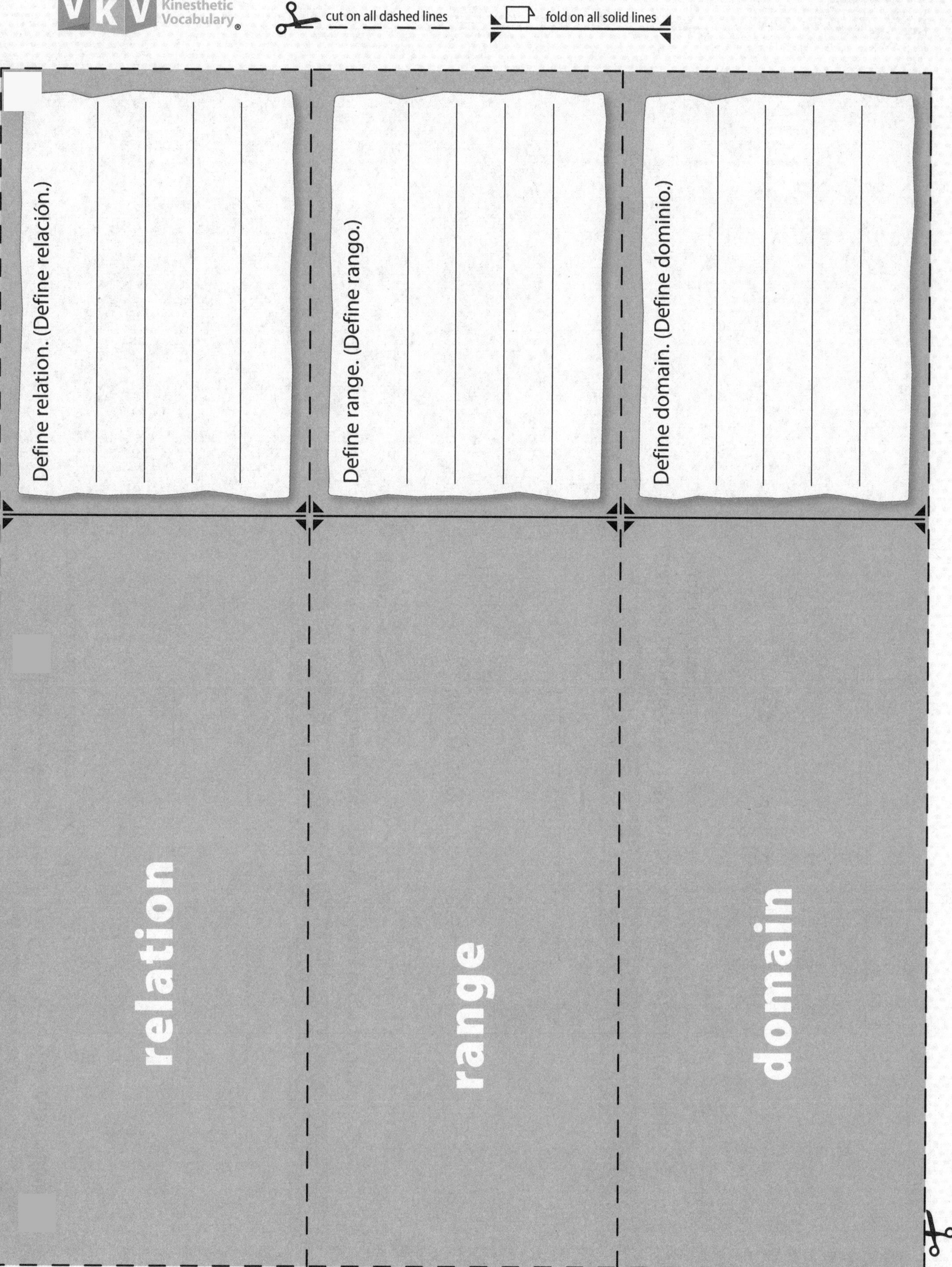
Define relation. (Define relación.)
Define range. (Define rango.)
Define domain. (Define dominio.)
relation
range
domain

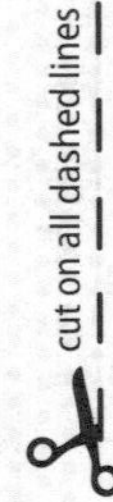
cut on all dashed lines
fold on all solid lines

ción

Find four ered pairs for the relation $y = x + 4$. (Enumera cuatro pare ordenados de la relación $y = x + 4$.)

(______, ______), (______, ______),

(______, ______), (______, ______),

o

State the range of the relation below. (Calcula el rango de la siguiente relación.)

{(6, –2), (8, 0), (12, 2), (18, 6)}

{______, ______, ______, ______}

inio

State the domain of the relation below. (Calcula el dominio de la siguiente relación.)

{(–5, 4), (–7, 3), (–12, 11), (–14, 13)}

{______, ______, ______, ______}

Grade 8 Mathematics Reference Materials

LENGTH					
	Customary			Metric	
1 mile (mi)	=	1,760 yards (yd)	1 kilometer (km)	=	1,000 meters (m)
1 yard (yd)	=	3 feet (ft)	1 meter (m)	=	100 centimeters (cm)
1 foot (ft)	=	12 inches (in.)	1 centimeter (cm)	=	10 millimeters (mm)

VOLUME AND CAPACITY					
	Customary			Metric	
1 gallon (gal)	=	4 quarts (qt)	1 liter (L)	=	1,000 milliliters (mL)
1 quart (qt)	=	2 pints (pt)			
1 pint (pt)	=	2 cups (c)			
1 cup (c)	=	8 fluid ounces (fl oz)			

WEIGHT AND MASS					
	Customary			Metric	
1 ton (T)	=	2,000 pounds (lb)	1 kilogram (kg)	=	1,000 grams (g)
1 pound (lb)	=	16 ounces (oz)	1 gram (g)	=	1,000 milligrams (mg)

Inches 0 1 2 3 4 5 6

Grade 8 Mathematics Reference Materials

Centimeters: 0 1 2 3 4 5 6 7 8 9 10 11 12 13 14 15 16 17 18 19 20

LINEAR EQUATIONS	
Slope-intercept Form	$y = mx + b$
Direct Variation	$y = kx$
Slope of a Line	$m = \frac{y_2 - y_1}{x_2 - x_1}$

CIRCUMFERENCE			
Circle	$C = 2\pi r$	or	$C = \pi d$

AREA	
Triangle	$A = \frac{1}{2}bh$
Rectangle or Parallelogram	$A = bh$
Trapezoid	$A = \frac{1}{2}(b_1 + b_2)h$
Circle	$A = \pi r^2$

SURFACE AREA	Lateral	Total
Prism	$S = Ph$	$S = Ph + 2B$
Cylinder	$S = 2\pi rh$	$S = 2\pi rh + 2\pi r^2$

VOLUME	
Prism or Cylinder	$V = Bh$
Pyramid or Cone	$V = \frac{1}{3}Bh$
Sphere	$V = \frac{4}{3}\pi r^3$

ADDITIONAL INFORMATION	
Pythagorean Theorem	$a^2 + b^2 = c^2$
Simple Interest	$I = Prt$
Compound Interest	$A = P(1 + r)^t$